Hampshire
Bird Atlas

2007–2012

Hampshire Ornithological Society

Published by Hampshire Ornithological Society
www.hos.org.uk

Requests for permission to reproduce material from this work should be sent to
Hampshire Ornithological Society

First published 2015

British Library Cataloging-in-Publication Data is available

ISBN 978-0-9567712-6-1

Production and design by **WILD**Guides Ltd., Old Basing, Hampshire UK.

Printed in Poland

10 9 8 7 6 5 4 3 2 1

Hampshire Bird Atlas

2007–2012

Edited by John Eyre

Atlas Steering Group

Charirman: Glynne Evans

Members: Keith Betton, John Clark, John Collman, John Eyre, Richard Ford, Hugh Kent, Andy Page, Barrie Roberts, Brian Sharkey, John Shillitoe and David Thelwell

Publication Steering Group

Charirman: John Eyre

Photographic Editors: Martin Bennett and Richard Ford

Members: Keith Betton, John Clark, John Eyre, Richard Ford, Andy Page, Barrie Roberts, Brian Sharkey, John Shillitoe, Robert Still and David Thelwell

Hampshire Ornithological Society

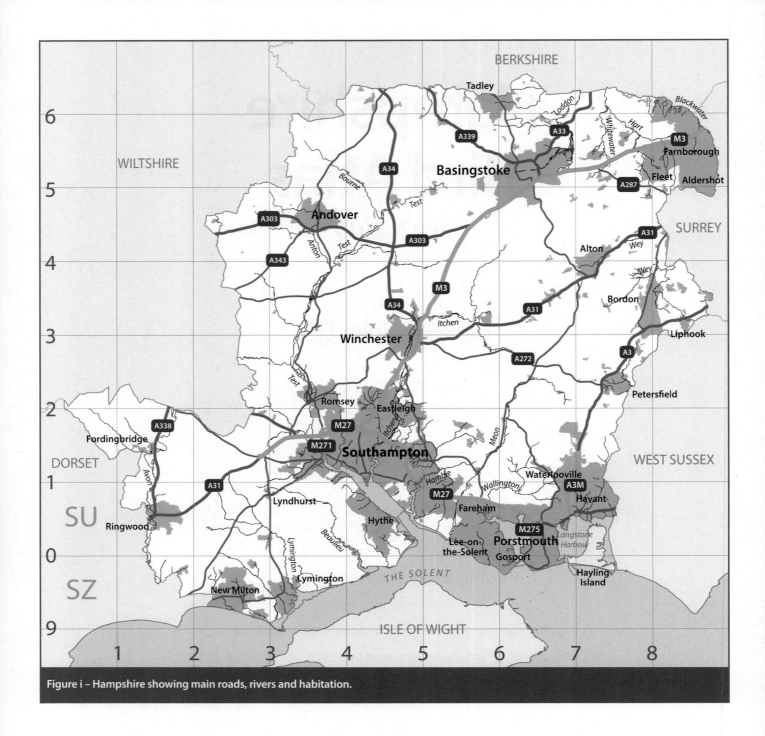

Figure i – Hampshire showing main roads, rivers and habitation.

Contents

LIST OF FIGURES AND TABLES

Hampshire Ornithological Society acknowledges the generous support of the following companies and organisations. As the main sponsors of *Hampshire Bird Atlas 2007–12* they have all played a key role in its publication.

www3.hants.gov.uk/biodiversity/hbic

www.ecosupport.co.uk

www.naturetrek.co.uk

www.mottmac.com

www.nats.aero

www.farnboroughinternational.org

www.berkeleygroup.co.uk

www.epr.uk.com

www.birdworld.co.uk

www.portsmouthwater.co.uk

www.ecosa.co.uk

www.vitacress-conservation.org

www.appliedecology.co.uk

www.ethosep.co.uk

www.hants.gov.uk

www.naturalengland.org.uk

www.hiwwt.org.uk

www.easthants.gov.uk

Great Spotted Woodpecker,
New Forest, January 2012 –
Martin Bennett

Foreword

I'm in my kitchen watching a Great Spotted Woodpecker lord it over my feeder which they do all winter long. Then they return in spring to smash open my nest boxes and systematically remove all my young Great Tits and Blue Tits. Last spring they stole the first brood of House Sparrows to have chirped since I arrived here seven years ago. I've retaliated! I've spent out, gone woodcrete, so hopefully a few broods will make it out alive this spring. And I already have another first . . . Starlings are stuffing the extractor fan in my toilet with a ragged wig of straw. I've disconnected it as I don't want a confetti of nestlings wafting across the lawn. But isn't it odd . . . the first Sparrows and Starlings nesting in years but loads of Great Spots; what a reversal from the early seventies when I first took a keener interest in the birds in my back yard. In those days the red flash of the pecker was unseen and the drizzled song of the Starlings competed with the chatter of the innumerable spadgers above my bedroom window.

Back then pawing through the Peterson in fits of fantasy drew me to the Peregrine, a national rarity, and the Goshawk, allegedly extinct in the county. Now I've seen both through this same window; even better I've had a Gos perched in my garden and a Peregrine eating a Woodpigeon on my lawn. It's almost unbelievable, a fantasy come true in my lifetime, amazing. So is the fact that I've never heard a Willow Warbler in the woods around the house, nor seen a Redstart there and last year for the first time I failed to hear a Cuckoo in my garden. Very sad. But what are such recollections and observations worth, one child, one man, two gardens, a few birds gone, a few new ones arrived? Not much. It's pretty subjective, a bit nostalgic, you see it's not data, it's only memories.

That's why this book is invaluable, it presents measured and analysed trends in distribution and population. It's a magnificent triumph of voluntary labour and exceptional expertise. Now Hampshire is one of the best scientifically known areas on the planet and this volume represents essential information to those concerned with the task of conserving many of the species considered.

Hampshire's south coast continental proximity and varied habitats make it one of the UK's best birding counties, a great place for young ornithologists to learn their skills. But already devoid of breeding Yellow Wags, with Turtle Doves and Corn Buntings on the same slippery downward slope it urgently requires some dramatic conservation effort. So please don't get depressed or smug about the losers and winners in here. Get active now you are equipped with the facts. Your county's birds need you more than ever.

Chris Packham
New Forest March 2015

Introduction and Background

Hampshire is privileged to have such a rich and varied birdlife. Its mix of habitats, including such gems as the New Forest, the Solent coastline with its estuaries and harbours, and the clear chalkland rivers running through verdant valleys to the sea, accounts for its diversity. The county is also fortunate in having an excellent historical record of its birds. Beginning with the writing of Gilbert White in the 18th century followed by the first county avifauna from Kelsall and Munn in 1905 and subsequently from Cohen (1963), Cohen and Taverner (1972) and Clark and Eyre (1993), we can trace how Hampshire's birds have changed over time. We can chronicle the disappearance of breeding species such as Black Grouse, Corncrake, Cirl Bunting and Red-backed Shrike and, more positively, the colonisation of the county by newcomers such as Little Ringed Plover, Collared Dove, Mediterranean Gull, Cetti's Warbler and Firecrest. In recent years we have seen the return of Red Kite and Raven, and more new arrivals including Little Egret, Goosander, Avocet and Peregrine.

It was not until the publication of *Birds of Hampshire* (*BoH*) in 1993 that information became available about the distribution and estimated numbers of the county's breeding birds. *BoH* presented the results of the first county bird atlas carried out by Hampshire Ornithological Society (HOS) in 1986–91. This was designed to map the distribution of the county's breeding birds at tetrad (2 km square) resolution. In 1988, two years into the Hampshire project, the second national breeding bird atlas was launched. In Hampshire, the two projects were then combined and ran concurrently until both ended in 1991.

The intention to carry out new national breeding and wintering atlases beginning in 2007 provided the motivation for HOS to embark on a second atlas of Hampshire's breeding birds and to combine it with the county's first winter bird atlas. This book presents the results of that project. Although it is not a complete avifauna but rather an extended snapshot of the county's winter and breeding birds, information about species recorded outside the atlas recording periods is also included. The atlas fieldwork, which spanned the five winters (November–February) 2007/08–2011/12 and the five summers (April–July) 2008–12, was designed to map the distribution and relative abundance of all birds breeding and wintering in Hampshire. For the first four years, it ran alongside the country-wide project which covered the whole of Britain and Ireland and was led by the British Trust for Ornithology (BTO), partnered by Birdwatch Ireland and the Scottish Ornithologists' Club. Both the national and Hampshire projects were devised to repeat previous breeding atlases and, for the first time, to carry out a winter atlas over the same period. Fieldwork for the national project, which covered Britain and Ireland at a 10 km square level, began on November 1st 2007 and ended on July 31st 2011. The results have been published in *Bird Atlas 2007–11*. Fieldwork for the Hampshire Bird Atlas (HBA), again covering the county at tetrad level, also began on November 1st 2007 but was extended for an additional year to end on July 31st 2012.

The repeat of the Hampshire breeding bird atlas, approximately 20 years after the first, was intended to allow direct comparison between the two, thereby showing the changes in distributions over the intervening years. The winter distribution patterns and abundance data collected in both winter and breeding seasons would be new information and would provide a baseline against which to monitor future change.

The HBA project was overseen by an Atlas Steering Group (ASG), the members of which are named in the Acknowledgements. Approximately 1,200 observers took part in the surveys and these are named in *Appendix 1*. The large number of people involved reflects both on the scale of the project and on the high level of local interest in Hampshire's birds. It is thanks to their dedicated efforts that it has been possible to collect the mass of information presented in the following pages.

Survey methodology

Fieldwork
The methodology for the HBA was based on that developed for the national project which is detailed in *Bird Atlas 2007–11*. Observers were requested to carry out bird surveys in two ways. These were:

- **Timed Tetrad Visits** (TTVs), which involved a nominated observer recording and counting all the birds encountered in a tetrad during two two-hour visits, in both the winter and breeding seasons.
- **Roving Records**, which involved any observer recording any bird, at any time, in any tetrad during the breeding and winter seasons.

The prime purpose of the TTVs was to map the relative abundance of each species located during the timed visits in both seasons. In Hampshire, HOS aimed to achieve 100% TTV coverage i.e. two two-hour TTV counts in both winter and summer in all of the county's tetrads which were predominantly land-based (see *Survey coverage* opposite). In both seasons, observers were required to make two survey visits to their allocated tetrads, one early and one late. In winter the first visit was in November/December and the second in January/February; in the breeding season the first was in April/May and the second in June/July.

It was anticipated that the four hours of TTV fieldwork alone would be insufficient to locate all the species occurring in a tetrad. Furthermore, with the key thrust of

TTVs being to count the birds seen and heard, recorders were likely to give less attention to obtaining breeding evidence which had been a core aim of the 1986–91 Atlas. Observers were therefore encouraged to collect Roving Records by visiting tetrads at other times throughout the project, both to complete the species list and to improve the evidence of breeding. Coverage of nocturnal and crepuscular species presented particular problems because these were not properly surveyed during TTVs and received only limited coverage through Roving Records. To compensate for this potential under-recording, towards the end of the project one of these, Tawny Owl, was targeted in a species-specific survey, and for another, Nightjar, the HBA findings were augmented by adding in the results of a 2013 survey carried out in the New Forest.

Survey coverage

In total, 1,029 tetrads were included in the survey. These included many boundary tetrads shared with neighbouring counties. To facilitate direct comparison with the 1986–91 Atlas, the same criteria were adopted for either including or excluding them in the HBA. Tetrads with at least one third of their area in Hampshire were included. In a few cases, where particularly bird-rich areas in Hampshire would have been excluded based on this criterion, some tetrads with less than one third of their area in the county were included.

Some coastal tetrads also presented a boundary-related problem. Here all tetrads with accessible land above the low water mark were included but where the centre point of the tetrad fell below the low water mark they were not eligible for TTV coverage, although Roving Records were collected from them. This removed 23 coastal tetrads from those requiring TTVs.

Table 1 gives the TTV coverage achieved in the 1,006 eligible tetrads. During the breeding season 938 (93·2%) received the full four hours of coverage. A farther 66 received varying levels of reduced coverage and just two no coverage at all. In the winter the equivalent figures were 927 (92·1%) full coverage, 78 reduced coverage and just one no coverage. These figures take no account of the time spent collecting Roving Records which was additional to that dedicated to TTVs.

Breeding evidence

Observers were requested to record evidence of breeding during both breeding season TTVs and when gathering Roving Records. Each surveyor was provided with a set of status codes which distinguished between four breeding categories:

● **Non-breeding.**
● **Possible breeding.**
● **Probable breeding.**
● **Confirmed breeding.**

Full descriptions of all the evidence categories and their associated field codes are given in *Table 2*.

		Breeding season		Winter season	
		No. of tetrads	Percentage	No. of tetrads	Percentage
2 × 2 hr		938	93·2	927	92·1
2 hr+1 hr		23	2·2	41	4·1
1 hr+1 hr		36	3·6	36	3·6
1 × 2 hr		5	0·5	1	0·1
1 hr		2	0·2	0	0
0 hr		2	0·2	1	0·1
Total		**1,006**	**100**	**1,006**	**100**

Table 1 – TTV coverage.

Non-breeding birds		
F	Flying over	
M	Species observed but suspected to be still on migration	
U	Species observed but suspected to be a summering non-breeder	
Possible breeding		
H	Species observed in breeding season in suitable nesting habitat	
S	Singing male present (or breeding calls heard) in breeding season in suitable nesting habitat	
Probable breeding		
P	Pair observed in suitable nesting habitat in the breeding season	
T	Permanent territory presumed through registration of territorial behaviour (song etc.) on at least two different days a week or more apart at the same place; or many individuals on one day	
D	Courtship and display, judged to be in or near potential breeding habitat; caution needed with wildfowl	
N	Visiting probable nest site	
A	Agitated behaviour or anxiety calls from adults suggesting presence of nest or young nearby	
I	Brood patch on adult examined in the hand suggesting incubation	
B	Nest building or excavating nest hole	
Confirmed breeding		
DD	Distraction display or injury feigning	
UN	Used nest or eggshells found (occupied or laid within the survey period)	
FL	Recently fledged young (nidicolous species) or downy young (nidifugous species). Careful consideration should be given to the likely provenance of any fledged juvenile capable of significant geographical movement. Evidence of dependency on adults (e.g. feeding) is helpful. Be cautious, even if record comes from suitable habitat	
ON	Adults entering or leaving nest site in circumstances indicating an occupied nest (including high nests or nest holes, the contents of which cannot be seen) or adults seen incubating	
FF	Adult carrying faecal sac or food for young	
NE	Nest containing eggs	
NY	Nest with young seen or heard	

Table 2 – Categories and codes used to record breeding evidence.

Data collection and validation

All atlas records, including both TTV and Roving Records for both the national and Hampshire projects, were submitted to a central database constructed and managed by the BTO. For Hampshire, and other counties continuing local surveys, the facility to input records to the database was extended beyond the end of the national project in 2011.

In addition to the records collected directly as part of the atlas projects, HOS uploaded records submitted to the Society during the HBA period. The BTO added farther data collected via their on-line BirdTrack recording system and from other national datasets and surveys such as the Breeding Bird Survey (BBS), the Nest Record Scheme (NRS), the Heronries Census, the Wetland Bird Survey (WeBS), the Waterways Breeding Bird Survey and the national Ringing Scheme. Information from other bodies such as the Royal Society for the Protection of Birds (RSPB) and local surveys such as the Thames Basin and Wealden Heaths Breeding Bird Surveys and the New Forest Wintering Bird Survey was incorporated. In all cases, records were only included with sufficiently accurate grid references to allocate them to a tetrad (or 10 km square for the national survey).

The on-line database was a particularly valuable tool. Not only did it facilitate submission of records but also provided rapid feedback of progress during the survey period. It also enabled Hampshire records, some 800,000 of them from whatever source, to be validated by a team of experienced local observers (Keith Betton, John Clark, Glynne Evans, John Eyre and John Shillitoe). Records from some Hampshire tetrads located in 10 km squares allocated by the BTO to neighbouring counties, were validated by teams from Dorset, Wiltshire, Berkshire, Surrey, West Sussex and the Isle of Wight. The validation process required substantial effort but was necessary to ensure that all the records and the maps produced from them were as accurate as possible. Where errors were suspected the validation system allowed a record to be queried directly with the observer who then had the option of editing or deleting it, or of providing additional information to confirm it. If the observer did not respond to the query, the relevant record was omitted from the final data set. Records of local rarities were assessed by the HOS Records Panel.

At the beginning of the validation process, Willow Tit and Tree Sparrow were singled out as requiring special attention. All records of Tree Sparrow, and those of Willow Tit submitted from areas where the species was not known to breed, were reviewed by contacting the observers to seek confirmation of positive identification.

Data analysis and mapping

The main part of this book is devoted to descriptions of the status of all the bird species recorded in Hampshire during the five winters and breeding seasons covered by the HBA fieldwork. The accounts are based on the distribution, breeding status and relative abundance data gathered during the survey. Where relevant, comparison is also made with breeding data from the 1986–91 Hampshire Atlas. Supplementary information about migration and other aspects not covered by atlas fieldwork, but collected by HOS, is also included in the accounts.

The HBA results are presented in three types of maps:
- 2007/08–2011/12 winter distribution and abundance.
- 2008–12 breeding distribution and abundance.
- Change in breeding distribution between 1986–91 and 2008–12.

The methodology used to produce the maps is described below. Farther information about the symbols, colours and interpretation of the maps is given in the *Introduction to the species accounts* on *page 44*.

Winter distribution and abundance maps

The atlas data identified which Hampshire tetrads were being used by each species (excluding birds flying over) during the winter and the numbers of individuals of those species in each tetrad as recorded during TTV counts. The information has been plotted directly onto a map of the county to show the species' winter distributions and relative abundances.

Breeding distribution and abundance maps

Although observers were requested to provide the highest level of breeding evidence observed during both TTV counts and Roving Records visits, many records were submitted without any such evidence. In general, the level of breeding evidence, particularly of confirmed and probable breeding, was felt by the ASG to be lower than in the 1986–91 survey. This is perhaps to be expected, given that the collection of breeding evidence was a primary requirement of the earlier survey but was possibly overshadowed by the emphasis on TTV counts in the later one. As a result, this created difficulties both in presenting an accurate picture of current breeding distributions and also for identifying change between the two atlases (see *Breeding change maps* opposite). To overcome the problem, the ASG adopted a method used successfully in *The Norfolk Bird Atlas – Summer and Winter Distributions, 1999–2007* (Taylor & Marchant 2011). Rather than relying solely on the breeding evidence as submitted, an assessment of the data was made on a species-by-species basis to decide where breeding was considered likely (BCL). This included not only confirmed and probable breeding records but also allowed some of the possible breeding and presence-only records to be upgraded to BCL. While this may seem somewhat arbitrary, it is perhaps most easily appreciated for resident sedentary species (for example Green Woodpecker) where all records during the breeding season are likely to indicate breeding nearby. It becomes more problematic for migrant species, where the presence of a bird does not necessarily indicate likely breeding. As a partial solution to this problem, the date of a record could be used to assess the likelihood of breeding, early-season records being more likely to refer to migrants. For some, mainly resident, species dates outside the HBA April–July breeding season were adopted. This allowed available information to be used to supplement the breeding evidence for early or late breeders. The big advantage of the BCL approach was that it allowed flexibility in the assessment of records both to upgrade and downgrade the likelihood of breeding. For example, local knowledge was used to downgrade records of some species (particularly some ducks and gulls) which qualified as probable breeding records (usually on the basis of display or pairs in suitable breeding habitat) but were considered not to be actually indicative of breeding. A similar approach was used for wide-ranging species such as Hobby, where it is easy to over-estimate breeding numbers from atlas data. By adjusting the breeding criteria for each species on a case-by-case basis, it was possible to raise or lower the level of breeding evidence required to assign BCL status to each record. The evaluation of which field codes and dates to use for each breeding species was made by John Clark, Glynne Evans and John Eyre and is reproduced in *Appendix II* on *page 436*. The list includes several species that were seen during the HBA breeding season surveys but were not considered likely to be breeding. For most species, records that were expressly identified by the observer as non-breeding (those in categories F, M and U) were excluded from the assessment although in a few cases some birds seen in flight were included. Similarly, some records where no evidence of breeding was submitted (shown as 'Null' in the table) were included as providing evidence of likely breeding.

The breeding distribution and relative abundance maps have been plotted to differentiate between the tetrads where breeding was considered likely and those where the species was recorded as being present, but not considered likely to be breeding. In all cases the 'presence' records cover the entire April 1st–July 31st atlas recording period and therefore provide accurate pictures of each species' distribution during the breeding season (including migrants and non-breeding birds).

Breeding change maps

The purpose of the change maps is to compare breeding records obtained in the 1986–91 Atlas with those from 2008–12. In *BoH* the 1986–91 breeding distribution maps were plotted in terms of possible, probable and confirmed breeding records. As discussed above, the evidence of breeding submitted for the 2008–12 Atlas was less comprehensive so direct comparison of the two would run the risk of producing a pessimistic impression of how the breeding status of species has changed.

Since the intention was to use the BCL approach to identify the breeding distribution in the current atlas, as far as possible the same methodology was applied to the results from the earlier atlas. However, since we were not able to apply modified date ranges to the data from the first atlas, the HBA BCL results have been compared to the April-July BCL data from the 1986–91 Atlas. This has, inevitably, introduced inaccuracies to the change maps for some species, particularly to those of some summer visitors. It means that the absolute magnitude of change, in terms of the numbers of tetrads lost or gained, should be treated with caution.

Despite having some advantages, it has to be recognised that the BCL methodology is not ideal. Nonetheless, given the limitations in the data, the ASG considered it to be a workable and pragmatic approach to take.

Confidentiality and sensitive species

There are several nationally scarce and sensitive species breeding in Hampshire. Prior to producing and publishing the HBA maps the ASG gave considerable thought to how the distribution of these species should be displayed. There were similar concerns about a smaller number of sensitive wintering species, for example those that might be disturbed from accessible winter roosts. For the national project, the BTO provided detailed proposals based (for the UK) on advice from the Rare Breeding Birds Panel (RBBP), but since this had to be appropriate across the country, for some species, it was considered too restrictive to be applied locally. For example, species such as Dartford Warbler and Firecrest which are rare in some parts of the country, are relatively common in Hampshire. After careful consideration it was decided that all species would be mapped accurately at tetrad level with the following exceptions: Honey-buzzard, Goshawk, Stone-curlew, Long-eared Owl and Peregrine. The approaches adopted for these differ from species to species; farther details are given in the relevant accounts.

Scientific names

The scientific names of birds are given in the species accounts or, for rarities and escapes, in the sections following these accounts. The scientific names of other taxa are given in *Appendix III* on *page 440*.

Place names, abbreviations and references

All place names mentioned in the text are collected in a gazetteer which forms *Appendix IV* on *page 441* of the book. The names are listed alphabetically, each with its appropriate map reference to enable easy location on an Ordnance Survey map.

Abbreviations and references are given in *Appendix V* on *page 444*. The latter include both abbreviated forms of frequently used references as well as standard author-date references.

Acknowledgements

The HBA project and the subsequent publication of its findings in this book would not have been possible without the input and support of many people. On behalf of HOS, I would like to thank all those listed below and throughout the following pages for their contributions, from the organisation and execution of the survey through to analysis and publication of the results.

Planning and organisation of the HBA depended to a considerable degree on work done by the BTO for the national breeding and wintering bird atlases, the results of which have been published in *Bird Atlas 2007–11*. The survey methodology and data handling tools developed for the national project were carried over to the local one. These proved particularly valuable and our thanks go to the BTO as an organisation and, specifically, to staff members Dawn Balmer and Simon Gillings who provided ongoing guidance and answered many atlas-related queries throughout the project. Special mention must also be made of Jeremy Greenwood CBE who was Director of the BTO during the planning stages of the national Atlas, and his successor Andy Clements who took over as Director when Jeremy retired in 2007. Both were keen Atlas supporters and worked constructively with county bird clubs, including HOS, to ensure smooth interfaces between the local and national projects.

In Hampshire, planning and organisation of the local project was the responsibility of the ASG, chaired by Glynne Evans and comprising the following members: Keith Betton, John Clark, John Collman, John Eyre, Richard Ford, Hugh Kent, Andy Page, Barrie Roberts, Brian Sharkey, John Shillitoe and David Thelwell. Glynne, as BTO representative in Hampshire, took the lead in organising the fieldwork and managing the database. With that in full swing, the ASG morphed into the Publication Steering Group (PSG), chaired by John Eyre. Robert Still and Martin Bennett joined the team, Martin taking over as Photographic Editor when Richard Ford stood down and Rob providing expert advice on all aspects of book production. While some of the specific tasks carried out by members of both the ASG and PSG are acknowledged below, space does not permit a detailed breakdown of the individual contributions of all those involved. Suffice it to say that all played their part and without their input, this book would not have been published.

The HBA fieldwork was carried out by many people who are listed in *Appendix I*. Thanks go to all those whose individual observations have combined to paint the fascinating picture of Hampshire birds presented in these pages. The names listed are those who submitted records directly to the Atlas project but not necessarily those whose records came via other national surveys or directly to HOS and were subsequently incorporated into the Atlas database. Apologies to anyone who has been inadvertently missed from the list. Some information was provided after completion of the HBA fieldwork including, particularly, the 2013 Nightjar survey results from the New Forest. Thanks go to Ian Barker of the New Forest National Park Authority for permission to incorporate these data into the Atlas.

With the beginning of the book production phase of the project, other individuals and organisations were involved. We are particularly grateful to David Price who converted the data from the 1986–91 Hampshire Atlas into Excel format to allow comparison with the HBA results. The Hampshire Biodiversity Information Centre (HBIC) was also very helpful and thanks go to Nicky Court and Wolfgang Ritter for access to HBIC data and assistance with production of habitat maps.

The writers of the species accounts are named alongside their individual contributions; all of them must be congratulated both for their expertise and for their patience in following the sometimes serpentine paths to arrive at the finished product. Similarly we were very fortunate to have Peter Thompson on hand to write the chapter on Hampshire habitats. Peter's extensive knowledge of the county's many habitats and the environmental factors impacting upon them, has proved invaluable. Thanks are also due to Eddie Wiseman and Keith Betton who, in addition to writing species accounts, also prepared the Rarities and Escapes sections, and the Gazetteer respectively. Another major contribution to the book's content has been from the many photographers who have so generously provided their pictures to illustrate its pages. The photographers' names are given alongside their excellent work and appreciative recognition goes to all of them. Special thanks go to Martin Bennett who, as photographic editor, spent considerable time sourcing, sorting and classifying the images that appear here. Both species account authors and photographers are also listed on *page 46*.

Proof-reading can be a thankless task, so I am grateful to Keith and Esther Betton, Mike Chalmers, John Clark, Alison Cross, Laura Darling, Glynne Evans, Rob Hume, Andy Rhodes, Jodie Southgate, Alan Snook and Marcus Ward for taking it on. Many errors were found and corrected but some will inevitably have slipped through the net for which I accept full responsibility. I should also mention that John Clark's unrivalled knowledge of Hampshire ornithology, records, locations and history, has been very helpful in correcting factual errors. Similarly, Alison Cross provided valuable expertise and input to the Habitats chapter.

Robert Still has also played an important and much-appreciated role. His knowledge of book design, production and publishing proved invaluable and I am personally grateful to him for sorting out problems which, at times, seemed insoluble.

Although HOS is a relatively large bird club, publication of this book still represented a substantial financial liability. The Society is therefore particularly grateful to all those members who have supported the project by sponsoring species. Their names are given at the end of the accounts of their chosen species. Thanks go to John Shillitoe for organising this aspect of the project and also for setting up the book ordering and payment system aided by Bryan and Sandy Coates. Keith Betton took on the job of seeking external sponsors. As a result of his sterling efforts we are appreciative of the following companies and organisations who, as our main sponsors, have generously provided funds: Applied Ecology, Berkeley Homes, Birdworld, East Hants District Council, ECOSA, Ecosupport, EPR, Ethos Environmental Planning, Farnborough International, Hampshire County Council, Hampshire & Isle of Wight Wildlife Trust, Hampshire Biodiversity Information Centre, Mott MacDonald, NATS, Natural England, Naturetrek, Portsmouth Water and Vitacress Conservation Trust. Our thanks also go to Chris Spooner, Footprint Ecology, Hampshire Ecology and RPS for their financial support.

I want to thank Chris Packham, HOS President, for writing the Foreword and, to end on a personal note, my wife Sue. There were times when 'the book' occupied too much of my time. Without her patience, understanding and support it would not have been completed.

John Eyre

Woodlark, Bourley and Long Valley, May 2015 – *John Eyre*

Hampshire Habitats

How habitat change may affect bird populations

Peter Thompson

Introduction

The HBA species accounts and maps which form the major part of this book describe the current distributions and relative abundances of Hampshire's birds and show how their ranges have changed over the past twenty years. Some of the changes, both positive and negative, are obvious – for example, we are all familiar with the appearance of Red Kites after their re-introduction into southern England – but many are not so noticeable and are less easy to understand. While many of them have happened as a result of changes operating over a wide geographic area, at a local level, changes to Hampshire's habitats have also played their part. As a forerunner to the accounts, this chapter is intended to describe the county's key habitats and how the pressures upon them are influencing the birds that they support.

Hampshire is, arguably, one of the most bio-diverse counties in England and those of us who live there are extremely fortunate to have such an amazing array of different habitats and species right on our doorstep. Birders are able to visit the coast, marshes, water meadows, lakes, rivers, ancient and semi-natural woodland, heaths and farmland all within an hour's drive of each other. It should, therefore, come as no surprise that a carefully planned and executed day's birdwatching at the best time of the year and with the right weather conditions can record in excess of 140 species. A total of around 260 species occurs in a typical year and the county supports an assemblage of over 125 regular breeding species.

Despite its diversity, we should never become complacent about this beautiful part of England. All of these habitats and species are under constant assault from external pressures, which must be managed if we are to have any hope of retaining the rich wildlife we have at present. The problems that need attention are often complicated and difficult to resolve. They range from simple neglect and accidental loss, for instance from pollution incidents, through direct destruction from housing development and road building, to longer term and insidious deterioration brought about through changes in land management practices. Our burgeoning population puts huge pressure on the surrounding countryside in many different ways, from the more obvious such as recreational disturbance issues, especially by dogs, through to the less noticeable such as increased pressure on natural resources like water. Add to this the uncertainties of climate change, disease and alien species and it's easy to see why there is concern.

Direct destruction is clear for all to see; however, the slow erosion in the quality and general well-being of habitats and their associated wildlife is far less apparent. A national survey has recently shown that (when all vegetation sampling plots are analysed together) overall species richness of plants growing in fields, woods, heaths and moors decreased by 8% between 1978 and 2007 (*Countryside Survey* 2007). Hampshire is no different. Despite having the New Forest and South Downs National Parks and numerous excellent wildlife reserves and protected areas, almost without exception, everywhere is facing an increasingly wide range of issues which need addressing.

This, Hampshire's second bird atlas, clearly shows that some relative newcomers, such as Little Egret, Cetti's Warbler and Firecrest, are faring extremely well in the county, while others – both long term residents such as Willow Tit and Corn Bunting, and migrants such as Turtle Dove and Yellow Wagtail – are in real trouble. Of course the populations of many species have remained relatively stable over the two decades since the previous atlas. However, for any species it is important for ornithologists to understand what causes their numbers to change. Hopefully this chapter will help to shed some light onto why the populations of Hampshire's birds are performing in the way that they are.

Hampshire's National Character Areas

Hampshire's biodiversity can be attributed to its varied landscape and geology: it has ten different National Character Areas (NCA) lying entirely or partially within its boundaries (*Figure iii*). These are dependent on the county's underlying geology as shown in *Figure ii* and although some share common features, each has its own particular identity. The Hampshire Downs NCA is the largest and is part of the broad belt of chalk downland which runs through central/southern England. This belt includes the Salisbury Plain & West Wiltshire Downs to the west and the South Downs to the south-east.

The northern boundary of the Hampshire Downs forms a ridge rising to over 290 m and creating a striking escarpment overlooking the Thames Basin. To the east, the downland is interrupted by a second escarpment at the edge of the Western Weald. Here the chalk has been eroded away to expose the clay and sandy layers beneath.

The world-famous Avon, Test and Itchen rivers rise on the chalk, the latter two on the Hampshire Downs, and flow in a southerly direction through the Hampshire Basin to the sea. The mouth of the county's fourth chalkland river, the Meon, was dammed in the 17th century creating an important wetland area at Titchfield Haven.

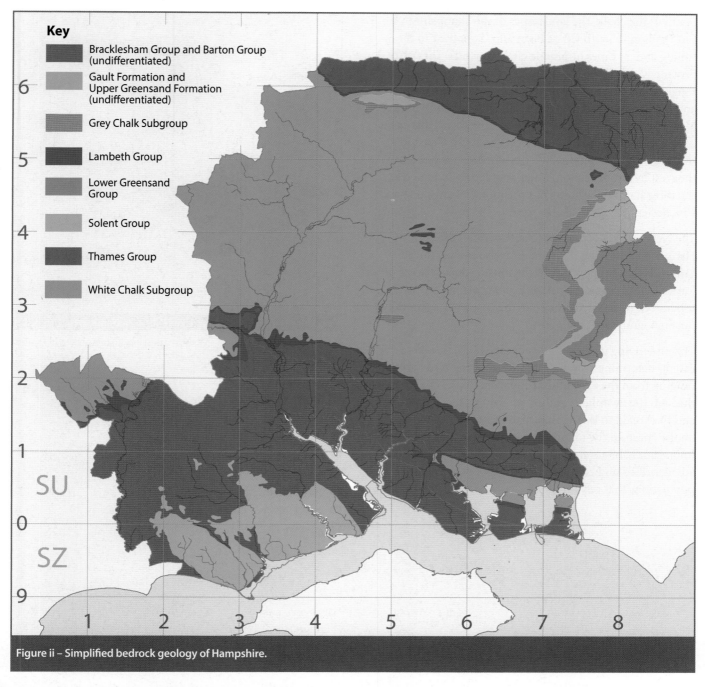

Key

- Bracklesham Group and Barton Group (undifferentiated)
- Gault Formation and Upper Greensand Formation (undifferentiated)
- Grey Chalk Subgroup
- Lambeth Group
- Lower Greensand Group
- Solent Group
- Thames Group
- White Chalk Subgroup

Figure ii – Simplified bedrock geology of Hampshire.

Looking east along the north Hampshire Downs from West Woodhay (Berks) – *Robert Still*

South of the chalk, the landscapes of the Hampshire Lowlands and South Coast Plain afford contrast to the rolling and, at times, dramatic chalk uplands. They also provide widely differing sceneries of their own which range from the large urban settlements of Southampton and Portsmouth to expanses of ancient woodland in the New Forest, a legacy of the royal hunting forest that once covered the area. In the south-east the South Coast Plain slopes gently down to the Solent shoreline bordered in the west by Southampton Water and deeply indented by the three natural harbours of Portsmouth, Langstone and Chichester.

The New Forest occupies the south-west of the county. Here, the underlying clays and gravels have produced acid soils that support one of the most extensive areas of lowland heath in Europe. The Solent coast in the west is less influenced by urbanisation than the east with a generally unspoilt landscape.

The underlying geology and geography has, to a large extent, determined land usage and resulting bird habitats, ranging from the agricultural expanses on the chalk through the heathland of the New Forest, the Thames Basin and the Weald to the dense urban zones and wilder areas on the coast. In the following pages, each of the county's important habitats and the pressures acting upon them are identified and considered with respect to the bird populations that rely on them.

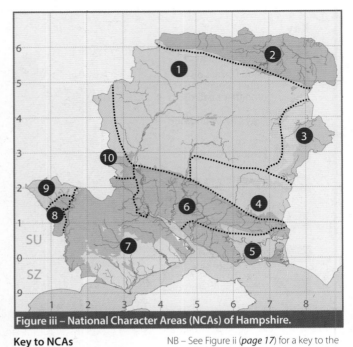

Figure iii – National Character Areas (NCAs) of Hampshire.

Key to NCAs

1. Hampshire Downs
2. Thames Basin Heaths
3. Wealden Greensand
4. South Downs
5. South Coast Plain
6. South Hampshire Lowlands
7. New Forest
8. Dorset Heaths
9. Dorset Downs and Cranborne Chase
10. Salisbury Plain and West Wiltshire Downs

NB – See Figure ii (*page 17*) for a key to the underlying geology

New Forest heathland, coniferous and broadleaved woodland – *Robert Still*

Farmland

Farmland makes up around 85% of Hampshire's countryside split 50% arable and 35% grassland (*Figure iv*). Of the latter only a little over 2000 ha remains as unimproved calcareous grassland (*Figure v*). Farmland is perhaps the habitat that has changed more than any other in the last 60 years, and still continues to do so. These changes, which can often be quite subtle, have impacted greatly on those birds that are farmland specialists, as frequently-shown graphs, with lines plummeting towards the base line, have demonstrated for a number of years. In fact no other group of birds has suffered so badly. The decline of species, such as the Turtle Dove, are already causing ornithologists to talk about possible extinctions, not just within Hampshire, but nationally. Hampshire bird indices show massive decreases within the farmland bird community, added to which there have also been some complete losses within the county. As we shall see, species such as Tree Sparrow and Yellow Wagtail have been lost as breeding species since the 1986–91 Hampshire Atlas was undertaken – and before that Cirl Bunting and before that Corncrake.

In order to understand why these farmland specialists are suffering such declines, it is necessary to look at the farming methods that have supported their populations and how these practices have changed over recent decades. Individual changes may, in isolation, not have too significant an effect but their cumulative impact on bird populations can be catastrophic, particularly when they are applied over a large area of land. It is possible, starting at the end of the agricultural year with harvest time and following the farming calendar from a bird's point of view, to run through some of the ways that Hampshire farms have evolved. It is these changes, most of them brought about by farmers making business decisions simply so that they remain profitable, that have had such a negative impact on birds.

While some farmland species, including the Turtle Dove and Yellow Wagtail, leave our shores for warmer climes, many others remain here to over-winter in, or close to, their breeding habitats. The majority of these are seed-eaters, depending on weed seeds and grain to survive through the cold winter months. This food source has, in the past, been gleaned from weedy stubbles left after harvest and not ploughed up until the following spring. Historically, huge mixed flocks of finches, buntings and sparrows gathered together to forage on the seeds of annual plants such as Common Chickweed, Fat-hen, knotgrasses and meadow-grasses. Weed killers (herbicides) were first introduced in the 1950s and have become commonplace on all but organic farms. The amount of herbicide sprayed on agricultural land has actually fallen over the last twenty years or so but this is primarily due to the fact that modern herbicides are vastly superior to their predecessors. Their effectiveness has resulted in stubbles with virtually no weeds in them, as all were killed back in the spring and summer months.

Skylark plot in cereal crop near Cheriton – *Peter Thompson*

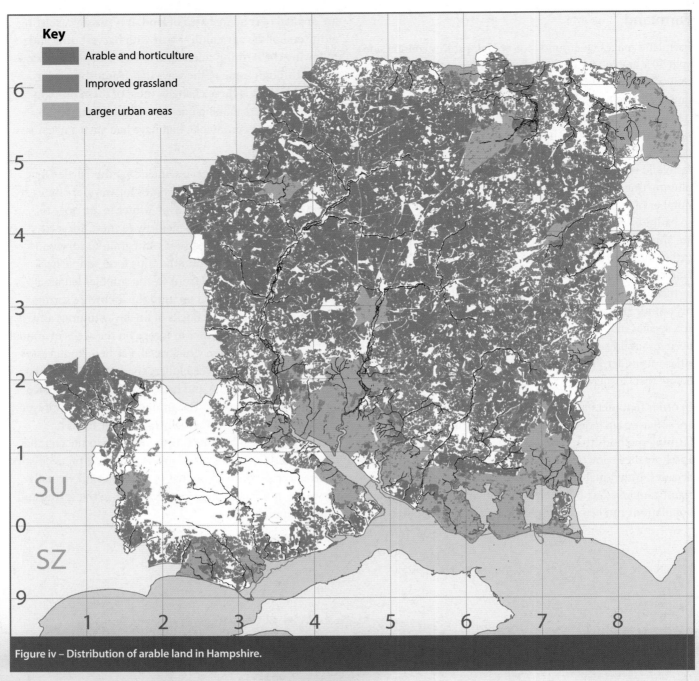

Key

- Arable and horticulture
- Improved grassland
- Larger urban areas

SU

SZ

Figure iv – Distribution of arable land in Hampshire.

Improved grassland/grazing near Overton – *Robert Still*

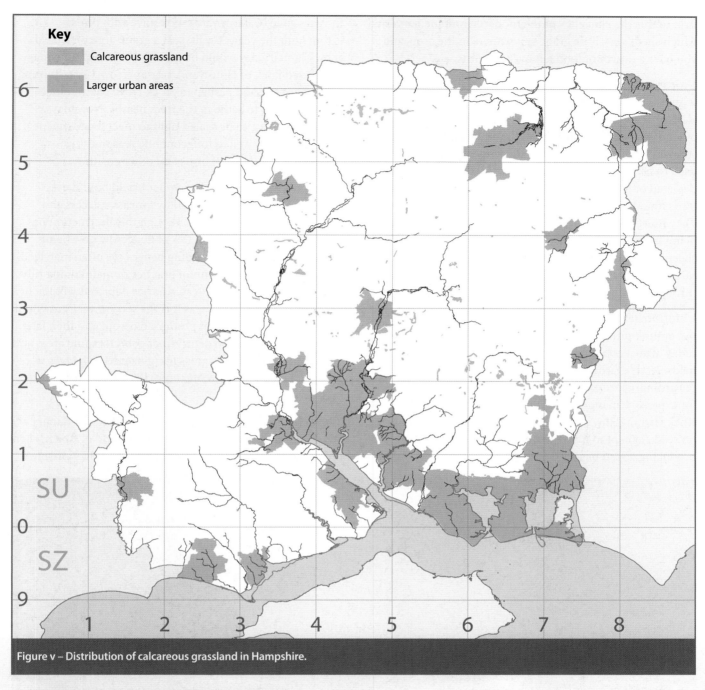

Key

- Calcareous grassland
- Larger urban areas

Figure v – Distribution of calcareous grassland in Hampshire.

Calcareous grassland, Old Winchester Hill – *Robert Still*

Add to this the efficiency of the modern combine harvester, which sheds very little grain as it gathers in the crop, and you have a dearth of food left over for birds.

Crops planted in the autumn, known as winter crops, tend to produce much better yields than those planted in spring. Consequently there has been a big increase in the amount of land cultivated and drilled in the autumn, meaning that stubbles are not as common in the winter landscape as they used to be. In the past, when the stubbles began to become depleted of food in the first couple of months of the year, birds found an alternative source alongside farm animals. They moved into farmyards and foraged amongst the cattle being fed their rations of hay and cattle cake, or joined the sheep and cows out in the fields, munching away at weedy turnip or kale crops, specially grown to feed the stock through the winter months while there is no grass growth.

Unfortunately, economic trends have forced many farmers out of milk production, a movement that still continues today, with a consequent exodus of stock from Hampshire's fields. Arable farming has become more financially rewarding, especially as technology has reduced the need for expensive manpower. Those who have remained in stock farming now generally feed cattle on silage, which has no seed element to it as, unlike hay, it is harvested before producing a seed head.

In years gone by, farm yards were alive with birds throughout the year. A walk past a grain store on a bleak, snowy January day would be met by a "whoosh" of wings as a mixed flock of House and Tree Sparrow, Corn Bunting, Yellowhammer and perhaps a Stock Dove or two burst out of the barn to settle in the trees nearby. Nowadays, grain stores have to be sealed tight to meet food hygiene requirements as well as for economic reasons, thus preventing the access of birds and other creatures.

With the advent of larger machinery, field boundaries of all sorts were removed to allow for easier access and bigger areas of land to work. Though this destruction has stopped, with many kilometres of hedgerow now being replanted, numerous remaining hedges are often managed inappropriately. The common practice of maintaining tidy hedges by cutting them every year has deprived wildlife of an important food source, as it is the second year growth of most shrubby species that produce blossom and then later, berries. Birds were also deprived of good foraging areas and over-winter cover when grass margins next to hedges were ploughed up, in order to maximise the area available for crop production.

These changes have resulted in what is called the hungry gap, the period between January and the end of April, when little food is available as most seed and grain has already

Flower-rich margin, Rotherfield – *Peter Thompson*

The Stewardship Farmland Bird Package

National experts from the BTO, RSPB, GWCT and NE have targeted those species of farmland bird that have been particularly affected by the loss of the 'big three' – nesting habitat, summer and winter food – and decided on the 'big six' farmland bird species that most need our help: Lapwing, Yellow Wagtail, Turtle Dove, Corn Bunting, Tree Sparrow and Grey Partridge.

It is believed that if farmers can apply the in-field Stewardship options identified in the table in each of the three resource categories, then farmland birds will thrive on their farms.

Resource	Options	Minimum per 100 ha
Winter seed food	Wild bird mixture (WBM) or weed-rich stubble (or a combination)	**2 ha WBM** or **5–10 ha Stubble**
Spring-summer invertebrate food	Conservation headlands, low input spring cereals, field corners, beetle banks, blocks/strips of nectar mix/flower-rich margins	**1–3 ha**
Places to nest in-field	Skylark plots or Fallow plots	**20 Skylark plots** or **1 ha Fallow plot**

been eaten, leaving farmland birds struggling to find enough to eat. This time of year, especially if the winter is harsh, is a time when big losses can occur.

In the spring, birds begin to pair up and start to choose nest sites, with many species such as Grey Partridge and Yellowhammer looking for uncut grass next to the hedge to nest in, whilst other species such as Linnet and Song Thrush prefer to nest in the hedge itself. There is some evidence to show that flat topped hedges that have been regularly cut may be easier for predators such as Magpies to hunt along and spot nests, as they simply hop along the hedge peering in. This is far more difficult if the hedge has an 'A' shape to it and has last year's growth still in place.

A number of farmland bird species nest on the ground but away from the field boundary, actually choosing the crop itself as the ideal habitat. However, these species do not like thick, tall crops that have already begun to grow away by the time they are choosing to nest, so this largely rules out autumn-sown crops which, as mentioned before, have become more widespread. Skylark, Lapwing, Stone-curlew and Corn Bunting are therefore generally reliant on spring-sown crops to nest in, although all will utilise nutrient-poor, open grassland but not thick fertilised, rye-grass swards.

Farmland bird species, with a few exceptions, feed their chicks on invertebrates, the numbers of which have dropped considerably. The declines in insect abundance within crops can be attributed in part to direct causes such as the use of broad-spectrum insecticides which kill not only the target species – aphids for instance – but also most of the non-target insect species too. However, perhaps an even bigger cause of decline is the success of broad-spectrum weed killers that remove virtually all weeds from the crops. These assorted weeds act as host plants for the mixed variety of invertebrates within the field. So, as an indirect result of removing the weeds, very few insects remain as food for hungry chicks, which in turn can result in very low fledging success.

These therefore are the main reasons for farmland bird declines, remembering that individual species are affected in different ways. However, on a brighter note, hedges are now protected by law and a farmer needs to seek permission, coupled with a sound reason for the removal of a hedgerow, before he or she may be allowed to grub it out.

There has also been much research into farmland birds since the findings of previous atlases, including the 1986–91 Hampshire Atlas were published in *BoH*. This knowledge has fed into Government-funded Stewardship schemes first introduced in England under the Countryside Stewardship Scheme in 1991 and evolving into the Environmental Stewardship Scheme in 2004. They are voluntary but are designed to reward farmers who manage existing habitats in a way that will benefit wildlife and also to increase biodiversity by creating new habitats for farmland wildlife.

For example, as shown in the box *above*, farmers can now be paid to leave stubbles over winter, plant areas of wild bird seed mix (seed-bearing crops left over winter for birds to utilise), cut hedges on rotation so that blossom and berries occur, establish grass margins next to hedges and watercourses and create insect-rich habitats for birds to forage in. Hampshire farmers have been very good at taking up these options, with approximately three quarters of them entering a Stewardship scheme.

Disappointingly, despite increased understanding and practical steps taken to reverse the downward trends, as the following species accounts show, the declines in Hampshire's farmland birds have continued over the past two decades. The implementation of the Stewardship options have not, to date, shown a dramatic change in these trends, but there is room for optimism. Initial results suggest that if the options are implemented on a wide enough scale across the county, these populations should start to recover. However, following cut-backs, less money will be available in future so the number of farmer agreements is expected to fall, more than halving over the next few years. This risks leaving us with a landscape containing distributed hot-spots where farmland birds are readily found, while populations in the wider countryside continue to decline.

Heathland

The UK has approximately 20% of Europe's remaining lowland heath. However, over 90% of Hampshire's heathland outside the New Forest has been lost since the late 1800s (*Figure vi*); today we have a total area within the county of approximately 13,000 ha of which 11,400 ha are in the New Forest. Heathland in Hampshire is classified as lowland heath, a diverse mosaic of dry, damp or wet habitats found up to 300 m above sea level. A defining characteristic of heathland is nutrient-poor acidic soils, often sandy and free draining. Few plants can flourish on these types of soil, which means that species tolerant of such conditions have an advantage.

Hampshire's heathlands are almost totally confined to four areas: the New Forest; Ringwood Forest (part of the Dorset Heaths); the Thames Basin and the western Weald. There are smaller, more fragmented heaths to be found in the south coast plain and Hampshire lowlands. Most areas of lowland heath are now protected by national and international designations. Hampshire includes parts of three heathland Special Protection Areas (SPA) and five Special Areas of Conservation (SAC). The three heathland SPAs have been designated under the European Birds Directive to protect the populations of three scarce heathland birds – Nightjar, Woodlark and Dartford Warbler – that breed on them. The New Forest, in particular, also holds significant numbers of woodland and wetland birds. The former include nationally important populations of Honey-buzzard, Wood Warbler, Firecrest

and Hawfinch while the marsh and mires are the breeding grounds for waders such as Curlew, Redshank and Snipe. In winter, the larger areas of open heathland provide refuge for Hen Harrier, Merlin and Great Grey Shrike.

Lowland heath is predominantly a man-made habitat and requires management to prevent succession to woodland. Pollen studies indicate that areas of traditional heathland such as the Breckland in East Anglia, were covered in trees prior to the establishment of heathland vegetation as early as 900 BC. It is thought that heaths developed via clearance and grazing of woodland, thereby preventing regeneration of the trees.

In Medieval times, heathland was a valued resource and many areas were protected as common land. In the Middle Ages the introduction of Rabbits provided a motive for maintaining heaths. They shared the grazing with the commoners' animals and provided the landowner a good return on land which otherwise yielded little financial benefit.

Nowadays, although there is little agricultural value to be gained from heathland, other forms of human intervention continue to threaten the very existence of this important ecological habitat. Many commercial softwood plantations have been established on heaths in the past. Today, ongoing urban developments in the surrounding areas combine to mount farther pressure on the remaining heathland fragments. These include increased recreation and amenity use, mineral extraction and road and pipeline extensions. Climate change too, potentially increasing the frequency of

Acid grassland, Emer Bog – *Trevor Codlin*

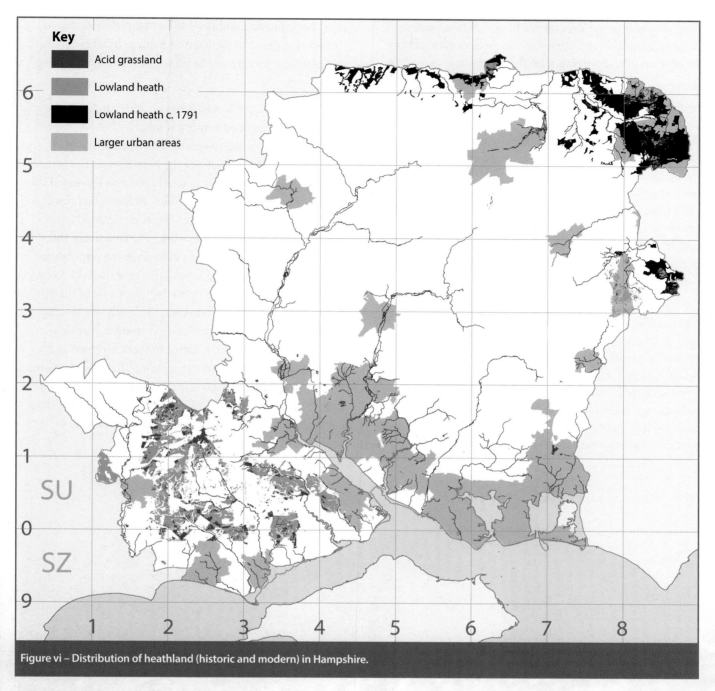

Key

- ■ Acid grassland
- ■ Lowland heath
- ■ Lowland heath c. 1791
- ■ Larger urban areas

SU

SZ

Figure vi – Distribution of heathland (historic and modern) in Hampshire.

Heathland, Browndown, Gosport – *Trevor Codlin*

long, dry summers, raises the likelihood of fires, both natural and deliberate. These can have a devastating effect on vegetation and sedentary heathland species.

Probably the biggest remaining threat to heathland is neglect and lack of management. If areas of heathland are not regularly cut, grazed and possibly burnt (often in combination), they soon become overgrown by scrub and then trees. Grazing is often not possible as the impracticalities of fencing loom large, because people feel their access is being restricted so cut holes in fence lines, or object because they are frightened of livestock. Additional problems are that, in many cases, heaths tend to be small and fragmented, so that grazing becomes even harder to implement, with access to fresh water sometimes also being a handicap.

So, the big issues that need to be addressed are tree felling, where either timber production has been introduced in the past or where trees have naturally developed over time, and control of scrub where it has begun to dominate areas of heath. It is important to note though that some scrub and a few scattered trees are an important part of the heathland habitat, especially for species such as Nightjar and Hobby. Invasive non-native species such as rhododendron, which particularly thrive on acidic soils, can invade heathland at an alarming rate and need to be completely removed. Action also needs to be taken to manage bracken as often this plant can swamp out heather and other low growing plants.

Despite all these problems, between 2001 and 2006 the Hampshire Heathland Project, funded by the Heritage Lottery Fund, worked to restore 75% of the county's degenerate heathland outside the New Forest. The project also recreated over 300 ha of heathland and increased the area of grazed heathland by 370 ha. In 2009 the project was awarded a grant from the SITA Trust Enriching Nature Programme to continue this work. The benefits of this management programme can be seen in the populations of Dartford Warblers and Woodlarks that reached record levels in the years leading up to the beginning of the HBA. It should be recognised, however, that both species also benefited from the long run of mild winters over this period and more recently, their numbers dropped as a result of hard winters and wet springs. These fluctuations in their populations underline the vulnerability of two iconic Hampshire species and the importance of ongoing management of their remaining heathland habitat to maintain it in optimum condition.

Housing adjacent to heathland, Elvetham Heath – *Robert Still*

Woodland

With woodland covering around 67,000 ha, or 17·7% of the total area, Hampshire is a relatively well-wooded English county (*Figure vii*). Only Surrey (22·4%) and West Sussex (18·9%) have higher proportions. Cambridgeshire (3·5%) is the least wooded. About 28,000 ha of Hampshire's woodland is classified as ancient, having had a continuous history of woodland cover since the year 1600. This includes, of course, parts of the New Forest which was created as a royal forest by William I in about 1079.

Some bird species associated with Hampshire woodland have shown worrying signs of decline, with both Willow Tit and Lesser Spotted Woodpecker in particular ringing alarm bells. In contrast, some other woodland species such as the Great Spotted Woodpecker and Nuthatch are faring well. So what changes have been occurring within Hampshire woodland that may be impacting on this community of birds?

In days gone by, Hampshire woodland was generally a busy place with a thriving coppicing industry creating hurdles, spars and charcoal amongst other things. Timber was also extracted to be used in a wide array of building operations and so woodland not only employed people but was also profitable to the landowner. However, many woods have now become neglected with little or no management taking place. Coppice that is abandoned rapidly loses its under-storey of plants and assumes a relatively stable, simple, multi-stemmed, open structure. Such woods support extremely low densities of breeding birds and depleted numbers of species.

Even within managed woodland, owners have tended to reduce the amount of thinning out of the least good trees, which have become uneconomic as timber prices have fallen, resulting in woods that are heavily shaded with little, if any, under-storey. Therefore many of Hampshire's woodlands have now become very uniform in age and structure, with a high canopy that has closed over, shading out the shrub and field layers below. It is this under-storey that is so important to many bird species such as Nightingale, Dunnock, Song Thrush, Willow Warbler, Marsh Tit, Willow Tit and Bullfinch.

To exacerbate things farther, the number of deer within Hampshire has exploded in recent times, especially the Roe Deer and Fallow Deer populations with Reeve's Muntjac too now being found across the whole of the county. The intensified grazing and browsing pressure caused by this growing deer population is very likely to have resulted in a reduction of habitat quality and contributed to the declines of some woodland birds. For instance, research in Bradfield Woods in Suffolk found that Nightingales spent 69% of their time in the 6% of the woodland from which deer had been excluded using fencing, and that territory density was 15 times greater in deer-free areas than in browsed vegetation of the same age (*Holt et al.* 2010).

Beech wood near Kingsclere – *Robert Still*

Key
Broadleaved woodland
Coniferous woodland
Ancient woodland
Larger urban areas

Figure vii – Distribution of woodland in Hampshire.

Abandoned Hazel coppice, nr Odiham – *Robert Still*

Loss of open space has occurred within some woods as rides and glades have become overgrown; this may have affected a number of species such as Blackcap, Garden Warbler and Chiffchaff that prefer more open woodland. The lack of light reaching the woodland floor is likely to lead to a decline in plant diversity which in turn diminishes the quality of a year-round food supply. Indeed, a national survey found that the woodland ground flora deteriorated by 19% between 1990 and 2007, the fall being particularly sharp for ancient woodland indicator species, which declined by 34% against the 1990 baseline (Defra 2009).

The reduction in shrub and field layers may also have exposed some woodland species to increased predation thereby reducing their productivity. For example, a reduction in the amount of cover may not only reduce the number of suitable nest sites but also make it easier for Foxes, Grey Squirrels and corvids to locate the nests and predate them.

So a lack of general woodland management, coupled with a burgeoning deer population, has resulted in many Hampshire woods becoming rather uniform in structure with a dense closed canopy, few medium sized trees and poor shrub and field layers. This lack of diversity might well have led to changes in food supply, increased predation, and competition for suitable nest sites, which may all be exerting a combined effect on bird populations.

Natural events can maintain some diversity in Hampshire woods. For example, the two great storms of 1987 and 1990

created for a while plenty of open areas along with a rich source of damaged and fallen timber, ideal for many species of wildlife. Unfortunately, most woods were quickly tidied up and replanted so, to maintain the habitat more suitable for birds, a return to more sympathetic management is vital. With the help of Government grants and the creation of new markets that utilize wood products, we can once again start a sustainable exploitation of Hampshire's woodland that will let in light and help restore structure. This, coupled with a well-organised, joined-up policy of deer control across the county, could reverse the decline of many of the woodland birds that we have witnessed in recent times.

Finally, there are two additional factors, potentially looming on the horizon, which may well have an impact on our woodland. These are disease and climate change. Ash constitutes 16% of broadleaf tree cover in Britain and oak 26%. Both are at risk of significant disease impact in coming years that could radically change the whole aspect and structure of Hampshire's woodland habitat. The Forestry Commission is also currently advising landowners to diversify the tree species planted and to use national broadleaf stock. The predicted drier, more drought-prone summers could, for instance, make shallow rooted trees such as Beech a non-viable long term choice, so the Commission suggests that it would make sense to use native species such as Small-leaved Lime, Alder, Aspen and Hornbeam in new plantings.

Alder carr, River Loddon, Old Basing – *Robert Still*

Coniferous woodland, Emer Bog – *Trevor Codlin*

Mature oak woodland,
Denny Wood, New Forest
– Robert Still

Inland water

Hampshire is blessed with a rich and diverse variety of rivers and wetlands (*Figure viii*), including a significant number of groundwater-fed chalk rivers, which are of national and international importance for nature conservation. The combined length of rivers and streams in Hampshire is 1,125 km, including 632 km of braided chalk rivers. Larger man-made open water areas such as fish ponds (e.g. Alresford Pond) and gravel pits (e.g. Blashford Lakes) have also created important habitats for waterfowl. Gravel pits in particular have undoubtedly increased the numbers and variety of Hampshire's birds in recent years with species such as Gadwall, Tufted Duck, Common Tern and Little Ringed Plover benefitting from the increased availability of suitable habitat.

Less obvious perhaps have been the changes in the number of smaller ponds. Before mechanisation, there were around one million plough horses kept on farms in Britain and when ploughing it was very convenient to have a pond situated in the corner of most fields so that the horse could drink. The switch from horses to tractors took away the usefulness of ponds, so that the number found in the countryside drastically declined, due to either neglect (scrubbing up and drying out) or because they were deliberately filled in. However, a recent national survey showed that the number of ponds increased by 11% between 1996 and 2007, which is most encouraging news. Unfortunately, the same survey also highlighted that, over the same period, their biological condition deteriorated, with only 8% of ponds found to be in good overall condition (*Countryside Survey* 2007). So let us take a closer look at some of the issues facing our remaining inland water bodies.

For centuries, man has had a major impact on the rivers and the water environment by taking and using water, agricultural intensification, discharging waste water back into rivers and the sea, the modification of river channels and, through development in both urban and rural areas, changing the speed of surface water run-off. Soil, fertilisers and pesticides have also found their way into our watercourses from adjacent farmland, sometimes causing severe problems in the case of spillages but more often creating subtle changes within the ecosystem. Such factors have combined to bring about big declines in some of the birds dependent on riverside habitat. For example, breeding waders such as Snipe and Redshank have almost disappeared from Hampshire's river valleys and Yellow Wagtail, another species associated with the habitat, no longer breeds in the county. But it is not all bad news. Over the past two decades we have seen the arrival of a new breeding species – the Goosander – on the River Avon, and spectacular numbers of Black-tailed Godwits on the Avon floods in winter.

The majority of water consumption in Hampshire is by people in their homes. Average domestic water use per person in the south-east is around 160 litres a day, although there is a wide variation with house occupancy, income and lifestyles. Water is becoming increasingly scarce as demand continues to increase and changes in lifestyle mean that we use 55% more water per person now than 25 years ago. Most is extracted by water companies directly from the rivers Itchen and Test as well as from groundwater under the chalk. The potential impacts of a changing climate on supply and demand are expected to be significant. We are likely to see more variable weather conditions with wetter winters and more frequent droughts in summer. This could

Chalk stream, River Itchen near Winchester – *Martin Bennett*

lead to more frequent flooding during winter and reduced river flows and lower groundwater levels during the summer which could result in pressure on water resources. In addition, population growth and economic regeneration, particularly in South Hampshire, will mean increasing demand on water (and other natural resources).

Eutrophication, the enrichment of water bodies by nutrients, can be a naturally occurring phenomenon but there is increasing concern over the number of rivers, lakes and coastal waters in which it is developing into a major problem, aggravated by human inputs. The eutrophication of water is increased where fertilisers are washed off farmland by rainwater or where sewage, which is high in phosphate, leaks from septic tanks and cesspits directly into rivers and lakes. The resulting increase of nitrate and phosphate levels in the water encourages plant growth, which in turn can slow water flow and can lead to serious flooding issues. Reduced water flow can also allow the silting up of gravel spawning beds, which are important for species such as Atlantic Salmon, Brown Trout and lampreys.

In very slow-flowing brackish waters or lakes the increased nutrient levels can lead to algal blooms on the surface. These can prevent sunlight reaching other water plants which can then die. Bacteria break down the dead plants and use up the oxygen in the water so that, in the worst case, the water can become completely lifeless. All of these issues can have a knock on impact on the waterfowl and other birds that depend on these areas of water. Whether they eat fish, invertebrates or vegetation, birds can be severely affected by poor water quality.

To combat these problems, a joint project between EA and NE, funded by Defra and the Rural Development Programme for England, has been set up to work in priority catchments within the country. Catchment Sensitive Farming (CSF) delivers practical solutions and targeted support to enable farmers and land managers to take voluntary action to reduce diffuse water pollution from agriculture and to protect water bodies and the environment.

Farmers can gain free advice and capital grants through local partners to enable them to address farm-based problems that may occur. Local events giving advice, information and encouraging changes in behaviour are regularly organised. Sometimes farmers are simply not aware of the problems that certain fields may be causing to adjacent watercourses. For instance research has demonstrated that freely draining soils with good soil structure typically have less than 2% water run-off, whereas compacted 'sealed' soils can often have up to 60% run-off (Environment Agency 2012).

Ploughing can substantially decrease the number of earthworms living within the soil, whereas cultivation which only disturbs the very top layer of the soil (known as minimum tillage) results in the establishment of high populations. Given plenty of earthworm tunnels, water can be absorbed at a rate of four to ten times that of fields without worm tunnels. This in turn helps the soil to take up water during storms and retain it during drought. Increased worm numbers can of course also benefit farmland bird species such as Lapwing, Stone-curlew and Song Thrush.

The European Water Framework Directive is currently being implemented throughout Member States and is intended to establish a framework for the protection of surface waters and ground waters. We are beginning to see some encouraging improvements, although there is a long way to go if we are to really address the multiple problems that our aquatic ecosystems face.

Fleet Pond – *Robert Still*

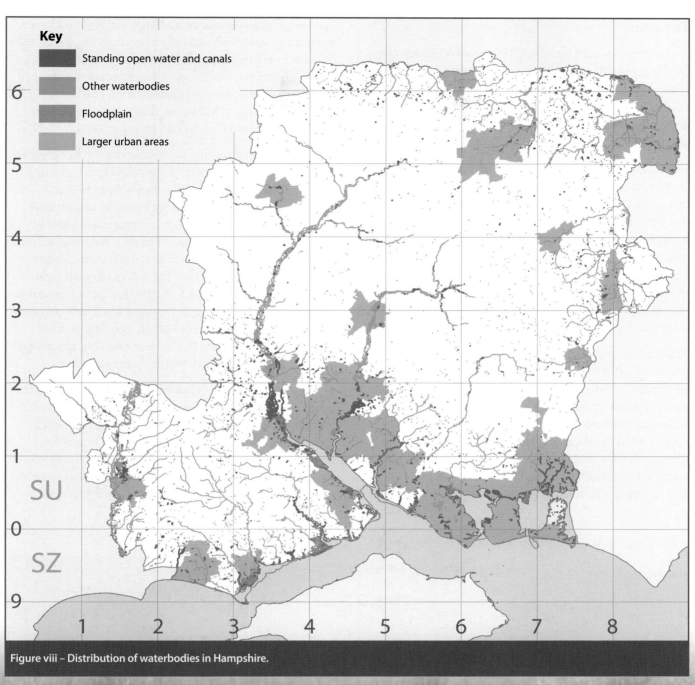

Key

- Standing open water and canals
- Other waterbodies
- Floodplain
- Larger urban areas

Figure viii – Distribution of waterbodies in Hampshire.

Titchfield – Martin Bennett

The coast

Arguably, along with farmland, Hampshire's coastal areas (*Figure ix*) are being subjected to more pressures and change than any of the county's other habitats. Climate change, house building, recreation, disturbance, predation and competition for space are all increasingly likely to impact on the county's coastal bird populations.

In fact, the two habitats – farmland and coast – are directly connected because mudflats can be adversely affected by nutrients from farmland, homes and industry being discharged into the estuaries by rivers. This may encourage a mat of vegetation to form on the surface, smothering the mud and changing bird feeding behaviour. A dense layer of seaweed causes de-oxygenation of the underlying mudflats reducing the diversity of invertebrates. Decomposing seaweed mats can produce hydrogen sulphide which, in large quantities, is toxic to marine life.

Many of the county's coastal breeding bird colonies are on low-lying saltmarsh or shingle islands. These are already susceptible to tidal flooding but if current climate change predictions are realised, this problem can only get worse. Although estimates cover a wide range, the latest mid-range forecast by the Intergovernmental Panel on Climate Change (IPCC) puts the most likely sea level rise about 20 cm above current levels by 2050 (IPCC 2014). This, coupled with weather patterns that may well include more severe storms and high winds, could have a devastating impact on seabird nesting colonies. Predicted changes to existing intertidal habitat across the north Solent, regardless of defences or nature conservation designations, are estimated at an increase of 60 ha for mudflat and a loss of 812 ha for saltmarsh over the next 100 years (Channel Coastal Observatory 2008).

The relative scarcity of suitable nesting sites in the Solent area has resulted in many sites having gull and tern breeding-colonies intermixed, with birds often obliged to nest closely together. This can have both positive and negative effects. The high density of birds can provide a degree of protection from predators but it can also lead to Little Terns being forced to seek alternative sites when their colonies are annexed by larger species. The lack of large sites and competition from other birds, means that Little Terns must also nest at high density, thus putting a whole sub-colony at risk of total failure from predation, flooding or other hazards. Many nests may be clustered into tight groups with nests as close as one or two metres from each other.

A reduction in the area of saltmarsh will also impact on the internationally-important populations of birds that winter in the Solent. For example, it will most probably result in some coastal species becoming increasingly dependent on terrestrial habitat for feeding and roosting. The Brent Goose already feeds on agricultural land as well as on urban playing fields and other amenity grasslands where it is

Coastal grazing marsh, Farlington Marshes – *Ian Cameron-Reid*

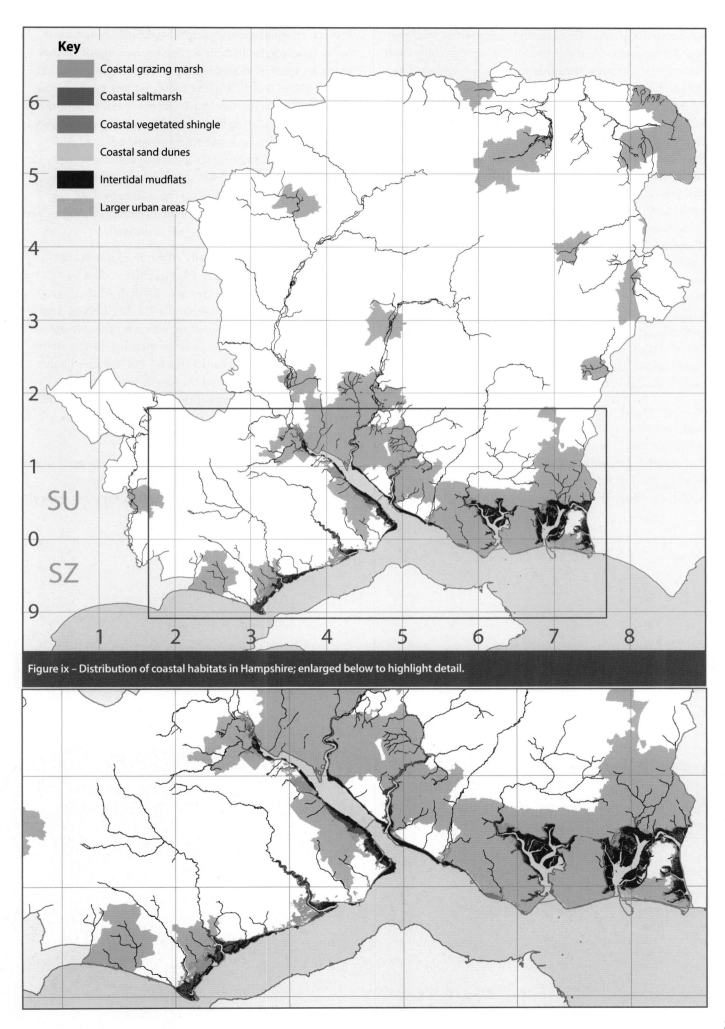

Key

- Coastal grazing marsh
- Coastal saltmarsh
- Coastal vegetated shingle
- Coastal sand dunes
- Intertidal mudflats
- Larger urban areas

Figure ix – Distribution of coastal habitats in Hampshire; enlarged below to highlight detail.

subject to disturbance. Several roost sites used by waders at high tide are also vulnerable to disturbance, especially from recreational activities. The birds are therefore subjected to the combined pressures of coastal squeeze and increasing urbanisation. There have been relatively recent losses of several Brent Goose feeding sites and wader roosts due to development and these have had a cumulative impact or knock-on effect on other sites. To secure the Solent's Brent Goose and wader populations into the future it is essential that planning authorities take steps to protect existing feeding and roosting sites and, where possible, to create new ones. A survey of Brent Goose feeding sites confirmed that disturbance is an increasing issue and that accordingly, sites farther away from buildings, in particular residential homes, are preferred; the bigger the site the better, as geese like to see danger approaching to avoid being caught by surprise. Considering that there are 1·7 million residential properties (equating to approximately three million residents) within 50 km of the Solent shoreline (including Dorset and West Sussex), one can start to surmise the pressures that roosting geese and waders may be subjected to.

More general disturbance from an assortment of land-based activities takes place in varying degrees throughout the whole length of the Hampshire coastline. These include bait digging, dog walking (with dogs on and off of leads), jogging, cycling, fishing, family outings and, dare I say it, birdwatching. The Solent Disturbance and Mitigation Project, set up to monitor impacts on birds, found some worrying evidence that the increasing number of visitors to the coastline is indeed having an impact on birds. The project found that 14% of the routes visitors use go below the mean high water tide mark where waterfowl commonly feed, especially during the winter. The level of disturbance recorded was determined by how people behaved and where they went rather than the actual volume of use. Activities that took place on intertidal areas were more likely to result in disturbance. Dog-walking was of particular concern with 27% of disturbances causing major flight by birds when the dog was off the lead.

Any nesting bird is potentially vulnerable, at varying degrees of risk, to having its eggs or chicks taken by a predator. However, research has highlighted that all Little Tern colonies throughout the UK and Ireland have regularly experienced predation, which is probably the largest and most common cause of their low productivity. Once predators have found a fruitful site, they are likely to make repeated visits and the longer-lived predator species will regularly exploit the prey source in future years. In fact, predation has in certain circumstances led to complete failure of nesting tern colonies.

It is the Fox, Carrion Crow and Brown Rat that are particularly problematic. These can, where the situation allows, be controlled using legal methods though this is often difficult

Mudflats, Langstone Harbour – *Robert Still*

in areas frequented by people and dogs. Various non-lethal methods have been used with varying levels of success, including electric fencing to keep Foxes out, supplementary feeding, nest caging and chick shelters to help deter avian predators including Kestrels and gulls. Even so, lethal control of predators by humane means is often the only satisfactory solution but, given the large population-reservoirs of all the main culprits, such programmes need sustained management effort to be successful.

The Hampshire coastline is, on paper, well protected with three SPAs – Solent & Southampton Water, Portsmouth Harbour and Chichester & Langstone Harbours. These sites are additionally designated under the Ramsar Convention (commonly known as Ramsar sites). Both designations include recognition of the international importance of the Solent harbours and estuaries for wintering water bird assemblages, and/or individually important populations of one or more species. Together they support a total wintering population of around 150,000 birds although numbers are declining. While this may be due in part to local factors, the more important cause is thought to be the impact of warmer winters. Milder conditions are allowing migrants to over-winter nearer to their northerly breeding grounds, stopping short of onward movement to the UK.

Sites designated as SPAs are given special protection and as a consequence any plans or projects (including development) can only go ahead if it can be proven that they will have no adverse effects on the SPA. Since 1992, the Solent Forum (a regional coastal group made up of councils, harbour authorities and other organisations) has provided a platform to deliver Integrated Coastal Zone Management in the Solent sub-region of the South East. It operates at a strategic coastal management level, providing a network for closer working relationships, information dissemination and discussion of topical coastal issues.

It needs to be remembered that it is not just the designated sites that are of importance to birds, but also the wider area around them as has been discussed. Current pressures from development (residential, industrial and port/marinas), recreation, coastal re-alignment, climate change, sea-level rise and coastal squeeze all highlight the urgent need to identify currently important locations and the potential changes in their usage by birds over time. All data gathered will help to influence planning and development management and assist in assessing plans and projects which could impact on these important sites for birds. So, despite the designations and protection which are in place, our coastal habitats and the wildlife that they support continue to be under enormous and increasing pressures. There still remains a constant nibbling away – sometimes literally – of suitable habitat for our coastal birds.

Coastal vegetated shingle, Browndown Point – *Trevor Codlin*

Urban areas

Hampshire has a population of approximately 1·8 million, making it the third most populous county (after Kent and Essex) in England and home to one in seven people in the South East region (excluding London). What is particularly interesting is that 77% of people live in just 15% of the area, tightly packed into the southern coastal area or alongside the M3 corridor in the north of the county (*Figure x*).

For some bird species, the urban environment is a key habitat. For the House Sparrow, Swift, House Martin and Starling in particular, our towns and cities are important breeding areas as they all rely on buildings for nest sites. In recent years Peregrines have opted increasingly to nest inland, using tall buildings which offer them a habitat similar to natural coastal cliffs with ample Feral Pigeons as a handy source of food.

Parks, gardens and churchyards within built-up areas, along with green corridors introduced by many local councils in an attempt to encourage connectivity between habitats through the urban landscape, are also important habitats for species such as Spotted Flycatcher, Bullfinch, Dunnock, Song Thrush and Mistle Thrush. Green spaces within urban areas are often planted with ornamental trees and shrubs, many of which produce fruits and berries in the autumn and winter, providing a rich source of food for city-dwelling birds. In fact, supermarket car parks have become well known places for spotting one of the most colourful of our winter visitors, the Waxwing! As has already been pointed out, in coastal areas, some of the larger open green spaces such as playing fields are commonly frequented by Brent Geese along with several species of gull and some waders.

It has been estimated that up to 75% of households provide food for wild birds at some point during the year and, nationally, the bird-feeding industry is estimated to be worth some £200 million annually. This may well be important for the over-winter survival of some birds and it is interesting that species such a Goldfinch, Siskin, Long-tailed Tit and even Bullfinch are becoming common visitors to garden bird feeders nowadays.

Many people, with even the smallest of gardens, not only feed birds but have also put up a nest box or two, perhaps providing suitable sites for hole-nesting species when otherwise breeding might not have been possible in the locality. This connection with birds through feeding and providing nest sites for them in gardens is, for many folk, one of the few real contacts that they may have with nature and therefore becomes a hugely important aspect of encouraging an interest in birds and other wildlife.

Reserves

Hampshire is fortunate to have many top quality nature reserves which placed it (perhaps surprisingly) as the number one county in a poll carried out by the online magazine Wildlife Extra, with three out of the top 15 most visited reserves being in the county (Blashford Lakes, Old Winchester Hill and Swanwick Lakes). Excellent coastal sites such as Farlington Marshes, Langstone Harbour, Titchfield Haven, Keyhaven & Pennington Marshes offer top quality habitat, while inland fresh-water reserves, in addition to Blashford and Swanwick Lakes, also include areas such as Anton Lakes and Fleet Pond.

The New Forest is a wonderful county resource offering a wide range of habitats for birds, particularly heathland and ancient woodland. Heathland areas outside the New Forest include many excellent sites such as Woolmer Forest in the Weald and Yateley Common in the Thames Basin. Although much smaller than the New Forest, these areas hold most of the same heathland species and often at higher densities.

Garden feeders with recently fledged House Sparrows, Basingstoke, June 2015 – *Phil Dixon*

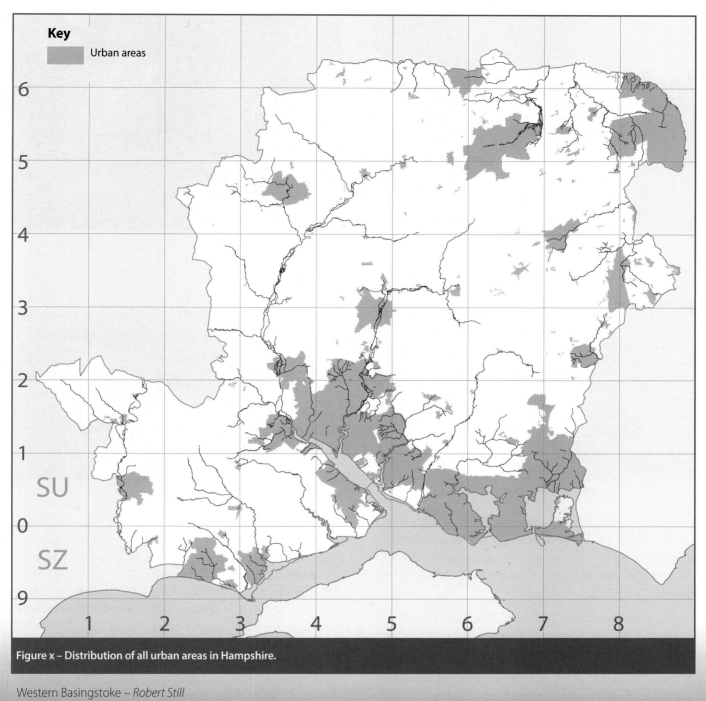

Key
Urban areas

Figure x – Distribution of all urban areas in Hampshire.

Western Basingstoke – *Robert Still*

Blashford Lakes – *Robert Still*

Pamber Forest – *Robert Still*

Martin Down – *Martin Bennett*

Hampshire has too many great expanses of woodland to mention them all, and of course they are not all official reserves; some of the larger areas include Pamber Forest, Alice Holt, Queen Elizabeth Country Park and Harewood Forest.

On the chalk, areas such as Martin Down and Beacon and Butser Hills are all good for birds, especially during migration periods.

As I have discussed throughout this chapter, as wonderful as these reserves are, they are just that – reserves. These oases for nature within an often otherwise increasingly hostile environment, will undoubtedly struggle for survival unless we work hard to stop encroachment from numerous outside influences. We must look at conservation management much more on a landscape scale, endeavouring to link these important reserves together in a far better way than we currently do, so that wildlife, including birds, can move more easily between their favoured habitats.

Factors affecting all habitats

So far, I have concentrated on Hampshire's habitats and the pressures impacting on them one by one but some threats are likely to affect all habitats. To conclude this chapter, I will touch on two of these: climate change and invasive species and disease.

Climate change

The first 14 years of the 21st century ranked as the hottest since record keeping began in 1880, with global average temperatures having risen by nearly 0·8 °C since the late 19th century, and rising at about 0·2 °C/decade over the latter part of the 20th century, although much slower more recently. Sea-surface temperatures around the UK coast have also risen over the past three decades by about 0·7 °C and as mentioned previously, global sea-level rise has accelerated between the mid-19th and mid-20th centuries and is now about 3 mm per year.

Over the past 45 years all regions of the UK have experienced an increase in heavy rainfall events, while in the summer all regions except northeast England and north Scotland show a decrease in rainfall.

The impacts of global warming on biodiversity include changes in species distribution and range, a good example of this being the Cetti's Warbler which has moved 150 km farther north within the UK in the past 40 years. Changes in the timing of seasonal events may also impact on the productivity of nesting birds. For example earlier springs could result in the nesting cycle of birds such as the Blue Tit becoming 'out of sync.' with peak caterpillar numbers. Meanwhile, changes to habitat character could occur as a result of hotter, drier summers. These could adversely affect shallow-rooted plants such as Beech and thus slowly, over time, change the composition of existing habitats and the invertebrates that are dependent upon them.

If the forecasted changes in average temperature and precipitation levels do actually occur, they are likely to lead to changes in vegetation composition and faunal distribution. Some species and habitats are likely to benefit, while others will suffer. For example, some heathland species are at the northern limit of their range in the UK and may be able to spread northwards. However, hot, dry summers may lead to more heathland fires. Although often used as a management tool to promote new heather growth and clear invasive scrub, extensive, uncontrolled fires can be very damaging to wildlife. They can devastate animal and plant populations and kill the rootstock of desirable plant species. Bird populations on small, fragmented heathlands are especially vulnerable to local extinctions but are fortunate in that they are mobile and can seek out new haunts. It remains to be seen whether, in such a crowded island as Britain, particularly in southern England, there is available space for new habitats to evolve.

Impacts on the landscape might arise not only from rising sea level, which has already been discussed, but also from an increase in flood events and soil erosion. These could reduce the productivity of some breeding birds through, for example, having a detrimental effect on the quality of our waterways. The raised levels of carbon dioxide in the atmosphere are also affecting the oceans, causing acidification of the water which impacts on marine life and affect ocean currents. We are already seeing the negative effects of this on northern colonies of shallow-feeding sea birds such as Puffin and Guillemot.

These direct effects of climate change are likely to result in measures being put in place that may also impact on the wider natural environment. For example, growing new crops, increases in summer irrigation and geographical shifts in arable and livestock production could well occur, but how these indirect changes may affect biodiversity remains less certain. Indeed, it needs to be said that not all wildlife will be affected in a negative way, with many species liking the new climatic conditions within Hampshire. We are probably already experiencing such changes with formerly Continental breeding species such as Little Egret, Mediterranean Gull and Firecrest now firmly established in the county.

Invasive Non-Native Species And Disease

The impact of disease and the arrival and spread of non-native species can have dramatic impacts on native wildlife, particularly when the affected populations are small or fragmented. Hampshire is already inundated with invasive non-native species, some of which have been around for a considerable time. These include the Grey Squirrel (bringing Squirrel Pox which kills native Red Squirrels) and American Mink (a major predator of the Water Vole and

water birds); others are relative new-comers such as New Zealand Pigmyweed (which out-competes our native pond flora) while at least one more, the Ring-necked Parakeet (a potential competitor of nest sites), is waiting on the side-lines ready to invade the county. We should not forget, of course, that some of the birds that we now take for granted as Hampshire residents, were originally introduced. These include common and familiar species such as Canada Goose and Pheasant. It is probable that the decline in our native species will be balanced to a degree by additional introductions as we are already seeing with Egyptian Goose and anticipating with Ring-necked Parakeet.

Often, these human introductions can cause quite a lot of turmoil in the conservation world, as shown, for example, by the case of the Ruddy Duck. This attractive duck is native to North America and closely related to the endangered White-headed Duck which breeds in Spain, North Africa and western and central Asia. It was brought to the UK in the 1930s and 1940s for captive wildfowl collections. Escapees first bred in the wild in 1952 and by 2000 the UK population numbered around 6,000 birds. Unfortunately, Ruddy Ducks can interbreed with White-headed Ducks, producing fertile hybrids. This is happening in Spain and there was concern that if the number of incoming Ruddy Ducks was allowed to increase, they would inundate the local White-headed Duck population. As Ruddy Ducks are more promiscuous in their mating behaviour, international conservation organisations and European governments feared that hybridisation posed a very serious threat to the survival of the White-headed Duck. The UK held the largest population of feral Ruddy Ducks in Europe and it was therefore considered vital that action was taken to remove the source of birds reaching the Continent. However, many birders were unhappy with this action and the stance taken by government and some conservation bodies who support this view.

This is just one well known example of an alien species causing conflict but it is likely that the increasing movement of people and products, including exotic pets and horticultural imports from around the world, will continue to bring in new diseases and species. Only recently, the UK has discovered Ash Dieback disease, brought into the country on infected stock from Europe. We are yet to find out if we are to lose 90% of our Ash trees as has been the case in parts of the Continent and, if so, what impact that might have on our native wildlife. Trichomonosis, a disease caused by microscopic parasites, which has been found for some time in pigeons, doves (including Turtle Dove) and birds of prey, now seems to be expanding (since 2005) to effect garden birds, particularly finches such as Greenfinch and Chaffinch. Reasons are unclear as to why this particular disease is on the increase.

Looking into the future, it is probable that foreign species and new diseases reaching our shores will create many more headaches both for Hampshire birds and Hampshire birders.

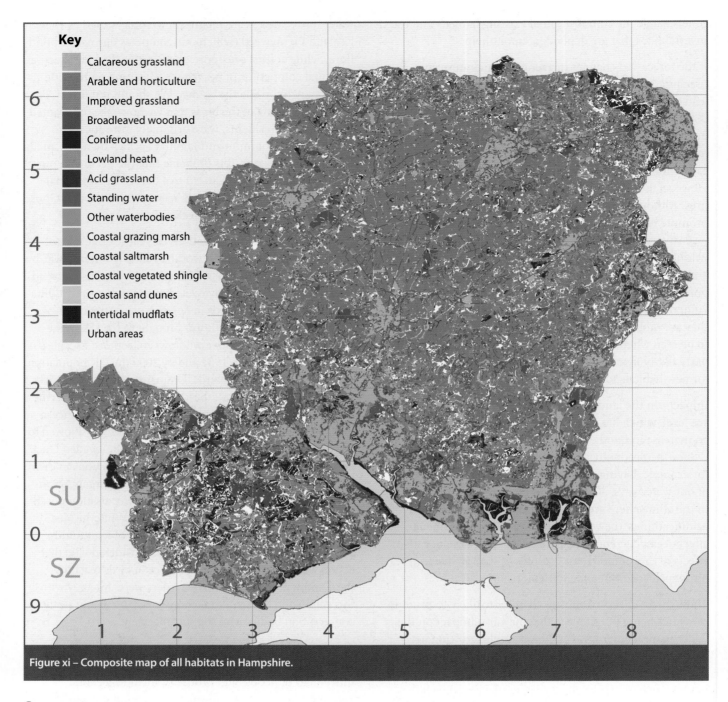

Key
- Calcareous grassland
- Arable and horticulture
- Improved grassland
- Broadleaved woodland
- Coniferous woodland
- Lowland heath
- Acid grassland
- Standing water
- Other waterbodies
- Coastal grazing marsh
- Coastal saltmarsh
- Coastal vegetated shingle
- Coastal sand dunes
- Intertidal mudflats
- Urban areas

Figure xi – Composite map of all habitats in Hampshire.

Summary

I started this chapter by stating how wonderful the county of Hampshire is for birds and birdwatching and that this is directly linked to the superb array of habitats that the county has to offer and that of course remains true. *Figure xi* shows a composite picture of those habitats as they exist today and provides an explanation for many of the bird distribution patterns mapped in the following pages. However, I also hope that readers will be reminded of the multitude of difficulties our local wildlife face and that it is often a combination of these various pressures, acting together, that can cause such major problems for a number of our precious Hampshire bird species.

We can, of course, all do our bit in helping to protect and enhance the habitats that our birds rely on within the county, supported by recording the birds that we see. The data that the Hampshire Ornithological Society collects through its members' recording efforts play a crucial role in being able to influence a wide range of decisions that might affect the welfare of our county's birds. Hopefully, as you enjoy studying the pages of this book, this chapter may have given you a précis of the issues that Hampshire birds face in our ever changing local landscape and, thereby, help you to put some of the changes you see described in the Atlas into context.

Red Kite crossing the M3 – *Robert Still*

Introduction to the Species Accounts

Coverage

The accounts which follow cover all wild bird species recorded in Hampshire during the five winters 2007/08–2011/12 and the five summers 2008–12. Wild species, invariably rarities, recorded during 2007–12 but outside the eight HBA recording months are included in a separate section following the accounts (*page 427*). Some introduced or escaped species which have established breeding populations in Hampshire or neighbouring counties are included in the accounts, even in some cases where the population has ceased to be self-sustaining. Known escapees from captivity, including those deliberately released with the aim of establishing a sustainable breeding population but have not yet done so, and those known to have arrived with human assistance (for example on board ship) are listed in a final section following the accounts (*page 428*).

Taxonomy

The naming of the species follows the eighth edition of the British list of wild birds recorded in Great Britain, published by the British Ornithologists' Union Records Committee in June 2013 (BOU 2013) and subsequent changes included in BOURC reports up until January 2014. British vernacular names are used although sometimes simplified where common usage allows. The order in which the species accounts are presented is based on the same list but has been modified in places to facilitate the page layout.

The accounts

The species accounts have been written by a team of experienced Hampshire birders most of whom have built up expertise through writing about the same species in the annual Hampshire Bird Reports (HBR). The names of the authors are given at the end of each account.

Each account begins with a brief statement of the species' current status in Hampshire. These are, with minor exceptions, the same as those used in the HBR. Certain terms are used that have an approximate numerical range associated with them as shown in *Table 3*.

In most cases, no attempt has been made to produce more accurate population estimates for Hampshire's birds as was done in *BoH*.

The maps

Where relevant, the species accounts are accompanied by maps showing the seasonal distributions and relative abundances of the species concerned. For most winter visitors, just one map is given showing the species'

Status	Number of breeding pairs	Number in winter or on passage
Very rare	Fewer than 5 records	Fewer than 10 records
Rare	Less than annual	Less than annual
Very scarce	1–10 per year	1–20 per year
Scarce	11–100	21–200
Moderately common	101–1,000	201–2,000
Common	1,001–5,000	2,001–10,000
Numerous	5,001–30,000	10,001–60,000
Abundant	30,000+	60,000+

Table 3 – Numerical ranges associated with status descriptions.

Figure xii – Hampshires's 10 km squares with inset DINTY square.

distribution and relative abundance over the November–February periods for the five winters 2007/08–2011/12. Most summer visitors have two maps showing likely breeding distribution and relative abundance during the 2008–12 April–July breeding seasons and change in likely breeding distribution between the 1986–91 and 2008–12 Atlases. For some species records outside the April–July period were included to determine breeding distributions. Residents generally have all three maps showing winter and breeding distributions plus breeding change. For reference, the three maps for Mute Swan are shown opposite.

All maps show the Hampshire county boundary and main river systems and are overlain with the Ordnance Survey 10 km square grid with the eastings and northings identified for the relevant parts of the SZ and SU 100 km grid squares. The distribution and relative abundances of birds are shown at tetrad resolution. Although not labelled on the maps, each of the 25 tetrads in a 10 km square can be identified using the conventional alphanumeric method (as used in the Gazetteer) or by means of the DINTY system. The latter approach identifies each tetrad by combining the appropriate 10 km square grid reference, as shown in *Figure*

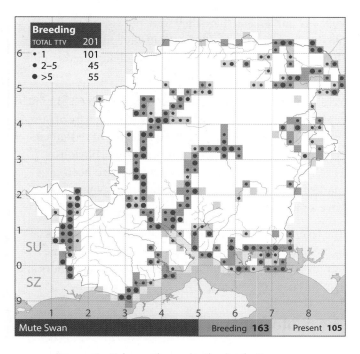

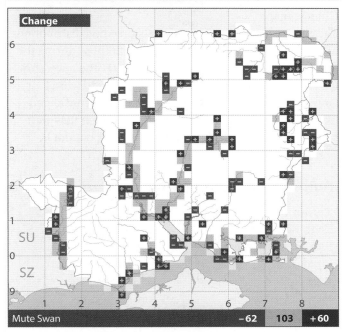

Figure xiii – Colour codes used in the distribution maps.

Breeding

■ Breeding Considered Likely (BCL)

■ Present but not considered to be breeding

● TTV: high count band

● TTV: middle count band

• TTV: low count band

NB: the associated band ranges are indicated on each map

Winter

■ Present using tetrad

● TTV: high count band

● TTV: middle count band

• TTV: low count band

NB: the associated band ranges are indicated on each map.

Change

– Breeding Loss: BCL 1986–91; not breeding 2008–12

■ No Change: BCL 1986–91 and 2008–12

+ Breeding Gain: not breeding 1986–91; BCL 2008–12

E	J	P	U	Z
D	**I**	**N**	**T**	**Y**
C	H	M	S	X
B	G	L	R	W
A	F	K	Q	V

DINTY square

xii, with a letter (excluding 'O') – shown as an inset square in the figure and in expanded form above. The system gets its name from the second row of letters in the square. As an example, this method identifies Hurst Point, the most southerly point of the Hampshire mainland, as being is SZ38E. Some species accounts refer to tetrads using the DINTY scheme.

Winter maps

The winter maps show the distribution of the species as blue-shaded tetrads. To be included the species must have been recorded actively using the tetrad, i.e. feeding, hunting or roosting in it but not simply over-flying it. White areas indicate those tetrads where the species was not recorded actively using them. The legend at the bottom of the maps gives the species name and the number of tetrads in which it was recorded.

Some of the blue-shaded tetrads also contain dark blue dots. These indicate that the species was recorded in those tetrads during one or more TTV visits. The dots vary in size representing the numbers of individuals recorded in three bands. Generally, the abundance numbers refer to the larger of the early and late season two-hour TTV counts. For those tetrads where full TTV coverage was not achieved, the numbers are the higher of those achieved in the available early or late season counts. Where possible, the mapped ranges have been chosen to result in roughly equal distributions of dot sizes. The legend in the top left corner of the map gives the total number of tetrads in which the species was recorded during TTV visits and the numerical bands associated with each size of dot, small dots representing fewer birds than larger dots.

Breeding season maps

The format of the breeding season maps is the same as the winter maps but with the species' breeding season distribution shaded in green. However, for these maps two colour-shades are used (in addition to white), light green tetrads showing where a species was present but not thought to be breeding and dark green tetrads showing where breeding was considered likely (BCL). The legend at the bottom of the maps gives the species name, the number of tetrads in which it was present but not thought to be breeding and the number where breeding was considered likely.

As with the winter maps, some tetrads also contain dots of three sizes representing the numbers of birds counted during TTV visits. The legend in the top left corner again gives the total number of tetrads in which the species was recorded during TTV visits and the numerical bands associated with each size of dot.

Change maps

The change maps compare the likely breeding distributions of species recorded during the HBA with those during the first Hampshire breeding atlas in 1986–91. The maps show tetrads shaded in three colours (in addition to white). Grey tetrads are those where the species was considered likely to be breeding in both atlases, red where they were considered likely to be breeding in 1986–91 but not in 2008–12 and green where they were not considered likely to be breeding in 1986–91 but were in 2008–12. More simply, grey tetrads represent no change, red tetrads losses and green tetrads gains.

While the green and red colour-coding will give a graphic representation of gains and losses for the majority of readers, for anyone suffering from a degree of red/green colour-blindness, the distinction will be less obvious. For this reason, the red loss squares have also been marked with a minus sign while the green gain squares have a plus symbol.

The legend at the bottom of the maps gives the species name plus the numbers of gains, losses and no-change tetrads colour- and symbol-coded to match the colours and symbols used on the maps.

The photographs and species sponsors

The species accounts (and other sections of the book) are illustrated with photographs the majority of which were taken in Hampshire by Hampshire photographers. Many, but not all, of the bird photographs were taken during the HBA period. In addition, most of the species have been sponsored by individuals whose names appear at the end of their chosen accounts. As already acknowledged, HOS is most grateful to both sets of contributors.

Authors and photographers

Authors	Photographers		
Keith Betton	Steve Bassett	Brian Fellows	Dave Perrett
Richard Carpenter	Martin Bennett	Richard Ford	Ian Pibworth
John Clark	Alex Berryman	Jacquie Frampton	Andy Pullen
Alan Cox	Keith Betton	Linda Fuller	Gareth Rees
Mark Edgeller	Tom Bickerton	Aaron Gee	David Ryves
John Eyre	Dennis Bright	Hugh Harrop	Gordon Small
Andy Johnson	Paul Brock	Alan Hayden	Barry Stalker
John Jones	Bill Brooks	Charlotte Hellewell	Robert Still
Nigel Jones	Ian Cameron-Reid	Josie Hewitt	Joe Stockwell
David Minns	Trevor Carpenter	Manny Hinge	Andy Swash
Nick Montegriffo	Trevor Codlin	Simon Ingram	Peter Thompson
Paul Norris	Steve Copsey	Richard Jacobs	Daniel Trim
Graham Osborne	Hilary Cornford	Andy Johnson	Simon Vale
Andy Page	Jason Crook	Nigel Jones	Marcus Ward
Peter Potts	Mike Crutch	Ian Julian	John Whichall
John Shillitoe	David Cuddon	Simon Layton	Ian Williamson
Matt Stevens	Mark Darlaston	John Levell	
Peter Thompson	Mike Darling	Alan Lewis	
Dave Unsworth	Caroline and Alan Dawson	Andrew Madgwick	
Marcus Ward	Phil Dixon	Elaine Mallion	
Keith Wills	Peter Drury	Bob Marchant	
Eddie Wiseman	Mike Duffy	Keith Maycock	
Simon Woolley	Darren Evans	Roger Murfitt	
Russell Wynn	John Eyre	Mark Palmer	
		Robin Pascal	

Mute Swan

Cygnus olor

A moderately common resident species

The Mute Swan is arguably the most familiar and recognisable species on the British List. Swans can be found on almost any reservoir, gravel pit, river valley, harbour or parkland with significant stretches of open water. Although they feed mainly on submerged, aquatic vegetation by reaching under the water with their long necks, they will also graze on grassland and crops and, in many localities, benefit from man providing bread and seed.

The HBA maps indicate that during the breeding season Mute Swans were recorded in over a quarter of the county's tetrads, with breeding considered likely in about 60% of them. This may underestimate the actual breeding range slightly because a few probable breeding records were discounted. Their distribution is strongly associated with the county's river system. Not surprisingly, they are largely absent from the chalk uplands and the central New Forest. In terms of breeding abundance, numbers are highest in the main river valleys, particularly the Avon, Test and Itchen, although counts during the HBA, particularly late in the breeding season, include both breeding and non-breeding birds. The highest site count during 2008–12 was a record 244 at Blashford Lakes in the Avon Valley on July 31st 2011.

The change map shows little variation in breeding range between the 1986–91 Atlas and HBA periods. Although there have been gains and losses, the overall picture in Hampshire remained basically unchanged. Nationally, the UK range has spread north and west over this period (*Bird Atlas 2007–11*). The population increased markedly following the banning of lead fishing weights in 1987 but plateaued around 2000 (*BirdTrends*). In south-east England, the population fell by 16% between 1995 and 2011 (*BBS*).

As expected for what is generally considered a sedentary species, the HBA maps show that the Mute Swan's winter and breeding distributions are very similar. As in summer, the main wintering populations are centred on the major river valleys of the Avon, Test and Itchen. Other important wintering areas are the gravel pits and lakes in the north-east of the county and the coastal harbours and estuaries, where numbers increase during hard winters. Overall, in terms of tetrads occupied, the species' range was about 9% larger in winter (293 tetrads) than in summer (268 tetrads). This reflects post-breeding dispersal to favoured wintering areas and displacement when inland waters ice over.

Although most birds don't move far from their natal areas, immigrants from farther afield do reach the county. During the HBA period a bird ringed in Greater Manchester on January 13th 2007 was seen at Hook Spit, Warsash, 295 km SSE, on September 8th 2008. Other movements included a bird ringed in Regent's Park,

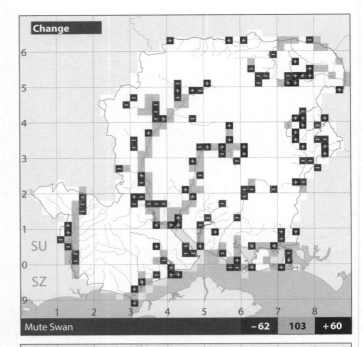

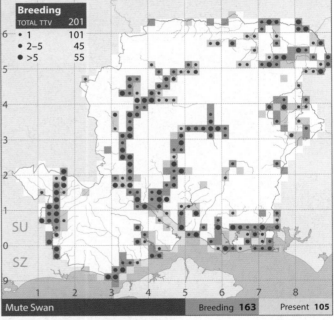

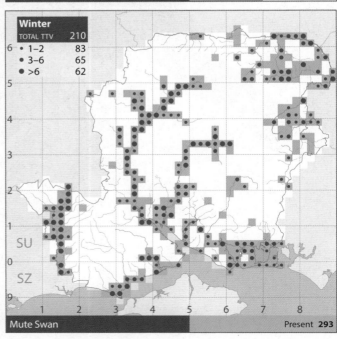

London on July 7th 1998 seen in Andover on February 24th 2011 and another ringed at Chew Valley Lake on June 29th 2004 recovered at Twyford on July 23rd 2011. Movements to and from the Continent also occur.

A nestling ringed in Gelsenkirchen, Germany on August 17th 2011, was recovered 620 km W in Ringwood on August 20th 2012.

Paul Norris

Sponsored by Tim Walker

Mute Swan, Hillhead Harbour, May 2015 – *Robert Still*

Bewick's Swan

Cygnus columbianus

A scarce and declining winter visitor

The Bewick's Swan was evidently a very rare visitor to Hampshire during the 19th and first half of the 20th centuries, with only eight dated records known for this period (*K&M, Cohen*). Severe cold spells in early 1954 and 1956 produced substantial herds, with between 105 and 165 estimated for the latter year. There were no further records until 1960 but from the winter of 1961/62 small numbers were regularly recorded in the Avon Valley at Ibsley. Until 1965/66, no more than ten were present but from then until 1974/75 peak counts varied between 17 and 52. The following season produced the first three-figure count; in subsequent winters up to 1997/98 numbers failed to reach that level on only five occasions. The peak count was of 314 during severe weather in February 1987. Numbers exceeded the threshold level for international importance of 170 in seven, mostly cold, winters during this period and exceeded that for national importance of 70 annually. This contributed to the notification of the Avon Valley SPA in 1998. Since then there has been a progressive decline. Between 1998/99 and 2003/04 maxima were in the range 23–45 but subsequently peak counts have been between ten and 18, except in December 2010, when 27 occurred in cold weather and a further 38 were present elsewhere in the county, and the 2011/12 winter, when a maximum of only seven was recorded.

At their peak, groups of Bewick's Swans could be found throughout the Avon Valley between Sopley and Woodgreen, although the fields above Ibsley Bridge and across towards Harbridge remained the favoured location. Most birds flew into roost at Blashford Lakes after dark although at times of extensive flooding some roosted overnight in the water meadows. The HBA winter map shows records from most tetrads in this core area; indeed in the 2011/12 winter some were feeding in fields at

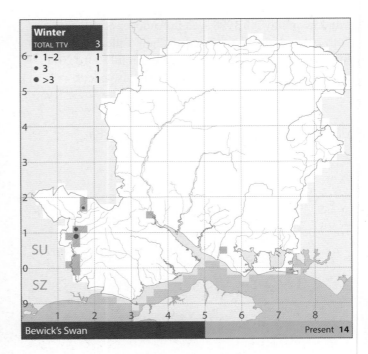

Kingston above the valley floodplain to the east of the Ringwood-Sopley road, a habit not previously noted. Other registrations on the map represent sightings in December 2010 when an influx occurred. Two flyover records, which were reported during late November/early December 2010 from Hayling Island (SZ79P) and South Warnborough (SU74D), are not shown on the map.

Numbers of wintering Bewick's Swans have declined at many locations in southern England in recent years, although they have increased at the principal site at the Ouse Washes, peaking at 6,176 in severe weather in February 2011 (*WeBS 2012*). However, in 2011/12 the maximum at the Ouse Washes was only 1,969 (*WeBS*). This is presumably due to 'short-stopping', with an increasing proportion of the population wintering in Continental Europe instead of continuing farther west.

John Clark

Sponsored by Ian Julian

Bewicks Swan, Harbridge, November 2008 – Martin Bennett

Whooper Swan

Cygnus cygnus
A rare winter visitor

Whooper Swans breed across northern Europe and Asia, from Iceland to north-east Siberia. In winter, most migrate south from their breeding grounds, those reaching Britain and Ireland originating mainly from Iceland. In the UK, most winter in the north with relatively few reaching the south coast of England. They have never been common in Hampshire, at least in recent times, although *K&M* described them as sometimes numerous in severe weather. "Numerous" certainly doesn't describe the species' status in the county today with annual numbers rarely reaching double figures. Over the 20 year period 1993–2012 there has been a total of 43 records with occurrences in just nine years (*HBR*).

During the HBA period, Whooper Swans were recorded in all five winters (although not in every year) as shown in *Table 4*. Note that these counts include some birds that were seen only in flight and others that occurred, most probably as migrants, outside the November-February HBA winter recording period and are, therefore, not included on the accompanying map.

The map shows that most records of grounded birds came either from the coast or the Avon Valley where Whooper Swans are typically found grazing in fields with other swans or geese.

The year 2008 was an exceptional one, which began with a group of five flying over Stubbington on January 26th, to be followed by a family party of five grounded at Testwood Lakes on March 26th/27th. In the late year there were four at Winchester Sewage Farm on October 22nd, three at Rockford, Blashford on November 23rd, five over Bedhampton on November 1st, one at Farlington

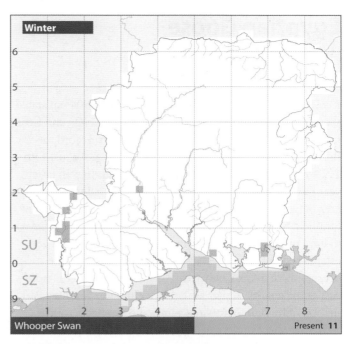

Winter	2007/08	2008/09	2009/10	2010/11	2011/12
Max. WeBS	10	14	4	1	2

Table 4 – Whooper Swan: WeBS count maxima during the HBA winters.

Marshes from November 25th to 30th and one by the Test at Romsey that arrived in November and subsequently over-wintered into 2009 (the only record for 2009). The 2008 total of 24 made this the best year for Whooper Swans in Hampshire since 1963 when 53 were recorded during severe winter weather (*BoH*).

In contrast to Bewick's Swan, numbers of Whooper Swans being recorded in southern England have been increasing in recent years. The most likely cause for this is an increase in the Icelandic breeding population which grew by around 11% between 2005 and 2010 (*Bird Atlas 2007–11*).

Paul Norris

Whooper Swan, Testwood Lakes, December 2008 – Richard Ford

Egyptian Goose
Alopochen aegyptiaca
A scarce and increasing feral resident

K&M cited several records between 1823 and 1904 but stated that all had probably escaped from captivity. *Cohen* and *C&T* ignored the species, although the first modern record for the county was of one at Pennington Marsh on August 13th 1971. Between 1977 and 1993 there were sightings in every year but three, including up to five in the Nursling/Lower Test area between December 1985 and February 1986 and five at Stratfield Saye Park in October 1990. The latter were believed to have originated from the small breeding population established at Dinton Pastures, Berkshire, and were the precursors of increasingly frequent occurrences in the north-east of the county. A pair nested at Wellington Country Park in 1994, although their two goslings did not fledge, and in 1995 they successfully raised one young. No further successful breeding was noted in the north-east until 2003, when a pair raised nine young at Hartley Wintney Golf Course. In the meantime, a pair raised one young from a nest in a pollarded willow in the Somerley Estate in 1998, while two pairs nested successfully farther south in the Avon Valley between Wattons Ford and Bisterne in 2001.

The HBA summer map shows that the Egyptian Goose has consolidated its position in the north-east of the county and to a lesser extent in the Avon Valley, with a scattering of registrations elsewhere. Records of successful breeding during 2008–12 suggest a maximum of around 20 breeding pairs in the north-east, ten in the Avon Valley and one at Heath Pond (Petersfield). As with other goose species, the population contains a large proportion of presumed non-breeding birds and this is shown by the size of post-breeding gatherings, which form from July to December and then break up through the winter. The largest of these is at Lyndridge Farm, Eversley, from where they commute to and from their roost at Eversley Gravel Pits. The first double-figure count was of 20 in September 2003, with numbers rising steadily to 108 in October 2007. Autumn maxima during the HBA period were never below 138 and peaked at 191 at Lyndridge Farm in October 2011. The increasing size of the Avon Valley population is suggested by a record of 24 at Avon Causeway on September 30th 2012. A flock of 14 in flight off Hurst Beach on October 21st 2012 may have been Avon birds dispersing, while 14 at Heath Pond on November 13th 2012 was the largest gathering recorded away from the core areas and was presumably of local birds.

The HBA winter map shows a wider distribution than the summer map, indicating dispersal from the autumn roosts. It is also an indication of pairs prospecting new breeding sites early in the year; indeed breeding has been recorded in Hampshire from January onwards.

John Clark

Sponsored by Ian Julian

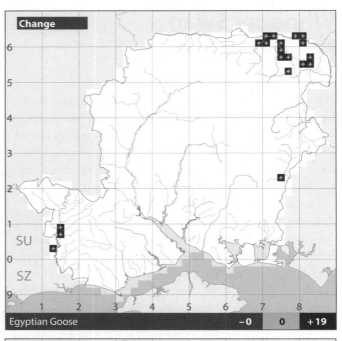

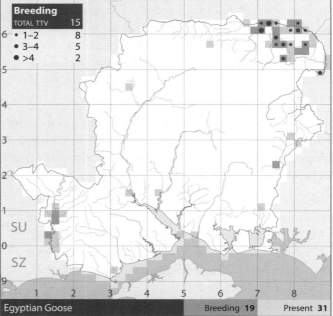

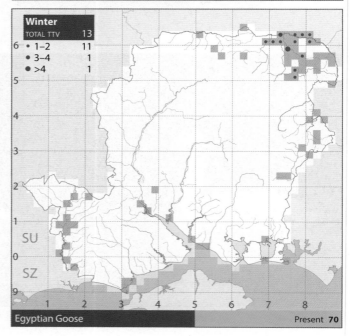

Egyptian Goose, Passfield Pond, April 2013 – *Richard Ford*

White-Fronted Goose, Tundry Pond, February 2009 – *Daniel Trim*

White-fronted Goose

Anser albifrons

A scarce and declining winter visitor, most frequent in severe winter weather

The first ever record for Hampshire appears to be of a pair shot near Ringwood in December 1788. *K&M* described the White-fronted Goose as the commonest of the grey geese which visit the coast in winter, frequently straying inland. However, *Cohen* suggests that the wintering flock in the Avon Valley did not become established until the 1940s. Several hundred were recorded each winter from 1947/48 with numbers peaking at 1,550 in the winters of both 1968/69 and 1969/70, at the time when the total wintering population in Britain reached its maximum of 13,000 (Ogilvie 1978). Subsequently there has been a considerable decline, relieved only by influxes in severe weather in early 1979, 1982 and 1986. The last three-figure count in the Avon Valley was of 172 in January 1992 and in the 2001/02 winter none were recorded for the first time.

During the HBA period, small numbers were recorded in the Avon Valley in four winters with four briefly in late 2008, up to 11 wintering in cold weather in 2009/10, 15 wintering in 2010/11, also a cold winter, and two briefly in late 2011. Two of these winters produced influxes to other parts of Hampshire. There were 51 in 2008/09, all moving over, apart from four which stayed at Tundry Pond from late December until early March. In 2010/11 there were 73, which included 35 at Pennington Marsh from late December until late January and up to 19 at Farlington Marshes from late December until early March. The winter of 2011/12 produced the lowest total ever with only nine recorded including six at Needs Ore from mid-January until late March. Note that some flyover records are not shown on the accompanying map.

Most records in Hampshire refer to the Eurasian race *A. a. albifrons,* which typically arrives from late October onwards and departs by mid-March, with peak numbers between mid-December and February. As with Bewick's Swan and several other waterfowl species, the decline in

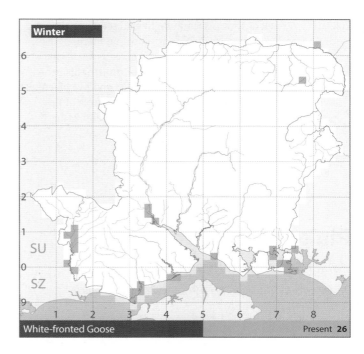

the county is at least partly attributable to 'short-stopping'. Birds are only forced farther west when frozen conditions prevail in north-west Europe, as happened in three winters during the HBA period (*WeBS 2012*). Single birds of unknown origin are sometimes recorded in spring or summer, such as one with Canada Geese at Hamer Warren (SU11F) on May 17th 2009 and another with Canada Geese at IBM Lake and Titchfield Haven in June 2010.

There were also three records of the Greenland race *A. a. flavirostris* during the HBA period. An adult stayed for the day at Farlington Marshes on November 6th 2007, a group of five flew north-west over Weston Shore on February 17th 2008 and a first-summer, which first appeared at Testwood Lakes in late June 2011, remained in the lower Test Valley for a year, being last recorded on June 30th 2012. This bird was unringed and may well have been of wild origin. Prior to these occurrences, only two single birds of this race had been recorded in Hampshire, both in the winter of 2000/01.

John Clark

Bean Goose

Anser fabalis

A rare winter visitor

The Bean Goose breeds in northern Europe and Asia, migrating south in winter. Two distinct races winter in Western Europe, the taiga form, *A. f. fabalis*, and the tundra form *A. f. rossicus*. Both are rare in Hampshire but *rossicus* is the more frequently recorded. Bean Geese were recorded in three of the five HBA winters as follows:

2008/09: One of the race *rossicus* was seen with Greylags and Canada Geese at Needs Ore on November 27th 2008. It moved to the Avon Valley where it remained until April 26th 2009.

2009/10: A flock of 13 was seen in flight at Testwood Lakes on December 6th 2009 (not shown on map). These were identified by the observer as *fabalis* but there was insufficient evidence to confirm this. Later in the winter, nine (four adults and five juveniles) were seen daily in the Balancing Ponds area of Iley Lane, Keyhaven between February 7th and 24th. All were of the race *rossicus*.

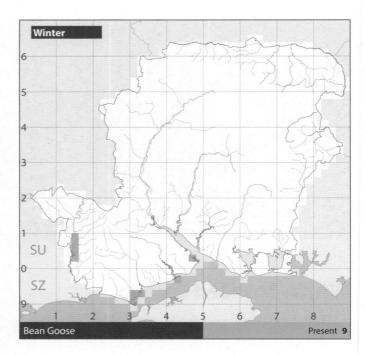

2011/12: A lone adult of the race *rossicus* was found resting on a shingle bank at Calshot near Fawley on November 11th 2011 but was not seen subsequently.

John Eyre

Pink-footed Goose

Anser brachyrhynchus

A rare winter visitor, although presumed feral birds have occurred in most months

The Pink-footed Goose breeds in eastern Greenland, Iceland and Svalbard. The Greenland and Iceland populations winter almost entirely in Britain, mainly in Scotland and northern England. It is a rare visitor to Hampshire, usually associating with other grey geese on the coast or in the Avon Valley. During the five HBA winters there were records of 19 birds, all considered to be of wild origin, as follows:

2007/08: One flew south over Lower Test Marshes on October 13th 2007 and two were present in the Avon Causeway area from December 31st 2007 to March 2nd 2008 in association with Greylags.

2008/09: Four were between Sopley and Avon Causeway from November 23rd–28th 2008 with one remaining in the area until December 8th. In the first winter period of 2009, a further four flew south-west over Sway on February 19th.

2009/10: A group of four was present at Oxey Marsh on January 21st 2010.

2010/11: In late 2010 up to three were recorded. The first was an adult that roosted intermittently at Ibsley Water from September 26th to October 25th. This was followed by one present with other geese, including

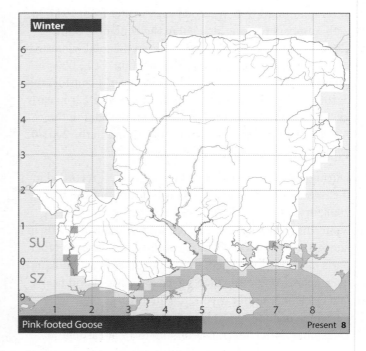

15 White-fronts, at Farlington Marshes from December 25th remaining until January 6th 2011. A third individual was discovered in the roadside fields at Lower Pennington, also in the company of White-fronts, on December 30th 2010.

2011/12: One was heard flying west over Ocknell Plain, New Forest on January 13th 2012.

John Eyre

Bean Goose, Keyhaven, February 2010 – *Keith Maycock*

Pink-footed Goose, Petersfield Heath Lake, February 2007 – *Ian Julian*

Greylag Goose

Anser anser

A moderately common and increasing feral resident

This species, the biggest and bulkiest of the 'grey' geese, now breeds widely across the UK, although only patchily in south-west England and Northern Ireland (*Bird Atlas 2007–11*). Following re-introduction into southern Britain from the 1930s onwards, it now has a fairly large and rapidly growing British population estimated to be around 46,000 pairs (*APEP3*). This is supplemented by wild, migratory wintering birds arriving mainly from Iceland.

As a breeding species, the Greylag Goose is a relative newcomer to Hampshire. Prior to the establishment of the feral population, few were seen. It was first recorded breeding in 1964 when an introduced pair raised young at Stratfield Saye in the north-east of the county. Over the following 50 years, numbers increased. Today, resident birds can be found year-round on ponds, lakes, gravel pits and riverside meadows, where they graze on grass, crops and other plant material. They breed across the county where there is suitable habitat, their distribution closely matching the main river valleys and gravel pits. The accompanying maps show that there has been a notable range expansion since the 1986–91 Atlas. During the HBA period, breeding was considered likely in 42 additional tetrads and lost from just eight, with the largest gains centred on the north-eastern gravel pits and the Avon Valley. New breeding areas have also been established on the Lower Itchen, the Beaulieu Estuary and in scattered tetrads in the north and east of the county. The increased range in Hampshire is consistent with the national picture, which shows that breeding numbers have grown significantly in recent years. In the 1990s the growth rate was estimated at 12% per annum in southern Britain (*BirdTrends*) and between 1995 and 2011 the English population grew by an estimated 248% (*BBS*).

The HBA winter map shows a distribution very similar to that during the breeding season although, as the birds gather together into post-breeding flocks, their distribution is more restricted than during the summer months. Flocks build up in the autumn with high counts during the HBA years of 532, a county record, in the Avon Valley between Sopley and Ringwood in September and 520 at Blashford Lakes in November 2010, 158 at Testbourne in the Test Valley in October 2011 and 206 at Tundry Pond in September 2011. Annual WeBS count maxima averaged about 950 during the HBA period but varied from winter to winter (see table *below*) possibly reflecting both missing and double-counting of flocks.

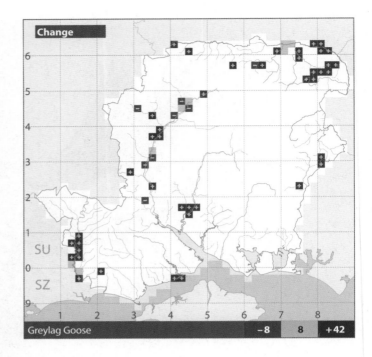

Greylag Goose | −8 | 8 | +42

Although Hampshire's feral population is essentially sedentary, short distance movements occur as the wintering flocks wander in response to disturbance and in search of food. Longer distance movements also occur. During the HBA period, an individual ringed at Sevenoaks, Kent on June 25th 2006 was recovered at Ramsdell, 94 km W, on October 24th 2008. One ringed at Hawley Lake in July 2003 was seen at Kensington Gardens, London, 47 km NE, in January 2012. Historically, Hampshire's long distance record for a movement made by a 'resident' Greylag involves a first year ringed in Sevenoaks on June 24th 1990 and seen at Titchfield Haven, 112 km SW, on January 31st, 1992.

Paul Norris

Sponsored by Brian Cozens & Val Lowings

Greylag Goose, Woolmer Pond, March 2009 – *Richard Ford*

Winter	2007/08	2008/09	2009/10	2010/11	2011/12
Max. WeBS	768	691	1,022	1,377	863

Table 5 – Greylag Goose: WeBS count maxima during the HBA winters.

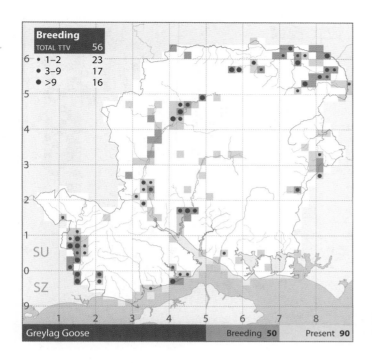

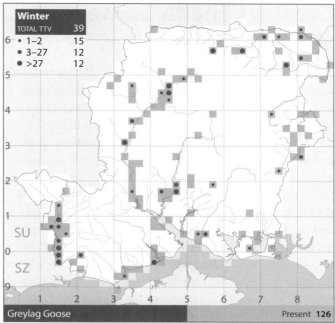

Breeding
TOTAL TTV	56
• 1–2	23
• 3–9	17
• >9	16

Greylag Goose — Breeding **50** — Present **90**

Winter
TOTAL TTV	39
• 1–2	15
• 3–27	12
• >27	12

Greylag Goose — Present **126**

Snow Goose

Anser caerulescens

Previously a scarce feral resident; now extinct as a breeding bird in the county

A small feral population of Snow Geese was established in the north-east of the county in the 1970s. Although the origins of the first free-flying birds is not certain, they may have come from the wildlife collection at Stratfield Saye. It is known that a pinioned pair bred there in 1979 producing three free-flying young. Numbers increased and by the time of the 1986–91 Atlas, a flock of up to 34 was present in Stratfield Saye and surrounding areas. Records from elsewhere in the county also increased, usually of small numbers, but occasionally of larger flocks including ten at Lymington in March 1980 and 14 over Titchfield Haven, and two days later at Fareham Creek, in January 1983.

The flock in the north-east peaked at 35 in 1993 but breeding success was low and, thereafter, numbers began to decline. As shown in the table, by 2007, the first year of the HBA survey, the flock had dwindled to just four birds. By 2009 it had disappeared completely, although a possible lone survivor was seen at Eversley Gravel Pit on January 19th and February 5th 2010 and, following the HBA, at Bramshill Police College Lake on September 11th 2012. The latter bird was known to have spent most of the year over the county boundary in Berkshire.

The reason for the rise and fall of the breeding population is not known but probably represents a classic case of

reduced fertility and genetic disorders arising from in-breeding in a small, isolated population. The presence of several Snow Goose hybrids with other species of goose throughout the lifetime of the flock is another indication of the breeding pressures that the birds were under.

During the HBA period, away from the north-east, there was a scatter of records around the county. These were usually of single birds but included three at Itchen Valley Country Park on December 9th–22nd 2009 and a flock of 32 over the same site on March 2nd 2012. These were probably displaced birds from the feral flock in Oxfordshire.

John Eyre

Sponsored by Betty Hansell

Snow Goose, Baffins Pond, November 2003 – *Brian Fellows*

2000	2001	2002	2003	2004	2005	2006	2007	2008	2009
20	19	17	13	11	6	4	4	3	0

Table 6 – Snow Goose: numbers in north-east Hampshire 2000–2009.

Greater Canada Goose
Branta canadensis
A common resident and partial migrant

This species was first introduced into Britain from North America as an ornamental bird in the second half of the 17th century. It subsequently spread slowly through further introductions but, in recent times, both its range and population have expanded rapidly. It is now common across much of Britain to the extent of being considered a pest species in many areas. The most recent estimates put the UK breeding and winter populations at 62,000 pairs and 190,000 individuals respectively (*APEP3*). Over the period 1995–2012 the English breeding population grew by 34%. However, indications are that numbers may have peaked during this period (*BBS*). Winter counts showed a rapid rise up to 2001 since when the growth rate has slowed and the population appears to be reaching a plateau (*WeBS*).

Canada Geese are well distributed across Hampshire, their breeding range reflecting the county's main river systems and larger gravel pits. Key breeding sites include Needs Ore, Titchfield Haven, Fleet Pond and Yateley Gravel Pits. They are more catholic in their choice of sites than Greylag Geese, nesting on tributaries, farm ponds, golf-courses and in urban parks. Consequently their range extends more widely, notably into parts of the central New Forest but, like Greylags, they are absent from large areas of chalk downland. Although there have been both gains and losses at the tetrad level, the HBA maps show little overall change in breeding range between the 1986–91 Atlas and the HBA. The rapid growth in their numbers has raised many social, economic and environmental concerns. Increasingly steps are being taken to reduce the population where they create a specific nuisance, for example at IBM Lake where 100 birds were culled in July 2007. Such measures may be responsible for the slow-down in their growth or even peaking in their numbers.

Outside the breeding season, Canada Geese form large flocks feeding on agricultural fields and amenity grasslands. Post-breeding numbers build, reaching their peak in autumn and then declining through the winter. WeBS count maxima during the HBA years ranged between 2,850 in November 2010 and 4,112 in September 2008 (see *Table 7*), although the latter count may have involved some double-counting. At the time of the 1986–91 Atlas the maximum county post-breeding population was estimated at around 3,600 (*BoH*) so indications are that, overall, there has been relatively little change in numbers between the two atlases. However, this may mask changes at a local level.

The HBA winter map shows a distribution very similar to that during the breeding season although the number of occupied tetrads was significantly lower in winter than

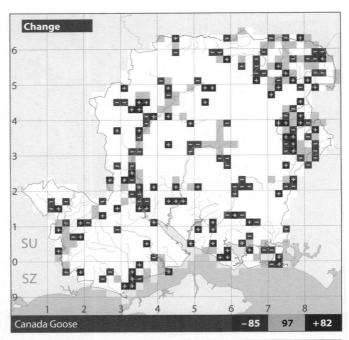

Canada Goose   −85   97   +82

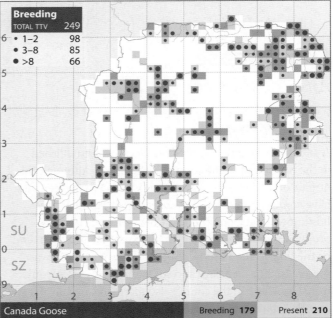

Breeding
TOTAL TTV 249
- 1–2   98
- 3–8   85
- >8   66

Canada Goose   Breeding **179**   Present **210**

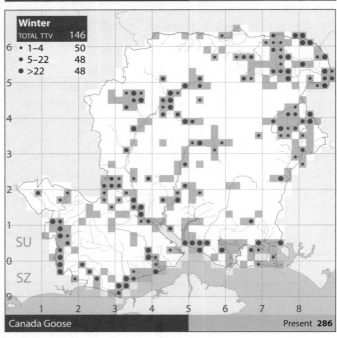

Winter
TOTAL TTV 146
- 1–4   50
- 5–22   48
- >22   48

Canada Goose   Present **286**

in summer with more concentrations around the main river valleys, gravel pits and at the coastal harbours and estuaries. TTV counts were higher which is consistent with the formation of flocks in favoured wintering areas.

The Canada Goose is a partial migrant in Hampshire. Most Hampshire-ringed birds are recovered within the county but some interchange with neighbouring counties also occurs. The longest movements during the HBA period involved one ringed at Regents Park, London on July 7th 1998 and seen in Andover, 98 km WSW, on February 24th 2011; another ringed at Chew Valley Lake, Avon, on June 29th 2004, reported at Twyford, 98 km ESE,

Winter	2007/08	2008/09	2009/10	2010/11	2011/12
Max. WeBS	2,892	4,112	3,680	2,850	3,915

Table 7 – Canada Goose: WeBS count maxima during the HBA winters.

on July 23rd 2011 and a further bird ringed at Chew Valley Lake in June 2006 recovered at Beaulieu Estuary, 100 km SE, in September 2012. Longer distance movements, such as those that occurred in the second half of the 20th century (*BoH*), have not been reported in recent years.

Paul Norris

Sponsored by Julie Moon

Canada Goose, Blashford Lakes, December 2014 – *Martin Bennett* (above); Blashford Lakes, May 2008 – *Martin Bennett* (below)

Barnacle Goose
Branta leucopsis

A scarce and declining resident (feral populations) and rare winter visitor (wild populations)

Records of this attractive goose are always clouded by questions over the birds' origins. Presumed escapees from local collections have been recorded annually since 1963 and feral birds descended from them have bred in the county since 1979. Records of presumed wild birds are usually associated with severe winter weather and involve discrete flocks or single birds accompanying White-fronted or Brent Geese. They are assumed to emanate from the Russian breeding population. However, an increase in such records in the 21st century almost certainly involves some birds displaced from expanding feral populations in south-east England and the Netherlands.

Gilbert White recorded that three were on a pond at Bramshott on April 10th 1778, one of which was shot and sent to him. *K&M* listed four 19th century records involving six birds. In the following century, three at Pennington Marsh in December 1946 and six at Eling in November 1961 were presumably wild birds, while one at Fleet Pond in October 1950 was probably of captive origin.

Escaped and feral birds were recorded in the north-east of the county annually from 1964 and breeding was first recorded at Potbridge Fishery in 1979. Subsequently, a colony became established at Stratfield Saye which, between 1995 and 1998, held up to 24 pairs with a total of 162 young fledging during that period. The post-breeding flock, which increasingly wintered at nearby Eversley Gravel Pit, peaked at 237 in December 2001. During the HBA period, breeding was recorded at Stratfield Saye (in 2008 and 2011) and Wellington Country Park (annually) but 11 attempts produced a total of only seven fledged young. The wintering flock has progressively declined (Clark 2009) and held only 14 birds in the 2011/12 winter.

A second feral population, centred on Baffins Pond, Portsmouth, was first noted in 1986, when it numbered 16. Up to three pairs bred annually between 1993 and 1998 which resulted in the flock increasing to a peak of 42 in the 1998/99 winter. However, it was decimated by an outbreak of botulism in summer 1999 and fell to only 12. Numbers have declined slowly since then and numbered only five during the final winter of the HBA in 2011/12. A single pair hatched five young at Baffins Pond in 2008 but it is not thought that any survived. The Baffins Pond flock, colloquially known as 'The Baffins Gang', ranges widely along the Hampshire coast in winter and has particularly favoured the Titchfield Haven and Needs Ore areas. A bird paired with a Canada Goose at Titchfield Haven in 2010, raised two hybrid young (shown erroneously as confirmed breeding of Barnacle Goose in *Bird Atlas 2007–11*), and another similar pairing at Needs Ore in 2012, raised four young.

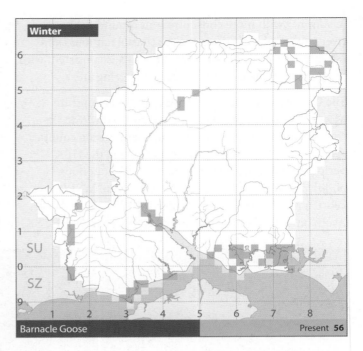

Barnacle Goose — Present **56**

Single birds, usually with Canada Geese, have also been recorded frequently in the Avon and upper Test Valleys.

Records of presumed wild birds, or certainly birds of more distant origin, during the HBA period included up to 43 in the Chichester/Langstone Harbours area from February 14th–26th 2008; 25–30 circling Hurst Beach on November 28th 2010 before heading off west; up to six with White-fronted and a single Pink-footed Goose at Farlington Marshes from December 6th–31st 2010; 107 at Pennington Marsh from January 1st–15th 2011, first noted at Freshwater, Isle of Wight, in late December 2010; 21 in Chichester Harbour from January 21st–31st 2011 and five in the Blashford/Ibsley area from February 3rd–26th 2012. All of these records occurred during severe winter weather.

John Clark

Sponsored by Ken Prior

Barnacle Goose, Baffins Pond, December 2014 – *Ian Julian*

Barnacle Goose, Pennington, January 2011 – *Alan Hayden*

Red-breasted Goose

Branta ruficollis

A rare vagrant

Prior to the HBA, there had been only eight records of this distinctive Arctic goose in Hampshire. A further three wild birds were added during the five HBA winters, all associating with coastal Brent Goose flocks.

During the 2007/08 winter an adult at Gutner Point, Hayling Island on November 10th 2007 remained in the area until March 6th 2008, sometimes commuting over the county boundary from East Hayling to West Wittering in West Sussex. This was presumed to be the same bird first located at Ferrybridge, Dorset in November 2006 and relocated at Keyhaven from January 26th–31st 2006. It returned for its third Hampshire winter to the Keyhaven/ Normandy area from October 31st 2008 to February 6th 2009 before again moving to the entrance of Chichester Harbour until March 6th 2009.

In 2011, an adult found at Chilling on January 20th, remained in the area until February 6th. In 2012, a first-winter was at Pennington Marsh on February 25th/26th and at the Beaulieu Estuary from February 27th– March 24th.

As with many rare species of waterfowl, it is not always possible to distinguish between wild vagrants and escapes from wildfowl collections. During the HBA period, other Red-breasted Geese, additional to the above, were seen in the county but assessed as escapes (see Escapes and Others on *page 428*).

John Eyre

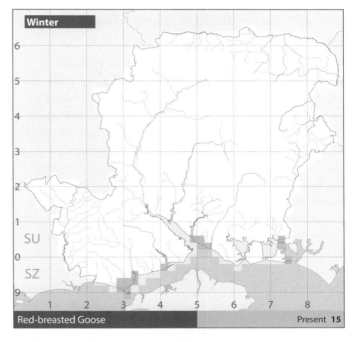

Red-breasted Goose, Farlington, November 2012 – *Steve Bassett*

Brent Goose

Branta bernicla

Three subspecies of this small Arctic goose occur in Hampshire. They are treated separately in the following accounts.

Dark-bellied Brent Goose

Branta bernicla bernicla

A numerous winter visitor and spring and autumn passage migrant; a few sometimes remain through the summer

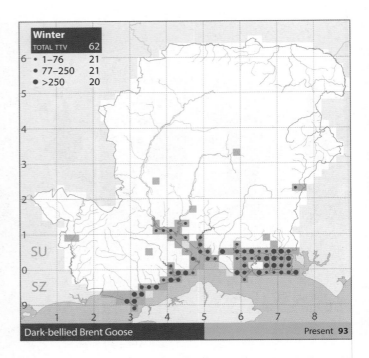

The Dark-bellied Brent Goose, which breeds predominantly in Arctic Russia, has greatly expanded its range around Britain although the highest concentrations remain on the east and south coasts from the Humber Estuary around to Poole Harbour in Dorset. Its wintering population has largely remained stable following a peak in the early 1990s (*Bird Atlas 2007–11*).

This goose can perhaps be described as *the* Hampshire goose and is to be found in all suitable localities along the coast, from Chichester Harbour in the east to Keyhaven in the west. Its history in the county is well documented thanks to wildfowlers of bygone days, particularly Colonel Peter Hawker and William Mudge, who bequeathed us accounts of winter goose numbers in the Keyhaven and Southampton Water-Beaulieu Estuary area in the first halves of the 19th and 20th centuries, respectively. The population declined, reaching a low point in the early 1950s; the long and continuous record from Langstone Harbour thereafter illustrates its recovery. From a paltry 70 in early 1953, numbers increased gradually through the 1950s and 1960s, rising to more than 8,000 in 1985/86. The large populations in Hampshire and elsewhere in Britain at that time were able to supplement natural intertidal food sources by feeding on pasture and autumn-sown cereals, inland of the seawalls. The fortunes of this goose in Hampshire have been fully researched by Tubbs (1997). He concluded that sustained wildfowling kills, prior to its protection in the early 1950s, contributed to diminishing numbers. He also argued that firm evidence for the theory that the loss of Eelgrass *Zostera* spp. to disease in the mid-1930s caused the Brent Goose decline was often lacking or less than convincing, although low numbers in Langstone Harbour in the early 1950s were partly attributed to die-off of marine food sources (*Tubbs & Tubbs* 1982).

During the HBA winter period there were many counts of 2,000 or more from Langstone Harbour, where the peak was 5,690 in January 2012. Maxima at other important Hampshire sites also occurred in early 2012 including at least 2,819 in Portsmouth Harbour, 2,496 in Southampton Water and 2,195 at Hurst–Sowley. Most Brents vacate the county by the end of March although, during the HBA period, occasional high counts in April included 500 in the Beaulieu Estuary in 2012. Occurrences between May and July included a maximum of 26 on the west Solent in mid-May 2008. Inland records are rare and usually involve birds flying over.

The British population in 2011/12 was 91,000 birds, equating to 50% of the world's total, of which Hampshire's estuaries provided refuge for more than 13,800. On account of attaining qualifying thresholds of 2,400 and 910 birds respectively, over the five-winter period 2007/08–2011/12, both Langstone and Portsmouth Harbours qualified as sites of international importance and Southampton Water and Hurst–Sowley as of national importance (*WeBS 2014*). In comparison, during the five-winter period immediately prior to the HBA, Beaulieu Estuary also attained national importance for its Brent Goose wintering population; over this period the British population was 88,738 in 2006/07, including more than 14,000 individuals on Hampshire's estuaries (*WeBS 2008*).

Two additional and distinct Brent Goose races, the Light-bellied Brent Goose (*B.b. hrota*) and the Black Brant (*B.b. nigricans*), were recorded during the HBA period although they are not distinguished on the accompanying map. Brief accounts of both forms are given *opposite*.

Eddie Wiseman

Sponsored by Jeremy Clark

Dark-bellied Brent Goose, Farlington Marsh, March 2010
– *Ian Cameron-Reid*

Light-bellied Brent Goose, Hill Head, October 2008 – *Bob Marchant*

Black Brant, Gosport, January 2010 – *Mark Palmer*

Light-bellied Brent Goose
Branta bernicla hrota

A scarce but increasing winter visitor and passage migrant

This race breeds in eastern Canada, Greenland, Franz Josef Land and Svalbard and, in Europe, winters south to Britain and Ireland. Historically, it has been a very scarce visitor to Hampshire. In the 23 winters leading up to publication of *BoH* in 1993, there were records in 16 of them, mostly of small numbers and with a maximum of eight at Weston Shore on November 15th 1983. In recent years numbers have increased, both as winter visitors and passage migrants. During the HBA, there were records in all five winters with an average of around 18 birds in each of them. There were also more records in spring and autumn with an unusually high count of 38 in Langstone Harbour on April 14th 2011. Also in 2011, a first-winter bird arrived in Hook-with-Warsash on April 28th and remained until July 27th, the first record of an individual summering in the county.

Eddie Wiseman

Sponsored by Jeremy Clark

Black Brant
Branta bernicla nigricans

Formerly rare but now a very scarce winter visitor

Black Brants are relatively scarce visitors to the south and east coasts of Britain, from eastern Siberia, Alaska and western Canada (*Bird Atlas 2007–11*).

An individual that spent most of its stay in Chichester Harbour in West Sussex, from early November 1986 until early March 1987, constituted the first record for Hampshire when it was known to visit east Hayling and Langstone Harbour between February 7th and 12th 1987. This individual returned to West Sussex in each of the following six winters and again visited east Hampshire in early January 1990. Thereafter, Black Brants were increasingly recorded in the county with a further 19 individuals between 1991 and early 2007 (*HBR*).

During the HBA period, at least seven birds were considered new to Hampshire, additional to those previously accounted for; they increased the county's total to 27 individuals.

Eddie Wiseman

Sponsored by Jeremy Clark

Shelduck
Tadorna tadorna
A decreasing breeding resident and a common, but decreasing, winter visitor

Estuaries are the preferred habitat of breeding Shelducks in the UK and as such, other than the Eider, they are unique among British breeding ducks in that the majority are confined to maritime counties (Sharrock *et al.* 1976). In Hampshire this large and colourful species was described by *K&M* as a scarce resident on the coast, occasionally wandering inland. One hundred years later it had become much commoner in winter and was also breeding at inland localities as far north as the Berkshire border.

Compared with the 1986–91 Atlas, HBA data show an apparent overall small contraction of the breeding range, with losses in the Avon Valley, from the south-east of the New Forest and from north of Portsdown. For example, inland of Portsmouth and Hayling Island, at least five tetrads have apparently been abandoned and on about 2,100 hectares of predominantly New Forest heathland, breeding was considered unlikely where, during the 1986–91 Atlas, 21 tetrads were occupied. This is probably a true reflection of its status as 'on guard' male Shelducks are very visible and not likely to be overlooked by the majority of observers. Conversely, towards the coast in the south-west and south-east, along the valleys of the Rivers Test and Itchen and in the north-east of the county, there was an expansion in range with breeding confirmed in an increasing number of tetrads. In 1992 the county breeding population was considered to be 80–100 pairs; during the HBA it was probably at least 75.

Wintering Shelducks are mainly coastal, from Hurst to the eastern harbours and along the River Avon in the south-west. During the HBA period wintering populations averaged more than 200 at only two sites, Langstone Harbour and Hurst–Sowley, with averages of 499 and 219 and maxima of 645 in February 2012 and 242 in January 2011 respectively. A high count of 926 in Chichester Harbour in January 2010 included 410 in Hampshire. The average county maxima of about 1,300 in 2007/08–2011/12 fell from around 2,400 in 1985/86–1989/90. Declines of similar magnitudes were reported from Dorset and West Sussex. This is thought to be due to milder winters in north-west Europe where Shelducks wintering in the Netherlands have increased since the mid-1990s, implying an eastwards shift in distribution across the North Sea in that time. However, in January 2011, the reverse applied when, due to cold weather conditions in the Wadden Sea, there was an apparent influx into Britain (*WeBS 2012*). No Hampshire site qualified for international or national importance during 2007/08–2011/12 although Chichester Harbour, the west shore of which is in Hampshire, did so for the latter category with an average count of 627 individuals.

Eddie Wiseman

Sponsored by David Phillips

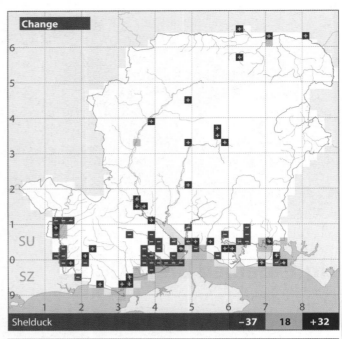

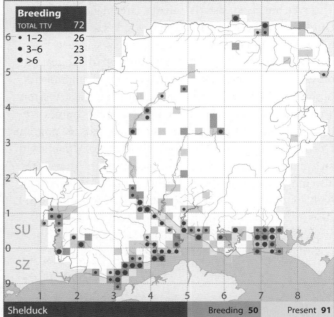

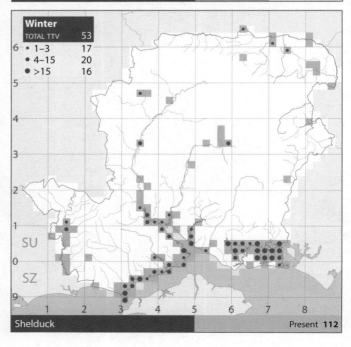

Shelduck, Blashford Lakes, April 2011 – *Martin Bennett* (above); Titchfield, May 2009 – *Richard Ford* (below)

Mandarin Duck

Aix galericulata

A moderately common resident

Native to East Asia, the Mandarin was initially brought to Britain in 1747 but became an established breeding resident only in the 20th century as a result of escapes and deliberate releases, primarily into Berkshire and Surrey (Sharrock 1976). It first bred in a wild state in Hampshire close to Leckford on the River Test following escapes from the local wildfowl collection in the 1950s. It is now a widespread resident having recently colonised the south-east of the county, although remaining absent from much of central Hampshire. Both summer and winter maps clearly show its affinity to river valleys as well as to woodland streams.

The Mandarin's breeding distribution during the HBA period shows a marked similarity to that during 1986–91 Atlas but with a notable increase in the number of tetrads in which breeding was considered likely. The range has increased by 62% since the previous Atlas, with net gains across the county other than in the New Forest. Significant expansion has occurred in the Thames Basin, the Weald and the lower Test and upper Itchen Valleys. Mandarins have also extended their range into south-east Hampshire. In contrast, the picture in the New Forest is more balanced, with a mixture of both gains and losses. Mandarins nest in holes in trees and readily in artificial sites, such as nest-boxes. They appear to be finding sufficient nest sites and are not out-competed, other than perhaps in the New Forest, by tree-nesting Jackdaws. Their increased breeding range in Hampshire is consistent with the findings of *Bird Atlas 2007–11*, that showed a 123% expansion in Britain and Ireland since the 1988–91 Atlas.

The HBA winter distribution was broadly similar to that of summer although Mandarins were recorded in fewer tetrads, probably reflecting post-breeding concentrations on favoured waters. The highest count during the HBA winter period was 80 at Headley Mill Pond in January 2009. Wintering Mandarins are easily over-looked. On larger waters, especially those with restricted access or where considerable overhanging bankside vegetation affords thick cover, they can be remarkably inconspicuous; in such situations they are often visible in open and deeper water only in freezing conditions. On some waters they may fly at dusk to nocturnal woodland feeding sites.

There is no evidence that Hampshire's Mandarins are anything other than sedentary but this belies the ability of the species to traverse great distances. For example, one in St James Park, London, in the summer of 1930, was found the following April in Hungary and two which left Oslo, Norway, on November 8th 1962, were shot together the next day 900 km away in Northumberland (*BWP*).

Eddie Wiseman

Sponsored by Steve Hodgkinson

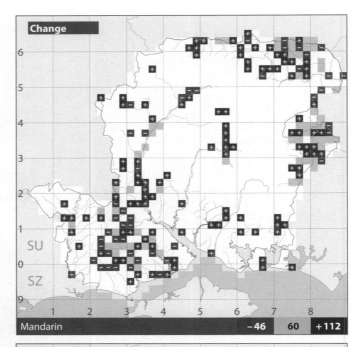

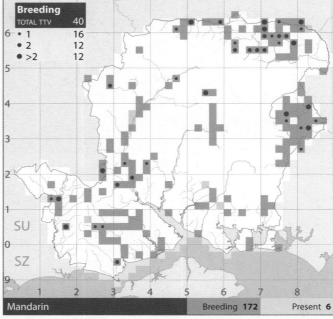

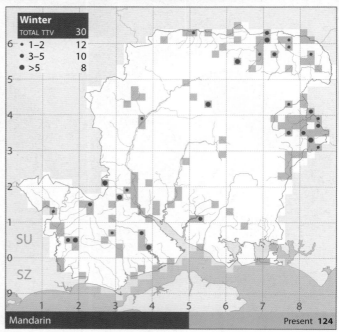

Mandarin Duck, Eyeworth, March 2015 – *Martin Bennett* (above); Eyeworth Pond, March 2015 – *Steve Bassett* (below)

Wigeon

Anas penelope

A common winter visitor and passage migrant; a few summer each year

The Wigeon has an extremely large global range, breeding across northern Europe and Asia and migrating south as far as southern Asia and Africa in winter. Those wintering in south-east England originate mainly in Fennoscandia and Russia.

In Britain, the species was recorded nesting for the first time in Sutherland in 1834 (*1968–72 Atlas*). It subsequently spread southwards although the small breeding population of 300–500 pairs (*APEP3*) is still centred principally in Northern Scotland, the Northern Isles and the Uists. Those breeding in the south probably originate from escapes or releases (Mead 2000). Breeding has never been confirmed in Hampshire, although a few over-summered in each year of the HBA breeding survey and gave rise to possible or probable breeding records.

During the five HBA winters, Wigeon were widely distributed across the county, the principal concentrations being at coastal locations in the eastern harbours, Southampton Water and the west Solent. The highest coastal counts came from Chichester Harbour, peaking at 3,502 during cold weather in December 2010, although the majority of these birds were in West Sussex. Other notable counts included 1,730 at Lymington/Hurst in January 2010 and 1,696 in Southampton Water at Lower Test, Eling and Bury Marshes in January 2011. Inland, the Avon Valley is another very important site, particularly when the river is

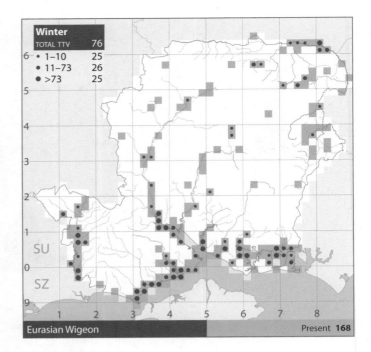

in flood. Wildfowl are often concentrated between Sopley and Harbridge when such conditions prevail and where, for example, there were 2,227 at Blashford Lakes, following a shoot in the valley on December 31st 2010. Elsewhere smaller populations occurred particularly in the east and north-east of the county.

The majority of wintering Wigeon leave the county by early April and those recorded in that month and beyond include migrants as well as sick and injured birds.

Eddie Wiseman

Sponsored by Josie Allen

Wigeon, Bunny Meadows, February 2012 – *Mike Crutch*

Wigeon, Bunny Meadows, January 2010 – *Steve Copsey* (above); Blashford Lakes, October 2009 – *Martin Bennett* (below)

Gadwall

Anas strepera

A scarce but increasing resident, a passage migrant and a
moderately common winter visitor

The Gadwall has an extremely wide global distribution
across the Palearctic and Nearctic regions and extension
of the species' range is possibly linked to climate change
(*RBBP* 2009). In England pinioned, wild-caught Gadwall
were introduced into Norfolk where they first bred in 1850
(*1968–72 Atlas*).

K&M's assessment of the Gadwall in Hampshire as a
rather scarce winter visitor remained true until the early
1970s. A pair at Marsh Court in May and June in most
years from 1971 to 1982 did not breed and it was not until
1983 that the first broods were raised, two at Winchester
Sewage Farm and one at Northington Lake. The breeding
population continued to expand during the 1986–91
Atlas, when successful nesting was reported from 15
localities with up to 13 broods in 1987 and 1988. A county
summering population of 100–150 birds in that period
was concentrated around Blashford Lakes, Overton in the
upper Test Valley and in the Alresford and Northington
areas (*BoH*). A post-breeding flock of 98 was at Alresford
Pond in August 1998.

The current situation, revealed during the HBA period, is
one of continuing county-wide increase, principally along
the Avon and Test Valleys, in the east and north-east of
the county, the west Solent coast and around the upper
reaches of Langstone Harbour. Other than in a few coastal
localities, it remains absent from much of the New Forest
and from the chalk hinterland. Breeding was considered
likely in 140 tetrads, almost three times the number at the
time of the 1986–91 Atlas. Although this estimate may be
on the high side, it is a valid indication of how the species'
range has expanded over the past two decades.

National wintering totals now appear to be stabilizing
following a sustained rise over the past thirty years.
The increase has been mirrored in other European countries,
for example the Netherlands and Switzerland (*WeBS 2012*).
Between 1960 and 1985, the increase of Gadwalls wintering
in Hampshire reflected the wider expansion in Britain and
north-west Europe and was attributed in part to additional
habitat created by an increase in lowland artificial waters
such as gravel pits and reservoirs. During the period of the
1986–91 Atlas, the maximum site count was 366 at Blashford
Lakes in December 1989. In the following years, numbers
continued to rise, for example to 557 in December 1992
at Blashford Lakes and to 243 in January 1991 at Eversley/
Yateley Gravel Pits (*BoH*). During the HBA, principal
concentrations were along the rivers Avon, Test and Itchen,
in the east and north-east of the county, but also on the
Solent between Hurst and Hayling Island. On the River
Avon, between Fordingbridge and Ringwood, there were

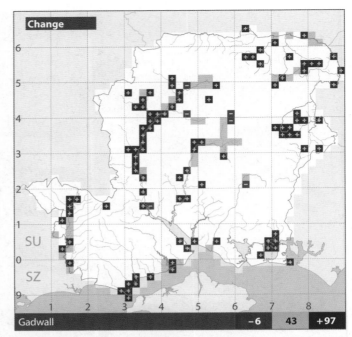

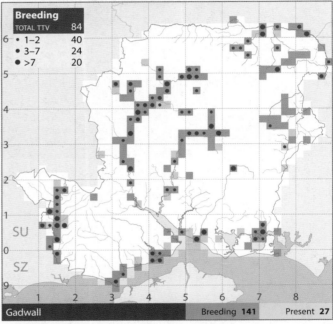

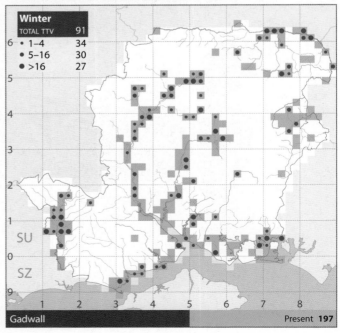

15 counts in excess of 600, mostly in December. Over the five HBA winters, 2007/08–2011/12, an average of 830 Gadwall (maximum 1,149 in 2010/11) was recorded, making this one of seven UK sites attaining international importance (*WeBS 2011/12*).

Eddie Wiseman

Sponsored by John Clark

Gadwall, Blashford Lakes, November 2008 – *Martin Bennett* (above); Blashford Lakes, September 2009 – *Martin Bennett* (below)

Teal

Anas crecca

An increasingly scarce breeding resident and common winter visitor, although in smaller numbers since the mid-1980s

The Teal has a world-wide distribution and populations are large. Nationally, a decline in the breeding range and population in the final 20–30 years of the 20th century was attributed partly to habitat loss from afforestation (Mead 2000).

During the HBA period there were four spring counts of 100 or more in early to mid-April, including a maximum of 175 at Keyhaven in 2008; these consisted of late winter visitors or spring migrants. Although birds were present in 74 tetrads during April–July, breeding was not proven in any of them. Teal are secretive and broods are often difficult to detect. They do not venture much into open water, preferring to remain hidden in vegetation (*BoH*). The presence of so many birds in April, with occasional pairs throughout the breeding season at apparently suitable breeding sites, makes it difficult to be sure of the species' true breeding status. However, breeding has not been proven in the county since 2005. For this reason, and perhaps being over-cautious, the accompanying change map is based on proven breeding records only. During the 1986–91 Atlas, when the county population was estimated at 30–35 pairs, breeding was confirmed in 12 tetrads. A preferred habitat at that time was peaty, heathland pools, for example in the New Forest and in the Woolmer area. Unfortunately, the entire population appears to have been

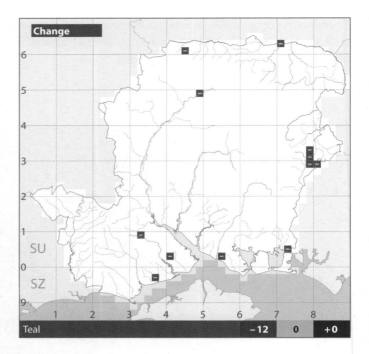

lost from the Woolmer area and much reduced in the New Forest, where breeding was not proven during the HBA period. The change map therefore shows the complete loss of Teal as a Hampshire breeding species.

Teal wintering in Britain originate mostly from Iceland, Scandinavia and north-west Russia, with the national population stabilizing in recent years after a period of steady increase (*WeBS 2012*). During the HBA winter surveys, Teal were widely distributed throughout the county with principal concentrations in coastal localities and along the Avon Valley. On the coast, maxima occurred in the Keyhaven area where 3,000 were reported in early

Teal, Pennington, February 2011 – *Martin Bennett*

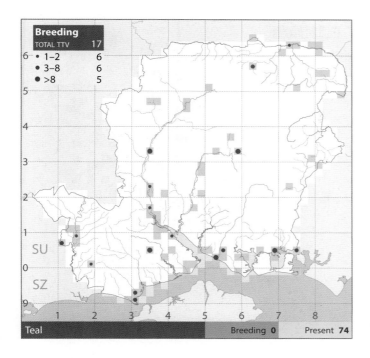

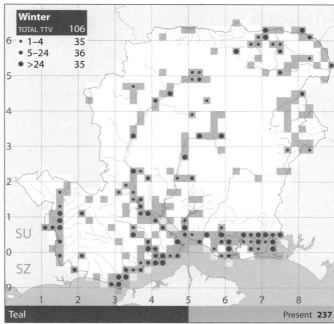

December 2010 and 2,000 a week later, and in the Avon Valley with 1,730 in December 2009. No Hampshire site qualified for international or national importance over the HBA period, although 3,400 from Hurst–Sowley in December 2010 exceeded the threshold for national importance. The average of winter maxima in the county 2007/08–2011/12 was about 5,600, compared with around 6,200, boosted by a very high count in the flooded Avon Valley in February 2003, in the preceding five-year period 2002/03–2006/07 (*HBR*).

Very high numbers of Teal in December 2010 and January 2011 in Hampshire and elsewhere in the country were possibly the result of birds concentrating, for example, in south-west England, during cold weather. Alternatively, this was possibly a response to flocking of birds forced onto open water in frozen conditions (*WeBS 2012*).

Eddie Wiseman

Sponsored by Ray Hiley

Green-winged Teal

Anas carolinensis

A rare vagrant

There were five records of this Nearctic duck during the HBA period bringing the Hampshire total to 23:

2008: Single males were at Hook-with-Warsash from April 22nd–28th and at Farlington Marshes from October 13th–November 9th.

2010: A male was at Budds Farm Sewage Farm on January 9th. The next day it was re-found off West Hayling Local Nature Reserve where it remained until the 13th. It was not seen again until January 30th, when it had returned to Budds Farm, remaining there until February 19th.

2012: A male was at Farlington Marshes from February 23rd–March 11th and again from March 30th–April 9th. A different male was on floods at Titchfield Haven from April 7th–14th.

Eddie Wiseman

Green-winged Teal, Keyhaven, March 2013 – *Gordon Small*

Mallard

Anas platyrhynchos

A common resident and winter visitor

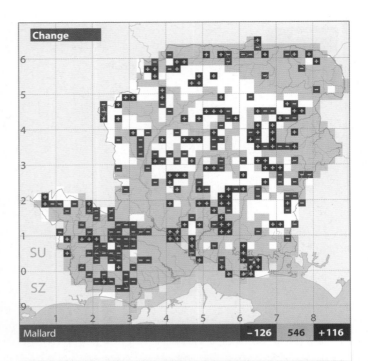

Mallard   − 126   546   +116

In the UK, the Mallard's breeding population has shown a steady increase since the 1960s, especially in England, partly attributable to releases of large numbers by wildfowling organisations for shooting (Marchant *et al.* 1990).

It is widespread with breeding considered likely in almost two-thirds of the county's tetrads. It occurs most commonly in wetland sites, including the river valleys, gravel pits and ponds, but is more thinly spread in the drier chalkland areas. The breeding maps show little difference in the number of occupied tetrads between 1986–91 and 2008–12 although there have been changes in distribution. These include infilling on the chalk and losses in the south-west, particularly in the central New Forest, for which there are no obvious reasons. Post-breeding maxima in April-July exceeded 200 only in the Keyhaven/Pennington area (411 in July 2008 and 215 in May 2010) and inland at Ewhurst Lake (301 in June 2011).

The winter distribution during the HBA was broadly similar to that in summer, with a lack of records from many squares on the chalk, as well as in the New Forest. Counts of 200 or more during the 2007/08–2011/12 winters, were confined to 17 sites with day maxima at Ewhurst Lake of 716 in February 2012 and 634 in January 2011, with 440 on Sowley Pond in January 2009. Overall, there has been an apparent decline in wintering numbers in Hampshire over the past 20 years. A five-year mean of autumn/winter maxima, 1985/86–1989/90, was about 5,500, with a peak count of a little under 1,000 at Lower Test in December 1989 (*BoH*). This fell to about 4,000 over the HBA five-winter period, with a site maximum of about 1,150 on the River Avon between Ringwood–Fordingbridge in October 2007 (*HBR 2007–2012*). National WeBS counts also indicate a steadily declining British wintering population since the 1990s. This has now stabilised, partly in response to recent cold winters when increases in December 2010 and January 2011 probably consisted of Continental immigrants. This supports the theory that the recent downward trend is linked to a fall in this immigration.

Ring recovery data up to the late 1990s suggested 75% of Mallards wintering in Britain and Ireland were Continental immigrants (*WeBS 2012*). No such recoveries were detected in Hampshire during the HBA period though one ringed at the Volga Delta, Ukraine on August 24th 1941 and shot at Otterbourne, 3,728 km west, on February 12th 1944 and one, ringed as a chick at Murmansk, Russia on July 8th 1972 and found dead at Totton, 2,617 km south-west, on January 30th 1977, are indicative of the great distances individuals are capable of covering (*BoH*).

Eddie Wiseman

Sponsored by Glyn Young

Mallard, Titchfield, May 2015 – *Robert Still*

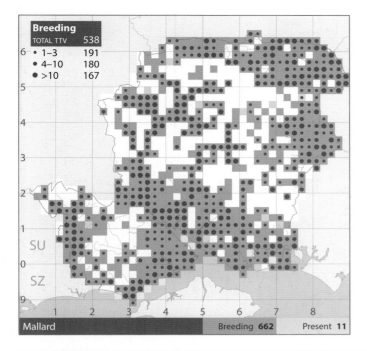

Breeding
TOTAL TTV	538
• 1–3	191
• 4–10	180
● >10	167

Mallard — Breeding **662** — Present **11**

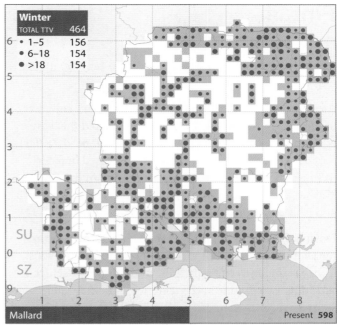

Winter
TOTAL TTV	464
• 1–5	156
• 6–18	154
● >18	154

Mallard — Present **598**

Mallard, Blashford Lakes, May 2009 – *Martin Bennett* (above); New Forest, April 2008 – *Martin Bennett* (below)

Pintail

Anas acuta

A moderately common winter visitor and passage migrant that occasionally summers

As a breeding bird, the Pintail is a 19th century colonist of the UK. In the mid-1970s it was considered the least common of our breeding dabbling ducks (*1968–72 Atlas*). Some four decades later, it remains a localised breeder in England with clusters of records only from the Ouse Washes and the Norfolk coast and only a few additional and isolated records from elsewhere (*Bird Atlas 2007–11*).

During the 20th century there were few summer records for Hampshire. Between the mid-1930s and early 1960s, *Cohen* was able to cite only three mid-summer occurrences, including two in June and one in July. A decade later, summer records were still unusual in the county and between 1971 and 1992 cumulative totals were of about 15 records for May and 11 for June, mostly in Langstone Harbour (*BoH*). Perhaps unsurprisingly, the summer status of this species was similar during the HBA period; it was recorded in only six tetrads in May and three in June with no evidence of breeding.

As a winter visitor, *K&M* described the Pintail as scarce in Hampshire and this remained so through to the early 1960s, although there was some indication of an increase at that time with one exceptional count of 110 in the Avon Valley in 1961 (*Cohen*). Over the five-winter period 1985/86–1989/90, routinely submitted records to HOS for five major sites indicated an average county winter maximum of a little over 400, with a peak of about 300 in Langstone Harbour in January 1989. It is of note that numbers in the Avon Valley were at a particularly low level during this period due to lack of persistent winter flooding, even though the Hampshire population at the time averaged about 2·2% of the British total (*BoH*).

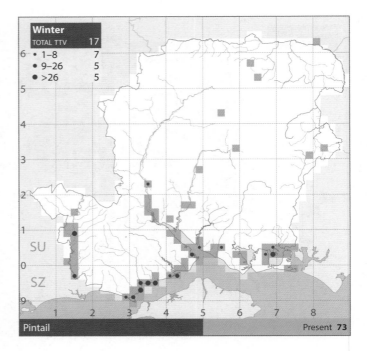

Winter

TOTAL TTV	17
• 1–8	7
• 9–26	5
● >26	5

Pintail — Present **73**

Numbers in Hampshire peaked in the early years of the current century when extensive flooding in the Avon Valley attracted maxima of 1,383 in January 2001 and 2,329 in February 2003. As recently as 2005/06 the number of Pintails wintering in the UK attained an historic peak but by 2009/10 the population index was at its lowest for over thirty years (*WeBS 2012*).

During the HBA, when the annual county maxima averaged 774, peak counts were 550 at Hurst–Sowley in January 2012, 510 there in January 2011 and 507 in the Avon Valley between Sopley and Ringwood in February 2008. In the five winters, 2007/08–2011/12, the Hurst–Sowley area qualified as a site of national importance, with an average population of 408.

Eddie Wiseman

Sponsored by Kevin Sayer

Pintail, Eastrop Park, February 2012 – *Barry Stalker*

Garganey

Anas querquedula

A scarce passage migrant and rare summer visitor

The Garganey, on the western edge of its range in the UK, is a summer migrant and is thus unique among our waterfowl. Numbers reaching the British Isles fluctuate greatly from year to year, with the highest numbers occurring in warm springs with anticyclonic conditions. Spring migration may continue until late May or early June and return passage sometimes commences as early as mid-June so summer occurrences are not necessarily indicative of nesting (*1968–72 Atlas*).

In *K&M*, the Garganey was described as a scarce spring and summer visitor. These authors mention only one confirmed breeding record when, in early July 1897, a female with three young able to fly was observed near Fareham. Breeding also took place in south-east Hampshire in 1935 and in the Avon Valley in 1937 and 1940 (*C&T*). A pair possibly attempted nesting in 1976 and breeding may have taken place in the county in 1991 (*BoH*). Confirmed breeding occurred in 1993 when two pairs reared young (*HBR*).

During the HBA period, the number of individuals recorded in spring averaged around 19 per year. Most involved passage migrants mainly from coastal locations such as Lymington/Hurst, Titchfield Haven and Farlington Marshes. There was also a scatter of records from inland sites including Blashford Lakes, Fishlake Meadows, Alresford Pond and Fleet Pond. Records of pairs indicative of possible breeding were reported in June and July from three sites but breeding was confirmed at only one, where a pair successfully raised three young in 2008. Breeding was also considered likely at two other sites in 2008 and was

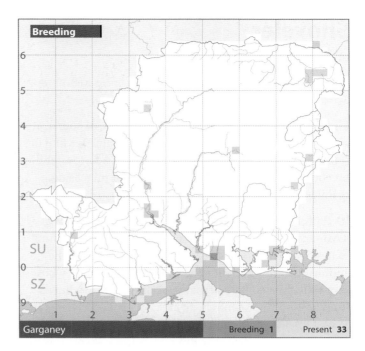

possibly attempted at one site in 2011 and at another in 2012. Only the confirmed breeding record is shown on the accompanying map.

Although largely outside the HBA recording period, return passage occurred between mid-July and late October at seven coastal and four inland sites. The majority of records were in August and September, with day maxima of up to three at Keyhaven between July 31st and September 1st 2010 and on August 19th 2012. Six singletons in October included one at Farlington Marshes on October 16th 2009 and at Ivy Lake, in the Blashford Lakes complex in the Avon Valley, on October 20th 2010.

Eddie Wiseman

Sponsored by Dr Bob Lee

Garganey, Normandy Marsh, May 2006 – *Marcus Ward*

Shoveler

Anas clypeata

A moderately common winter visitor and passage migrant; a few pairs probably attempt breeding annually

The most distinctive feature of this species is, of course, its broad spatulate bill especially adapted for filter-feeding in shallow brackish or fresh water. It has been a long-standing breeding bird in the UK, formerly rare, but increasing, mainly from 1900–1950 (*1968–72 Atlas*).

Its Hampshire status was described in the early 1900s as a winter visitor in small numbers, occasionally remaining to nest (*K&M*). The first record of breeding was on the authority of the eminent taxidermist Edward Hart, whose skin collection contained many locally-killed specimens from around Christchurch, an area conceded to Dorset in 1974. Other breeding records for the early 1900s were also from the Avon Valley, near Ringwood and at Avon Tyrrell. Between 1952 and 1979, Shovelers bred on at least a further nine occasions, while during the 1986–91 Atlas, five broods were recorded when breeding was confirmed in three tetrads and pairs were present at two other sites where no nesting evidence was obtained (*BoH*). During the HBA at least 14 pairs nested in eight tetrads along the Solent, between Hurst and Langstone Harbour and on the rivers Avon, Test and Meon, where seven broods were noted at Titchfield Haven in 2010. A number of other records were obtained of pairs present during the breeding season but without nesting evidence. Only proven breeding records have been included as indicative of likely breeding on the accompanying maps.

As a winter visitor, numbers had greatly increased by the time Taverner, writing in the early 1960s, described it as "an itinerant bird" and "the nomadic duck of Hampshire". He was intrigued by the enormous fluctuations, not necessarily confined to the spring and autumn migration periods, at many localities. Extremely cold weather was often instrumental in bringing exceptionally large numbers to Hampshire, particularly to the Avon Valley

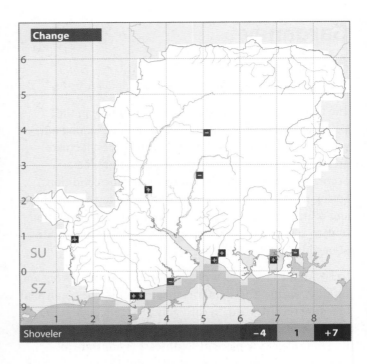

and Keyhaven in 1947. However, the highest post-war site counts of over 200 occurred in the mild but very wet winter of 1960/61 and the county maxima in both winters was probably in the order of 300–400 birds (Taverner 1962).

During the five HBA winters, 15 sites supported in excess 50 individuals with day maxima exceeding 100 reported from Hurst–Sowley (255 in February 2011) and from the Avon Valley at Blashford Lakes and Sopley–Bisterne (respectively 280 and 144 in February 2008) and from Ibsley/Harbridge Green (110 in January 2010). Reduced numbers at British WeBS sites over the period led to a fall in the national Shoveler index, possibly as a result of two cold winters, and coincided with an influx into southern Europe, for example France and Iberia. The River Avon between Fordingbridge and Ringwood qualified for national importance with an average winter maxima of 217 over the HBA period (*WeBS 2014*).

Eddie Wiseman

Sponsored by Diana Westerhoff

Shoveler, Titchfield, March 2009 – *Simon Ingram*

Shoveler, Blashford Lakes, November 2013 – *Martin Bennett*

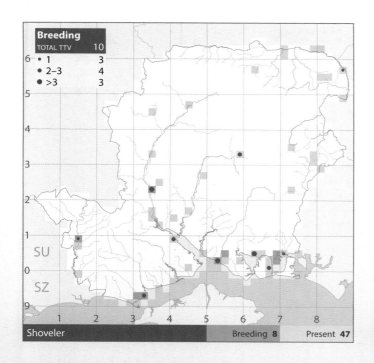

Breeding
TOTAL TTV 10
- • 1   3
- • 2–3   4
- ● >3   3

Shoveler   Breeding **8**   Present **47**

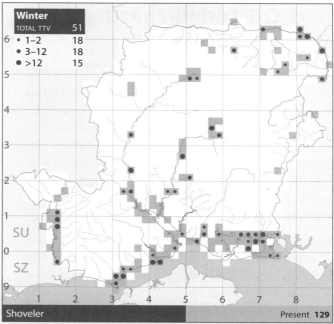

Winter
TOTAL TTV 51
- • 1–2   18
- • 3–12   18
- ● >12   15

Shoveler   Present **129**

Shoveler, Blashford Lakes, October 2009 – *Martin Bennett*

Red-crested Pochard
Netta rufina
A very scarce feral visitor, or escape

The vast majority of the Red-crested Pochards recorded in Hampshire are most likely either escapes from captivity or wanderers from the small feral populations centred on such sites as Cotswold Water Park on the Gloucestershire/ Wiltshire border or elsewhere in south-east England. In the absence of compelling evidence, it is impossible to be certain whether any of the Hampshire birds are genuine vagrants.

During the HBA period, this species was recorded in 20 tetrads during the winter and in just two during the breeding season. The latter included a pair at Farlington Marshes on April 11th 2008. Although this date would be consistent with overshooting Continental migrants, the birds were considered too approachable to be wild. The other breeding season record included a male at Whitten Pond, Burley on July 5th 2011.

In winter, records were obtained from both inland and coastal sites, the former including Dogmersfield Lake, Heath Pond (Petersfield) and Woolmer Pond as well as from several gravel pits in the Avon Valley. Favoured coastal sites included Needs Ore and Titchfield Haven. As in summer, there was little evidence to suggest that the birds were genuine vagrants. In December 2007 an unringed drake at Badminston Gravel Pits was initially very flighty but became more settled on flooded pig

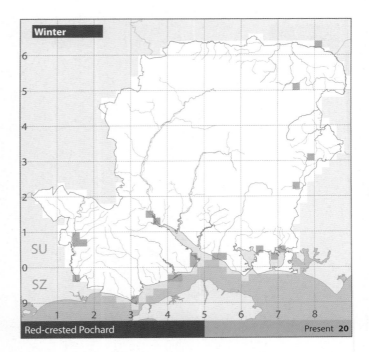

fields adjacent to the pits later in its stay. The arrival date coincided with the onset of a particularly cold spell during the first half of that month. There was a small influx into the county during January 2010, which coincided with severe winter weather throughout much of southern England probably resulting in cold weather movement from inland sites. Up to 13 birds were seen including six at Blashford Lakes, four in Langstone Harbour, two in the Hill Head/Titchfield Haven area and one at Lower Test Marshes.

Nick Montegriffo

Red-Crested Pochard, Bedhampton, January 2010 – *Andy Johnson*

Ring-necked Duck

Aythya collaris

A rare vagrant

A first-winter drake was present during the HBA survey period at Passfield Pond. It was found on December 10th 2008 and remained until December 21st. It was present at Frith End Sand Pit on December 29th/30th and then intermittently at both sites until March 27th 2009. This brought the number of individuals recorded in the county to eight, all since 1979.

Nick Montegriffo

Ring-necked Duck, Frith End, March 2009 – *Steve Copsey*

Ferruginous Duck

Aythya nyroca

A rare vagrant

This species breeds in southern and eastern Europe and southern and western Asia. It is also kept in captivity so some records may refer to escapes from wildfowl collections. During the HBA period, a male was found on December 4th 2011 at Fishlake Meadows, Romsey, the first in the county since 2000. Probably the same individual was present at Spinnaker Lake, Blashford on December 30th/31st, subsequently moving to nearby Ivy Lake with intermittent sightings until February 27th 2012. Although asleep for much of the time, it was eventually seen sufficiently well for its identification to be confirmed, hybrid origin having been eliminated. What was assumed to be the same bird returned to the Blashford area on October 22nd 2012 remaining until November 30th. This record brought the county total to 12, all post-1950.

Nick Montegriffo

Sponsored by Chris Spooner

Ferruginuous Duck, Blashford Lakes, January 2012 – *Martin Bennett*

Pochard

Aythya ferina

A scarce breeder and moderately common but declining winter visitor

The Pochard's breeding range extends across the temperate zone of Europe into Russia and China. Post-breeding, the northern populations migrate south and west, some of those from the Baltic countries and farther east reaching the UK, where they vastly outnumber the non-migratory resident birds. Numbers reaching Britain depend on conditions in mainland Europe, particularly the extent to which suitable wintering habitat remains ice-free. The trend during the first decade of the 21st century has been sharply downwards, possibly because of 'short-stopping' brought about by the longer-than-normal run of mild winters that occurred over this period or, conceivably, due to longer-term climate change.

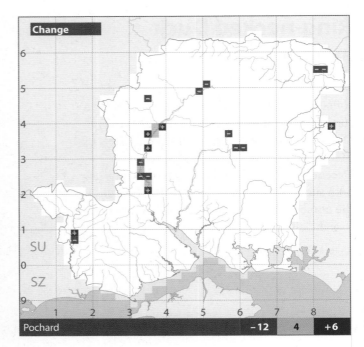

The size of the Hampshire population in winter is also dependent on the extent to which waters in southern England remain ice-free. In very cold winters, the birds arriving from the Continent are forced south and west, resulting in higher numbers in the county than in mild winters. During the five HBA winters, the maximum WeBS count varied between a low of 342 in February 2012 and a high of 640 in February 2011. December 2010 was exceptionally cold across the UK which concentrated the birds on to ice-free waters near the coast and resulted in the high count later in the winter. The peak count of 640 was the highest since 2003 but only approximately 50% of the 1,260 in February of that year.

The main wintering site in Hampshire is at Blashford Lakes where numbers peaked at 259 in January 2011. Other high counts at this time included 147 at Titchfield Haven in February 2011 and a combined three-site total of 110 in the north-east at Tundry Pond and Eversley and Yateley Gravel Pits in January 2011.

Pochard, Blashford Lakes, November 2009 – *Martin Bennett*

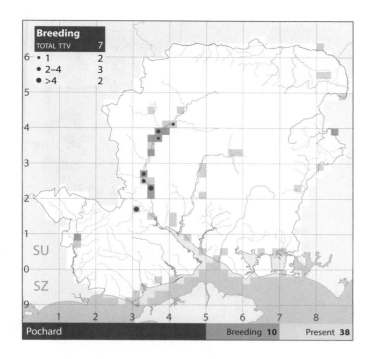

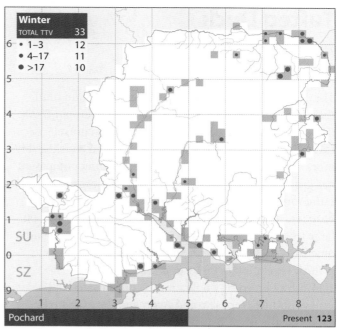

Breeding was first confirmed in Hampshire in 1935 (*BoH*) and in 1978 the total breeding population was estimated at 70–80 pairs (Clark 1979). By the time of the 1986–91 Atlas numbers had fallen to around 40–50 pairs (*BoH*) and this downward trend appears to have continued to date. The HBA maps show that although breeding continues to be concentrated in the Test Valley at sites such as Mottisfont, Fishlake Meadows, Timsbury and Longstock, it no longer

occurs at several other sites including the Overton area, Alresford Pond and Fleet Pond. The reason for these declines is not clear and may vary from site to site. For example, at Fleet Pond, siltation and declining water quality have made the site unsuitable.

Nick Montegriffo

Sponsored by Mark Painter

Pochard, Blashford Lakes, October 2009 – *Martin Bennett*

Tufted Duck

Aythya fuligula

A regular breeding resident and common winter visitor

The Tufted Duck didn't begin breeding in Britain until the mid-19th century. It first bred in Hampshire in 1890, its range expanding slowly until increases in gravel extraction from the 1960s onwards provided considerably more suitable habitat. Since then the breeding population has grown steadily; the species is now the second most numerous breeding duck in the county, exceeded in numbers only by the Mallard. It is generally common on large freshwater lakes, ponds, reservoirs, gravel-pits and quiet stretches of slow-flowing rivers, wherever there is thick vegetation close by to provide nest sites. The Hampshire breeding population is concentrated in the valleys of the Rivers Test and Avon and the gravel pits alongside the River Blackwater in the north-east, with scattered pairs wherever suitable habitat occurs elsewhere.

Although there have been no major changes in its breeding range between the 1986–91 and 2008–12 Atlases, the change map shows a scatter of both gains and losses and, overall, a slight contraction particularly in the Avon Valley and the north-east. It would appear that, after a long period of expansion, Tufted Ducks may now have occupied most suitable wetland areas in the county.

The breeding population is thought to be largely resident so it is not surprising that the summer and winter distributions are very similar. However, counts typically decline after the breeding season suggesting that some post-breeding movements do occur prior to numbers

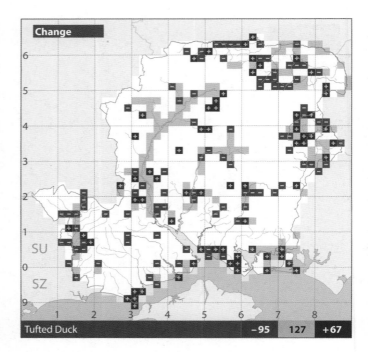

| Tufted Duck | −95 | 127 | +67 |

increasing again as winter visitors arrive. Cold weather also results in movements to areas of open water. Due to their size, Blashford Lakes remain ice-free longer than Hampshire's other inland waters. When they eventually freeze, as they did in at least one of the HBA survey years, Tufted Ducks and other water birds are forced to move onto the River Avon or into the Solent.

The county's winter population is swelled by visitors from northern Europe although there is a growing body of evidence to suggest that Tufted Ducks, along with other wildfowl, are now arriving in the UK later in the year than in the past. Studies of data from the Hanko Bird Observatory in southern Finland have found that Tufted

Tufted Duck, Blashford Lakes, August 2011 – *Martin Bennett*

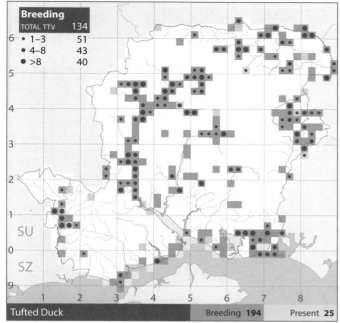

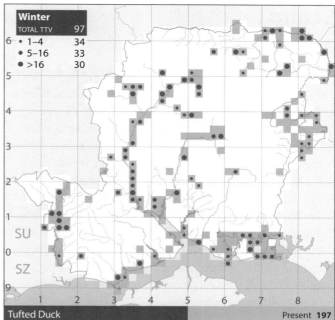

Ducks demonstrate the strongest lag in autumn migration with a delay of more than a month over the past 31 years (Lehikoinen & Jaatinen 2011). It is presumably only a matter of time before this trend is reflected in the arrival and departure dates in Britain and Hampshire but no direct evidence of this has revealed itself in records of the species in the county to date.

Numbers reaching Hampshire vary from year to year. During the five winters of the HBA survey, WeBS count maxima varied from a low count of 1,322 in February 2009 to a peak of 1,782 in February 2012. The average over the period was 1,557, remarkably close to the previous five-year average (2002–07) at 1,568, but considerably higher than the 1997–2002 average of 1,294. In winter, the UK holds internationally important numbers of Tufted Ducks with an estimated population of 120,000 (*APEP3*). Based on this, Hampshire holds approximately 1·3% of the national total. This is substantially lower than the 4% estimate given in *BoH*.

Nick Montegriffo

Sponsored by Steve Hodgkinson

Tufted Duck, Blashford Lakes, April 2009 – *Martin Bennett*

Scaup

Aythya marila

A very scarce winter visitor and passage migrant

This species is, for the most part, a winter visitor to Britain and Ireland from its Icelandic and north-west European breeding grounds. It is usually very scarce in Hampshire but during periods of hard weather higher numbers can occur. Of the five HBA winters, the 2010/11 winter was particularly severe with record low temperatures and an Arctic airstream affecting southern England in December 2010. These conditions brought unusually high numbers of Scaup to the county – more than had been seen since 1997. *Table 8* shows the approximate numbers recorded during each of the HBA winters. These counts include a small number of birds seen on passage outside the November–February winter recording periods.

The high count in 2010/11 included a group of 18 in the mouth of Chichester Harbour on January 18th 2011 and seven in Portsmouth Harbour on January 1st/2nd 2011, but such concentrations are unusual. Most counts were of one or two birds. As the HBA distribution map shows, the vast majority of records were coastal, although freshwater pools close to the sea were also used. There were also occasional inland sightings. During the HBA winter period, inland records came from: Tundry Pond, January 4th–March 30th 2008; Andover area from late December 2008 to March 16th 2009; Testwood Lakes, January 17th/18th 2009 and Alresford Pond, November 25th 2010. Outside the HBA winter survey period there were additional inland records from: Ibsley Water, March 20th and 25th/26th 2011; Testwood Lakes, March 29th 2011 and Blashford Lakes,

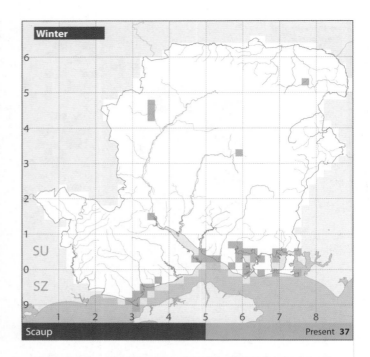

Winter	2007/08	2008/09	2009/10	2010/11	2011/12
Birds	16	11	17	52	11

Table 8 – Scaup: approximate numbers recorded during the HBA winters.

March 13th–April 13th 2012. Particular care needs taking to identify Scaup inland because of possible confusion with Scaup-like *Aythya* hybrids.

Breeding season records are rare. During the HBA period there was an unseasonal record of a moulting male at Hook-with-Warsash on July 28th 2009 and subsequently at Farlington Marshes on August 2nd, and a male at Fleet Pond on May 26th 2010.

Nick Montegriffo

Scaup, Titchfield, March 2009 – *Steve Copsey*

Long-tailed Duck
Clangula hyemalis
A very scarce winter visitor and passage migrant

Long-tailed Ducks have a circumpolar range, breeding almost wholly within the Arctic Circle. In winter they move south, those reaching the British Isles originating mainly from Fennoscandia and north-west Russia (*Migration Atlas*). In Hampshire the species occurs in very small numbers, both as a winter visitor and passage migrant. Numbers vary from year to year but generally winter totals do not exceed 15 (*BoH*). The HBA period was typical with numbers as given in *Table 9*. Records outside the HBA winter recording periods are not included either in the table or on the accompanying map.

Inland records are rare. During the HBA period, there were only two, both from Blashford Lakes. An adult male was on Ibsley Water from November 14th–25th 2008 and a first-winter on Rockford Lake from November 15th–19th 2010.

Breeding season records are also very unusual although lingering winter visitors and late migrants can occasionally be seen in April and beyond. During the HBA breeding survey, notable examples included a pair wintering in Chichester Harbour in 2009 which remained until April 13th when they were seen displaying. In 2010, an adult female was present between April 25th and June 13th off

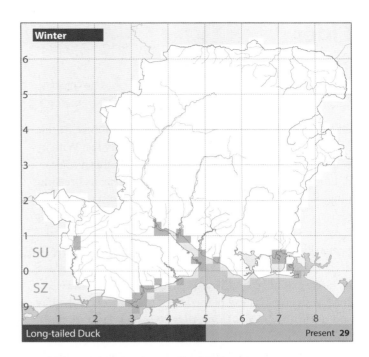

Winter	2007/08	2008/09	2009/10	2010/11	2011/12
Birds	7	8	5	1	3

Table 9 – Long-tailed Duck: numbers recorded during the HBA winters.

Keyhaven Marsh, and an adult male was off Hurst Beach from April 26th–29th in 2011.

Nick Montegriffo

Long-tailed Duck, Hook-with-Warsash, February 2009 – *Bob Marchant*

Eider

Somateria mollissima

A scarce but increasing winter visitor and passage migrant; small numbers usually summer; bred for the first time in 2003

Of all Hampshire's breeding species, the Eider must be one of the most surprising additions to the county list. With a world distribution extending around the northern coasts of Europe, North America and eastern Siberia, its breeding range is restricted to Arctic and some northern temperate regions. In Britain, it is at the southern limit of its European range and has been very much a northern breeder found primarily in Scotland and north-east England. Over the two decades between the 1988–91 and 2007–11 national atlases, its range extended southwards particularly down the west coast with colonisation of the Isle of Man, Morecambe Bay and north-west Wales (*Bird Atlas 2007–11*). Even so, the discovery, in June 2003, of a female incubating a clutch of six eggs on the Hampshire coast was a major surprise. The nest was not successful but, in subsequent years, further breeding attempts were made with two pairs in 2006 and up to ten in 2007, at least one of which successfully raised young.

During the HBA period, although breeding was attempted in each year of the survey, success was achieved only in 2010 when pair formation in the western Solent commenced in the second half of April and a female with three young was seen in late June. In the other years it is likely that nests were washed out by high tides or, in some cases, possibly taken by predators.

The confirmation of breeding followed a long term increase in the numbers of Eiders recorded in the county both in summer and winter. Prior to the mid-1950s, the species was rarely seen but in the second half of the 20th century it became a regular winter visitor and passage migrant. Numbers fluctuated but increased progressively, reaching a peak in February 2006 when 220 were recorded off the favoured site at Hill Head. The county total in April 2006 was estimated at 404. During the HBA winter surveys, numbers were lower with counts at Hill Head varying between a maximum of 164 in 2007/08 to a minimum of 52 in 2010/11. Sightings were made from 35 coastal tetrads including Langstone Harbour and Southampton Water. There were no inland records during the HBA period.

The first county summer record was obtained in July 1958. Thereafter records were intermittent with occasional high counts including unprecedented numbers in 1976 when up to 23 summered in the Lymington/Hurst area, 13 at Sowley/Pylewell and five at Needs Ore. Numbers off Lymington/Hurst were higher in 1989 with 32 present in August, but the population continued to fluctuate with some years having no mid-summer records at all. From 2001 onwards, a regular summer population was established and by 2003, the year that breeding occurred for the first time, around 90 were present in the Solent

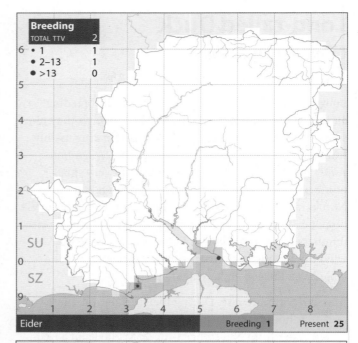

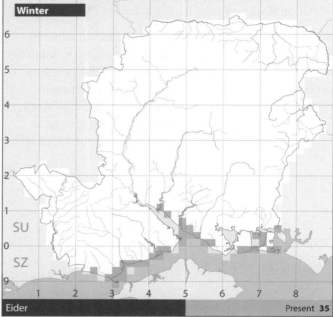

in June and July. During the HBA period, mid-summer numbers were generally in the 30–50 region, with records mainly from the west Solent between Lymington/Hurst and Lepe/Needs Ore. Records in the east Solent were generally of passage birds.

The establishment of sustained numbers of Eiders off the Hampshire coast in both summer and winter is presumably a result of the availability of suitable food supply in the Solent. It is surprising given the predictions that global warming would be expected to shift populations northwards. Unfortunately, the saltmarsh on which they nest is subjected to periodic flooding, so it remains to be seen whether the unexpected range expansion is short-lived or the Hampshire coast becomes firmly established as the most southerly breeding site in Europe.

Nick Montegriffo

Sponsored by Steve Hodgkinson

Eider, Oxey Marsh, May 2010 – *Marcus Ward* (above); Fareham Creek, February 2014 – *Steve Bassett* (below)

Common Scoter

Melanitta nigra

A moderately common passage migrant; scarce in summer and winter

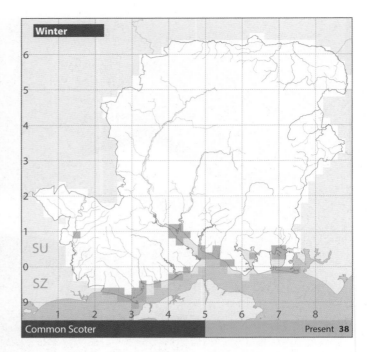

Although Common Scoter breeds in small numbers in Scotland and winters around much of the UK coast, it is best known in Hampshire as a spring migrant. The best time to see appreciable numbers in the county is in April and May with movement continuing through June and July. Since the timing of their migration coincides with the HBA breeding season, most Atlas records during this period referred to birds moving along the coast. In fact one of the harbingers of spring is the lines of Common Scoter offshore heading east towards their northern breeding grounds. At the western entrance to the Solent, the birds gather, appearing reluctant to pass through the narrows off Hurst Castle, and sometimes retreating back towards Christchurch Harbour before passing eventually to the south of the Isle of Wight. Consequently relatively few birds enter the Solent and counts off Hayling Island are generally lower than off Hurst.

During 2008–12, spring passage numbers counted off Hurst Beach peaked at 647 in 2010, including a high day-count of 103 on June 4th. Although the seasonal pattern has changed little since *BoH* was published in 1993, numbers appear to have declined. For example, large gatherings off Hurst Beach such as the 400 recorded on April 4th 1987 and 600 on April 10th 1991, no longer occur. The reason for the decline is not known but may possibly be due to a deterioration in the local food supply related to the shingle extraction from submerged banks off Hurst.

Inland records during the breeding season are unusual; during the HBA period there was only one, a female at Ibsley Water on July 18th 2009.

In winter, numbers are generally much lower than in spring/early summer. Most reports during the HBA winters were of single-figure flocks from coastal watch points, although 2007 was unusual with a total of 202 logged in November, including 80 in the Lymington/Milford on Sea area. As the accompanying map shows, although predominantly coastal, the birds do penetrate into the Harbours and to the upper reaches of Southampton Water. During the winter survey period there was only one inland record, an adult male at Ibsley Water on February 16th 2010.

Nick Montegriffo

Common Scoter, Stokes Bay, August 2015 – *Alan Lewis* (left); Stokes Bay, February 2015 – *Steve Bassett* (right)

Velvet Scoter

Melanitta fusca

A scarce passage migrant and winter visitor

The Velvet Scoter has a similar circumpolar breeding range to the Common Scoter but, unlike its smaller relative, does not breed in the UK nor winter as far south in Europe. Numbers occurring in Hampshire are, therefore, lower. Annual counts vary, depending on weather conditions and the level of observer activity but, historically, have typically been in the 10–50 range made up of both winter visitors and passage migrants. Approximate numbers occurring during the HBA years (including those parts of 2007 and 2012 prior to and after the HBA recording period) are given in *Table 10*.

In general, numbers were higher than normal with 2008 and 2009 being particularly good years. Most records were from the western end of the Solent and involved just one or two birds. Double-figure counts off Hurst Beach during the survey period included 14 on May 4th 2008, 11 on April 18th 2009, 12 on May 7th 2010, 11 on April 14th and ten, presumed the same, on April 17th 2012. The only double-figure count from the eastern end of the Solent was 14 off Sandy Point on April 20th 2009.

There were no inland records during the HBA period.

Nick Montegriffo

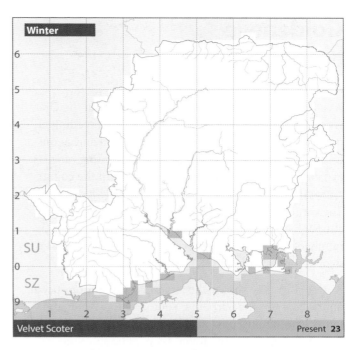

Year	2007	2008	2009	2010	2011	2012
Birds	39	66	76	47	53	46

Table 10 – Velvet Scoter: numbers recorded 2007–12.

Velvet Scoter, Titchfield Haven, March 2010 – *Mark Palmer*

Surf Scoter

Melanitta perspicillata

A very rare vagrant

The Surf Scoter breeds in Canada and Alaska and is seen annually in small numbers off the coasts of Great Britain, mostly in Scotland. There have been a few well-documented records in recent years along the south coast of England. Only one was recorded in Hampshire during the HBA period. A female/immature was seen off Hurst with Eiders on November 19th 2011 before flying west. This was only the fourth county record, the previous one being a first-winter female in Langstone Harbour on December 18th 2006.

Nick Montegriffo

Surf Scoter, Stokes Bay February 2015 – *Andy Johnson*

Goldeneye
Bucephala clangula
A scarce and declining winter visitor

As a breeding species, the Goldeneye's range in the UK is concentrated in Scotland with confirmed breeding in only two English counties, Northumberland and Avon (*Bird Atlas 2007–11*). Although its UK breeding range is expanding, the vast majority of birds seen in the country are winter visitors from Fennoscandia (*Migration Atlas*). The winter population in Hampshire has been declining; although cold winters generally result in higher totals, numbers reaching the county are generally much lower than at the time of the 1986–91 Atlas.

As the HBA map shows, the largest concentrations occur on the coast, in the harbours, Southampton Water and in the Lymington/Hurst area. Inland, the prime site is Blashford Lakes and the River Avon, although small numbers occur at several other locations including the north-east ponds and gravel pits, Alresford Pond, Anton Lakes, Heath Pond (Petersfield) and Testwood Lakes.

The winters during the first years of the HBA period were relatively mild but the cold winter of 2010/11 resulted in the highest number of Goldeneyes in the eastern harbours for five years, halting the decline noted there over the preceding years. The peak count in Langstone Harbour was 54 in January 2011 compared with the all-time maximum there of 153 in January 1970. Cold winters also bring increased numbers to inland waters providing they are not iced over. During the 2010/11 winter, numbers at Blashford Lakes peaked at 36 in February 2011 although the highest

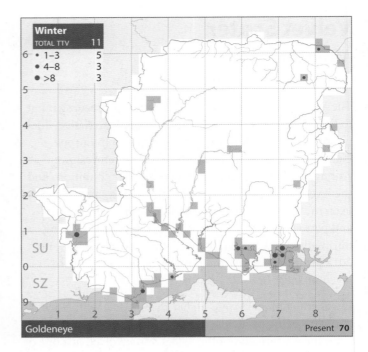

count during the 2007–12 period was 37 in March 2009. Peak numbers generally occur in March, possibly due to the winter population being augmented by migrants.

Summer records are rare although some lingering winter visitors remain into April and were therefore present at the beginning of the HBA breeding season surveys. There were only two summer records, both in 2008: two flew past Hurst Beach on May 20th and a female was at Ibsley Water on July 25th.

Nick Montegriffo

Sponsored by Matt Coumbe

Goldeneye, Blashford Lakes, January 2011 – *Martin Bennett*

Smew

Mergellus albellus
A very scarce winter visitor

This attractive sawbill breeds in the taiga zone from northern Sweden to eastern Siberia. The bulk of the north-west European breeding population winters in the Baltic and North Sea, particularly in the Dutch Ijsselmeer. An estimated 180 reach the UK each winter (*APEP3*), although the total varies depending on the severity of the weather farther east.

Small numbers reach Hampshire in most winters but are sometimes absent as shown in *Table 11* for the five winters of the HBA period.

The 2007/08 winter was mild with generally above average temperatures. In contrast, December 2010 was particularly cold and resulted in an influx of at least 11 Smew during the month. A cold spell in February 2012 led to a further influx which included a group of seven at Testwood Lakes on February 5th. As the HBA map shows, most records were from the inner harbours and larger inland ponds and lakes.

Most birds occur in mid-winter and records outside the November-March period are extremely rare. During the HBA there was a single summer record, the first for the

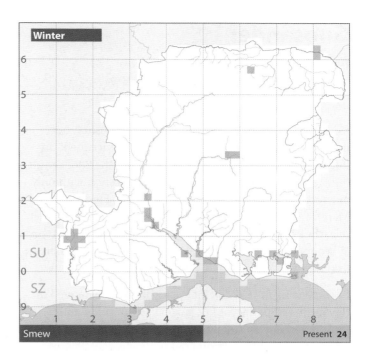

Winter	2007/08	2008/09	2009/10	2010/11	2011/12
Birds	0	2	5	14	14

Table 11 – Smew: numbers recorded during the HBA winters.

county. A female flew in off the sea at Needs Ore on June 13th 2009. It flew up the Beaulieu River and was later relocated at Blackwater.

Nick Montegriffo

Smew, Romsey, January 2011 – *Martin Bennett*

Goosander

Mergus merganser

A moderately common winter visitor and very scarce breeder

K&M described the Goosander as a winter visitor, not uncommon during hard weather, and more frequent on inland waters. In the first seven decades of the 20th century they remained scarce and erratic in occurrence, with only one record of a double-figure count – 13 at Fleet Pond on March 1st 1936 – except in the notoriously severe weather in early 1963, when up to 100 gathered on the River Avon at Woodgreen and a further 90 were recorded elsewhere in the county.

Commencing in 1977/78, increasing numbers wintered in the north-east of the county, particularly in cold winters. Birds fed by day on still waters and rivers in the area, returning at dusk to a communal roost site. Initially this was at Wellington Country Park, but by the 1988/89 winter the main roost had largely shifted to a lake on the Berkshire side of the River Blackwater at Eversley Gravel Pit. Peak counts reached 26 in February 1979, 44 in February 1985, 79 in January 1994, 132 in February 1996 and 210 in January 1997, which comprised 184 at Eversley and 26 at Wellington Country Park. Mild winters in the succeeding decade produced five-yearly mean maxima of 68 in 1997–2002 and 39 in 2002–2007 but during the HBA period the mean increased to 70 largely due to a peak count of 118 during a cold weather influx in December 2010. High counts at feeder waters included 12 at Bramshill Police College Lake on December 9th 2007, 41 at Yateley Gravel Pits on December 12th 2008, 42 there on December 12th 2012, 15 at Tundry Pond on February 1st 2011, and a peak of 22 at a satellite roost at Bramshill Plantation on March 5th 2011.

Elsewhere in the county the species was scarce until a wintering flock gradually became established in the Avon

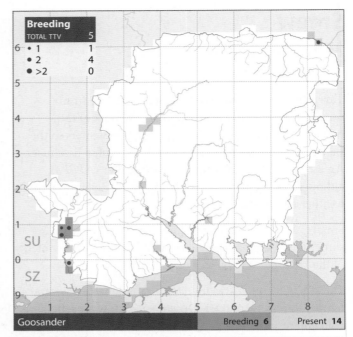

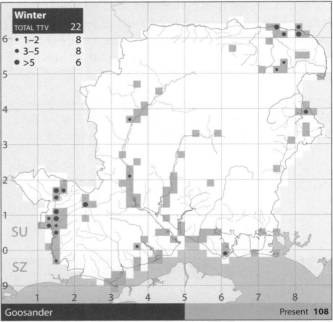

Goosander, Cadman's Pool New Forest, December 2014 – *Martin Bennett*

Valley, feeding by day on the River Avon and the New Forest ponds and roosting on Ibsley Water at the HIWWT Blashford Lakes reserve. Peak winter maxima were in the range 16–30 between 1995/96 and 2003/04, then rose to 60 in 2004/05 and, during the HBA period, to 92 in 2008/09, 103 in 2009/10 and 231 in 2010/11, before falling to 124 in 2011/12. As at Eversley, the peak count of 231 occurred during the cold weather in December 2010 with numbers remaining above 200 until early February 2011. Exceptional numbers occurred on the New Forest ponds in early 2010, with a maximum of 48 at Eyeworth Pond on February 6th, which presumably were attracted by a profusion of fish; generally numbers are much lower at individual ponds and parties of up to ten or more are scattered along the length of the Avon.

The HBA winter map shows the expected concentration of sightings in the north-east and south-west, but also a scattering of registrations elsewhere, particularly along the coast, in the Test and Itchen Valleys and on waters in the east. Small flocks were frequent between Fawley Reservoir (adjacent to Southampton Water) and the Test Valley up to Longstock, particularly in cold weather with, for example, maxima of 17 at Longstock on December 19th 2010, 15 at Fawley on December 30th 2010, 12 at Kentford Lake on January 29th 2011, 15 at Testwood Lakes on February 9th 2012 and 14 at Broadlands Estate on February 12th 2012. Nocturnal roosting at Testwood Lakes was confirmed in February 2012 (S. S. King *pers. comm.*). Other double-figure counts included ten at Wishanger near Frensham

on December 29th 2007, 11 at Sowley Pond on January 13th 2011 and ten at Sleaford Reservoir on February 23rd 2012. A few were also regular at sites such as Heath Pond (Petersfield) and Sinah Gravel Pit (Hayling), while opportunistic birds fed at small ponds at Newlands Farm (Fareham), Passfield and adjacent to a golf course and a cricket pitch at Eversley.

Goosander was perhaps one of the more surprising additions to the list of Hampshire's breeding birds. On July 1st 1998 John Arnold saw a female with six ducklings on the River Avon at Oakford Coppice below Ringwood. Birds were present in the Avon Valley in summer in the next few years and undoubtedly attempted breeding but success was not recorded again until 2004, when a female raised eight young from a nest in a hole in a tree in Somerley Park. Since then, successful breeding has been recorded annually from 2006–12, with two broods in most years. As the HBA summer map shows, most instances of confirmed breeding have continued to be in the well-watched Somerley Estate in the Blashford/Ibsley area. There was also one report of recently-hatched young from south of the Avon Causeway in 2008, and it is probable that other instances of breeding have been overlooked in the valley. Registrations elsewhere in the county refer to late-departing winter visitors (in early April) or wandering non-breeders, while some of those in the upper Test Valley refer to a resident individual.

John Clark

Sponsored by Ed Bennett

Goosander,
Cadman's Pool New Forest,
December 2014
– *Martin Bennett*

Red-breasted Merganser

Mergus serrator

A moderately common but declining winter visitor and passage migrant; rare inland

An estimated 2,200 pairs of Red-breasted Mergansers breed in Britain (*APEP3*). Their breeding range is concentrated in Scotland and north-west England, extending southwards to north Wales although, during the 2007–11 national atlas, probable breeding also occurred on the south coast in Devon (*Bird Atlas 2007–11*).

In Hampshire it is largely absent during the summer, except for a few lingering non-breeders. The majority return to their wintering quarters from early November onwards, with numbers building rapidly throughout the month. There are rather few records of birds on visible migration and it is believed that this is conducted mainly at night. As the HBA map shows, in winter it is mostly confined to coastal waters, particularly in the eastern Harbours. It occurs only occasionally inland, most regularly at Blashford Lakes, where one may sometimes be found amongst the roosting Goosanders on Ibsley Water.

The number of Red-breasted Mergansers which over-winter in Hampshire increased steadily in the second half of the 20th century, probably due both to an expansion in the national breeding population and an increase in the number of Scandinavian birds wintering here. Numbers peaked in the 1990s and, more recently, have declined with the mean maximum WeBS totals falling from 415 over the 1997/98–2001/02 winters to 337 during the HBA period.

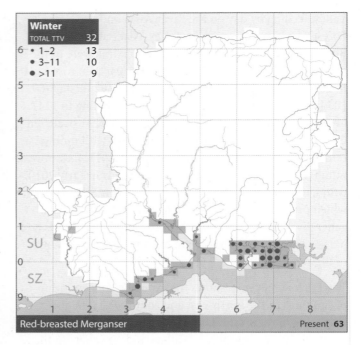

Winter
	TOTAL TTV	32
•	1–2	13
•	3–11	10
●	>11	9

Red-breasted Merganser — Present **63**

This is consistent with the national picture and may be a result of a long run of mild winters enabling a greater proportion of birds to winter farther north in Europe. Both Langstone and Chichester Harbours continue to hold nationally important numbers with peak counts during the HBA period of, respectively, 205 on March 10th 2012 and 221 on December 5th 2009. Most birds remain well into April by which time displaying males are a common sight up and down the coast.

Nick Montegriffo

Sponsored by Joanna Lowis

Red-Breasted Merganser, Pennington, March 2013 – *Gareth Rees*

Ruddy Duck
Oxyura jamaicensis
A declining resident and winter visitor

Following the first confirmed breeding in Hampshire at Fleet Pond in 1978, this North American species bred sporadically until a small resident population was established at Blashford Lakes in the mid-1980s. Breeding also occurred intermittently elsewhere in the county before Alresford Pond became the second regular breeding site from 1990 onwards. The decision to eradicate the species from Britain, to protect the threatened Spanish population of White-headed Duck *Oxyura leucocephala*, was confirmed in 2003 but, despite almost 2,700 Ruddy Ducks being shot in the UK between September 2005 and January 2007, it had little effect on the small Hampshire population by 2008, the first year of the HBA breeding survey. Thereafter, numbers dropped quickly following culls in 2010 and 2011. For example, the only significant count on Ibsley Water in 2011 was five on February 3rd but these had been eliminated two days later.

Small numbers continued to be seen in the county to the end of the HBA period but the species was, by then, in rapid decline. The Food, Environment and Research Agency (Fera) aimed that work to eliminate the remaining birds would continue in line with the commitment to eradicate Ruddy Ducks by 2015.

Since the eradication programme began, reports of birds in Hampshire made public were followed, a few days later, by them being culled. This outcome was not universally popular and, consequently, some observers withheld information about the occurrence of the species in the county. However, with so many observers and the speed of dissemination of news, it is most probably just a matter of time before the Ruddy Duck's relatively short history as a Hampshire resident draws to an end.

Nick Montegriffo

Sponsored by Tony Blakeley

Ruddy Duck, Blashford Lakes, March 2008 – *Martin Bennett*

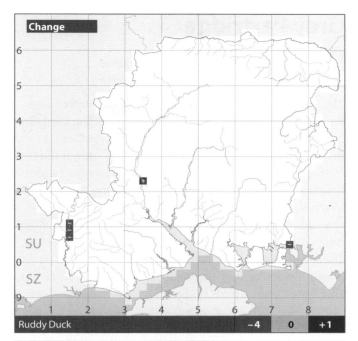

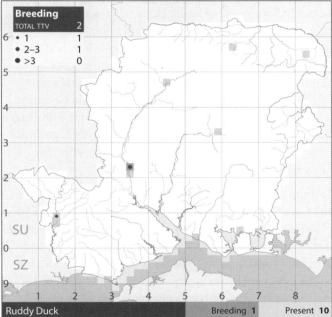

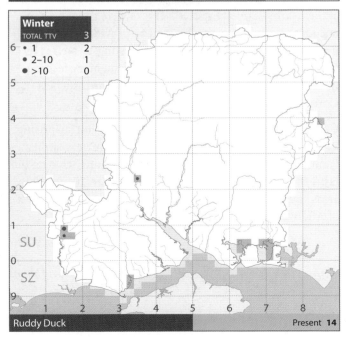

Grey Partridge
Perdix perdix
A scarce and declining resident

The Grey Partridge is one of the most rapidly decreasing bird species in Europe. In the UK, the population has fallen by around 90% over the past 40 years. In Hampshire, a dramatic decline was already obvious at the time of the 1986–91 Atlas as described in *BoH*. This downward slide has continued to date. The HBA breeding and change maps show that the total of 602 tetrads where breeding was considered likely in 1986–91 plummeted to just 125 in 2008–2012, with confirmed breeding from only 11 tetrads. The species is now mainly restricted to limited areas on Martin Down, around The Wallops, Andover and Overton, East Tisted and on parts of the South Downs.

The primary reason for its decline is the deterioration of farmland habitat due to agricultural intensification. In particular the use of herbicides and insecticides has resulted in reduced chick survival because of decreased availability of invertebrate food (Rands 1985). Supplementary causes include loss of nesting cover through the removal of hedges, smaller broods because of subsequent increased predation, particularly by Foxes, and accidental shooting and disturbance during Red-legged Partridge shooting drives. There is no evidence that direct competition from Red-legged Partridges has affected Grey Partridges.

Despite the continuing downward trend in the population, the Environmental Stewardship Scheme currently provides payments for measures such as conservation headlands and beetle banks which should benefit these birds and other farmland species. At the Middleton and Portway Estate in the Longparish area, with advice from the GWCT, the number of breeding Grey Partridges has been increased from three pairs in 2007 to 32 pairs in 2012. Also in 2012 at the nearby Trinley Estate, 53 chicks were ringed. These encouraging results were obtained by providing insect-rich field margins and tussocky grass for nesting, as well as by sowing wild-bird seed mixes and supplementary feeding in winter. Such measures can also benefit birds such as Corn Bunting, Skylark and Lapwing.

Grey Partridge is a sedentary species so it is not surprising that its winter and breeding distributions are very similar. Family parties stay together through the winter. During the HBA the highest winter counts were between 20 and 30 in areas south-east of Alton, along the Berkshire border, west of Andover and in the Martin Down area.

David Minns

Sponsored by David Minns

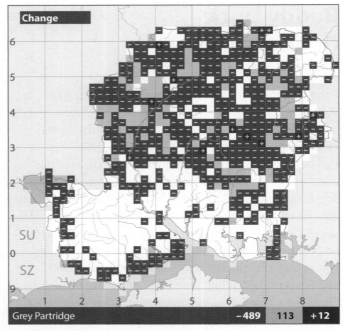

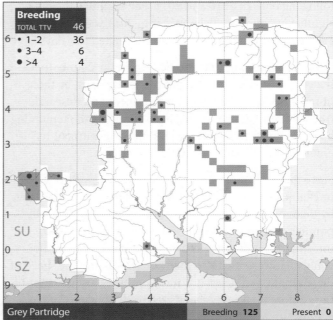

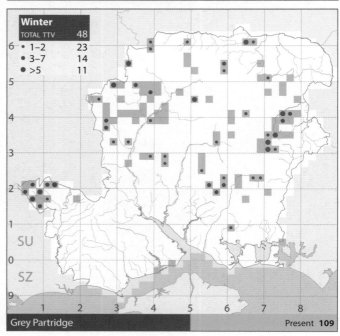

Grey Partridge, Stockbridge, May 2012 – *Mike Darling* (above); north Hampshire, September 2011 – *Martin Bennett* (below)

Red-legged Partridge

Alectoris rufa

A common resident, its numbers supplemented by releases

In 1972 *C&T* described the Red-legged Partridge as widely spread but generally much less common than the Grey Partridge. Today the situation has reversed with Red-legs now by far the more numerous of the two. Comparison of the HBA maps for the two species shows that Red-legs were found likely to be breeding in 605 tetrads (approximately 60% of the county) whereas the corresponding number for Grey Partridges was just 125 tetrads (approximately 12% of the county).

Regrettably, the reason for this reversal in fortunes owes more to the dramatic decline of our native species than to the success of its introduced relative. In fact the number of Red-legged Partridges has also been declining since the time of the 1986–91 Atlas. Over the intervening period, their population in England has fallen by 21% (*BirdTrends*) although for a species that is released in its millions every year, such trends may not mean a great deal.

In Hampshire, although the species remains widespread, its range has contracted by around 8% since the 1986–91 Atlas, with losses particularly in the New Forest and the eastern parts of the county. In contrast, some infilling has

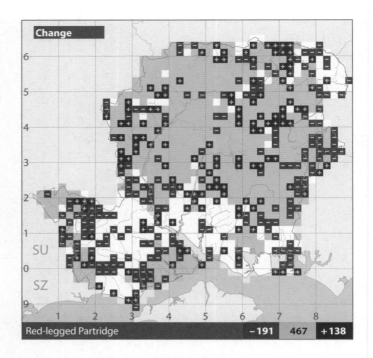

Red-legged Partridge | – 191 | 467 | + 138

occurred on the central agricultural belt where breeding densities are generally higher. It is possible that this pattern of change is due to losses in the wild population and gains as a result of more widespread releases. However, given the vast numbers put down annually in the UK, it is perhaps more likely due to variations in locations and numbers of releases.

Red-Legged Partridge, Cheriton Wood, September 2010 – *Peter Thompson*

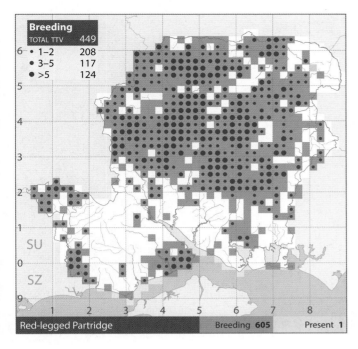

Breeding
TOTAL TTV 449
• 1–2   208
• 3–5   117
• >5   124

Red-legged Partridge | Breeding **605** | Present **1**

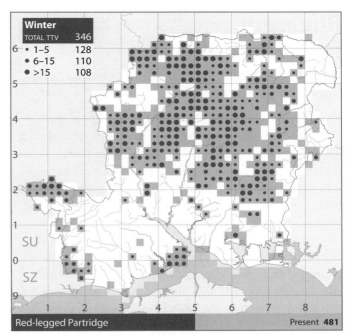

Winter
TOTAL TTV 346
• 1–5   128
• 6–15   110
• >15   108

Red-legged Partridge | Present **481**

Red-legs can turn up anywhere, including unlikely locations such as parks, gardens and even busy urban areas, but are generally far more common in large open agricultural regions than in heathland and woodland habitats.

Red-legged partridges are essentially sedentary so it is to be expected that their winter distribution largely mirrors that in the breeding season. The fact that fewer tetrads were occupied in winter than in summer, yet counts in occupied tetrads were higher, suggests that some local movements leading to concentration in better feeding areas may take place in winter.

David Minns

Sponsored by Geoffrey Farwell

Lady Amherst's Pheasant
Chrysolophus amherstiae

Golden Pheasant
Chrysolophus pictus

Very scarce and declining introduced residents

The first Golden Pheasants probably arrived in Hampshire from Dorset in the late 19th century but none were recorded during the 1968–72 Atlas. By the time of the 1986–91 Hampshire Atlas, however, following small-scale releases on several estates, there were apparently self-supporting populations in the Beaulieu and Exbury areas, a few parts of the New Forest and in the Queen Elizabeth Country Park. Most of these populations seem to have died out by the time of the HBA, with only two records obtained, both in 2008: one of two birds in the Kimbridge area in January and the other of an immature male at Ampfield Wood near Chandler's Ford in December.

Lady Amherst's Pheasants were released on the Exbury estate in the 1950s, with a flock of 11 recorded there in 1973. Occasional reports of pure Lady Amherst's continued

Golden Pheasant, Norfolk – *Alex Berryman*

to the time of 1986–91 Atlas but most records were of hybrids with Golden Pheasants and there is no evidence of a self-supporting feral population. Only one record from near Sherfield English in February 2008 was received during the HBA.

The continuing, occasional records of both species presumably refer to escapes from local collections.

David Minns

101

Pheasant

Phasianus colchicus

An abundant resident, the naturalised population being supplemented by releases

It is somewhat ironic that at a time when many of our farmland birds are in decline, the Pheasant, an introduced species which is bred to be shot, is one of the most common and best known birds in the British countryside. It is maintained as an abundant resident thanks to millions being reared and released each year. In autumn, following release, it contributes a greater avian biomass than any other 'wild' bird species in the UK. It qualifies as one of our best known birds because it is large, spectacularly-plumaged and conspicuous, its loud and distinctive call also making it hard to miss. In England, its population has almost doubled since the 1960s (*BirdTrends*) presumably as a result of larger numbers being released. In recent years the upward trend has peaked, possibly due to a reduction in demand for an expensive pastime caused by the economic slowdown.

This species is widespread across Hampshire, the main gaps in its distribution being in built-up areas such as Southampton, Portsmouth and in the north-east around Aldershot and Farnborough, although even in urban areas it sometimes turns up unexpectedly and naively in town parks and gardens. It is most common on the agricultural heartland of the county where it is found in woodland and farmland, particularly on shooting estates where it is bred for release and cover is provided for its benefit (and, one has to admit, for the benefit of many other species). During the HBA survey, the highest breeding season TTV count, no doubt based on insider information, was 2,500 on the Somerley Estate in the Avon Valley in July 2008. There has been little change in its distribution over the last 20 years, with a net loss of only six tetrads in the breeding season.

Although the Hampshire population is dependent on the annual release of huge numbers of birds, a smaller wild population exists. This is confirmed by the presence of

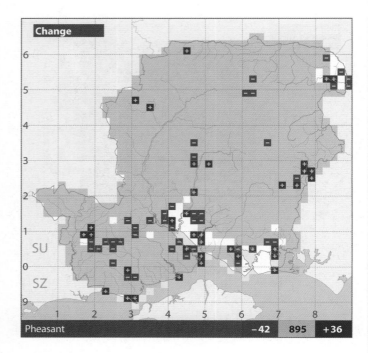

breeding birds in areas that are not shot over including both farmland and heathland habitats. How big this population would be without the annual replenishment provided by escapees from the cull is unknown, although one might speculate that it would reduce in line with many other farmland species without the regular injection of new blood.

Pheasants are sedentary although they tend to form flocks in winter and may move in search of good feeding areas. Comparison of the HBA breeding and wintering maps shows similar distributions although with fewer tetrads occupied in winter than in summer. This is particularly noticeable in the New Forest where large areas are apparently devoid of birds in winter. This may be a result of the local population moving on to nearby farmland or because the birds become much less vocal outside the breeding season and are therefore less easy to detect.

David Minns

Sponsored by Geoffrey Farwell

Pheasant, New Forest, May 2010 – *Martin Bennett*

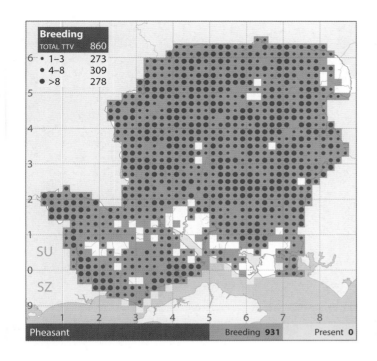

Breeding
TOTAL TTV 860
- 1–3   273
- 4–8   309
- >8   278

Pheasant   Breeding **931**   Present **0**

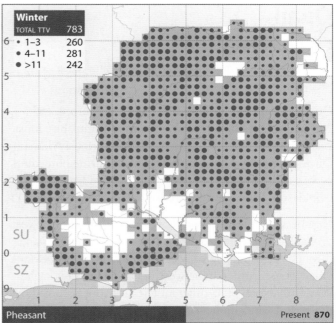

Winter
TOTAL TTV 783
- 1–3   260
- 4–11   281
- >11   242

Pheasant   Present **870**

Pheasant, Cheriton, June 2010 – *Peter Thompson*

Quail
Coturnix coturnix

A normally scarce and erratic summer visitor; very rarely recorded in winter

Quails are summer visitors from southern Europe and Africa. Their distinctive song is heard in Hampshire most years, but obtaining breeding proof is notoriously difficult. During the HBA period there was no confirmed breeding reported although a young bird was rescued from the Cholderton Estate during harvest on September 16th 2011.

Numbers vary year to year, those recorded in any one year probably representing only a fraction of the total passing through the county. During the 2008–12 breeding seasons, Quail were recorded in between six and 24 tetrads each year, with a total of 55 different tetrads being occupied over the period. The number of singing males was more variable, from seven in 2009 to 61 in 2011. The latter year, a so-called 'Quail year' saw an exceptional record of 40 during harvesting on the Cholderton Estate on September 8th. The factors affecting how many reach the UK are complex, and include breeding success and weather conditions in southern Europe, conditions in the Sahel region of Africa, winter survival and weather at migration time. Observer effort also determines how many are located.

The majority of records are of singing males. With breeding success being so difficult to prove, the accompanying HBA breeding map has been based on those records received after May 15th being indicative of likely breeding. However, many of these records may refer to unmated males. The protocol of recording probable breeding based on the presence of a territorial singing male for a week or more may not be appropriate for this species as extended singing more likely indicates an unmated, rather than paired, bird.

Similar to Grey Partridge, Quail records were largely confined to certain areas of the chalk, in particular Martin Down, around the Wallops, Overton and Binsted, and other parts of the South Downs.

The change map shows a decline in likely breeding from 68 tetrads in the 1986–91 to 52 in 2008–12, but this should not necessarily be taken as indicative of a downward trend in the breeding population. It is possible that such changes may simply reflect the annual variance in numbers and recording effort, or that some likely breeding records, particularly from the first Atlas, were migrants. That said, in Europe, Quail populations declined significantly during 1970–90.

Birds occasionally winter in Hampshire (*BoH*), though there were no records during the HBA period. The most recent winter record was of one at West Hayling Local Nature Reserve in January 2003.

David Minns

Sponsored by Rupert Pyrah

Quail, Martin Down, May 2014 – *Alan Lewis*

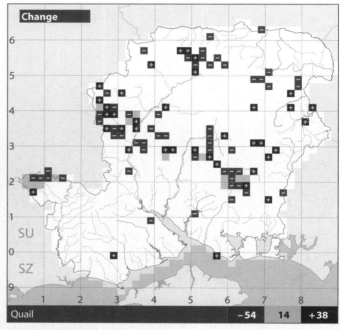

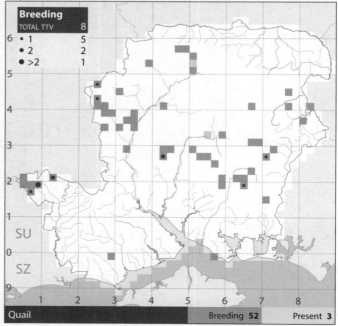

Red-throated Diver
Gavia stellata
A scarce winter visitor and passage migrant

The Red-throated Diver has a circumpolar distribution, breeding on tundra lakes into the Arctic Circle as far north as the ice thaw will allow by late May. The world population is between 200,000–500,000. In Britain, 1,300 pairs summer north from the Scottish Highlands to the Northern Isles (*APEP3*). In autumn, West Palearctic birds migrate south to winter in tidal waters around the British and west European coasts and east along some north Mediterranean shores to the Black Sea. Evidence from aerial mapping suggests the British wintering population is a minimum of 17,000 individualss (O'Brien *et al.* 2008). The species is thinly spread in winter in shallow waters around the entire British coast, although now there appears to be significant offshore concentrations in the south-east.

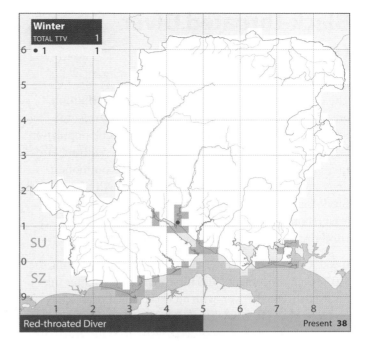

Wintering patterns in Hampshire have changed substantially this century. Previously, it was at best a scarce winter visitor to sheltered coastal waters in the early winter but by mid-winter it was more likely to be reported from the open sea. From 1980–85 the five winter totals averaged 12 individuals. From 2007–12 numbers in sheltered coastal locations were of ones or twos in winter whereas during sea-watching at the east and, particularly, west of the county, far greater numbers were encountered than previously. During the HBA period the species was recorded in 38 tetrads. For the majority of these (25) there were only registrations in one or two months during the five winters and these normally of single or occasionally two individuals. These tetrads were all located within the inner Solent, the eastern harbours or Southampton Water and the same few individuals roamed between several tetrads. It suggests that these localities are only now used by weakened, or storm-driven, birds – in any case in lower numbers compared to the previous Atlas and prior periods. Certainly, fewer birds appear weakened by sea pollution as only two were reported oiled in the whole period.

Movements, however, were reported on 50% of winter months within the Solent between Hill Head and Chilling – exceptional counts being five east on November 15th 2007

and 11 west on December 15th 2010. On the open sea in the west of the county, from Hurst to Barton on Sea, birds were seen in all mid-winter months during the HBA period and in the east on most months across Hayling Bay (80%). At Hurst small flocks were occasionally seen settled on the sea or into the north-west Solent. Most observations were of movements, some off Hurst, which were particularly large and at previously unrecorded levels in Hampshire waters. These included an easterly movement of 71 on January 17th 2009 and a westerly movement of 394 from February 4th–7th 2011. Prevailing south-westerly winds up to gale force seem to precipitate these large movements consistent with the evidence above that the species winters out of visual range off the south coast.

Spring and autumn passage records over the calendar years 2007–12 were as follows. Light easterly spring passage totalled 201 individuals typically from late March to mid-May. By contrast very few were noted on return passage, just 16 individuals from 2008–2012 but an exceptional 16 in 2007 from September 18th into October.

Alan Cox

Sponsored by Jenny Jones

Red-Throated Diver,
Hayling Island, September 2009
– *Richard Ford*

Black-throated Diver

Gavia arctica

A very scarce winter visitor and passage migrant

The Black-throated Diver has a Palearctic distribution, breeding only at northern latitudes, reaching west to Scotland and Scandinavia. The West Palearctic population is between 120,000–230,000 individuals. In autumn, birds migrate south. In winter it is generally the commonest diver around European coasts from the North to the Black Seas. This is not the case in Britain where it is the least recorded of the three commoner divers with the wintering population estimated at 560 (*APEP3*).

It was a very scarce winter visitor to the county during the HBA; even movements off Hurst were much lighter than for Red-throated Diver, with an exceptional peak of six on December 7th 2008. The HBA map shows 25 tetrads where the species was recorded. Away from the Hurst area, all records were of singles, apart from two at Calshot and Sandy Point on single dates. Some individuals lingered for several weeks, for example ten of the 11 tetrad registrations in Southampton Water could have related to just three individuals, including one present from December 2011 until February 2012. At Hurst/Milford on Sea the species was recorded in 60% of winter months, mostly movements of one to three birds, but three settled on the sea there from December to January 2010–11. The species is hence a very scarce county winterer, as noted for the whole of Britain above, but long-staying birds make for easier viewing than

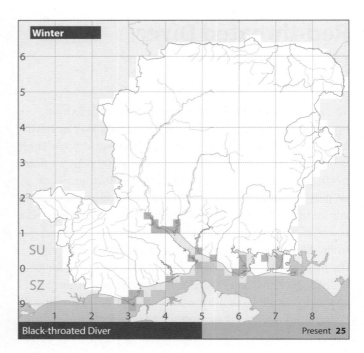

the greater, but more transient, numbers of Red-throated Divers.

It is more numerous on spring passage than in winter. During 2007–12 a cumulative total of 59 east between April 2nd and May 20th included 27 in 2011. Some of these lingered for several days including one into early June. By contrast only three were recorded in autumn including the earliest return ever on September 8th 2009.

Alan Cox

Sponsored by Ray Morley

Black-Throated Diver, Forton Lake, November 2008 – *Steve Copsey*

Great Northern Diver

Gavia immer

A scarce but increasing winter visitor and passage migrant

The Great Northern Diver is essentially a Nearctic breeding species with a tiny footprint into the Palearctic, mostly by virtue of 100–300 pairs in Iceland. The North American breeding population is stated by Cornell Laboratories (2010) as 252,000–264,000 breeding pairs out of a total population of 607,000–635,000 individuals, the additional birds being first and second years, breeding not being attempted before the third calendar-year. Nearctic breeders disperse along both east and west North American coasts but there is also a trans-Atlantic passage (estimated at <1% of the population) to winter along European Atlantic coasts and even a small population off the French Mediterranean coast. *Bird Atlas 2007–11* noted registrations in a surprising 27% of British 10 km squares, with many inland records on scattered lakes and reservoirs boosting the predominantly coastal distribution. The British population is estimated at 2,500 (*APEP3*) with the main concentration wintering around the Northern Isles, the Hebrides and off the north-west coast of the Scottish mainland.

In Hampshire numbers increased from an average of seven in the five-winter periods from 1980–85, to 15 from 2007–12. As the map shows, there were registrations in 48 tetrads within 14 10 km squares, including three inland records of singles from Blashford Lakes. Most winterers arrive in late November or early December, including dramatic influxes of 17 and 24 in the winters of 2008/09 and 2009/10. Adults are flightless for a period in mid-winter and hence such arrivals generally lead to sightings of settled birds for several weeks when there are very few records of offshore movements. In consequence, most coastal localities recorded the species for more than 50% of mid-winter months in the five-year period. Southampton Water held a peak of at least ten in 2009/10 when county winterers

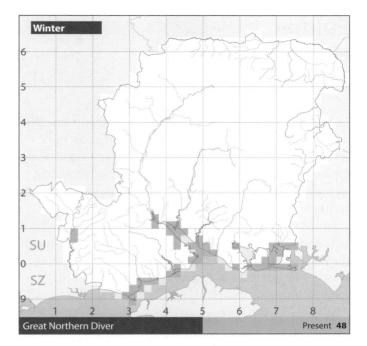

reached the record total of 24, approaching 1% of the estimated British wintering population. Elsewhere, peaks of three to four were recorded at five other coastal localities over the Atlas period. The species thus was the most likely of the three commoner divers to be encountered wintering within the county. It was often seen close to shore foraging for crabs.

Spring passage totalled 53 from 2007–12 but this is possibly an over-estimate as some individuals rested offshore for several days; indeed very few were reported moving purposefully east. Birds were present into late May in four years and one year into June (on 9th 2012 – the second ever record for the month). A total of just nine was recorded in autumn from 2007–12 between September 18th and October 30th; it is arguable that of these, three in late October were local winterers rather than on passage.

Alan Cox

Sponsored by Kate Allen

Great Northern Diver, West Hayling Island, January 2009 – *Richard Ford*

Fulmar

Fulmarus glacialis

A scarce passage migrant most frequent in spring and early autumn

During the HBA period this species was regularly recorded during sea-watches on the open coast, particularly in spring and summer (April to August) off Hurst Beach and Sandy Point. Although this coincides with birds breeding on coastal cliffs in adjacent counties, the lack of records earlier in the year, when local breeders have already returned to their colonies, suggests that the spring peak in Hampshire may be due to non-breeders moving through the English Channel and visiting nearby colonies at that season. The influence of recording bias during spring sea-watching may also play a part.

Peak day-counts during the HBA period included 14 off Hurst on April 27th 2008 and 12 off Sandy Point on May 28th 2008. Smaller numbers were seen in the Solent, with a peak of four off Gilkicker Point on April 15th 2009. Birds were occasionally observed prospecting the cliffs between Milford on Sea and Barton on Sea during the spring and one was seen heading inland over Hill Head on June 5th 2009.

Few records were received in autumn and winter (September to March) with only single-figure day counts; this is when local populations disperse offshore. Overall, numbers of this species recorded in the county have shown a steady increase since the 1986–91 Atlas (*Figure xiv*), probably partly due to increased observer coverage.

Russell Wynn

Sponsored by Mike Adams

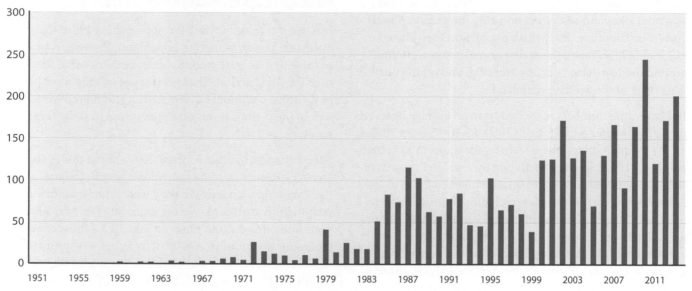

Figure xiv – Fulmar: annual totals 1951–2012.

Fulmar, off the Needles, July 2007 – *Nigel Jones*

Manx Shearwater

Puffinus puffinus

A scarce, but increasing, passage migrant most frequent in spring

Most records of this species are received from open coastal sites between April and June. Peak day counts off Hurst Beach during the HBA period included 82 on April 24th 2009, 73 on July 17th 2009, 133 on June 18th 2011 and 152 on April 30th 2012. Relatively few were seen in the August to October period, with a peak of 19 off Hurst on September 10th 2010. Sporadic records of birds picked up at inland sites in autumn presumably relate to recently fledged juveniles; recent examples included one in Basingstoke on September 19th 2011.

Numbers visiting Hampshire have dramatically increased since the 1986–91 Atlas, as indicated in *Figure xv*.

Russell Wynn

Sponsored by Royal Naval Birdwatching Society

Manx Shearwater, Milford on Sea, October 2009 – *Nigel Jones* (left and centre); Basingstoke, September 2011 – *Charlotte Hellewell* (right)

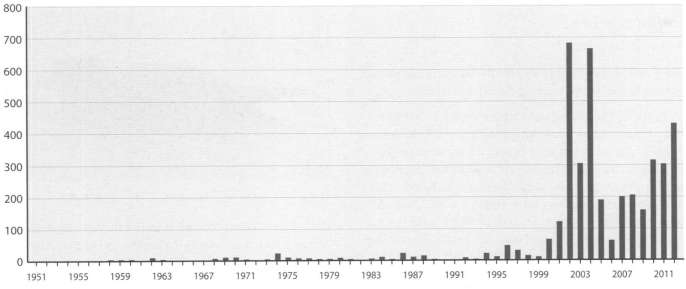

Figure xv – Annual totals of Manx Shearwaters 1951–2012.

Balearic Shearwater

Puffinus mauretanicus

A very scarce but regular passage migrant, mostly in late summer and autumn

Most sightings in Hampshire are of singles or small numbers seen during sea-watches from open coastal locations between late May and early October, particularly off Hurst Beach and Sandy Point. The peak day count in the 2007–12 period (although outside the HBA breeding and winter seasons) was eight (including a flock of seven) off Hurst on September 10th 2010. Annual totals ranged from ten to 34 each year from 2007 to 2012. However, calculation of accurate totals has recently become complicated due to birds lingering in Christchurch Bay for periods of a few days in summer and autumn.

Balearic Shearwater is Europe's only Critically Endangered seabird, although numbers recorded during post-breeding migration in UK waters have increased dramatically since the mid-1990s. This situation is reflected in Hampshire, with only four listed in *BoH* in 1993, but a further 67 up to 2006 (including an exceptional count of 40 in 2001) and 114 from 2007–12. The increase is clearly shown in *Figure xvi*.

Russell Wynn

Sponsored by Royal Naval Birdwatching Society

Balearic Shearwater, Lyme Bay – *Mark Darlaston*

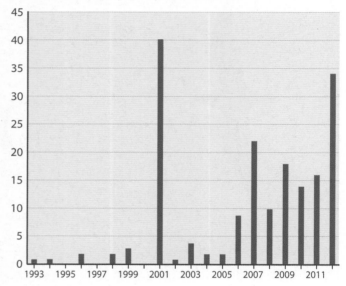

Figure xvi – Annual totals of Balearic Shearwaters 1993–2012.

Sooty Shearwater

Puffinus griseus

A rare passage migrant

The Sooty Shearwater breeds on sub-Antarctic islands and winters in the North Atlantic and Pacific Oceans.

During the HBA period there were as many as 20 birds recorded, including a peak count of eight in 2010. Most records referred to single birds seen during autumn sea-watches in August–November and usually associated with south-westerly gales and rain. Exceptions included a late bird seen in Hayling Bay on December 1st 2007, five off Milford on Sea on September 10th 2010, three off Hurst on September 11th 2011 and one found exhausted on the tideline at Hill Head on June 13th 2011 that later died in care.

Sooty Shearwater was formerly a very rare visitor to Hampshire waters, with only one bird from 1974 listed in

Sooty Shearwater, Hill Head, June 2011 – *Bob Marchant*

BoH. From 1993 to 2006 there were a further nine records. The recent increase means that by the end of 2012, the county total stood at 30.

Russell Wynn

Sponsored in memory of Tim Lawman

Storm Petrel

Hydrobates pelagicus

A very scarce visitor usually seen after autumn gales

This species is rarely seen from Hampshire, although there are occasional large 'wrecks' in association with stormy weather, *e.g.* 126 birds from May 19th–29th 2006. The only notable influx during the HBA period was in 2008 with up to 17 birds recorded, including a total of 12 between July 8th–10th off Sandy Point and Hurst. The county total stood at 323 birds at the end of 2012.

Russell Wynn

Sponsored by Andy Collins

Storm Petrel, Lyme Bay – *Mark Darlaston*

Leach's Petrel

Oceanodroma leucorhoa

A very scarce autumn and winter visitor, usually appearing after gales

This species is a rare visitor to Hampshire coastal waters, usually associated with severe and prolonged autumn and winter gales. However, during the HBA period a major influx occurred in 2009 with the likely total exceeding 100 birds. On November 29th at least 44 moved east off Hurst Castle, and birds were pushed well into the Solent with 20 off Hill Head and smaller numbers between Keyhaven and Beaulieu and in Southampton Water. At least seven were in the Hayling Bay and Chichester Harbour area, and three were seen inland. Many of the birds recorded during this influx were in a weakened state, with one taken into care, several pursued by gulls and Peregrines and one off Oxey Marsh consumed by a Great Skua. Outside of this influx, small numbers were recorded in most years at coastal sites between September and January.

Russell Wynn

Sponsored by Brian Leach

Leach's Petrel, Hill Head, November 2009 – *Steve Copsey* (both images)

Gannet

Morus bassanus

A common non-breeding summer visitor; scarce but increasing in winter

Gannets are regularly recorded from the Hampshire coast, most commonly in spring and summer. During the HBA period, the highest spring passage count was 202 moving east off Milford on Sea on April 29th 2008. The largest concentrations were seen feeding off Hurst Beach between late May and early August. Peak counts each year included 350 on July 19th 2008, 408 on August 7th 2009, 166 on 14th July 2010, 334 on July 15th 2011 and 464 on August 15th 2012. These birds were typically concentrated over offshore gravel banks, where interactions between topography and tide provide optimal feeding conditions. Flocks comprised predominantly adult birds and recent tracking studies indicate that the origin of these birds is likely to be the breeding colony on Alderney in the Channel Islands.

A change in behaviour observed during the HBA period was the regular appearance of birds in Southampton Water.

Until 2010, records were less than annual but became almost daily in June 2011 (up to five) and 2012 when a maximum of 14 was seen from Weston Shore on June 22nd. The numbers observed off Hill Head have also increased with a maximum of 70 on May 17th 2009.

Small numbers were seen feeding off Hurst until October, although sporadic large movements associated with autumn storms included 575 off Hurst on September 5th/6th 2010 and 434 off Hurst on October 23rd 2011. Lower numbers were seen moving through the Solent, with a peak of 72 off Normandy Marsh on July 18th 2008. There has recently been a marked increase in winter records, with peaks of 116 off Hurst on December 25th 2008 and 260 west off Sandy Point on January 15th 2011.

Inland records, mostly relating to juvenile or immature birds, included singles at Blashford Lakes on August 26th 2010 and Cheriton on September 26th 2010.

Russell Wynn

Sponsored by Doug Robertson

Gannet, Lyme Bay – *Mark Darlaston*

Shag
Phalacrocorax aristotelis
A scarce winter visitor and passage migrant

In Britain, the Shag is restricted as a breeding species mainly to the rocky coasts of the north and west. It is absent from much of eastern and south-eastern England with colonies on the Isle of Wight being the most easterly on the south coast. Although breeding adults remain close to their colonies throughout the year, immatures and non-breeders disperse so the species is seen more widely around the British coast in winter.

Prior to the 1950s, Shags were seldom seen in Hampshire but since then sightings have increased. Surveys during this period have shown that the national population has grown but, since around 1990, has been on a downward trend. This suggests that, in recent years, the increased number of Hampshire records is explained, at least in part, by the growth in sea-watching over the period.

The species can occur in any month of the year but is most numerous between September and November as immatures disperse from their natal colonies. They are seen most frequently at the eastern and western ends of the Solent – at Sandy Point and Hurst/Milford on Sea respectively. Most records are of ones or twos but high counts during the 2007–12 period included gatherings of up to 25 off Hurst Beach in October 2009 and 30 off Sandy Point in October 2011. As the HBA winter map shows, they also occur in the eastern harbours and at the head of Southampton Water, particularly as a result of stormy weather.

John Eyre

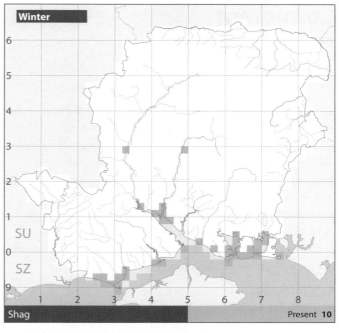

Shag, Winchester, December 2009 – *Hilary Cornford*

Shag, Port Solent, May 2009 – *Trevor Carpenter*

Cormorant

Phalacrocorax carbo

A moderately common resident, passage migrant and winter visitor

At the time of the 1986–91 Atlas, this species did not breed in Hampshire, the nearest breeding colonies being on the cliffs of the Isle of Wight and Dorset. The first tree-nesting colony in Great Britain had been founded at Abberton Reservoir, Essex, in 1981 and over the following 25 years increasing numbers of inland colonies were established, predominantly in east and central England. This change in behaviour from cliff-nester to tree-nester was most probably triggered by immigration of Continental birds of the race *P. c. sinensis* (Newson *et al.* 2007).

In 2006 two pairs attempted to nest at Fleet Pond. Both failed, but the following year two pairs raised five young at the same site, the first record of successful breeding by this species in Hampshire. In 2008 two pairs again nested successfully at Fleet Pond and a third pair bred at Ibsley Water, raising one young in a nest on the ground. Breeding was attempted, unsuccessfully, at Fleet Pond in 2010 but not in subsequent years. Given the current national policy, introduced in 2004, for controlling Cormorant numbers, it will be interesting to see whether the species succeeds in its bid to colonise Hampshire or whether its attempt during the HBA period proves to be a one-off and short-lived episode.

The number of Cormorants seen in the county has increased between the 1986–91 and 2007–12 Atlases. The mean maximum WeBS count over the HBA period was 720 whereas the total peak monthly site counts during 1986–91 were usually below 600. The numbers seen inland have also increased with a county record roost count of 450 in the Avon Valley in January 2011. This total involved birds feeding by day off the Dorset coast and flying inland to roost. Three-figure counts were also made at three other sites: Blashford Lakes, Fishlake Meadows and Eversley Gravel Pits.

As the HBA winter map shows, the Cormorant is now commonly seen not only on the coast but in all the county's main river valleys, the Thames Basin and the Weald. Ringing data has shown that the population is swelled in winter by immigrants from elsewhere in the British Isles and the near Continent. An example of such movements is illustrated by a bird ringed as a chick on 9th June 2011 at Maughold, Isle of Man and photographed four months later at Blashford Lakes (*facing page, top left*).

John Eyre

Sponsored by Peter & Pamela Strangeman

Cormorant, Blashford Lakes, October 2010 – *Martin Bennett*

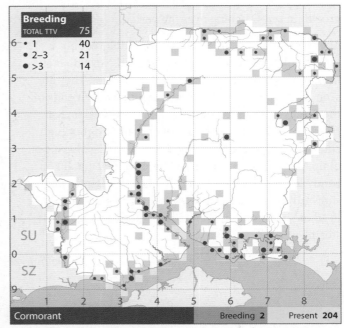

Breeding	
TOTAL TTV	75
• 1	40
• 2–3	21
• >3	14

Cormorant   Breeding **2**   Present **204**

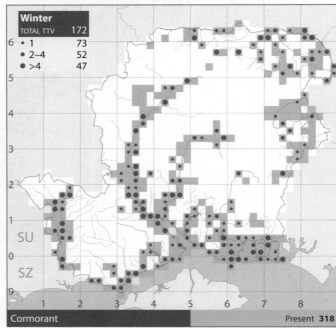

Winter	
TOTAL TTV	172
• 1	73
• 2–4	52
• >4	47

Cormorant   Present **318**

Cormorant, Blashford Lakes, September 2011 – *Martin Bennett* (above); Titchfield, August 2013 – *Mike Crutch* (below)

Cormorant ssp. *sinensis*, Sandy Point, April 2009 – *Andy Johnson*

Bittern
Botaurus stellaris
A very scarce but regular winter visitor

The Bittern is a species of temperate latitudes breeding across the Palearctic but wintering either in the extreme south, to India and sub-Saharan Africa, or to the far west in Europe where there is also a smaller resident population. It requires extensive reedbeds with large expanses of shallow water for breeding. In consequence it is localised over its summer range and in Britain is only successful in well managed, large wetlands where water is maintained at near constant levels. There were 110 territories in Britain in 2011 – an order of magnitude increase on the low point of just 11 in 1997 (Brown *et al.* 2012). The species does not breed in Hampshire although in 2012 there was a summering record.

In winter Bitterns are scarce visitors to the county. During the HBA period, overwintering occurred annually at Ivy Lake (Blashford) and Titchfield Haven where one to three individuals were present at each locality. Both reserves provide screened viewing of the reedbeds where the species appears to tolerate regular nearby human presence. Elsewhere, birds were certainly more difficult to locate, as they can hunt for small fish and amphibians amongst inundated reedbeds without breaking cover. In severe winter conditions, when shallower waters freeze over, birds are forced into the open and are recorded more widely.

During the HBA period the species was recorded in 61 tetrads with the most widespread occurrences in the severe winters of 2009/2010 and 2010/11. In the 2009/2010 winter, the British population was estimated at 600 (Wotton *et al.* 2011) of which at least 15 were present in the county. This represents perhaps a six-fold increase over the regular British wintering population. Such enhancements are probably the result of cold weather movements from the near Continent (Denmark, the Netherlands and Belgium). By contrast, breeding birds from Sweden, the Baltic countries and farther east are thought to migrate earlier in autumn to southern Europe and Africa. In the 2010/11 winter period, after a cold spell in December, a record total of 27 was scattered across Hampshire at 18 localities in January. During the five winters 2007/8 to 2011/12, county peak wintering numbers totalled 67 (6, 10, 15, 27, and 9). This is higher than either of the five-winter peak count totals of 43 from 1980–85 (included two severe winters) and 27 from 1985–90 (one severe winter). The increased five-year total from 2007–12 is perhaps indicative of an increase in the north-west European breeding and wintering populations.

Alan Cox

Sponsored by Paul & Jan Craven

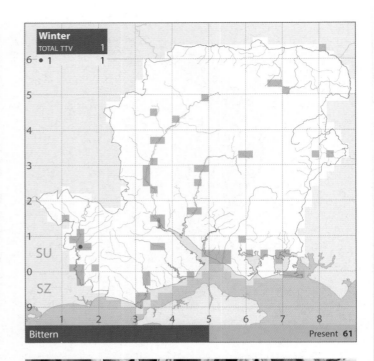

Bittern

Present **61**

Bittern, Blashford Lakes, February 2009 – *Richard Ford*

Bittern, Blashford Lakes, February 2011 (both images) – *Martin Bennett*

Cattle Egret

Bubuculus ibis

A rare vagrant

Unlike other herons the Cattle Egret is highly gregarious, often feeding away from water and, with a mainly insectivorous diet, regularly associating with cows and other farm animals. The breeding range of this cosmopolitan species has been expanding northwards in Europe reaching central France by the 1990s. During the 1986–91 Atlas, it was recorded in Hampshire for the first time and a further four records had been added to the total prior to the start of the HBA in 2007. Numbers were boosted by a small influx into Britain of approximately 23 which led to records of three in the county between January and May 2006 (BBRC). In December 2007, there was an unprecedented arrival of 80 individuals into Britain followed by subsequent smaller invasions in each of the HBA years.

As the map shows, registrations were made in 17 Hampshire tetrads during the winter Atlas recording period and the species was observed in every year. By 2012 the county total had increased possibly by 17 individuals with several overwintering and a few lingering into spring. It is not possible to be certain of numbers, as the species expands into the county from the near Continent; several individuals wander extensively in southern Britain and may in fact be annual returnees, as noted for colour-ringed Great White Egrets. There were also spring and autumn arrivals including five in August. One summer record at Titchfield Haven on May 29th 2008 coincided with first breeding in Britain on the Somerset Levels; another was found at Sandy Point Nature Reserve in early May the following year.

Alan Cox

Cattle Egret, Warblington, December 2011 – *Richard Ford*

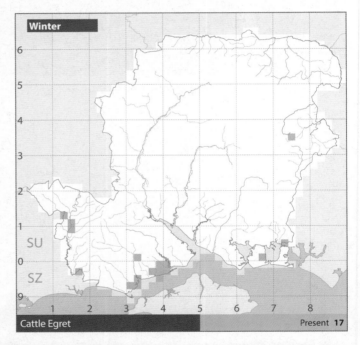

Winter

Cattle Egret — Present **17**

Cattle Egret, Keyhaven, September 2009 – *Mike Duffy*

Great White Egret

Ardea alba

A very scarce visitor, recorded in every month

Until the 1990s, the nominate subspecies of the Great White Egret was confined as a breeding species to central Europe and Asia. As recently as 1992, the European breeding population, present from Austria to the Ukraine, was estimated at 550 pairs (*HBW*) but has recently been re-estimated as at least 10,000 pairs (Ławicki 2014). This huge increase is dominated by revised estimates for the Ukraine, Belarus and Russia, which comprise 90% of the total but includes, for example, 200 pairs in France with initial breeding there as recently as 1994.

First breeding in Britain occurred in 2012. Even more surprising than the dramatic increase in European breeding numbers is a change in the species' wintering distribution. Until the 1990s, it was a rare winterer in central and western Europe as breeders migrated to the eastern Mediterranean and Africa. More recently birds have begun wintering in huge numbers in western Europe, a population now estimated as at least 11,200 (Ławicki 2014) and including some 6,300 in the Netherlands and France alone. In Britain, changes have been far more modest but the species has advanced from vagrant to now regular, but still very scarce, status. The wintering population of around 34 (*APEP3*) is confined to southern Britain with only scattered records farther north.

In Hampshire, one individual has been wintering at Blashford Lakes since 2003, when it arrived as a juvenile, and still appeared there in 2013 for its 11th successive winter. This individual has been colour-ringed as a nestling making it possible to track its arrival, typically from mid-August through to its departure in late January. It was ringed on May 3rd 2003 at Lac de Grand-Lieu, Vendée, France where, by the end of the HBA period, 160 pairs were breeding. During the Atlas a further 24 records of the species were registered in the county of which five were in summer and nine in winter. The map shows that in the Avon Valley winter records were concentrated in a cluster of seven tetrads. These included the regular winterer and another un-ringed bird that was present from January until April 12th 2010. Away from the Avon Valley other individuals were registered in ten tetrads: seven located in the Test, Itchen or Meon Valleys, one at Hatchet Pond, New Forest and two spanning Sinah Gravel Pit, Hayling Island. There were three records of two to four day winter stopovers and the remainder were on single dates. Individuals were recorded in every month of the year, including six in September. No pattern emerged in the

Great White Egret, Blashford, September 2008 – *Martin Bennett*

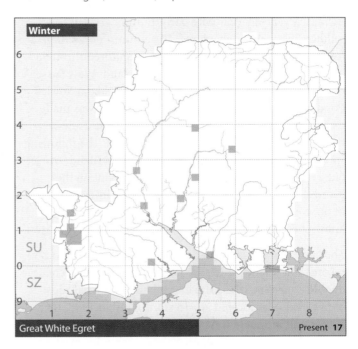

timing of arrivals and all but one record, outside of winter, was on a single date, the exception being April records from the Avon Valley. *Table 12* shows the cumulative monthly totals for the 22 years from 1985–2006 (first record June 15th 1985) and the 6-year 2007–12 period encompassing the HBA.

It is too soon to claim colonisation of the county, or indeed Britain, by this species, but a few pioneers during the Atlas survey and the rapid expansion of the near Continent population does suggest that may well be the case in the not too distant future.

Alan Cox

Month	Jan	Feb	Mar	Apr	May	Jun	Jul	Aug	Sep	Oct	Nov	Dec
1985–2006	5	1	0	1	0	2	6	7	2	4	5	7
2007–2012	9	6	4	3	3	1	4	7	15	11	7	10

Table 12 – Great White Egret: cumulative monthly totals in Hampshire.

Little Egret
Egretta garzetta
A moderately common winter visitor, passage migrant and increasing breeder

The species has a global population estimated between 0·64–3·1 million pairs (Wetlands International 2002). The nominate subspecies is highly migratory and has a Palearctic-wide distribution but in Europe it was thinly distributed, confined to southern and eastern regions, until a westward expansion in the late 20th century. The colonisation of northern France occurred in 1974 when significant numbers arrived in the autumn followed by first breeding in 1978 (Carr 2009). Its expansion into southern Britain followed the same pattern. The breakthrough year was 1989 when coastal arrivals in Hampshire included a flock of 17 at Keyhaven and Pennington Marshes. Numbers of overwintering birds increased year-on-year with early autumn arrivals followed by spring departures. The autumn population totalled at least 138 in August 1995, monitored through two nocturnal roosts, one at Thorney Island, West Sussex where Hampshire birds roosted, and the other at Sowley Pond in the west. The first three-figure count was made on December 4th 1995 when a total of 109 birds flew from Hampshire to roost at Thorney Island. The following spring, breeding was confirmed at Brownsea Island, Dorset but a recently fledged juvenile was also present on the Hampshire coast, near an existing heronry. In 1998, breeding in the county was confirmed when two, of a total of ten known breeding pairs in Britain, were located at Fort Elson.

The early years of colonisation were dominated by coastal records but inland winterers along river valleys reached double figures in 1996. The first inland nocturnal roost of five birds was located at Alresford Pond in 1998. By 2000 small numbers were present throughout the year above Ringwood in the Avon Valley. Along the coast, a coordinated count of four nocturnal roosts on October 5th 2000 totalled 334 and a further 18 were seen to fly from the Lymington area to the Isle of Wight to roost. The Thorney Island roost when disturbed relocated to Tournerbury, Hayling Island and 223 were present there on October 26th. In 2002, the wintering pattern changed with far greater usage of the river valleys exemplified by a nocturnal roost of 56 at Alresford Pond on January 6th. A coordinated county-wide roost count was made on a monthly basis, beginning in 2004 when totals ranged from 53 (May) to 359 (September).

Little Egrets breed locally in colonies (in mixed or single-species heronries) but because of their late breeding (usually May in Hampshire) fully-leafed tree canopies make nest detection very difficult. Complete surveys of known colonies totalled 87 pairs in 2007 and again, during the HBA period, in 2008. Thus far four coastal and two inland

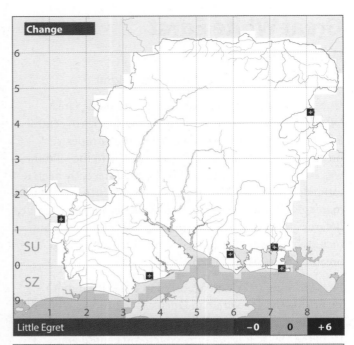

Change
Little Egret — −0   0   +6

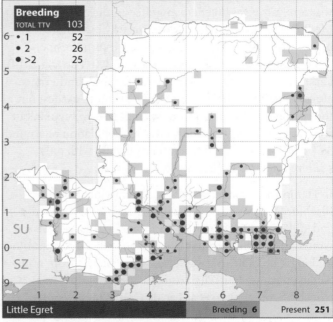

Breeding
TOTAL TTV 103
- 1   52
- 2   26
- >2   25

Little Egret — Breeding 6   Present 251

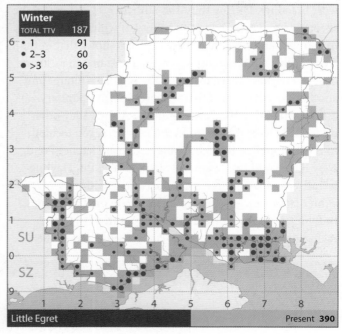

Winter
TOTAL TTV 187
- 1   91
- 2–3   60
- >3   36

Little Egret — Present 390

Great White Egret, Little Egret and Grey Heron, Blashford Lakes, September 2010 – *Martin Bennett*

Little Egret, Blashford Lakes, August 2009 (above); Blashford Lakes, September 2010 (below) – *Martin Bennett*

colonies have been confirmed. A colony near Ringwood (first breeding detected in 2004) was the first inland in Britain and one at Langstone Mill Pond was one of very few Little Egret colonies nationally to be exclusively of this species: it held 23 occupied nests in 2012. The breeding map shows birds summering in 25% of Hampshire tetrads, rising to 40% in winter; an extraordinary colonisation of virtually all suitable habitat in just over a decade. *Bird Atlas 2007–11* shows the breeding distribution of the species is principally confined to the Channel-coast counties and East Anglia.

Little Egrets occur typically in shallow wetlands feeding on large insects and their larvae, small fish and amphibians. The coastal WeBS data indicate a post-breeding dispersal when numbers along the coast build dramatically from July–August. A further surge occurs in October when perhaps the county population doubles in some years, as indicated by the winter distribution map. It seems likely that the increased early wintering population is of Continental origin and mainly transitory; however, some overwinter as indicated by the even denser distribution in winter along the river valleys and in the north-east of the county. Nationally, in winter, almost all 10 km squares in a line from Plymouth to mid-Lincolnshire were occupied during the 2007–11 national atlas period.

Alan Cox

Sponsored by Ian Calderwood

Grey Heron
Ardea cinerea

A moderately common resident, passage migrant and winter visitor

The Grey Heron is the largest European heron. Its range spans the whole of Africa and the Palearctic, from Great Britain and Ireland in the west to the Far East including Java and Japan. The population density is highest in the temperate zones of its range. Grey Herons frequent shallow water bodies, either inland or coastal, feeding mainly on fish and amphibians. Migratory or dispersive movements are largely dictated by food supply. In Hampshire, light coastal movements are observed in spring and autumn suggesting small variations in summer and winter populations.

Grey Herons breed locally in colonies (heronries) but because of their huge size are easily detectable in flight to and from the heronry, leading to widespread reporting away from these localities. In Europe the Grey Heron population has increased rapidly since 1980 (PECBMS 2011a). Heronry censuses have been undertaken in Great Britain since 1928 (annually from 1954). Population estimates are based on nest counts and estimates of nest occupancy. Problems encountered with censuses are inconsistent year-on-year coverage and counting inaccuracies at heronries in heavily wooded areas. These censuses, nevertheless, have demonstrated a steadily increasing population, albeit subject to falls and recoveries following harsh winters. Increased numbers are due to:

a) reduced persecution (see Witherby 1939 where human persecution is cited as a serious problem, naming a few counties, including Hampshire);
b) higher breeding productivity of prey species such as freshwater fish through improved water quality;
c) new feeding habitats created by fish farming with pond release of hand-reared fish.

In Britain and Ireland, the estimated breeding population increase has been slower than in Europe, numbers peaking at the beginning of the century at 13,000 pairs before, for as yet unexplained reasons, falling away slightly to 11,800 from 2007–2012. The county population has generally followed these national trends: 114 breeding pairs (occupied nests) in the first full survey in 1954, rising to peaks of 260 in both 1985 and 1998. The five-year means from 1999–2003 and 2004–2008 were 220 and 161–216 breeding pairs respectively. In 2009 there were 178–209 breeding pairs; unfortunately county records are incomplete from 2010–2012. The HBA change map is confined to confirmed breeding through observation of occupied nests. As the map shows, heronries were confirmed in 14 tetrads in the 1986–91 Atlas survey. These included 11 main heronries of which five are now extinct and a sixth, at Sopley, was abandoned in 1994 in favour of a new location nearby in Dorset. The remaining five traditional larger heronries at Somerley Park, Sowley Pond,

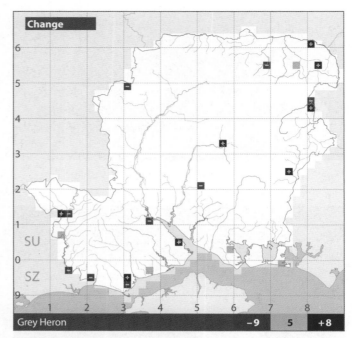

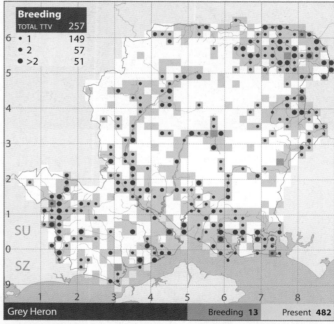

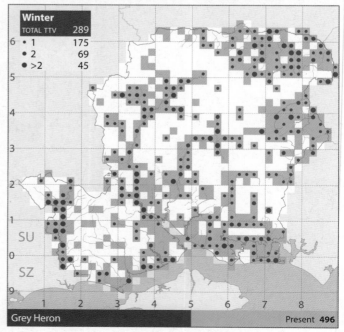

Grey Heron (with Sand Martin), Blashford Lakes, July 2011 – *Martin Bennett*

Fort Elson, Tournerbury and Elvetham were all occupied during the HBA period. In addition, larger heronries have developed at Arlebury Park (first breeding 1993) and at Midgham Wood in the Avon Valley (first breeding 2000). Smaller heronries, typically with single figure nest counts, were active during the HBA period in a further six tetrads contributing to a total of 13. The largest colony historically is on Crown land at Fort Elson at the edge of Portsmouth Harbour where numbers peaked at 85 pairs in 2004 and totalled 52 pairs in 2012. The only comparable heronry in size was at Midgham Wood where there were at least 61 pairs in 2009. Between the Atlas periods one to three Grey Heron pairs bred sporadically in a further five localities.

The winter map indicates increased numbers present in coastal estuaries and the Avon Valley, suggesting both local movements and immigration into the county. The highest post-breeding counts during the HBA period were 152 in the Avon Valley between Ringwood and Fordingbridge in September 2009 and 120 nearby at Blashford Lakes in September 2010. The fish farm at Bickton was probably responsible for these concentrations. Severe winters, such as the one experienced in December 2010, caused significant but temporary reductions in the wintering population. Along the coast, the highest numbers are typically reported from Portsmouth Harbour, including 45 in January 2008. By February, birds are returning to their colonies as egg laying is at least a month earlier than 50 years ago.

Alan Cox

Sponsored by Sarah & Martin Bredow

Night-heron

Nycticorax nycticorax

A rare vagrant

The Night-heron is widespread on four continents. The breeding population in south-east Europe is migratory, wintering in equatorial Africa. An increase in European wintering records, particularly from Belgium and the Netherlands (where it is a rare breeder) appears to involve birds that have escaped from collections. In France, a recent expansion northwards has resulted in good-sized colonies in the centre and west of the country. Nevertheless, it remains a rare vagrant in Hampshire, the three records during 2007–12 bringing the county total to 15:

2008: Adult east, Portsmouth, April 22nd.
Adult east, Chichester Harbour, September 27th.

2012: Adult, Pennington Marsh, on 17 dates June 2nd–August 19th.

Alan Cox

Night-heron, Pennington Marsh, June 2012 – *Andy Johnson*

Black Stork
Ciconia nigra
A rare vagrant

This elegant stork breeds across the Palearctic and migrates south in autumn, apart from a residential enclave in South Africa and part of the Spanish population. The European breeding population is small (approximately 7,800 pairs) but, nevertheless, comprises more than half of the total (Birdlife International 2004). In west Europe, where suitable open forest breeding habitat is scarce and local, the disjunctive population is largely confined to Belgium, France and Germany (390–430 pairs) and the Iberian Peninsula (400–1,100 pairs). In Britain migratory overshoots are rare, totalling 47 from 2007–2011 (BBRC) including two Hampshire records (one prior to the start of the HBA) as follows and bringing the county total to 11:

2007:   One adult east, Steep, July 12th.
2011:   One adult, New Forest, April 10th–22nd.

Alan Cox

Black Stork, Slufter's Inclosure NF, April 2011 – *Keith Betton*

White Stork
Ciconia ciconia
A rare vagrant

This large stork breeds across the Western Palearctic and just beyond into the south-western region of the Eastern Palearctic. White Storks migrate in autumn principally to equatorial Africa and India but some are resident in southern Spain. The population in the 1980s was estimated at 150,000 pairs but by then White Storks were largely extinct in west Europe, apart from the Iberian Peninsula (*HBW* 1992). The west European extirpation was attributed to prolonged drought in the Sahel region in the 1960–70s and intensive hunting on both passage and wintering territories, particularly in Mali (LPO 2014). A re-introduction programme in the Netherlands and conservation measures in France have led to a remarkable comeback: in 2012 a total of 322 pairs raised 460 young in one French Atlantic coastal department alone. White Storks migrate at relatively low altitude but require thermals for soaring, thus, as is well known, they avoid large expanses of open water. Despite this, 53 individuals had been recorded in Hampshire by the end of 2012. Of these 28 were seen from 2000–12 of which 11 were during the 2007–12 period. This recent surge of records must surely reflect the growth of population along much of the French Atlantic coast. A summary of Hampshire records during 2007–12 is given below:

2008:   One north, Little London, May 10th.
        One east then south, New Forest, May 20th.

White Stork, Ellingham, September 2010 – *John Levell*

One south, Ibsley Water, May 30th (presumed same west, New Forest, May 31st).
One in flight, Greatham, June 22nd.
One, Avon Causeway, July 19th (presumed same, Ringwood, August 6th and Ibsley, 7th then New Forest 14th).

2010:   One, Ellingham Bridge, Avon, September 21st/22nd.

2012:   Five, Havant, May 4th (presumably from the same group two, Eldon, May 8th and three, Up Somborne, May 17th).

Alan Cox

Glossy Ibis
Plegadis falcinellus
Previously a rare vagrant but annual records since 2008

Until the last decade of the 20th century the closest Glossy Ibis breeding population was around the Black Sea and, not surprisingly, Hampshire records totalled just four singles, in 1881, 1902, 1965 and 1977.

In 1996 a total of nine pairs first bred at Doñana, Spain in a new managed wetland area. Breeding success since then has been spectacular with several thousand pairs breeding by 2010 (Santoro *et al.* 2010). Post breeding the species is dispersive and highly nomadic. Following drought conditions in Doñana colonisation of the Camargue took place from 2006; by 2012 several hundred pairs were present. Further expansion has seen breeding for the first time in western France in 2011. In Britain the frequency of occurrences increased from 1996, including one briefly at Ringwood in 2004. Then, during *Bird Atlas 2007–11*, numbers rose dramatically, particularly in autumn. The national estimated cumulative total from 2007–11 was 132, including flocks of up to 25, compared with just 92 from 1950–2006. Many British records are of colour-ringed individuals and the ring codes suggest both the Doñana and Camargue colonies are represented.

None arrived in Hampshire in 2007 but there were annual records thereafter, including flocks of six in 2009 and 19 in 2010. In 2012 birds were present in Hampshire on 57 dates, scattered across eight months from February to December. Although most records occurred outside the HBA recording periods, a full summary of county records during 2007–12 is given below bringing the county total to 41 by the end of the period:

2008:   Pennington Marsh, one first–summer, May 17th–19th.

2009:   Pennington Marsh, six juveniles east, September 19th.

2010:   Keyhaven Marsh, one, August 14th–15th.
Keyhaven Marsh, 19 east, September 13th (same date earlier Devon, later Dungeness, Kent).
Ibsley Water, one, September 18th (presumed same, Stanpit Marsh, Dorset, later September 18th–Oct 10th).
Keyhaven Marsh, one east, September 26th (presumed same, later September 26th north, Titchfield Haven).

2011:   Lymington, one, October 17th, (presumed same, October 21st–23rd, Titchfield Haven).

2012:   Hamble Estuary, one west, February 11th.
Keyhaven, two, April 7th (of which one presumed same, later 7th to 8th, Beaulieu Estuary).
Hurst Beach, one, May 4th (possibly the same on 21 further dates until August 11th at three other localities – Keyhaven and Pennington Marshes, Needs Ore and Farlington Marshes).
Keyhaven Marsh, one, October 23rd/24th.
Avon floods at Bickerley Common, one, December 2nd into 2013.

Alan Cox

Glossy Ibis, Warblington, March 2013 – *Alex Berryman*

Spoonbill
Platalea leucorodia
A scarce visitor

Spoonbills breed widely across the Palearctic. They nest colonially in extensive shallow wetlands, hence in Europe they are scattered across countries, dependent on the availability of suitable habitat. In the UK, a small breeding colony is now established in Norfolk and isolated breeding records have occurred elsewhere in the country this century.

Post-breeding dispersal occurs from August to October (from Spain several weeks prior to the Netherlands), most migrating to West Africa (*Migration Atlas*). Some birds, however, migrate much shorter distances and a small wintering population of around 20 individuals (*APEP3*) is now established in south-west England. Colour-ringed individuals indicate that this population is from the Netherlands where breeding increased from 150–200 (*BWP*) to an astonishing 2,300 pairs by 2011 (Ecomare). Presumably reflecting this population growth, the frequency of occurrences within Hampshire has increased significantly since the 20th century, as shown in *Table 13* which compares the cumulative monthly totals for the 42-year period 1951–92 (*BoH*) with the 6-year period 2007–12.

Spoonbills were exceptional county vagrants in winter until 1994, never recorded in February and only two ever in March. Since then they have been recorded in ones and twos in March almost annually and the first ever February record was in 2000 at Needs Ore on 22nd. Although still scarce in winter, there is now evidence of a small late February-March movement through the county, staging at coastal wetlands. This included a county maximum of ten present at Needs Ore in late March 2012. Presumably, this movement is of birds wintering in Dorset, and farther west, returning to their breeding sites in the Netherlands. The only inland registration was at Ibsley Water on December 31st 2008, the second ever record in the Avon Valley. There is evidence of further passage in April-May (probably of equatorial wintering birds) and non-breeding or failed breeders into June-July. Return migration peaks in September but again numbers are much higher than previously. Regular stopover points in the county continue to be Titchfield Haven, Needs Ore and other suitable coastal wetland sites.

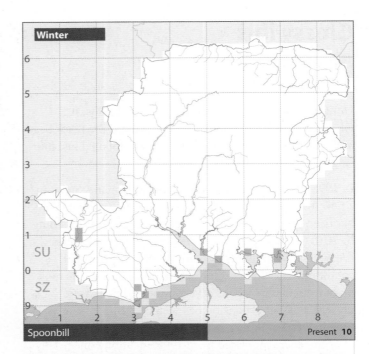

Spoonbill

Winter

Present **10**

Alan Cox Spoonbill, Titchfield Haven, May 2007 – *Richard Ford*

Month	Jan	Feb	Mar	Apr	May	Jun	Jul	Aug	Sep	Oct	Nov	Dec
1951–1992	2	0	2	5	15	8	10	14	17	7	1	2
2007–2012	0	8	27	28	28	19	20	14	39	10	7	2

Table 13 – Spoonbill: cumulative monthly totals in Hampshire.

Red-necked Grebe
Podiceps grisegena
A very scarce winter visitor and passage migrant

The Red-necked Grebe has a circumpolar distribution. In Europe it normally breeds no farther west than Germany/Scandinavia and although one or two summered in northern Britain during 2007–12, breeding was not confirmed. Autumn migration occurs either singly or in small flocks. The West Palearctic population winters principally along the coasts of the Baltic and North Sea. At the time of the 1986–91 Atlas, the British wintering population approached four-figures and included double-figure totals along the Hampshire coast, with birds occasionally appearing at large inland waters. The same county distribution was maintained during the HBA, as shown on the map. There were records from 23 coastal tetrads and one inland record from Kingfisher Lake, Blashford on December 28th 2007. Nevertheless, numbers during 2007–2012 were far lower than earlier with no double-figure totals recorded in any of the HBA years (*Table 14*).

The same pattern of lower numbers was experienced in the rest of Britain compared to the earlier Atlas period. A total British wintering population of just 55 was estimated from 2005 to 2009 (APEP3). Across the county, over the five winters tabulated, only one or two individuals were ever present on any given date. Most bird-days (57%) were recorded in Hayling Bay from the Chichester Harbour entrance west to Eastoke. There were long-staying individuals here in both 2010/11 and 2011/12, including

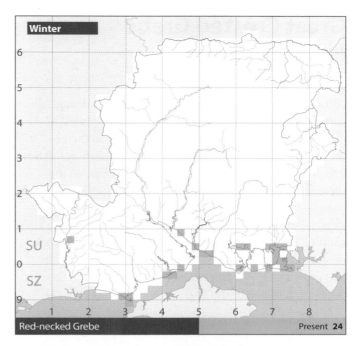

Winter	2007/08	2008/09	2009/10	2010/11	2011/12
Birds	6	7	7	8	5
Bird-days	14	27	18	45	55

Table 14 – Red-necked Grebe: counts and frequency of records during the five HBA winters.

the only record of two together (November 19th-December 2nd 2010); another, present from January 17th-March 5th 2012, was the only March record. One other coastal zone, from Gosport to Weston Shore, recorded birds in all five winter periods. Records were typically from late November to early February but there was one October record (presumed passage off Normandy, 13th/14th 2009).

Alan Cox

Red-necked Grebe, Oxon – *Alex Berryman*

Great Crested Grebe

Podiceps cristatus

A moderately common resident and winter visitor

Although distributed across most of southern Britain, this species is thinly scattered outside a region bounded in the west by counties from Dorset to Cheshire and then east to south Yorkshire. It breeds only on fresh waters – reservoirs, gravel pits, larger lakes and slow flowing rivers. At the time of the first national breeding survey in 1931 there were just 15 breeding pairs in Hampshire. There was a steady increase in population in the second half of the 20th century, principally due to the suitability of newly-created gravel pits for breeding. By 1991 the county population had grown to 90–95 pairs of an estimated total summering population of 220 birds (*BoH*).

Comparison of the HBA breeding map with that published in *BoH* shows that there has been a significant range expansion between the two atlases with 58 occupied tetrads in 1986–91 increasing to 126 in 2008–12. The picture is complicated by significant coastal populations still present as late as April and returning as early as July. It is estimated that breeding territories were established in 96 tetrads during the five HBA summers and that the total summering population was at least 400 birds, of which probably 180 pairs attempted to breed. At Blashford Lakes, a peak total of 72 birds was recorded in summer but in the best year only 15 successful pairs were reported. By contrast, at Yateley Gravel Pits, the number of pairs present rose from seven to 12 over the HBA period and annual breeding success ranged from 60–90% of pairs.

Post-breeding dispersal occurs as early as July. On arrival in winter quarters birds immediately start their post-breeding moult, which is completed by October. This presumably has an important influence on the choice of winter localities since birds are virtually flightless during the moult period and hence require large water bodies or open sea to avoid predation. The HBA winter map shows inland distribution was slightly reduced but very widely distributed across coastal waters. This is in accordance with Dutch and Danish studies which suggest that 50–60% of breeding populations migrate to the coast (*Migration Atlas*). No discernible passage or dispersal pattern has been established in Britain but there is evidence of, presumably weather-dependent, fluctuating coastal numbers in winter months. A recent observation is of large wintering concentrations along the English Channel coast from Kent to Hampshire. A count of 380 was made along the Solent between Chilling and Hill Head in December 2008, contributing to a county total of 854. The large offshore counts appear to occur in cold north European weather: in January, of the exceptional cold winter of 2009/10, a total of 1,735 was at Rye Bay on the Kent/Sussex border and 576 were found in a coordinated count between Southampton Water and Hill Head. The county total that month was

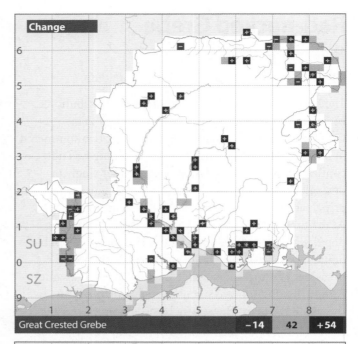

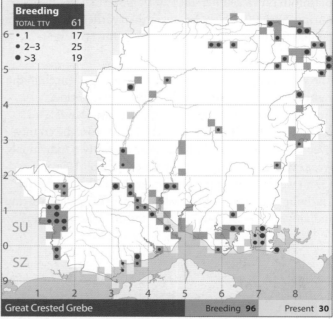

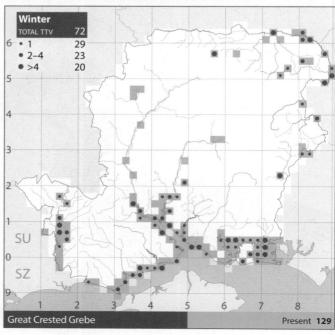

Great Crested Grebe, Blashford, November 2008 – *Martin Bennett* (right); Lakeside, March 2010 – *Simon Ingram* (below)

757, of which only 49 were reported inland, where many waters were ice-covered. The cold weather peaks suggest significant net immigration even allowing for good numbers of county-reared young. Nationally, a decline has been noted in wintering numbers as monitored by the WeBS counts from the winter of 2010/11 to date which corresponds to findings in the Netherlands. It is too early to conclude that this is a function of climate change-induced milder winters, as is being noted for other waterbirds. Nevertheless, for a species, where there is clearly a balance between sedentary and seasonal movements, it would be logical to assume that breeding birds from the Baltic and eastern Europe are opting to winter within their breeding territories or in continental western Europe.

Alan Cox

Sponsored by John & Edith Welch

Slavonian Grebe

Podiceps auritus

A scarce winter visitor and passage migrant

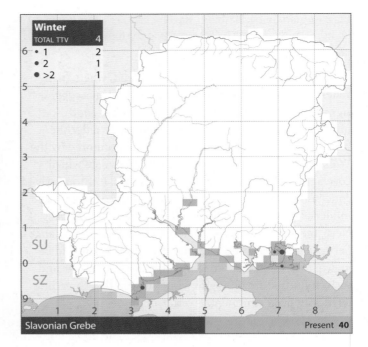

The Slavonian Grebe has a near circumpolar range, breeding from Iceland in the west, through central Asia and North America, as far as the Great Lakes region. It has a small but declining Scottish breeding population, 34 pairs raising just ten young in 2012 (*RBBP* 2012). This downward trend is offset by a significant growth in the Icelandic population since a survey of 400 pairs in the 1990s (*HBW*). Both Icelandic and British breeding birds are slightly larger and heavier-billed than those of Fennoscandia/Russia and have been split by some authorities from the nominate *auritus* into a separate subspecies, *arcticus* (Fieldså 1973).

The most recent estimate of the British wintering population of 1,100 individuals (*APEP3*) has shown a dramatic increase since the *1981–84 Winter Atlas* when it was estimated at 400. It suggests that winterers are principally of Icelandic origin because, in its more easterly European range at least, the population is thought to be in decline. These eastern birds also winter along the North Sea coasts including Britain. Numbers in wintering localities usually stay fairly constant from November onwards. Nevertheless the wintering distribution trends in Britain are indicative of two distinct populations with a marked increase in the Northern Isles and a decline along the south coast.

Hampshire winterers in the 1980s ranged from 20–40 (5–10% of the British population), larger numbers favouring Hayling Bay than elsewhere along the coast. There were a few records on larger inland waters but principally these were birds on passage. In the five winters of the HBA period annual maxima ranged from 21–37 with January and February averaging monthly maxima of 23 and 21 respectively. The map shows records from almost all coastal tetrads. Just one inland record was of a confiding individual, which made a 12-day visit in November 2007 to Lakeside, Eastleigh and presumably mid-December. Birds wintered regularly in three localities (numbers in brackets are the rounded average monthly maxima over the five HBA winters followed by the peak month): Black Point/Hayling Bay (nine, January); Lepe/Needs Ore (four, February) and Lymington/Hurst (six, January). Flocks into double figures were recorded in four winters but each on a single date; all were at the Chichester Harbour entrance including 19 on February 1st 2009 when nine were also off Normandy, Lymington.

Passage was recorded during the summer HBA surveys on nine April and two May dates, including two at Keyhaven from April 3rd–5th 2009 and the latest, at Hayling Bay, on May 4th 2011. There appears to be little change in either county numbers (perhaps a small decline), distribution or wintering patterns between the two national winter Atlas periods. The fact that numbers have not increased in line with those farther north reinforces the proposal made by Musgrove *et al.* (*APEP3*) that the south coast population may originate from north-eastern Europe.

Alan Cox

Slavonian Grebe, Oxey Marsh, April 2014 – *Marcus Ward*

Black-necked Grebe

Podiceps nigricollis

A scarce winter visitor and passage migrant, rare in summer

Black-necked Grebes are scarce breeders in Britain. In 2010, during the national atlas period, there were just 38 confirmed pairs spread between north, central and south-east England (*Bird Atlas 2007–11*). During the HBA, there was no breeding, or summering, in Hampshire where breeding was last confirmed in 2004. Post-breeding dispersal is protracted from August to mid-October. Most west European birds are thought to winter on coastal waters from Britain (mainly along the Channel) through Iberia to the Mediterranean and also inland on larger ice-free lakes and reservoirs.

The British wintering population over the five winter period 2004–09 was estimated at 130 individuals (*APEP3*), little changed since the *1981–84 Winter Atlas* (120). From 2007–11 individuals were located in 7% of British 10 km squares, a 69% increase on the earlier Atlas with increased coverage in the east Midlands, East Anglia, the south-east and along the Channel coast. There were, however, only a few wintering concentrations at Langstone Harbour, Studland Bay (Dorset), Tor Bay (Devon), the Fal Estuary (Cornwall) and one inland at William Girling Reservoir (London). These five concentrations accounted for 80–90% of the UK wintering population.

Langstone Harbour has been a major site since recording began in the 1950s with a fairly stable wintering population of 35–39 in the ten winters from 1979–88 (*BoH*). Numbers build up in the harbour from November and are then fairly stable through to February. In the five winters of the HBA period peak numbers ranged from 17–26. The distribution map shows registrations in other sheltered coastal waters and inland at Blashford Lakes in some winters; annual county peaks ranged from 25–33. Thus numbers away from Langstone Harbour were always low, with most records of ones or twos but winter maxima of up to four recorded at

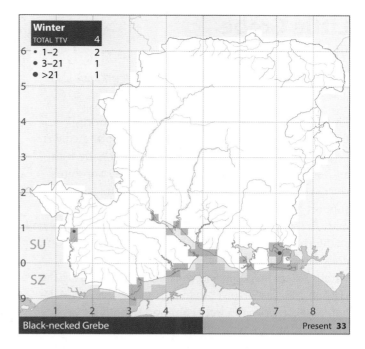

Blashford Lakes, Hayling Bay and also along the coast between Lepe and Needs Ore.

Whereas the county total remained stable during the HBA period, elsewhere along the Channel coast there was at least one notable January influx (2011) boosting the total population of the five main sites to 220. In addition national totals have exceeded 200 in each of the three winters since 2008/2009. This corresponds to the observations in Dutch coastal waters where there has been a marked increase this century. Unlike the rest of Britain, Hampshire has seen a decline in winter numbers between the two national winter Atlas periods, with no recent winter influxes (as seen nearby at Studland Bay), nor a surge in numbers since 2008/09. Such long-term fidelity to Langstone Harbour, of a group whose size runs counter to national trends, might suggest a unique population, perhaps originating from a specific, but yet unknown, breeding locality.

Alan Cox

Sponsored by Neil Luke

Black-necked Grebe, Blashford Lakes, February 2013 – *Martin Bennett*

Little Grebe

Tachybaptus ruficollis

A moderately common resident, passage migrant and winter visitor

Little Grebes require shallow still or slow-flowing freshwater for breeding; typically muddy-bottomed water bodies supporting vegetative life but additionally with an element of clear water nearby. Most of Hampshire's river systems, gravel pits, coastal lagoons and some ponds support breeding pairs, as shown by the HBA breeding map. Breeding distribution, although showing little overall change between the 1986–91 and 2008–2012 Atlases, does show some local variations. The total number of tetrads where breeding was considered likely during the HBA at 208 was 20 lower than during the 1986–91 Atlas but, of these, only 135 were common to both surveys. The variations are typically between adjacent tetrads and suggest local movements to maximise habitat suitability for breeding; this is particularly evident in the north-east of the county. There appears to have been a decline in the lower Avon Valley (Ringwood to Sopley) although it is doubtful whether the species ever bred on the river there. The highest breeding numbers were at Blashford Lakes where 50 territories were recorded.

An estimate of the county breeding population can be gained from maximum counts of adults at each of the tetrads over the Atlas period, which totalled 880. It is very unlikely that all individuals were seen or, conversely, that all seen were breeding, so 440 breeding pairs provides a rough median for the county (400 pairs 1986–91 (*BoH*)). Using statistical techniques, the British population has been estimated at 3,500–7,100 pairs (*APEP3*). Although this population is thought to have increased between the two survey periods, it is considered to be as a result of range expansion rather than increased breeding density.

Little Grebes are resident over much of their range but migrate typically east to west in autumn, leaving Scandinavia and Eastern Europe. Most, if not all, of the UK population is thought to be sedentary. There are, however, significant local movements, particularly in hard weather, from smaller inland waters to sheltered coastal estuaries and harbours. From the winter map it can be seen that, in Hampshire, more tetrads were occupied in winter than during the breeding season. While most, but not all, inland waters still have birds present in winter, tetrads along the main river systems, in particular the Avon, are more widely frequented. Numbers inland, however, are reduced whilst coastal numbers increase. The highest densities along the coast are often in the eastern harbours, particularly Portsmouth, where a count of 104 was made in January 2009. Estimating the total winter population is difficult in that birds may leave their breeding territories as late as November and return as early as February as *Table 15* shows.

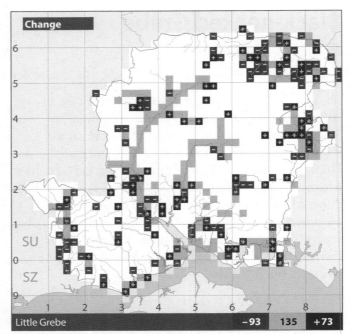

Change — Little Grebe — −93 | 135 | +73

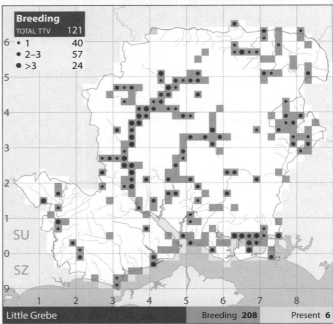

Breeding
TOTAL TTV 121
• 1 — 40
• 2–3 — 57
• >3 — 24

Little Grebe — Breeding **208** — Present **6**

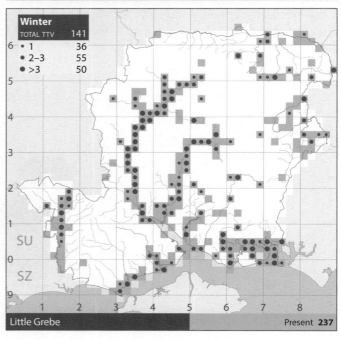

Winter
TOTAL TTV 141
• 1 — 36
• 2–3 — 55
• >3 — 50

Little Grebe — Present **237**

WeBS county totals for 2007–12 show an upper limit of just 400 individuals during the core winter months of November-December. One objective of the Atlas was to give a much broader coverage than WeBS for surveying more widespread species such as Little Grebe. An analysis of the HBA data over the November-December period shows 189 tetrads were occupied and the population range can be estimated at 900–1,500 individuals. There is no current method for determining the origin of this population but at the lower limit of the range, it would suggest some dispersal out of the county. The upper limit is consistent with the post-breeding population but could possibly include some minor immigration into the county.

Month	Sep	Oct	Nov	Dec	Jan	Feb	Mar
Mean 2007–2012	49	51	37	24	23	37	39

Table 15 – Little Grebe: WeBS counts for Blashford Lakes.

Evidence of immigration into Britain is slight but the few ringing recovery records do indicate birds of Baltic origin and there is visual evidence of cross-Channel movements (*Migration Atlas*).

Alan Cox

Sponsored by John Collman

Little Grebe, Blashford Lakes, August 2011 – *Martin Bennett* (above); Blashford Lakes, July 2010 – *Martin Bennett* (below)

Honey-buzzard

Pernis apivorus

A scarce summer visitor that breeds in small numbers each year

The Honey-buzzard has always attracted a disproportionate amount of interest amongst bird enthusiasts in the UK, despite it being one of the commonest breeding raptors in Europe. In Britain, it is at the edge of its range and has never been common. This, coupled with its elusiveness on its breeding grounds, has led to its almost mythical status. As far back as the 1968–72 Atlas, it was known that records for this species had been withheld from some UK areas, most notably its key sites in the New Forest; this remained the case during the 1988–91 Atlas.

More recent studies on Honey-buzzard have shown that much of our early information on the species had little basis in fact. They are not limited by the need for a warm southern climate nor by light soils to enable them to dig out wasp nests. Neither are they particularly vulnerable to disturbance. Much of our improved knowledge has been gained by colour ringing, nest cameras and satellite tagging. It is, therefore, pleasing to be able to say that attitudes have changed and information is now more forthcoming on the Honey-buzzard's status in Hampshire. Annual breeding totals have now been published for even those early Atlas years when records were previously withheld (Wiseman 2012).

As a summer migrant its fortunes ebb and flow but its association with Hampshire, and the New Forest in particular, has been long and reasonably well recorded. It is still, however, a very rare breeding bird in the county and for this reason it was felt unwise and unnecessary to publish a breeding map. Comparisons with previous surveys are also of limited value given the fact that previous atlas data are known to be incomplete and the species is extremely difficult to confirm breeding. It is also very secretive and easily overlooked where it does occur.

In recent years its fortunes in Hampshire have been well documented in the annual HBR. These reports have relied heavily on information from a small group of enthusiasts doing field work on the species to provide the overview of Honey-buzzard in the county. Suffice it to say that it has bred regularly in the New Forest and in other county localities throughout the HBA period. Indeed from 2000 the county has hosted singles or pairs of Honey-buzzard at between five and twelve sites each year (A. Page *in litt.*).

Where it is known to have attempted breeding, the species has achieved an 88·9% success rate and averaged 1·78 young per successful nest (Wiseman 2012). Continued monitoring of nests and their success rates in the New Forest is important given the recent but rapid colonisation of the area by Goshawks and published accounts of the serious threat they pose to adult Honey-buzzards as well as to their nestlings (Bijlsma 2004). Studies in Europe (Gamauf *et al.* 2013) have also shown that Honey-buzzard nests were placed significantly farther from nests of Goshawk than would be expected if nest-sites had been chosen at random and also that predation of Honey-buzzard young was higher in territories closer to breeding Goshawks.

Wasps' nest, almost certainly predated by Honey-buzzard, New Forest, July 2013 – *Martin Bennett*

Honey-buzzard, Dorset – *Martin Bennett* (right);
Test Valley, August 2013 – *Richard Jacobs* (below)

During the five years of the HBA survey, Honey-buzzards were recorded in 65 tetrads with breeding proven in 19 distributed across ten different 10 km squares. We know the species can turn up anywhere in the county where woodland is a feature of the landscape and can subsequently breed successfully in these areas. While not thought to be statistically important, it is quite likely that some pairs are going undetected in Hampshire in most years.

Andy Page

Sponsored by Andy Page

Red Kite
Milvus milvus
A moderately common resident, passage migrant and winter visitor

Until recent times, the last recorded Red Kite nest in Hampshire was near Broughton in the Test Valley in 1864. The species had formerly been present across much of the UK but human persecution resulted in it becoming extinct in every region apart from the deep valleys of mid-Wales. After reaching a low point in the 1930s, the population gradually spread into nearby lowlands, despite the activities of egg collectors. These birds may have been the source of Hampshire sightings in 1956 and 1970 followed by an additional 31 records up to 1992. However, it is also highly likely that Continental birds drifted across to Hampshire during this time as proven, in one case, by ringing results.

Today, as the maps show, Red Kites can be seen throughout the county although more commonly in the north than the south. The Hampshire population has resulted from the re-introduction programme undertaken in the Chilterns between 1989 and 1994. Juveniles from Spain were released in the hope that they would survive and nest (Wootton *et al.* 2002). Breeding in the Chilterns commenced in 1992 and in Hampshire a pair nested near to Overton in 1995 and 1996. These were apparently isolated attempts and breeding was not recorded again until 2003 when a pair nested near Corhampton. In addition to the official re-introduction, the Hawk Conservancy Trust released 12 captive-bred birds (four adults and eight juveniles) near to their centre at Weyhill between 2003 and 2005.

No additional nest sites were discovered until 2007, the first year of the HBA, when two pairs bred between Basingstoke and Stratfield Saye. The number of known breeding attempts then increased annually, reaching 14 in 2009 and 22 in 2012. The HBA period coincided with a rapid increase in sightings as juveniles from the core population in the Chilterns dispersed to find their own breeding areas. A winter roost of up to 60 became established at Faccombe in the 2004/05 winter; records submitted to HOS exceeded 600 in 2008 and over 1,000 in 2010. By the end of the HBA fieldwork there were probably in excess of 50 breeding pairs in the county, with a further 150 immatures wandering widely. This compares to over 800 pairs in the Chilterns.

In 2008 a project was set up to monitor breeding activity and the dispersal of locally-bred juveniles; a number of individuals were fitted with wing tags and radio transmitters up to 2010 (Betton & Jacobs 2009). From this work it is known that juveniles wander widely in their first two to three years, particularly on sunny spring days. These birds are mainly responsible for sightings in the south of the county. First-year birds tagged in this study have also been observed in Sussex, Cambridgeshire and Yorkshire.

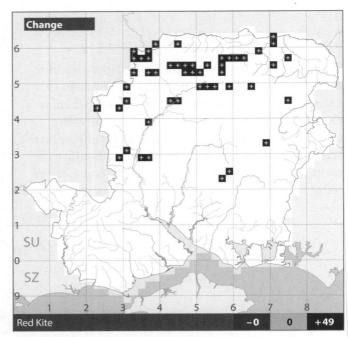

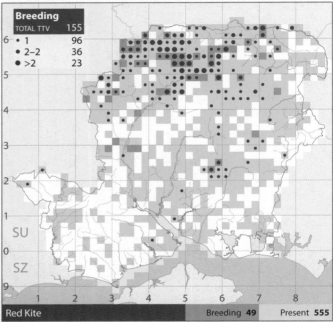

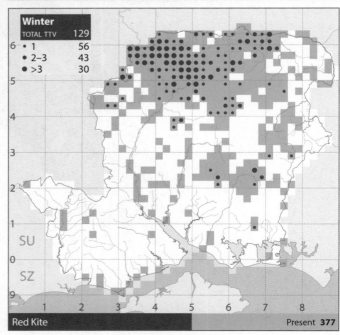

Red Kite, Ashley Warren, April 2011 – *Richard Ford* (right); Highclere, April 2015 – *Barry Stalker* (below)

Nationally there is still a problem of Red Kites being killed by illegal poison baits intended for corvids and Foxes; in addition, like all raptors, they are a target for illegal shooting. One of the Hampshire tagged birds was shot in Buckinghamshire and died in care. Young Red Kites first breed at the age of two or three years. Their first breeding attempt is often close to their natal site, so unless birds are forced to move due to lack of food, the population normally expands only gradually. By 2009 there were several pairs nesting in the northern part of the Test Valley and by 2010 birds had started nesting east of the M3 motorway and in the Meon Valley.

They particularly select private woodlands and parks as their preferred nesting areas, usually well away from public footpaths. By contrast, in the Chilterns there are now so many pairs that birds have been forced to nest in town parks and even large gardens. It would seem very likely that the gradual population spread will see birds becoming commoner in the south of the county, although poor breeding seasons in 2012 and 2013 have slowed that expansion temporarily. The UK population now stands at around 2,500 pairs and is likely to continue growing given current indications.

The return of the Red Kite has only been achieved through the concerted efforts of conservation organisations.

Although it was previously assumed that the ideal habitat for this species was the wet and wild Welsh oakwoods, it is now recognised that those birds were suffering from poor breeding success and a limited gene pool. The birds that we see in Hampshire have stronger ties to Spain than Wales but their return has been welcomed by most people and is widely viewed as one of the greatest bird conservation triumphs of the late 20th century.

Keith Betton

Sponsored by Keith Betton

Black Kite

Milvus migrans

A rare vagrant recorded in every month from April to September

Despite this species being one of the commonest raptors in the world it remains rare in the UK and a vagrant in Hampshire, although numbers do appear to be increasing. In 1991, at the end of the previous Hampshire Atlas, there had been just six records of Black Kite in the county. By the end of the HBA, there were 32 including 14 over the 2007–12 period. Most are recorded in the spring/early summer and therefore during the HBA breeding season but others are seen in the autumn. Records for the 2007–12 period, including those in autumn and all of single birds, are given below:

2007:   Hill Head on June 6th.
2008:   Bourley and Long Valley SSSI on April 1st.
2009:   Havant on May 31st.
        Somerley Estate, Avon Valley on May 31st.
        Straight Mile, Romsey on June 23rd.
        Keyhaven on September 21st.
2010:   Ranvilles Lane, Stubbington on September 12th.
2011:   Ibsley North Gravel Pit on April 25th.
        East Tisted on April 28th.
        Broadlands, Romsey on May 29th.

Black Kite, Spain – *Hugh Harrop*

2012:   Ibsley on May 5th.
        Needs Ore on May 7th.
        Hatchet Moor on May 8th.
        Goodworth Clatford on May 8th.

Keith Betton

Sponsored by Chris Spooner

White-tailed Eagle

Haliaeetus albicilla

A very rare vagrant

After a sixty-year absence from the county, this impressive eagle provided an unexpected start to the HBA survey when a first-winter bird was discovered on the Cholderton Estate on November 18th 2007. The bird had been colour-ringed as a chick in Finnish Lapland earlier in the year. It stayed in the area into January 2008 before moving south to Porton Down/Over Wallop where it was seen intermittently until April 8th/9th. It was also seen in Wiltshire during this period.

One White-tailed Eagle during the HBA period was special but a second bird, first seen flying west at Sandy Point on December 12th 2010, was extraordinary. This individual had previously been in Sussex, and was subsequently discovered near Hordle/New Milton on January 1st 2011. It stayed in the area until February 12th before re-locating north to the Old Basing area where it remained until March 24th.

These two individuals brought the county total to 13, the previous most recent record being in 1947.

Andy Page

Sponsored by Betty Hansell

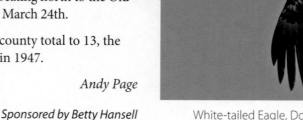

White-tailed Eagle, Downton, January 2011 – *Keith Maycock*

Marsh Harrier

Circus aeruginosus

A scarce but increasing passage migrant and winter visitor

The Marsh Harrier's story as a breeding species in Britain has been a mixed one. Following temporary extinction at the end of the 19th century, it re-established itself in the fens of Norfolk during the 1920s. It remained restricted in both range and numbers, recorded at the time of the 1968–72 Atlas in only 54 10 km squares and as a confirmed breeder in only four. Nearly all records came from the eastern counties of Norfolk and Suffolk. By the time of the 1988–91 Atlas, it had consolidated its hold on these counties and the number of breeding pairs had increased to 90. It was also being recorded in a number of other counties and more birds were overwintering in the UK.

Bird Atlas 2007–11 shows its breeding range has doubled since the 1988–91 Atlas with expansion into Cambridgeshire, Lincolnshire and Kent. It has also bred in other counties away from its core areas but only once in Hampshire, unsuccessfully at Needs Ore in 1957. It is however, now recorded in most months of the year but particularly during the winter. This is a change in behaviour since the 1986–91 Atlas when peak numbers occurred in spring and autumn and winter records were less frequent (*BoH*). It parallels the national picture, however, with an increasing wintering population occupying a broad band along the east and south coasts of England. In keeping with this distribution, the majority of records in Hampshire come from coastal sites. The areas between Keyhaven and Beaulieu, and Langstone Harbour and Farlington are the source of many of them. Sightings also come from the Avon Valley and Lower Test Marshes. Titchfield Haven is also a key area, and summer records are increasing there, suggesting that a county breeding record may not be far away.

Exactly how many birds are occurring in the county annually is difficult to assess with numbers fluctuating widely from month to month and even year by year. *Table 16* shows estimated monthly figures taken from *HBR* for the 2007–12 period, including some non-HBA periods (shaded pale grey).

Andy Page

Sponsored by Jeremy Peters

Month	Jan	Feb	Mar	Apr	May	Jun	Jul	Aug	Sep	Oct	Nov	Dec
2007	1	2	1	6	3	0	0	7	8	3	1	1
2008	1	2	0	5	6	1	0	6	12	3	6	5
2009	6	4	9	8	4	2	0	5	12	9	4	6
2010	9	13	11	3	4	0	0	5	9	8	6	8
2011	11	3	8	10	8	0	1	4	8	9	10	10
2012	8	10	11	12	6	2	5	5	7	9	12	15

Table 16 – Marsh Harrier: estimated numbers in Hampshire 2007–12.

Marsh Harrier, Titchfield Haven, January 2015 – *David Ryves*

Hen Harrier

Circus cyaneus

A scarce winter visitor and passage migrant

Like the Merlin, Hen Harriers breed in upland areas of heather moorland and young forestry plantations. In recent decades, its breeding distribution in Great Britain and Ireland has shown a mixed picture of significant losses and gains in different areas (*Bird Atlas 2007–11*). These include unexplained shifts in population centres in Ireland, large gains in Wales and considerable losses in south-west Scotland. The species also suffers continued illegal persecution in some parts of the UK, particularly in the grouse-rearing areas of northern England.

Hen Harriers do not breed on the heaths of Hampshire but do use this habitat in winter for feeding and roosting. The birds are, however, far ranging in their habits. They often hunt over many miles and frequently move on if prey becomes scarce or weather conditions deteriorate throughout the winter.

This distinctive and beautiful raptor is an eagerly awaited winter visitor with the first birds usually arriving in October and the majority having departed by early April. It is most reliably encountered around dawn and dusk near its traditional roost sites. As the accompanying HBA map shows, it is at its greatest density in the New Forest and is thinly spread throughout the rest of the county. Consequently, most records come from the Forest where a traditional roost provides regular sightings. However, up to seven different New Forest roosts are known to have been used throughout the HBA period and between five and nine individuals are thought to have been involved each year. Numbers can change significantly from month to month and occupancy of roosts ebbs and flows accordingly.

Away from the Forest, a roost at Alresford Pond can attract up to six individuals annually and regular records also

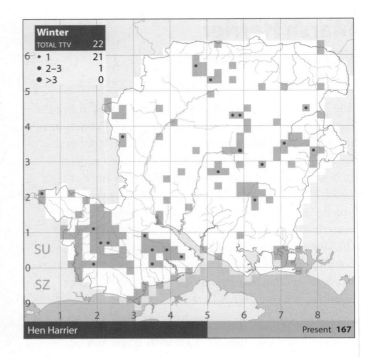

come from Bransbury Common, Ashley Warren, Woolmer Forest, Beacon Hill, Cheesefoot Head and the coastal zone.

Although Hampshire data at tetrad level is not available from the *1981–84 Winter Atlas*, comparisons of the two national winter atlases at the 10 sq. km level suggest that the Hen Harrier's range in the county has increased, mirroring the British picture of a 24% increase in winter distribution over the inter-atlas period (*Bird Atlas 2007–11*). Conversely, the number of individual birds observed at roosts in the New Forest has declined in recent years falling from 12–20 birds in the mid-1980s (*BoH*) to just five to nine during the HBA period. The reason for the decline is not known but care should be taken to avoid disturbance at these sensitive sites.

Andy Page

Sponsored by Adrian Martin

Montagu's Harrier

Circus pygargus

A scarce summer visitor and passage migrant

The Montagu's Harrier is an extremely scarce and enigmatic summer visitor to Britain most often encountered on spring passage. Historically it has bred on occasion in Hampshire but has not done so since 1998 when two pairs were known to have attempted breeding, one successfully and the other predated at the egg stage. Since then it has been recorded on only a handful of occasions each year, ranging from as few as two records in 2007 to ten, involving up to eight birds, in 2009.

Potential breeding birds can be seen as early as the third week of April. Females can be remarkably unobtrusive

when breeding but are particularly vulnerable to predation and farming operations when nesting in cereal crops and often require human intervention to be successful. Males cover very large distances when hunting and provisioning females and young.

Montagu's Harrier breeds more regularly in the adjacent counties of Wiltshire and Dorset and birds from there are undoubtedly recorded on occasion in Hampshire. The HBA data show only 21 records across the county. There were four coastal records, four in the Test Valley and six came from the New Forest and Martin Down. The remaining seven were scattered in other parts of the county.

Andy Page

Sponsored by Damian Offer

Hen Harrier, New Forest, March 2009 – *Martin Bennett*

Montagu's Harrier, undisclosed site, – *Martin Bennett*

Goshawk

Accipiter gentilis

An increasingly common resident

Goshawks are primarily birds of woodland and, in particular, larger forests. Persecuted close to extinction in Britain during the 19th century, the slow re-colonisation of the species was aided by escaped/released falconers' birds. During the 1968–72 Atlas, regular breeding was confirmed in only eleven 10 km squares in the UK and none were south of the Peak District in Derbyshire. By the time of the 1988–91 Atlas, breeding was confirmed in 91 10 km squares, with major increases throughout the Welsh forests. Southern England, however, was still almost devoid of Goshawks and there were no confirmed breeding records in Hampshire.

This situation changed in 2002 with the discovery of Goshawks breeding in the New Forest. Its fortunes in the county have subsequently been well documented, including the origins of the New Forest population published in *Birds of Wiltshire* (Ferguson-Lees *et al.* 2007). *Figures xvii* and *xviii* demonstrate more graphically than words their success in the New Forest since breeding began to the end of the HBA period.

In good habitat Goshawks can reach high breeding densities with one New Forest 10 km square containing fourteen occupied sites during 2012. Eleven of these held breeding pairs and the other three territory-holding singles. Productivity of New Forest birds is shown in the following chart. It mirrors the population chart, although the number of fledged young in 2012 was almost certainly affected by the extremely wet weather. It should be noted that fledging figures are based on brood sizes at ringing, which is usually at around four weeks of age, and not on actual fledging.

Throughout the HBA period, reports of Goshawk also came from sites well outside the New Forest with breeding proven at a number of these. While the New Forest birds have done very well and early caution about breeding information has been relaxed somewhat, it is strongly suspected that this species still suffers human persecution, particularly at some sites on private land. In view of this and the expressed wishes of some recorders, breeding records outside the Forest have not been specifically identified on the accompanying maps.

During the 2008–12 HBA breeding seasons, Goshawks were located in 66 tetrads and breeding was considered likely in 29 of them although only 23 are shown on the map. Since the species is largely sedentary, its winter and breeding distributions are very similar. The scatter of winter records away from the main breeding centres probably relate to dispersing first-winter birds.

Andy Page

Sponsored by Ken White

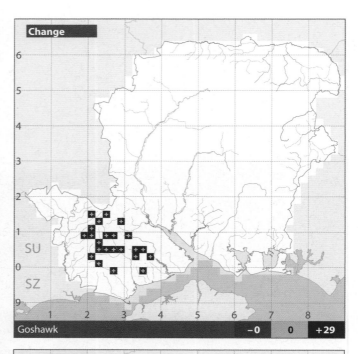

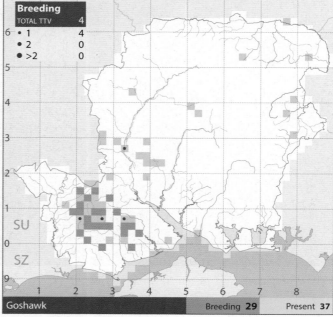

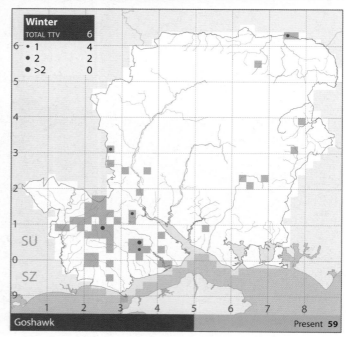

Goshawk, New Forest, March 2014 – *Mike Darling* (above); New Forest, February 2011 – *Martin Bennett* (below)

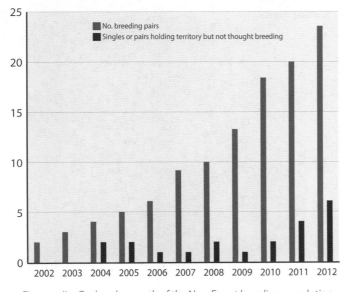

Figure xvii – Goshawk: growth of the New Forest breeding population 2002–12.

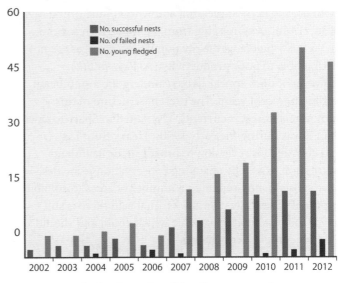

Figure xviii – Goshawk: number of New Forest nests and success rates 2002–12.

Sparrowhawk

Accipiter nisus

A common resident and passage migrant

Generally thought of as a common and widespread species of mixed woodland and farmland, the Sparrowhawk is probably more familiar to most people as a bird of towns and gardens where it has found a ready source of food thanks to the popularity of supplementary feeding for our garden birds.

Sparrowhawks, in common with other birds of prey, suffered a well-documented decline during the 1950s and 1960s due to contamination with organochlorine pesticide residues picked up through their prey species. This was particularly evident in the large agricultural areas of the east. Following the countrywide ban of these substances, the species underwent a period of rapid recovery. While the 1968–72 Atlas showed large losses across much of eastern England, subsequent range expansion was swift and, by the time of the repeat atlas in 1988–91, the Sparrowhawk was described as one of the most widespread and abundant raptors in England, second in number only to the Kestrel. The national population had stabilised by the mid-1990s but a small decline has been noted in the breeding population over the last ten years with *Bird Atlas 2007–11* showing there have been more significant decreases, particularly in the north and west.

In Hampshire the Sparrowhawk has remained fairly well represented throughout these periods. Analysis of HBA data shows a similar summer and winter distribution across the whole county, with a slight increase in presence in the winter mirroring the national picture.

For a species with a preference for breeding in conifers amongst mixed woodland it is now surprisingly absent from many once suitable parts of the New Forest. The species was well recorded here in the 1990s when the population was estimated at around 30–40 pairs. With 80% of nests successful, and with annual productivity of successful nests ranging from 3·2 to 4·2 with a mean of 3·6 this would suggest any population changes are not attributable to poor productivity (A. Page *in litt.*). However, it does appear to have undergone a significant decline in recent years. The present structure of this commercial forest is currently less suited to Sparrowhawks than it was during the early 1990s. Heavy thinning and clear fell for reversion to broadleaf, or heathland restoration driven by changing conservation priorities, have subsequently rendered a number of areas unsuitable as potential nest sites for hawks. That said there is still much suitable habitat available which could and should hold breeding Sparrowhawks.

The recent rapid colonisation by Goshawks in the New Forest from 2002 to date is also thought to be a factor

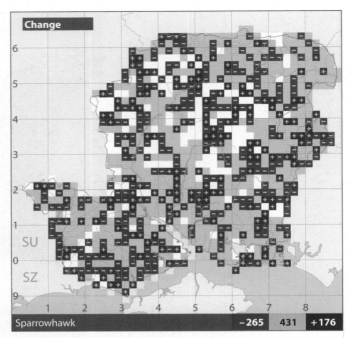

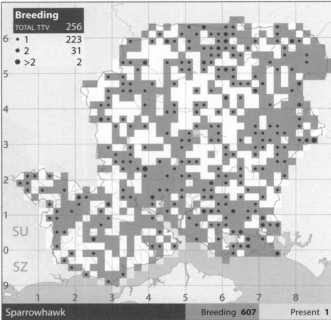

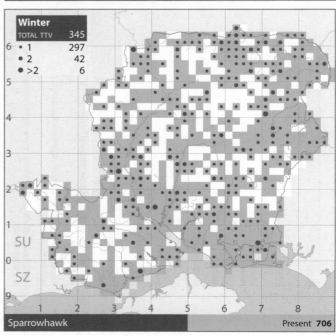

contributing to the decline, with instances of Sparrowhawk remains being found at Goshawk sites indicating direct predation of adults.

For the county as a whole a mixed picture is revealed with gains in 176 tetrads outweighed by losses in 265 tetrads. The factors outlined as possible causes of the New Forest decline are unlikely to be relevant across the rest of the county where the losses may be mirroring the national downward trend in abundance noted in the *Bird Atlas 2007–11*. However, further studies are needed to determine whether there has been a genuine decline in the range and abundance of the Sparrowhawk breeding population of Hampshire.

Andy Page

Sponsored by Michael Crutch

Sparrowhawk, Furze Hill, New Forest, May 2015 – *Martin Bennett*

Buzzard

Buteo buteo

A common resident

Over the past 200 years, this species has undergone a remarkable cycle in its range and numbers. From being widespread and common across Britain in the early 19th century, it underwent a major decline reaching its well-documented low point in the early part of the 20th century. Since then, a slow recovery began which has accelerated spectacularly in recent years.

At the time of the 1968–72 Atlas, the Buzzard was confined to the north and west of Britain. In southern England, the robust population that persisted in its Hampshire stronghold of the New Forest effectively marked the eastern edge of its range, apart from a few outlying pairs that occurred sparingly in other parts of Hampshire and Sussex. Twenty years later, the 1988–91 Atlas confirmed that the eastward spread of the species across the country was well underway, and Hampshire was no exception. *Bird Atlas 2007–11* shows this extraordinary range expansion is now almost complete with Buzzards occurring right across Britain. The increase in population has been linked both to reduced persecution and increased food supplies following the recovery of Rabbit populations from the effects of myxomatosis.

At the time of the 1986–91 Atlas, Buzzards were located in less than a quarter of the county's tetrads. As the HBA breeding map shows, they now occur in all parts of the county with close to 100% tetrad occupancy. The change map is probably the most dramatic and positive visual evidence of how the fortunes of this species in Hampshire have been transformed in a relatively short period of time.

The New Forest population has been well recorded and documented from the early 1960s up until very recently. From a stable population of around 35 pairs in the late 1960s, numbers dropped to around 20 pairs from 1973–93 then started to climb again. The population peaked in 2005 with 81 occupied territories and more than 60 successful nests. In 2008 and 2009, of 70 territories studied, the success rates differed markedly with 18 and 41 successful nests in the respective years. With the population this high, a number of pairs do not breed every year and this has been very evident over 2011 and 2012, the last two years of the HBA survey, when inclement spring weather and a poor natural food supply meant far fewer pairs of Buzzard attempted to breed or were successful in raising young.

As an essentially sedentary species, the Buzzard's winter and summer distributions are almost identical. In both seasons, it can now be seen anywhere in Hampshire making it the commonest raptor in the county.

Andy Page

Sponsored by Alan Snook

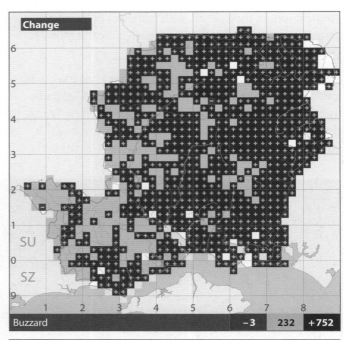

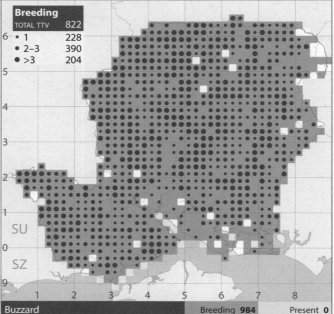

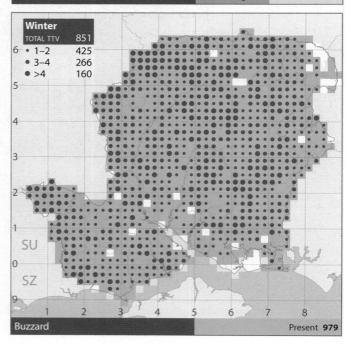

146

Buzzard (with Magpie), New Forest, November 2012 – *Martin Bennett*

Rough-legged Buzzard

Buteo lagopus

A rare winter visitor and passage migrant

There were three accepted records during the HBA period, bringing the total recorded in Hampshire since 1950 to 51. In 2009 a third calendar year male was present near Faccombe in the north-west of the county from February 15th–25th, the first since October 2004. In 2011 there were two records: a bird at Milkham in the New Forest on April 25th and an adult seen at Overton on May 3rd.

Andy Page

Rough-legged Buzzard, Jevington, Sussex – *Mike Darling*

Osprey

Pandion haliaetus

A scarce passage migrant

The number of Ospreys passing through Hampshire has increased following their recolonization of Scotland in the 1950s. As regular, though still scarce, passage migrants, they are seen in both spring and autumn, the latter falling mainly outside the HBA recording periods.

Sightings on spring passage usually begin in late March, with the 24th being the earliest during the 2007–12 period, and continue through April and into May. Most are made as birds move north following the river valleys of the Test, Avon and Itchen. Sightings from late May and into June are few and these encounters are presumed to be young non-breeding birds making their first return migration. Some of these occasionally summer in the county as did an individual in 2008 in the Langstone Harbour area.

Return passage is sometimes noted from July but begins in earnest around mid-August and continues until late October, with the 25th being the latest record for the 2007–12 period. Chichester and Langstone Harbours are a particular draw to returning migrants, with individual birds often staying for several days in the area and, less frequently, at other sites along the coast.

With Osprey now an established breeding bird well south of its Scottish stronghold, and the coast and rivers of Hampshire well capable of providing rich and plentiful feeding, it is hoped that this species will begin breeding in the county in the future. Artificial nest platforms have been erected at a number of strategic locations and Ospreys have been seen visiting these in recent years, including a colour-ringed male raised as a chick in the Rutland area in 2009, which frequented the Test Valley throughout the period June 21st to July 24th in 2011.

Andy Page

Sponsored by Ade Parker

Osprey, Romsey, May 2011 – *Simon Layton*

Spotted Crake

Porzana porzana

A very scarce passage migrant and rare winter visitor; has bred

Year	2007	2008	2009	2010	2011	2012
Birds	5–6	3	5–8	1	0	2

Table 17 – Spotted Crake: numbers recorded in Hampshire 2007–12.

Spotted Crakes were recorded in every year of the HBA period except for 2011. Numbers are given in *Table 17*.

The species occurs mainly as an autumn migrant so, of the 16–20 birds recorded over the 2007–12 period, most fell outside the HBA recording period. For example, of the maximum six birds in 2007, five were seen at Farlington Marshes between August 11th and September 8th with the sixth at Fishlake Meadows, Romsey, on October 23rd. Similarly, in 2009, all records were between August 2nd and October 14th.

Two individuals were recorded during the course of the HBA breeding survey: at Fishlake Meadows on May 19th 2008 and at Farlington Marshes on July 30th 2010. This represents a fairly typical showing for this shy and retiring species. In summer, the species is likely to be detected only by its territorial advertising calls, which can carry for a kilometre or more, but the male stops calling as soon as it has mated (*BWP*). There were no indications of any attempts at breeding in the county during the HBA.

Given the small numbers which appear annually there doesn't appear to have been any significant change in the frequency or pattern of occurrence since it was first recorded in the county in 1951.

Nick Montegriffo

Spotted Crake, Farlington Marsh, September 2007 – *Richard Ford*

Water Rail

Rallus aquaticus

A scarce resident, moderately common winter visitor and passage migrant

This is a difficult species to survey. In Hampshire most breeding sites are in inaccessible, wetland habitats, usually on the edges of still or slow moving water, in thick reed beds and sedges around lakes and estuaries or along rivers. During the breeding season, the birds are secretive and elusive; they remain largely silent during the day, which makes them even harder to detect using normal atlasing methods. Together, these factors make it likely that some were overlooked during the HBA breeding season survey and means that apparent changes in distribution might result from differences in the level of recording rather than in actual changes in numbers or range.

The HBA breeding map shows a scattered distribution with breeding considered likely in 38 tetrads and birds present in an additional 15. Many of the breeding locations are traditional and well-known, including coastal sites, such as Titchfield Haven and Warsash, and inland ones such as Woolmer, Alresford and Fleet Ponds. Breeding densities in ideal habitat can be high. For example a survey of the Keyhaven/Lymington Nature Reserve in 2008 produced a count of 35 territories and this was considered to be a gross underestimate.

In comparison with the 1986–91 Atlas, the change map shows both gains, particularly in the south-west on the coast and losses, notably on the River Test and in the Basingstoke area, with an overall net reduction of 17 tetrads. While it is possible that local factors have changed the suitability of habitat in these areas, it is likely that coverage and detectability issues are also involved. If the two Atlases are compared simply in terms of Water Rails' presence during the breeding season, which is reasonable given that the breeding population is mainly resident, the number of occupied tetrads was 55 in 1986–91 and 53 during the HBA, suggesting that there has been little change in the species' status.

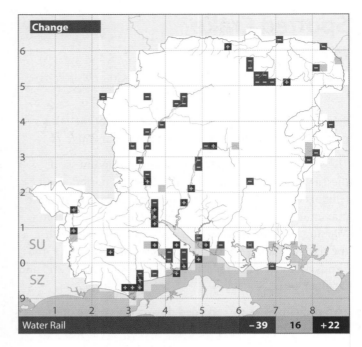

The population is augmented in winter by immigrants from the European mainland. The HBA maps show a similar distribution in winter as in the breeding season but with many more occupied tetrads along the coast, the main river valleys and on scattered ponds and lakes around the county. Although it is impossible to count all the birds present in a large reed bed, it does appear that numbers are lower now than they were at the time of the previous Atlas. In 1989, winter counts were made of 70 at Titchfield Haven and 40 at Fleet Pond (*BoH*), whereas maximum counts during the HBA, were 20 at both sites. It is possible that the long run of relatively mild winters in the intervening period has reduced the number of birds moving west from the Continent but such effects will probably vary from year to year making one-off comparisons of dubious value.

In 2006, Water Rail was added to the RBBP list with the intention of improving coverage of this under-recorded species. A more targeted survey of the species in Hampshire would be of value.

Nick Montegriffo

Sponsored by Tony Norris

Water Rail, Blashford Lake, March 2011 – *Martin Bennett*

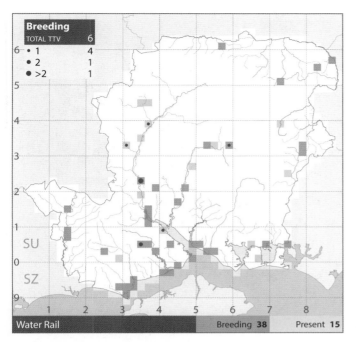

Breeding
TOTAL TTV   6
- • 1   4
- • 2   1
- ● >2   1

Water Rail   Breeding **38**   Present **15**

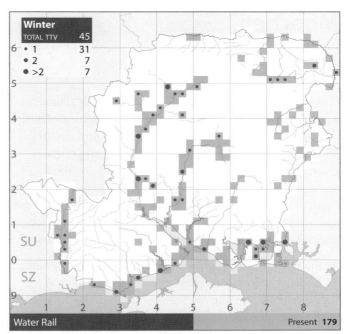

Winter
TOTAL TTV   45
- • 1   31
- • 2   7
- ● >2   7

Water Rail   Present **179**

Water Rail, New Forest, December 2012 – *Martin Bennett*

Moorhen

Gallinula chloropus

A numerous resident and winter visitor

Possibly with the exception of the ubiquitous Mallard, the Moorhen is the county's most widespread freshwater bird. It is conspicuous and familiar in both town and country, found almost wherever there is open water and often grazing conspicuously on nearby lawns and grassland. The resident population is highly sedentary and breeds in riparian vegetation adjacent to rivers, ponds, canals, ditches and marshes throughout the county, be it in town parks, on golf courses, on farmland, in river valleys or coastal marsh.

As the HBA maps show, it is widespread across the county, particularly in lowland areas – the Thames Basin and Weald in the north and the Hampshire Basin in the south. In the latter it is common in a broad swathe from Hayling Island north-west to the county boundary. It is more thinly spread on the chalk but occurs commonly along all the main river valleys and their tributaries, as well as on scattered ponds and lakes. The most surprising and striking feature of the HBA maps is the evident absence of the species from much of the New Forest. Given the availability of apparently suitable habitat throughout the Forest, this gap in its distribution is unexpected.

The change map shows that there has been a 17% breeding range reduction since the 1986–91 Atlas. While this is consistent with a 20% reduction of the population in southern England over the 1995–2012 period (*BBS*), other than in the Forest, the distribution changes in Hampshire show a mix of gains as well as losses. During the 1986–91 Atlas, most tetrads in the Forest were occupied; during the HBA, they were not. Although Moorhens were probably never common in the Forest, this means that whatever has caused the reduction of their population has taken place over the past two decades. It is not obvious what could have brought about such a localised and dramatic change. Possible reasons include a decline in habitat quality or an increase in disturbance or predation. Any one of these, or a combination, could be involved. Habitat succession over wetland sites has occurred extensively and has probably reduced open water. Conversely, over-grazing may have reduced water-side vegetation and hence potential nest sites. Increased disturbance from visitor and dogs is a major issue and increasing predation from the growing populations of Buzzards, Goshawks and possibly mammalian predators might be involved. Given that decreases have also occurred for other 'ground-nesting' water birds such as Mallard and Coot (see relevant species accounts), it is likely that the same factors are affecting them all.

The Moorhen's range in winter is almost identical to that during the breeding season. This is despite the winter population being swelled by incoming visitors from the near Continent. However, since most suitable habitat is already

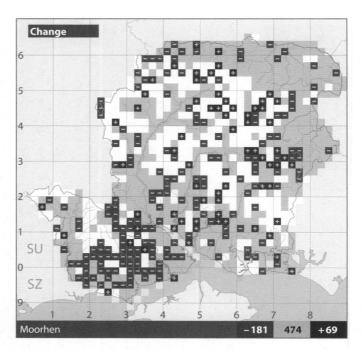

Moorhen   −181   474   +69

Moorhen, Titchfield Haven, March 2014 – *Tom Bickerton*

occupied by breeding birds, it is not unexpected that the range remains unchanged. The fact that the New Forest apparently holds few birds both in winter and summer could be explained by any of the factors discussed above.

Counts during the HBA winter periods included only one in three-figures, 100 in the Avon Valley on January 24th 2008. There were many counts exceeding 50, mainly from coastal sites such as the eastern harbours, Titchfield Haven and IBM Lake, but also from inland sites such as Arlebury Lakes and Yateley Gravel Pits. Overall, winter numbers may have declined with an absence of large counts such as 179 at Titchfield Haven in February 1984 and the record high count of 268 at Farlington Marshes in December 1967 (*BoH*).

Nick Montegriffo

Sponsored by Mike Wildish

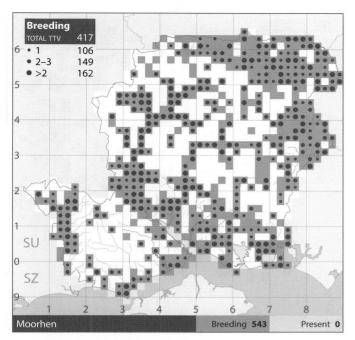

Breeding
TOTAL TTV 417

•	1	106
•	2–3	149
•	>2	162

Moorhen   Breeding **543**   Present **0**

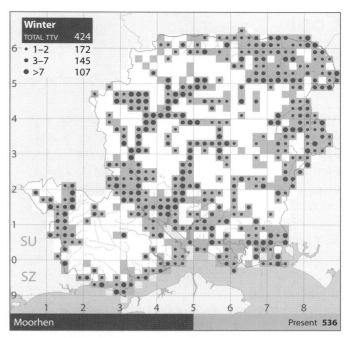

Winter
TOTAL TTV 424

•	1–2	172
•	3–7	145
•	>7	107

Moorhen   Present **536**

Moorhen, Blashford Lakes, December 2008 – *Martin Bennett*

153

Coot

Fulica atra

A common resident and winter visitor whose numbers increase considerably in winter

Although this species is often found sharing habitat with Moorhens, it generally prefers larger areas of open, and often deeper, water than its smaller relative. The HBA maps show similar distributions but with the Coot occupying fewer tetrads, consistent with the lower availability of suitable habitat in the county. Favoured areas include the major river valleys, lakes, ponds and gravel pits. Coots have benefited greatly in Hampshire from ongoing mineral extraction, which has provided additional habitat through the creation of new gravel pits. Those in the Avon Valley at Blashford and in the Blackwater Valley at Eversley and Yateley are important sites for the species (see below).

The change map shows both gains and losses since the 1986–91 Atlas with, overall, a small loss in breeding range. This is unexpected given the 20% increase in population in south-east England over the 1995–2012 period (*BBS*). However, since most suitable sites are already occupied, an increase in population would not necessarily result in range expansion. Furthermore, while gains and losses are balanced across most of the county, there has been a disproportionate number of losses from the New Forest. As with Moorhen, Coots have apparently disappeared from many New Forest sites which were occupied at the time of the previous atlas. It is likely that the same factors are responsible for the demise of both species (see Moorhen account *page 152*).

There is relatively little recent information on breeding numbers but counts of territories during the HBA period included 66 at Yateley Gravel Pit and 20 at Milton Common, Portsmouth, in 2008; 25 in the upper Itchen Valley in 2009 and 22 at Titchfield Haven in both 2010 and 2011.

In winter the Coot's population is swelled by visitors from elsewhere in Britain and the Continent. This is confirmed by ringing results, which show birds reaching England from as far afield as Russia, and consistent with site and TTV counts which, as shown on the HBA maps, are considerably higher in winter than during the breeding season. The number of immigrants is probably dependent on the harshness of the winter in north-west Europe but, given the increased population, it is surprising that the maps show fewer occupied tetrads in winter than during the breeding season. It is possible that, post-breeding, some birds leave their territories and move to larger, safer sites to moult and over-winter. Local movements also occur in response to cold weather when inland sites are frozen. At such times increased numbers occur on the coast on brackish pools, saltmarshes and in sheltered bays.

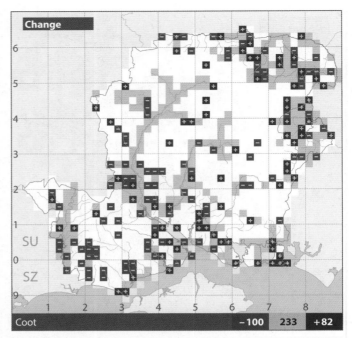

Coot — Change: −100 · 233 · +82

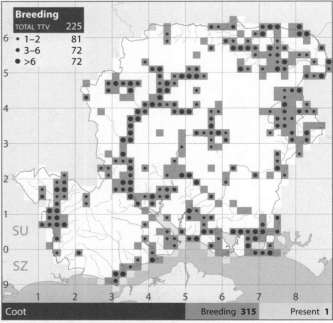

Breeding
TOTAL TTV 225
• 1–2   81
• 3–6   72
• >6   72

Coot — Breeding 315 · Present 1

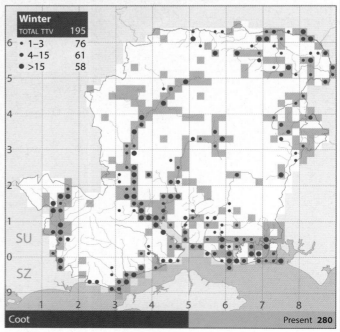

Winter
TOTAL TTV 195
• 1–3   76
• 4–15   61
• >15   58

Coot — Present 280

The highest winter counts during the HBA survey were at Blashford Lakes where the peak was 2,205 in December 2010. Numbers have increased considerably at this site as gravel extraction has created new habitat and existing pits have matured. The mean maximum count for the five winters of the HBA period was 1,938, some 70% higher than at the time of the previous atlas (*BoH*) and qualifying the site as of national importance. Although no other Hampshire site approaches these numbers, important locations include the Eversley/Yateley complex of gravel pits, where the maximum count during the HBA period was 618 in December 2009, and Fishlake Meadows, Tundry Pond and Dogmersfield Lake where recent counts have exceeded 200.

Nick Montegriffo

Sponsored by Alison Cross

Coot, Blashford Lakes, October 2010 – *Martin Bennett* (above); Blashford Lakes, June 2010 – *Martin Bennett* (below)

Crane

Grus grus

A rare passage migrant although likely to become
increasingly common if the British breeding population
increases

Although good fortune is still required to see a Crane in
Hampshire, the species does appear to be occurring more
often now than in previous years. This might be expected
given the increasing populations of both breeding and
wintering birds elsewhere in the country.

During the 2007–12 period, Cranes were recorded in the
county in every year other than 2007, as shown in *Table 18*.
The 44 birds bring the post-1950 county total to 131. All
but two of the records occurred during the HBA recording
periods in either April/May or November/December.

The 2011 count of 29 was exceptional due to a flock of 24
seen circling over Wickham and Southampton between
1420–1435 hrs on November 17th. Such large numbers
are extremely rare in Britain and only occur when weather
conditions drift migrating flocks from the Continent across
into the country.

Nick Montegriffo

Crane, Woolmer Forest, April 2008 – *Richard Ford*

Year	2007	2008	2009	2010	2011	2012
Birds	0	6	1	3	29	5

Table 18 – Crane: numbers recorded in Hampshire 2007–12.

Sponsored by Steve Mansfield

Black–winged Stilt

Himantopus himantopus

One breeding attempt, otherwise a rare vagrant

Small numbers of Black-winged Stilt nest as far north as the
Netherlands, otherwise the European breeding population
is centred on the Mediterranean. There were eight previous
breeding attempts in Britain, only two of which, those at
Nottingham sewage works in 1945 and in Norfolk in 1987,
were successful (*Bird Atlas 2007–11*).

In Hampshire, 11 records involved 17 birds between 1923
and 1990, including up to four at Warren Flats (Beaulieu
Estuary) in mid-May 1945 and a total of six individuals at
two coastal and at one inland site between May 3rd and
July 25th 1987 (*BoH*). A further six occurred between 1998
and 2007, including a pair at Titchfield Haven in mid-April
2002 (*HBR*).

During the HBA period five occurred: one at Ibsley Water
on May 10th 2008, two at Beaulieu Mill on June 30th of
that year which were almost certainly the pair which bred
unsuccessfully at Ashton's Flash, Cheshire and had left
the site the previous day, and a pair at Pennington Marsh
between June 2nd and 9th 2012, the female of which arrived
on May 27th. Coition and nest scraping was observed before

Black-winged Stilt, Pennington, June 2012 – *Richard Ford*

both birds abandoned the site due probably to poor weather
and much attention from marauding crows.

Eddie Wiseman

Sponsored by Tony Blakeley

Month	Jan	Feb	Mar	Apr	May	Jun	Jul	Aug	Sep	Oct	Nov	Dec
Birds	0	0	1	8	10	5	1	0	0	1	2	0

Table 19 – Black-winged Stilt: Hampshire records by month of occurrence 1923–2012.

Kentish Plover

Charadrius alexandrinus

A rare passage migrant; one wintering record

The loss of the Kentish Plover as a British breeding species has been attributed to persecution and disturbance. The species last nested in England in 1979 at Gibraltar Point, Lincolnshire (*Bird Atlas 2007–11*).

The first Hampshire Kentish Plover was at Titchfield Haven in late August 1948 and was followed by another at the same location in June 1949. Between 1951 and 1992 all but seven of around 49 occurred prior to 1981. Those in spring occurred from March 22nd (1974)–May 28th (1978) and in autumn from July 5th (1970)–October 28th (1987). Most records involved single individuals though up to four were present on two autumn occasions and there was one winter record. Between 1993 and 2007 they became scarcer and only a further six occurred including one at Needs Ore on August 7th 2007 prior to the beginning HBA survey.

Two more were recorded during 2008–12: a juvenile at Keyhaven on August 10th 2008 and a female at Black Point on May 4th 2009, the only one during the HBA

Kentish Plover, Black Point, May 2009 – *Andy Johnson*

recording periods. The latter brought the county total to approximately 59 birds.

Eddie Wiseman

Dotterel

Charadrius morinellus

A rare spring and autumn passage migrant with one record of wintering

The Dotterel is a summer visitor to montane breeding areas. In Scotland it is restricted to the Grampian Mountains and the north-west Highlands, where it breeds at altitudes above 700 m though as low as 500 m in the latter area (*Bird Atlas 2007–11*).

The first records for Hampshire were two shot at Ovington in late September 1893 (*K&M*), followed by six at Gorley in early May 1934. A further 66 were recorded up to 1991, the majority of which occurred between May 3rd and 6th. Most records consisted of one or two individuals, though groups in excess of ten were 17 and 14 in early May 1979 and 1980 respectively. Between 1992 and 2007 there were an additional 18 spring records, including Hampshire's earliest on April 15th 1996 and a trip of 11 in the New Forest in early May 2001. Autumn records between 1955 and 1991, included nine individuals at coastal sites and two at inland localities; an additional seven autumn birds between 1992 and 2007 involved three on the coast and four inland. The winter record concerned one in the Keyhaven area between December 2nd 1994 and January 29th 1995 (*HBR*).

During the HBA period a trip of nine, consisting of four females and five males, was present at Preston Candover on

Dotterel, Cheesefoot Head, May 2011 – *Keith Betton*

April 27th 2010 and nearby at Bradley Hill the following day. In 2011, two males and two females were at Cheesefoot Head on May 1st, remaining in the area until May 3rd. Although outside the HBA recording periods, the only autumn record during 2007–12 was of one flying over Fleet Pond on August 22nd 2010.

Eddie Wiseman

Sponsored by Steve Mansfield

Stone-curlew
Burhinus oedicnemus
A scarce summer visitor

The Stone-curlew was once widespread in England, from Dorset to Yorkshire. The UK population of around 1,000–2,000 pairs in the 1930s was already much reduced from that which had existed in the 19th century, but a more rapid decline followed with numbers hitting an all-time low of fewer than 170 pairs in the 1980s. The decline was largely due to the loss of suitable grassland habitat brought about by lack of grazing, both by sheep and Rabbits, and the conversion of permanent pasture to arable farmland (Green *et al.* 2000). As a result, the birds were forced to nest within sparsely-vegetated, spring-sown arable crops where the eggs and young were vulnerable to agricultural machinery. Work by the RSPB and others to protect the nests and young has led to a recent increase in numbers.

The first birds are usually back at their breeding sites by mid-March and are best detected at this time through their nocturnal calling. Most of the Hampshire population now breeds on specially-prepared plots created to provide safe areas away from agricultural operations. These have the additional benefit of minimising the impact of disturbance by the public, since very few are visible from public footpaths. They are managed to provide open stony ground for nesting plus buffer zones for chicks to hide in. Areas with trees and bushes are avoided as they provide opportunities for Carrion Crows and Buzzards to predate the nest. Fieldworkers locate nests and then alert the farmers to the birds' presence. These measures have allowed numbers to increase but without this level of intervention it has been estimated that the population would decline by about four per cent per year.

Most of the data reported here have been provided by the RSPB, whose staff and volunteers try to monitor every possible nest. Even for full-time staff it is often quite a challenge to establish whether birds are actually breeding as they may travel up to three kilometres to feed and, to complicate matters, there are non-breeders that move between sites.

Results for the period of the HBA breeding survey are shown in *Table 20*.

In 2008 there was a slight decrease in pair numbers and very low productivity, resulting in the worst breeding season since 1988. There was recovery in 2009 and by 2010 the number of breeding pairs had returned to previous levels; 2011 was an exceptionally good year but in 2012 the numbers fell back. The weather was very wet in 2012, which caused problems for many ground-nesting species, but a reduction in observer effort due to resource issues may have also contributed to the low count.

A productivity of 0·61 chicks per breeding pair is the target figure set by the RSPB to achieve a stable population. In 2010 and 2011 this was exceeded, suggesting growth, but in 2012 the figure was 0·47. This gives a five-year productivity of 0·56, below the target figure. Although this suggests that the population may be decreasing, the HBA period included two very wet summers (2008 and 2012).

For security reasons, in the accompanying breeding and change maps, tetrads have been plotted centrally in 10 km squares. The most important group of Stone-curlews in Hampshire is centred on Porton Down and the nearby farmland. This population appears to be relatively stable in terms of pair numbers but productivity varies widely, with some good years and some very poor years. Productivity in 2010 was high, with more chicks confirmed as fledged than in the previous three years put together, but fell away again in 2011 and 2012 when no fledged young were recorded at all. At the time of the 1986–91 Atlas there was still a west Hampshire population based around Martin Down. This was effectively kept going by one pair, particularly one female aged 14 in 2002, the last year that breeding was recorded there. The east Hampshire population was based around Micheldever but declined after the previous Atlas; a single bird was present in 2009 for one night only but there have been no records since. There has been a significant expansion of the north Hampshire population to the west of Basingstoke. The number of pairs in this area increased in both 2010 and 2011 and, although numbers declined in 2012, they were still better than in any year prior to 2010.

The change map shows a complete loss of birds in the south-west against a smaller increase in the north and north-west, much of which was in new areas. Almost all of these new sites are on arable land, indicating a continued shift away from downland.

While Stone-curlews continue to nest on working farmland the only way the population can be maintained is through proactive liaison with farmers. A sign of the success of 30 years of effort is that in 2009 the species was downgraded from red to amber in the list of Birds of Conservation Concern. Unless suitable areas of downland can be recreated and protected, such conservation action needs to be maintained at the current level. This is still one of Britain's rarest and most threatened breeding birds, so it is important that the Hampshire population of 20–30 pairs is sustained.

Keith Betton

Sponsored by Barry Stalker

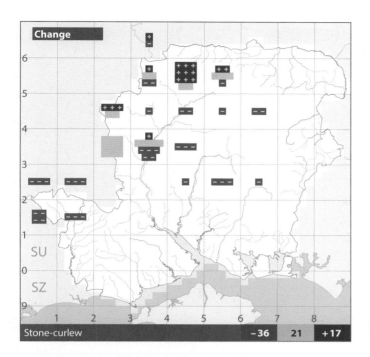

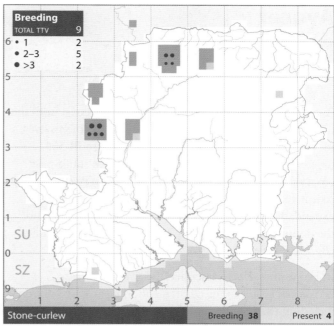

Year	2008	2009	2010	2011	2012
Pairs found	20	22	30	38	24
Pairs proved to breed	15	20	23	32	17
Breeding attempts recorded	19	24	28	40	20
Young fledged by monitored pairs	3	11	16	22	8
Number of fledged young per pair	0·20	0·55	0·70	0·69	0·47

] 20 – Stone-curlew: breeding numbers and productivity in Hampshire.

Stone-curlew, North Hampshire, May 2015 – *Keith Betton*

Avocet

Recurvirostra avosetta

A scarce passage migrant and winter visitor and a scarce but increasing breeder

Avocets formerly nested on the English east coast until the mid-nineteenth century, only re-establishing themselves, in Suffolk, in 1947. There are currently around 1,500 breeding pairs in Britain mostly on east and south-east coast estuaries from Lincolnshire to Kent (*APEP3*). In recent years the British wintering range has also greatly expanded, particularly along the south coast of England; the population currently numbers about 7,500 individuals (*Bird Atlas 2007–11*).

In Hampshire, *K&M* described the Avocet as a rare occasional visitor to the coast, mentioning at least 31 birds, including 18 in Southampton Water in September 1880. An additional 28 individuals were accounted for between 1900 and 1950, since when the trend during the latter half of the 20th century and until 2007, though fluctuating, has been one of increasing numbers and frequency at all seasons. Reports included 25 flying east at Gilkicker Point on 14th March 1965 and a flock of 24 at Keyhaven in September 2006. Large flocks were also occasionally observed in the late year including a total of more than 100 at three coastal stations between 23rd and 25th November 1958 and 32 in Langstone Harbour in late December 2006. Birds also occurred at inland sites and about 18 such records included a flock of 20 that left south-west from Frensham Great Pond (in Surrey) on 9th November 1992 (*BoH*).

Avocets first nested in Hampshire in 2002 when, on the east Solent, two pairs hatched a total of eight young, although only two fledged successfully. These were possibly the same individuals seen on several occasions at Keyhaven, on the west Solent, in August of that year. A further 27 pairs attempted breeding at three sites between 2003 and 2007 and fledged at least 42 young.

During the HBA period, relatively few spring migrants were observed although breeding groups were often on site by late February. Breeding was confirmed in four tetrads but predation clearly inhibited breeding performance. For example, between 2008 and 2012, only 47 young fledged from an overall total of 133 nesting attempts; it is unknown if any of an additional 17 young hatched at one site in 2011 or 19 young observed at one site in 2012, were reared to the flying stage. Autumn passage took place between early July and the end of October with a county maximum of seven at Langstone Harbour on 29th October 2009. Late year occurrences included 35 individuals on passage at three sites on 14th November 2011, of which 19 were at Winchester Sewage Farm. Wintering groups were regularly recorded at Langstone Harbour and the Beaulieu Estuary, with counts of 36 and 23 respectively contributing to a county maximum of 63 in December 2011.

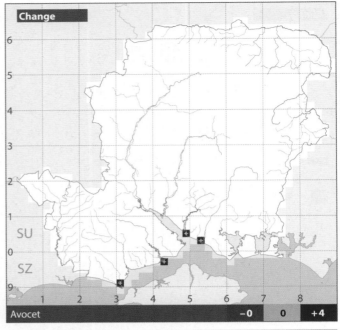

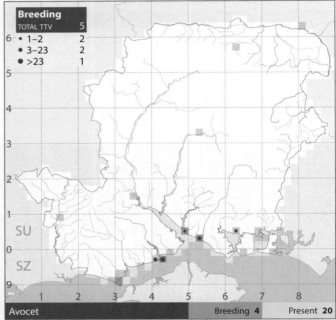

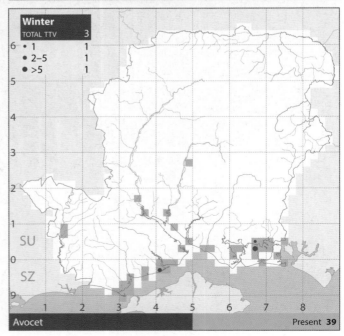

The origin of some individuals observed in Hampshire is indicated by the following records: one found dead at Otterbourne on January 28th 1942 had been ringed at Nyborg, Denmark in June 1941; one, ringed as a pullus at Holme, Norfolk, in August 1991, was seen at Farlington Marshes on 19th and 20th April 1992 (*BoH*); the male of a pair accompanied by a juvenile at Keyhaven on 15th August 2009, was bearing a French colour ring, as was a singleton at Langstone Bridge on 27th March 2010 (*HBR*).

The addition of Avocet to Hampshire's list of breeding species was perhaps overdue but was, nevertheless, a welcome change that occurred over the relatively short period between the two county atlases.

Eddie Wiseman

Sponsored by Bob Marchant

Avocet, Langstone Harbour, January 2009 – *Trevor Carpenter* (above); Titchfield Haven, July 2009 – *Mike Crutch* (below)

Oystercatcher
Haematopus ostralegus

A moderately common breeding resident, common passage migrant and winter visitor

Oystercatchers are found on rocky as well as estuarine shores with the largest concentrations in the latter habitat. Their winter range in the UK has greatly expanded, mostly at inland sites, where many February records are indicative of returns to breeding grounds. Wintering trends vary between regions though overall, a gradual increase in numbers in the 1980s was followed by a decline (*Bird Atlas 2007–11*).

Oystercatchers first nested in Hampshire in 1934 and a pair, suspected of breeding in Langstone Harbour in 1954, was confirmed as having done so in 1955 (*Cohen*). A greatly increasing population through the 1980s and early 1990s was partly attributable to protection afforded on wardened nature reserves, for example in Langstone Harbour, Beaulieu Estuary and Hurst–Sowley. The county population was considered to be at least 268 pairs by 1993 (*BoH*) most of which nested on shingle spreads or saltmarsh, though 27 pairs nested on fields in the Beaulieu Estuary and a pair did so at Pennington Marshes, in 1992.

Outside the breeding season, numbers increase from July onwards, though maxima may occur at any time between August and February and 2,400 were in Langstone Harbour, the principal Hampshire site, in November 1988. Oystercatchers were recorded at inland sites in 11 years between 1954 and 1970, then annually to 1992; the cumulative total of 141 individuals for the period 1954–1992 included sightings in all months though 21 were in April and 20 in August (*BoH*).

During the 1986–91 Atlas the county maximum was approximately 173 breeding pairs, including peak numbers at the three principal sites of 34 pairs in Langstone Harbour, 37 pairs in the Beaulieu Estuary and 90 pairs between Hurst and Sowley. During the HBA period numbers were significantly lower ranging between an incomplete total of 79 pairs and a maximum of 119 pairs. However, the HBA change map clearly shows a considerable range expansion from 24–38 tetrads where breeding was considered likely, including inland nesting at Blashford and around Southampton Water. Following the first reported instance in the county of such behaviour in 1999 at Totton (*HBR*), increasing numbers were reported nesting on flat-roofed buildings and other man-made structures. At the same time fledging success was sometimes poor; for instance in 2009, 35 pairs reared only two young at Langstone Harbour.

Although occurring all along the Hampshire coast, including both banks of Southampton Water and on the west Solent, the accompanying HBA map clearly shows

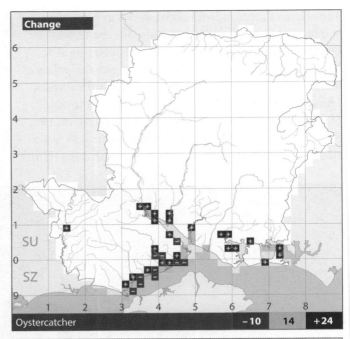

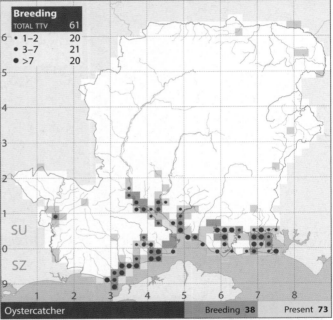

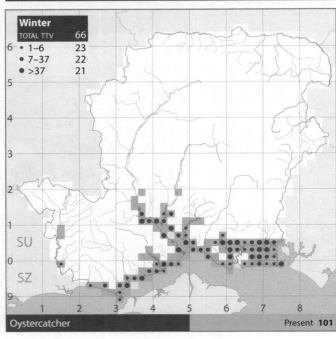

winter concentrations around the eastern harbours. Here, during the HBA, counts of 1,000 or more were forthcoming only from Langstone Harbour although the maximum of 2,100 occurred in August 2009. Winter maxima elsewhere were 779 in Southampton Water in December 2008 and 669 in Portsmouth Harbour in December 2009, these being the only other sites where 500 or more were recorded. Hampshire supports a relatively small percentage of the British wintering Oystercatcher population. The current threshold for internationally important sites is 8,200 and that for national importance 3,200. An overall total of 238,924, remarkably similar to that for Knot, was present in Britain in November 2010 (*WeBS 2012*).

Eddie Wiseman

Sponsored by Brian Leach

Oystercatcher, Hayling Oyster Beds, June 2009 – *Trevor Carpenter*

Golden Plover
Pluvialis apricaria

A common winter visitor and passage migrant: very scarce in summer

Wintering Golden Plovers are found throughout much of lowland Britain; numbers recorded on winter waterbird surveys since the mid-1980s indicate a significant increase, particularly on eastern estuaries. During the breeding season they are to be found in western and northern British uplands as well as in Ireland (*Bird Atlas 2007–11*).

In the early part of the 20th century, the Golden Plover was a winter visitor to most parts of Hampshire and often abundant in certain localities (*K&M*). By the early 1960s it was recorded in all months, though once only in June. The largest flocks were at inland sites and included 1,000 in the Andover area in early December 1941. In west Hampshire, where a regular and prominent spring passage was detected in late March and April, at least 1,000 were present at Bisterne in late March 1962 (*Cohen*). During the following three decades, preferred habitats in Hampshire included feeding sites such as permanent grassland, winter-sown cereals and newly ploughed land, and sometimes inter-tidal areas, particularly in severe weather. Diurnal and nocturnal roost sites were often on ploughed land, while those wintering close to the coast used saltmarsh or raised mud platforms. Inland roosts were sometimes on islands and spits within flooded ex-gravel workings, for example at Blashford Lakes in the Avon Valley. The annual wintering population in Hampshire was often in the order of 4,000–8,000 with site maxima of 2,000 on the coast in the Warsash/Calshot area in February 1984 and 1,700 inland at Danebury in January 1978.

During the HBA period, as the accompanying map shows, wintering Golden Plovers were widespread across the county, mainly on the coast and at chalkland sites. A significant proportion of the population was centred on estuaries, for example around Hayling Island/Langstone Harbour, on the Beaulieu Estuary and on flooded grazing marsh between Keyhaven and Lymington on the west Solent. At these localities winter maxima fluctuated between 1,400 at the latter in 2007/08 and four in the Beaulieu Estuary in the colder-than-average winter of 2010/11. At inland sites the few counts of 500 or more included 700 at Quarley Hill in early December 2007, 670 at Odiham in early November 2007, 600 at Binsted in late January 2012 and 530 at Lasham in late December 2007.

A significant proportion of four-figure flocks formerly wintered at inland sites but from the early 2000s, coastal localities were assuming greater importance. Such concentrations included 6,500, a county record, at Langstone Harbour/Hayling Island in January 2006. The apparent shift in preferred habitat from agricultural land to coastal wetland sites may have occurred because

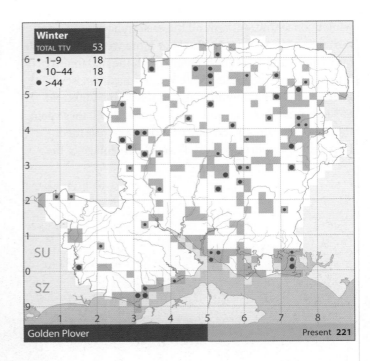

Golden Plover — Present **221**

traditional inland sites have become less attractive due to faster, climate-induced growth of autumn-sown cereal crops (Mason & Macdonald 1999).

In 2006, immediately prior to the HBA, the Hampshire population reached a peak, possibly as high as 10,000. Thereafter numbers fell, declining by almost 50% during the Atlas period. This picture is consistent with the national trend which saw a four-fold increase in population between the mid-1980s and the 2006 peak followed by a rapid fall of more than 50% by 2011 (*WeBS 2014*).

Golden Plovers were recorded as spring migrants in April during the HBA breeding season. Ringing data suggests that birds wintering in southern England are largely of Continental rather than British origin, many of the latter wintering close to nesting haunts (*Migration Atlas*). Those present in April usually consist of northern-form birds that breed in Iceland, northern Fennoscandia and Russia (Marchant *et al.* 1986). During the HBA period, little diurnal spring coastal passage was detected other than ten flying east at Hurst Beach on April 20th 2008. On the coast cumulative monthly maxima of grounded birds throughout the county did not exceed 196 in April 2008, or 315 in April 2010 at inland sites. To complete the picture of Golden Plover's status in Hampshire, autumn monthly maxima on the coast and at inland sites were 900 and 580 respectively in October 2008.

Eddie Wiseman

Sponsored by Brian Durham

Golden Plover, Bunny Meadows, January 2010 – *Steve Copsey* (above); Bunny Meadows, October 2011 – *Mike Crutch* (below)

Grey Plover

Pluvialis squatarola

A moderately common but declining winter visitor and passage migrant, often present in small numbers in summer

Grey Plovers breed on the Siberian tundra and are winter visitors and passage migrants to Britain and Ireland, where they are widely distributed around mud- and sandflat-dominated coasts (*Bird Atlas 2007–11*).

K&M made no reference to wintering or summering Grey Plovers in Hampshire, describing the species as a spring and autumn passage migrant, although half a century later winter flocks were found to be present in the low hundreds in the eastern estuaries and mid-summer gatherings there attained 350 in early July 1961.

Some 25 years later, in the late 1980s, the mean of Hampshire's winter peak counts over a five-year period was 4,375, with the largest concentrations continuing to occur in Langstone and Chichester Harbours. The increase was also reflected on estuaries west of Portsmouth. Grey Plovers were scarce at inland sites where 31 such records, involving 35 birds in 15 years, were recorded in all months but mostly in May or October or during hard weather. An easterly up-channel diurnal coastal movement, detected in the early 1960s, peaked at 140 at Hurst Beach on May 6th 1976 (*BoH*).

During the HBA period, Langstone and Chichester Harbours, Beaulieu Estuary and Hurst–Sowley qualified as sites of national importance for their wintering Grey Plover populations (*WeBS 2014*). The first of these continued to support the highest winter concentrations, including up to about 1,800 in November 2007 with 500–550 individuals at the latter two sites. The decline is consistent with the national trend, which shows numbers peaking in England in the winter of 1994/95 and declining thereafter.

Spring passage day maxima during the HBA period included up to 104 grounded individuals at a high-tide roost on the Beaulieu Estuary in April 2009, 51 flying east at Titchfield Haven on May 2nd 2011 and an all-season site maximum of 145 flying east at Hurst Beach in 2008.

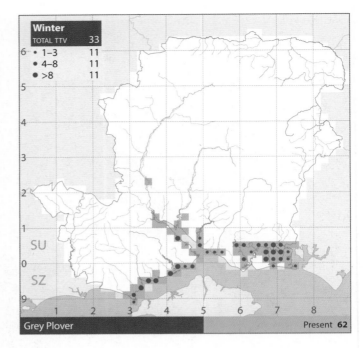

Winter	
TOTAL TTV	33
• 1–3	11
• 4–8	11
• >8	11

Grey Plover — Present **62**

These coastal movements account for most of the HBA 'breeding season' records as Grey Plovers remained scarce at inland sites; during the HBA summer surveys there were records of single birds from Ibsley Water on April 17th and May 14th 2008 and Woolmer Pond on April 8th and May 9th 2011. Grey Plovers migrating through Hampshire in autumn occurred from July–October though counts at that season did not exceed double figures at any site until August when up to 600 were in Langstone Harbour in 2012, with up to 820 there in September and 790 in October, both in 2009.

The Solent estuaries, from West Sussex to Hampshire and including those on the north shore of the Isle of Wight, were known to support up to 9·6% of the UK wintering Grey Plovers from 1986/87–2000/01 when Langstone Harbour qualified as of international importance and Beaulieu Estuary of national importance. Latterly the UK wintering population has exhibited an 18% reduction during the ten-year period 2000/01–2010/11 (*WeBS 2014*).

Eddie Wiseman

Sponsored by Pete Potts

Grey Plover, Farlington, August 2009 – *Steve Copsey*

Grey Plover, Hayling Island, September 2009 – *Trevor Carpenter* (above); Hook-with-Warsash, November 2009 – *Steve Copsey* (below)

Lapwing
Vanellus vanellus
A common but declining breeder, passage migrant and winter visitor

Though declining for decades, as a result of changes in agricultural practice, the Lapwing remains our most widespread breeding wader and, after Woodcock and Snipe, the third most widespread wintering wader in Britain and Ireland (*Bird Atlas 2007–11*). It is also one of our most conspicuous farmland birds. In Hampshire, at the beginning of the 20th century, *K&M* described them as common residents in all parts, breeding in great numbers. Their frenzied corkscrew-like, tumbling spring flight would have been well-known to a majority of countrymen and others, even to those with only a passing interest in birds. It remained a widespread breeding species until the mid-1980s when preferred habitats included arable farmland, coastal and river valley grasslands and New Forest heaths, especially those previously used as airfields. Winter concentrations were often also of considerable size, especially during flood conditions or severe weather such as occurred in the Avon Valley in late January 1984 and early February 1985 when 5,280 were present and 10,000 were in frozen fields, respectively (*BoH*).

Fieldwork during the HBA period has shown that the Lapwing remains a widespread breeder throughout the county. However, while the maps show significant concentrations in the south-west and north-west, many tetrads were devoid of nesting individuals and breeding-group densities were considerably lower than formerly. For instance, on one New Forest airfield in the 1970s, where more than 60 pairs of Lapwing were breeding within an area of approximately 190 hectares (*HBR 1972*), only four or five pairs now remain. During the HBA, breeding was considered likely in around 34% of Hampshire's tetrads, compared to 65% in the 1986–91 Atlas. Nationally, *BBS* results have revealed a decline of 41% in the UK breeding populations between 1995 and 2011 and during the past four decades, breeding Lapwings have been lost across much of western Wales and the western Scottish mainland, much of Ireland and south-west England, though this was not so in those counties bordering west Hampshire (*Bird Atlas 2007–11*). Fledgling success during the HBA was often poor and in part, attributed to factors such as disturbance, local flooding and even, on occasions, to illegal nocturnal fishing (*HBR 2012*).

As the maps show, the Lapwing's winter distribution during the HBA was similar to that in summer but was particularly evident at coastal sites and in the Avon Valley. The largest gatherings occurred on the coast, where 4,400 were counted in the Hurst/Lymington area in mid-February 2009 and 3,000 in January 2008. Inland, in the Avon Valley, about 2,500 were between Sopley and Ringwood

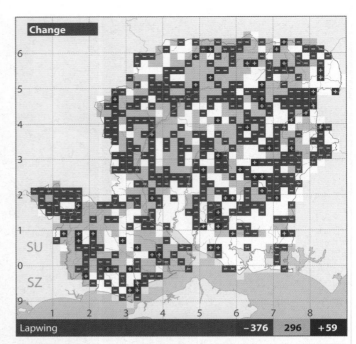

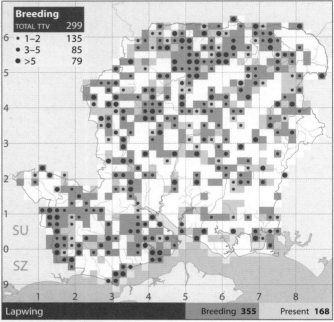

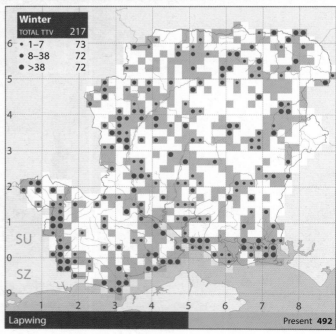

in February of both 2008 and 2010. WeBS monthly totals during the HBA period fluctuated between a maximum of 8,098 in January 2008 and a low of 1,901 in December 2010. These counts were significantly lower than in the previous five winters when county WeBS totals fluctuated between 17,250 (including 8,500 in the flooded Avon Valley, in December 2002) and 2,924 in November 2006, and when four other monthly counts exceeded 10,000 (*HBR*).

It is known that Lapwing numbers vary in response to temperature both in Britain and particularly in Continental Europe. Unlike Golden Plovers, whose numbers fell sharply, high Lapwing populations were present at some British sites during the cold winter of 2010/11, though it is unclear whether the January total included an influx of new arrivals from Continental Europe (*WeBS 2012*).

Eddie Wiseman

Sponsored by John Wood

Lapwing, Woolmer, August 2010, Richard Ford (above); Blashford Lakes, March 2009 – *Martin Bennett* (below)

169

Little Ringed Plover
Charadrius dubius
A scarce summer visitor and passage migrant

The Little Ringed Plover was first recorded breeding in the UK in Hertfordshire in 1938 but it wasn't until 1951 that the first was seen in Hampshire at Fleet Pond on June 3rd. In 1952 and 1953, a pair bred at a gravel pit near Sway and over the next decade one or two pairs bred intermittently on coastal flats at Ashlett and Dibden Bay, and gravel pits at Lee and Nursling. In 1964, a pair bred for the first time in the north-east at Warren Heath and in 1966 five pairs were located, three at the present day Wellington Country Park and one each at Warren Heath and Yateley Gravel Pits. Given the poor observer coverage in some areas of the county during that period, it seems likely that the species was missed in areas of the north-east and Avon Valley where gravel extraction was underway in the 1950s and early 1960s.

The favoured habitat of this species is provided by areas of flat, undisturbed gravel with scattered pools in recently worked-out gravel pits; it will also use gravel islands in rivers, the beds of temporarily drained lakes, ponds and sewage farm pools, building sites, disused car-parks, and partially-flooded fields and commons. The transient nature of these sites means that the species rarely remains in one area for long before seeking suitable alternatives elsewhere. As a result, coverage of known sites has been patchy with a proportion of pairs probably overlooked in most years. The highest county total ever recorded appears to have been of 33 pairs in 1980; peaks in subsequent years included 30 in 1987 (at the time of the previous county atlas) and 29 in 1995. A national survey in 2007 produced a county total of 23 pairs (Shillitoe 2008) although additional data which subsequently came to light produced a revised figure of 32 pairs. During the HBA period the

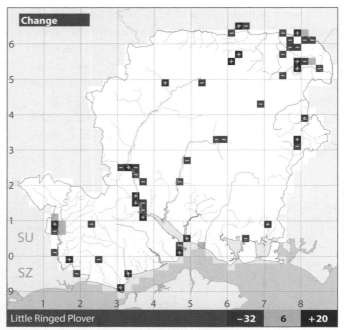

Little Ringed Plover   −32   6   +20

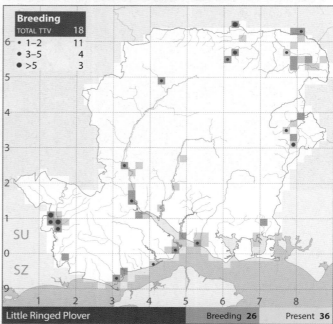

Little Ringed Plover   Breeding 26   Present 36

Little Ringed Plover, Blashford Lakes, July 2009 – *Martin Bennett*

peak recorded was 31 pairs in 2010 but only 18 pairs were located in 2012, the lowest total since 1994.

The HBA maps show the main breeding areas at sand and gravel quarries in the Avon Valley above Ringwood and the north-east, the lower Test Valley and various coastal lagoons and balancing ponds. The change map confirms the transitory nature of the species. Of 58 tetrads where breeding was considered likely in the two atlases only six were occupied in both, with 20 gains and 32 losses in the HBA survey. Little Ringed Plover has benefited from the creation of the HIWWT reserves at Blashford and Testwood Lakes but, even with the management of

suitable habitat at these sites, the species still suffers from a high level of predation, which often follows accidental disturbance.

Although a summer visitor that usually arrives from mid-March onwards and departs by September, there was one winter record during the HBA period which referred to an exceptionally early migrant at Ibsley Water on February 29th 2008.

John Clark

Sponsored by Barry Stalker

Little Ringed Plover, Blashford Lakes, June 2009 – *Martin Bennett*

Ringed Plover
Charadrius hiaticula
A moderately common but declining breeder, passage migrant and winter visitor

In winter, Ringed Plovers are widely distributed around British and Irish shores, their range remaining largely unchanged since the *1981–84 Winter Atlas*. In the south of England, their breeding distribution is also confined mainly to the coast (*Bird Atlas 2007–11*).

In Hampshire *K&M* described the Ringed Plover as a common resident and its breeding population increased further during the following decades (Munn 1920). Without quantitative information it is difficult to assess timing and extent of population fluctuations but by the mid-1980s, aided by increased observer coverage and protection measures, it was considered that about 165 pairs, including about 17 pairs at inland localities, were nesting in Hampshire (Steventon 1985). In 2007, the British breeding population was found to be in decline (Conway *et al.* 2008). This was evident in Hampshire and, as the HBA change map shows, the range has contracted markedly since the 1986–91 Atlas. The estimated population in 1986–91 of 140–160 pairs included concentrations of 35 pairs in Langstone Harbour, 42 in the Beaulieu Estuary and 34 between Hurst and Pitts Deep. By 2008, at the beginning of the HBA period, the county population had dropped to around 57 pairs and had fallen further to about 25 pairs by the end of the survey, although data were incomplete in 2012. Reductions were probably due to a number of factors, including poor productivity as a result of increased disturbance from recreational pressures, predation, loss of breeding habitat caused by sea-level rise and increasing wave attack on saltmarsh sites such as those between Hurst and Sowley.

Outside the breeding season, substantial populations were present on many Solent estuaries during the second half of the 20th century. Collectively, the estuaries between Pagham in West Sussex and Hurst–Sowley, including those on the north shore of the Isle of Wight, supported 3·2% of the wintering British Ringed Plover total between 1996/97 and 2000/01 (Unsworth 2003). The Hampshire and Langstone Harbour/Hayling Island maxima during this period were 1,177 and 739 in 1997 and 1998 respectively. November-February populations during the HBA period were lower, fluctuating between county maxima of about 640 in 2008/09 and 389 in 2010/11 with a site maximum of 375 at Black Point, Hayling Island in November 2009. Elsewhere, for example on the west Solent, maxima also occurred in November including 205 at Beaulieu Estuary in 2007 and 230 between Hurst and Sowley in 2009.

Overall totals of Ringed Plovers using British estuaries on spring and autumn passages are normally much

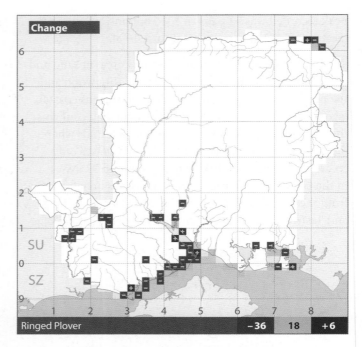

Ringed Plover, Sandy Point, September 2009 – *Steve Copsey*

greater than those remaining in winter (*WeBS 2012*) but the autumn peak at Langstone Harbour/Hayling Island, Hampshire's premier site for autumn migrants, was only 400 at Black Point in October 2008. The national decline over the past two decades has been attributed to an eastward shift in the core wintering range. However, populations in the Netherlands did not respond to frozen conditions in the Wadden Sea in 2010/11 by returning to UK estuaries as predicted. Instead national indices in the UK fell sharply to their lowest ever levels (*WeBS 2012*).

Eddie Wiseman

Sponsored by Caroline French

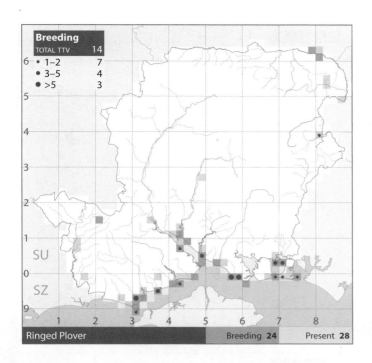

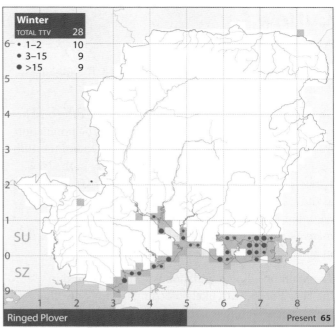

Ringed Plover, Blashford Lakes, May 2009 – *Martin Bennett*

Curlew

Numenius arquata

An uncommon breeder, common passage migrant and winter visitor

The status of the Curlew as a Hampshire breeding bird has waxed and waned over the past 100 years. The population increased from just one or two pairs at the end of the 19th century to around 120 pairs, predominantly in the New Forest, by the time of the 1986–91 Atlas (*BoH*). Today, as the HBA maps show, the range has contracted again. Although the breeding season distribution map shows many occupied tetrads, both on the coast and inland, the majority of these are occupied by non-breeding birds.

The main breeding population is still to be found in the New Forest, with likely breeding in only one other area around Woolmer Forest, in the north-east of the county. As the change map shows, the distribution in the Forest has contracted markedly since the previous Atlas. Furthermore, during the HBA period, there was no indication of breeding in the Avon Valley nor in some previously-occupied tetrads in the north-east. For the county as a whole, the number of tetrads where breeding is considered likely has fallen by 45%. This is consistent with the national picture, which shows a 43% fall in the UK breeding population over the period 1995–2012 (*BBS*). The reasons for the decline may vary from region to region but in the New Forest the most likely causes are associated with increased visitor pressure resulting in disturbance, particularly by dogs, and possibly increased predation by Foxes and corvids.

By mid-summer, flocks begin to build up on the coast as passage migrants and incoming winter visitors arrive, mainly from Fennoscandia. Numbers peak in late summer and then decline as winter progresses. The largest flocks are recorded in the eastern harbours where numbers in both Chichester and Langstone Harbours are of national importance. They also occur in good numbers on the mudflats around Southampton Water and between the Beaulieu Estuary and Hurst, but are less frequent on the shingle and rocky coastlines of Hayling and Portsea Islands, between Gilkicker Point and Titchfield, and to the west of Hurst. During the HBA winter period, the monthly maximum WeBS count at the main high tide roosts was 2,752 in November 2010.

Comparison of WeBS counts indicates that the Hampshire winter population has fallen from an average of around 4,000 in the 1980s (*BoH*) to around 2,300 during the five HBA winters. Over the same period, the UK population peaked in 1994/95 and then went into steady decline falling by almost a third by 2009/10. In common with other north-European waders, the fall is likely to be associated with a shift in wintering distribution from the UK to the near Continent.

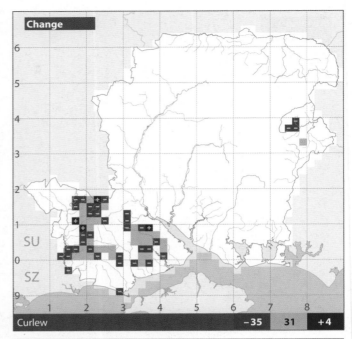

Change — Curlew — −35 | 31 | +4

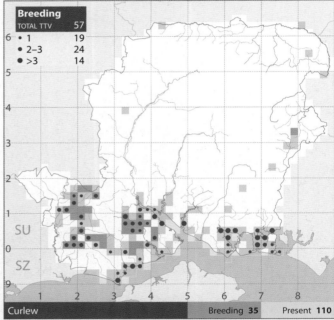

Breeding
TOTAL TTV 57
- 1 — 19
- 2–3 — 24
- >3 — 14

Curlew — Breeding 35 | Present 110

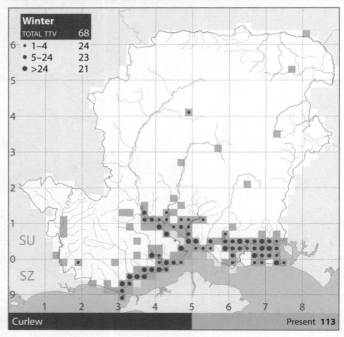

Winter
TOTAL TTV 68
- 1–4 — 24
- 5–24 — 23
- >24 — 21

Curlew — Present 113

In Hampshire, the overwintering birds feed on mudflats and nearby grasslands, moving from area to area depending on the state of the tide and sometimes flying farther inland to established feeding areas. The HBA winter map reflects these movements and shows there were also isolated records from farther inland. These were generally of single birds or small parties and often associated with hard-weather movements.

John Shillitoe

Sponsored by Jenny Jones

Curlew, New Forest, June 2014 – *Martin Bennett* (both images)

Whimbrel

Numenius phaeopus

A common passage migrant. Very scarce but increasing in winter

As a breeding species, the Whimbrel is restricted in Britain to the Northern Isles, Lewis, North Uist and the extreme north-east of the Scottish mainland. Elsewhere it occurs mainly as a passage migrant and, increasingly, as a winter visitor.

In Hampshire, most Whimbrels are seen during visible migration eastwards through the Solent in April and May. Passage numbers recorded vary from year to year, influenced by weather conditions and levels of observer coverage during the main migration period. The record day count during the HBA was 440 off Hurst Beach on April 20th 2008. In addition, grounded passage birds may stay for a few days in coastal and estuarine habitats and in small numbers inland. An estimated 400 at Lymington/Hurst on May 4th 2012 was the highest ever count of grounded birds in the county. Inland records came from scattered sites mainly in the river valleys and the north-east. Most were of one or two birds but higher numbers were seen, particularly of small flocks in flight. These included 24 flying south at Hundred Acres, Wickham on May 1st 2010.

Occasional birds over-summer and return passage is far less evident than in spring. Visible migrants and grounded flocks occur mainly in July and August with double-figure counts made at the same coastal sites as in spring. During the HBA, the peak count of grounded birds in autumn was 85 on the East Hayling WeBS count on July 24th 2009.

As passage counts can vary widely from year to year, it is difficult to draw any conclusions about trends in the numbers of migrating birds. However, the number of wintering birds has definitely increased over recent years. Following the first record during the 1958/59 winter, there were reports in only 14 winters up to the publication of *BoH* in 1993. These were all of single birds, apart from two in one year. During the HBA period Whimbrels wintered every year with a maximum count of 11 or 12 during 2008/09. Most records were still of one or two birds but there were three in Dibden Bay in January 2008 and on East Hayling during the second winter period in 2009 and the first in 2012. All wintering records were from coastal sites including Chichester, Langstone and Portsmouth Harbours, Hook links, the upper reaches of Southampton Water, the Beaulieu Estuary and between Pitts Deep and Keyhaven. It is likely that some of these individuals returned to winter in the same sites in subsequent years. The recent increased frequency of wintering, which has occurred nationally but particularly on the south coast, may be attributable to milder winters (*Bird Atlas 2007–11*).

John Shillitoe

Sponsored by Steve Mansfield

Whimbrel, Weston Shore, September 2012 – *Ian Pibworth*

Bar-tailed Godwit

Limosa lapponica

A moderately common but declining winter visitor and passage migrant; small numbers summer

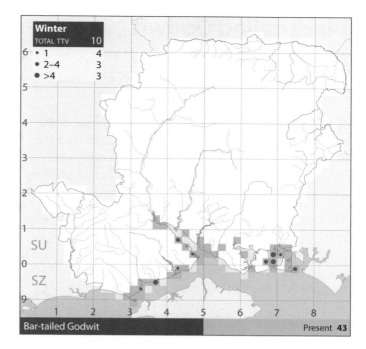

The Bar-tailed Godwits occurring in Hampshire are of two populations: those breeding in northern Fennoscandia to north-central Russia and those breeding farther east in western Siberia. The European breeders winter around the coasts of Europe, including the UK, south to west Africa while the more easterly breeders winter farther south in Africa but pass through the UK on migration.

In Hampshire, the wintering population of Bar-tailed Godwits is smaller and more concentrated than Black-tailed Godwits, with most of the birds found in Chichester and Langstone Harbours. Numbers in Chichester Harbour are generally higher than in Langstone Harbour, with the eastern shore of Hayling Island the favoured area for the species in the county. Away from the two eastern harbours, small groups (30 or fewer) winter along the shore of Southampton Water between Brownwich and Chilling and in the saltmarsh and mudflats between Pitts Deep and Hurst.

During the HBA winter period, the maximum WeBS count at the main high tide roosts was 387 in February 2008. The mean of the maximum counts over the five HBA winters was nearly 350. This number has been decreasing long term and is now substantially below the count of almost 1,300 for the 1985–90 period (*BoH*). The decline in Hampshire's wintering population is at odds with other parts of Britain. Both the national and regional populations, though erratic, have stayed relatively stable over the last forty years (*WeBS 2012*). There may have been a small shift of winter populations to the north and west of Britain, where the range has increased (*Bird Atlas 2007–11*). While the Hampshire wintering population is

almost entirely dependent on Langstone and Chichester Harbours, it seems that this site is becoming less attractive relative to others in the region. It is likely that site-specific pressures, possibly arising from changes in the use of the harbours, are having a detrimental effect, particularly to the more sandy areas which Bar-tailed Godwits favour.

Easterly passage of Bar-tailed Godwits, believed to be of the Siberian breeding population, occurs in April and May. Numbers vary from year to year dependent on weather conditions with the high count during the HBA period of 4,174 in 2011. Smaller numbers are grounded on the coast and, occasionally, inland at this time and also on return passage from late July. Although these periods coincide with the HBA breeding survey, as migrants the records are not mapped here.

John Shillitoe

Sponsored by Peter Hogan

Bar-tailed Godwit,
Hill Head, May 2013
– *Trevor Carpenter*

Black-tailed Godwit

Limosa limosa

A common passage migrant and winter visitor; small numbers summer

The Black-tailed Godwits wintering in the UK are of the race *L. l. islandica*. This population breeds in Iceland and has being undergoing sustained growth for many years; the British wintering population has seen a corresponding increase (*Bird Atlas 2007–11*).

The species did not begin to winter regularly in Hampshire until the 1940s. Numbers increased, levelled off in the 1970s and, although fluctuating from year to year, have not shown any further consistent upward trend despite the growth in the national population. During the HBA winter period, the maximum WeBS count at the main high tide roosts and inland sites was 3,253 in February 2010. The mean of the maximum monthly WeBS counts for the five HBA winters was just over 2,200. This was between the means of the corresponding numbers for the previous two five-year periods and in the same range as comparable five-year periods in the 1970s and 1980s (*Table 21*).

As the HBA map shows, the birds winter on the coast and in the Avon Valley. On the coast, they feed on mudflats, saltmarsh and damp grassland. The largest gatherings occur in the eastern harbours, on the Beaulieu Estuary and between the Lymington River and Hurst. There are smaller concentrations around the mouths of the rivers Test, Itchen, Hamble and Meon. Stony or rocky shores are generally avoided, so birds were not recorded from the Solent shores of Hayling Island, Portsea Island, much of the foreshore between Gilkicker Point and Titchfield Haven, sections of Southampton Water and west from Hurst Beach.

As the winter progresses the birds tend to move from the coastal mudflats to wet grassland particularly in the Avon Valley. This pattern of behaviour has developed mainly over the past 20 years. The timing and locations of the movements depend on the amount of rainfall and the degree of flooding of the river-side meadows. After heavy rains the upper stretches of the valley north of Ringwood flood too deeply for the birds to feed, so they congregate downstream between Sopley and Bisterne, moving up to the Blashford area as the floods there subside. Flocks in

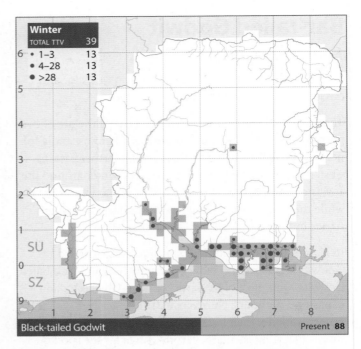

Year	1975/80	1980/85	1985/90	1997/2002	2002/07	2007/12
Birds	2,258	1,856	2,399	1,653	2,753	2,210

Table 21 – Black-tailed Godwit: comparison of mean maximum monthly WeBS counts over the 2007/8-2011/12 winters with earlier five-year periods.

excess of 2,000 were recorded in three of the five Atlas winters, with the maximum count of 2,655 in the Sopley-Bisterne area in December 2009. These large gatherings are made up of birds which have left their regular coastal haunts in both Hampshire and Dorset, so the Hampshire population is probably swelled at these times by visitors from across the county boundary. Winter records at other inland sites are rare.

In spring, prior to departing northwards on route to Iceland, numbers are swelled by incoming migrants from south-west Europe. Smaller numbers of non-breeding birds remain through the summer so the distribution during the HBA breeding season (not mapped) is similar to the winter one, with the exception that no large flocks occur in the Avon Valley. Inland records occur during both spring and autumn migration, most of them falling outside the HBA recording periods.

John Shillitoe

Sponsored by Pete Potts

Black-tailed Godwit, Farlington, February 2013 – *Trevor Carpenter* (above); Keyhaven, September 2007, *Richard Ford* (below)

Turnstone

Arenaria interpres

A moderately common passage migrant and winter visitor; small numbers summer

The Turnstone has a circumpolar breeding distribution and winters mainly along tropical and subtropical coasts. It also winters on the European Atlantic coast north to the British Isles. The population that winters in Britain breeds in Greenland and eastern Canada while birds breeding in Fennoscandia pass through on their way to and from more southerly wintering grounds. Summer records are mainly of immature birds and possibly late spring migrants.

In winter Turnstones feed on mudflats, often favouring weed-covered, rocky or stony areas. In Hampshire, in addition to being widespread in the harbours and estuaries, they are also found on some stretches of shoreline which are avoided by many other waders. These include the coasts of Hayling and Portsea Island, between Gilkicker and Titchfield Haven and also west of Hurst Beach. As the HBA map demonstrates, the Turnstone is one of the most ubiquitous waders on the Hampshire coast. At high tide, they use traditional roosting sites, along with other small waders. In the eastern harbours, they can often be found roosting on man-made structures and moored boats. There were no Atlas records away from the coast in the winter.

The mean of the maximum monthly WeBS counts for each of the five winters during the HBA years was around 870. This is substantially lower than the numbers in 1981–84 at the time of the first National Winter Atlas, which were in excess of 1,000. The national population grew rapidly during the early 1980s but peaked in 1987/88 and has since been on a steady downward trend to date. There has been a 41% national decline over the last 25 years (*WeBS 2012*). Although the causes of the decline are uncertain, they

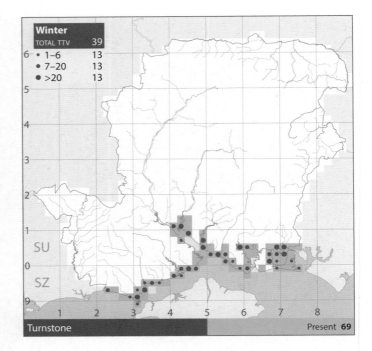

have been attributed to sea-level rise reducing habitat and changing invertebrate communities in rocky areas favoured by Turnstones. Warmer winters may also have resulted in northerly distribution shifts around the UK coast, which would not be detected via WeBS since it has relatively poor coverage of rocky shores.

Numbers recorded during the HBA summer period included both spring and autumn passage birds together with a small summering population. These latter birds are probably first-year non-breeders. They were distributed all along the coast using the same sites as wintering birds. There was also a small number of inland records, with reports from the Avon Valley and the north-east.

John Shillitoe

Sponsored by the Farlington Ringing Group

Turnstone, Keyhaven, September 2013 – *Martin Bennett*

Ruff

Calidris pugnax

A scarce but regular passage migrant and very scarce winter visitor

The Ruff breeds in northern Eurasia, the majority in Arctic Russia but with smaller numbers in more temperate regions including the UK. Post-breeding most migrate south to winter in sub-Saharan Africa but some go no farther than the British Isles and neighbouring Continental countries. In Hampshire, they occur in freshwater marshes and wet grassland adjacent to the coast and in the Avon Valley.

Ruffs did not begin wintering in Hampshire until the late 1950s. Numbers peaked in the 1970s and 1980s, with occasional three-figure flocks, including 171 at Keyhaven in February 1970, then declined rapidly until, by the early 1990s, they were restricted to a few birds at Titchfield Haven (*BoH*). WeBS and other counts made during the HBA period do not suggest any subsequent increase in the wintering population. The mean of the approximate monthly maximum counts for each winter of the Atlas period was 11. This average is elevated by some large gatherings attracted to extensive floods in the Avon Valley and at Pennington/Keyhaven Marshes.

In the HBA period, coastal records came from Keyhaven/ Lymington, the Beaulieu Estuary, Lower Test Marshes, Hook-with-Warsash, Titchfield Haven, Farlington Marshes and Hayling Island. These sites all have areas of freshwater habitat close to the inter-tidal mudflats and saltmarsh. The only inland records were from floods and gravel pits along the Avon Valley.

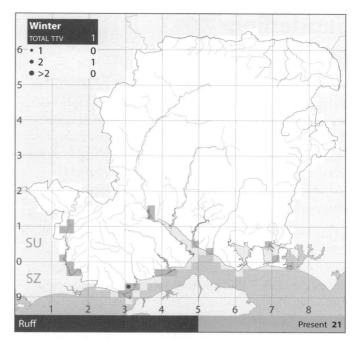

The changing fortunes of the Ruff in Hampshire roughly reflect the national picture, albeit the fall in numbers started earlier in Hampshire. The reasons behind the national decline are poorly understood, but may be caused by deterioration in staging grounds in the Netherlands which have resulted in an easterly shift in migration routes. This, in turn, has resulted in a redistribution of the breeding population from north-west Europe to western Siberia (*Bird Atlas 2007–11*).

John Shillitoe

Sponsored by Joanna Lowis

Ruff,
Blashford Lakes,
September 2013
– *Martin Bennett*

Sanderling

Calidris alba

A moderately common passage migrant and winter visitor

The Sanderling breeds in the high Arctic and occurs in Britain as a passage migrant and winter visitor. It is most abundant on sandy shores, preferring these to muddy estuaries. It has expanded its range by about 31% in Britain since the 1981–84 Winter Atlas (*Bird Atlas 2007–11*). National ringing data suggest that those wintering in Hampshire may be of Siberian origin (*BWP*).

At the beginning of the 20th century, *K&M* described the Sanderling as a common winter visitor to Hampshire's entire coastline, but very rare inland. Six decades later *Cohen* considered that it was no longer a common winter visitor with large flocks restricted to the eastern end of the coast. This description continued to be valid during the 1980s when a large proportion of a flock normally frequenting Chichester Harbour occasionally roosted on the shore of Hayling Island; for example 370 were present at Black Point in March 1989. Their feeding areas were widespread including the nearby Sussex coast, Ryde Sands on the Isle of Wight and the West Winner Bank in Hayling Bay. Elsewhere in Hampshire the Sanderling was mainly a spring passage migrant; up to 182 flew east at Hurst Beach in early May 1981. Inland, the Sanderling remained a scarce migrant. Between 1958 and 1992, 25 such records involved a total of 43 individuals at eight localities and of these, 38 occurred in May with three in August, one in September and one in November.

During the HBA winter periods, counts of 200 or more continued to be recorded from the county's eastern shores and harbours. Maxima usually occurred on Hayling Island where peak counts in Hayling Bay, a site qualifying as of national importance, included at least 330 at Black Point in late January 2009. Elsewhere in the county over the winter periods, other than 44 at Hill Head on March 28th, the maximum was 29 at Gilkicker Point on January 17th 2012. The mean of Hayling Island winter maxima of 312 for the 2007/08–2011/12 period, compared to 276 during the previous five-year period, suggests a stable population in line with the national trend (*WeBS 2012*). The wintering population often remained into early April; for example,

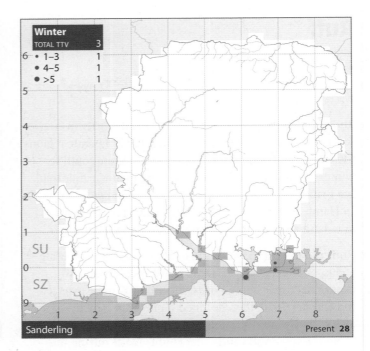

a flock of 200 on Hayling Island on April 3rd 2012, was considered too early for spring migrants.

Elsewhere on the Solent, the Sanderling is predominately a spring passage migrant and is particularly conspicuous on the west Solent in April and May. For instance at Hurst Beach over the 2008–12 period, a total of at least 829 was observed flying east between extreme dates of April 5th and June 11th (in 2008 and 2009 respectively). Similar numbers were reported during comparative springs over the preceding five-year period, 2003–07, when 906 were observed on diurnal easterly passage between March 20th and June 17th (in 2005 and 2006 respectively). Inland records over the five springs 2008–12, totalled 13 individuals at five sites with six in May, a group of five in June and two in July.

An increase in the British wintering population occurred simultaneously with a similar but more rapid expansion in the Netherlands; similarly the index for Northern Ireland has been at a high level following an unprecedented peak in 2007/08 though the reasons for these national trends are unclear (*WeBS 2012*).

Eddie Wiseman

Sponsored by the Farlington Ringing Group

Sanderling, Sandy Point, September 2009 – *Steve Copsey*

Dunlin

Calidris alpina

A numerous but declining winter visitor and moderately common passage migrant: small numbers summer

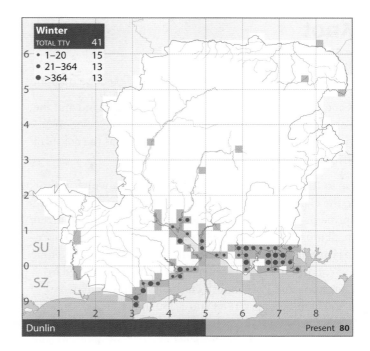

Most of the Dunlins wintering in Britain are of the race *C.a. alpina* which breeds in north-west Europe and Russia. The race *C.a. schinzii* breeds farther west in Greenland and Iceland, and in more temperate regions in Fennoscandia and the British Isles. These birds winter farther south in West Africa and pass through Britain and Ireland on migration, spring passage coinciding with the HBA breeding survey.

In Hampshire, Dunlins occur in large numbers, their distribution being essentially the same both on passage and in winter. They occur most commonly where there are extensive areas of inter-tidal mud. As a result, there are concentrations of birds in the Lymington/Hurst area, the Beaulieu Estuary, in parts of Southampton Water and in Portsmouth, Langstone and Chichester Harbours. Even though this is the most widespread and common wader on the Hampshire coast, as the HBA map shows, there are some stretches of coastline where birds were not reported. The most noticeable were the mainly shingle foreshores of Hayling and Portsea Islands, between Portsmouth Harbour and Titchfield Haven, between the mouths of the Hamble and the Itchen and west from Hurst Spit. The map also shows smaller gaps where birds are probably present, but military or industrial installations restrict survey access.

The HBA winter map gives a good representation of Dunlin distribution and relative abundance in the county but WeBS results give a better picture of total numbers and trends since the 1981–84 National Winter Atlas.

During the five winters of the HBA period, the maximum WeBS count at the main high tide roosts was 30,310 in February 2012. This total included 15,261 in Langstone Harbour qualifying the site as of international importance. The mean of the maximum monthly WeBS counts for the five winters was just over 24,000. This was down from 30,000 and 35,000, the corresponding numbers for the previous two five-year periods. It was also down

significantly from the time of the 1981–84 Winter Atlas when the comparable five-year count was approaching 60,000.

This reduction in numbers can be seen in the context of a national decline since the mid-1990s (*WeBS 2012*). This has been attributed to milder winters, which have allowed northern breeding species, including the Dunlin, to winter farther north and east in Europe by stopping short on their southern migration and has resulted, for example, in increased Dunlin numbers on the Dutch Waddensee but reductions in the UK.

Dunlins are scarce inland, occurring more commonly during migration than at other seasons and therefore often outside the HBA recording periods. During both the breeding and winter seasons, the gravel pits and wet meadows in the Avon Valley produced the most records, although no longer in the numbers seen twenty years ago on the winter floods (*BoH*). There were also isolated reports from elsewhere including the north-east and the Test and Itchen Valleys.

John Shillitoe

Sponsored by Mark Painter

Dunlin, Blashford Lakes, May 2009 – *Martin Bennett*

Knot

Calidris canutus

A moderately common winter visitor and passage migrant

Knots of the race *islandica*, breeding in Greenland and the Canadian Arctic, winter in north-west Europe; over 65% winter on muddy and sandy estuaries around the coasts of Britain and Ireland (*Bird Atlas 2007–11*).

Up to the early 20th century, the Knot was a winter visitor to the Hampshire coast and also occurred on autumn and spring passage (*K&M*). By the early 1960s, it had occurred in all months and three flocks of 1,000 or more included a maximum of 1,500 at the Beaulieu Estuary in early October 1957. From the 1960s wintering flocks were confined to Langstone and Portsmouth Harbours with site maxima of 2,950 in February 1988 and 1,260 in December 1975 respectively. West of Portsmouth, Knots occurred only on isolated dates, for example 180 at Hurst/Lymington in cold weather on January 27th 1963, 300 at the Beaulieu Estuary on January 17th 1965 and 180 at Dibden Bay on January 18th 1976.

During the HBA period the eastern harbours continued to support the majority of Hampshire's wintering Knots. The highest numbers were in the Sussex sector of Chichester Harbour but there were 2,000 at East Hayling in February 2008. This was a record count for the site and the highest in Hampshire since 2,500 in Langstone Harbour in January 2000. Numbers in Langstone Harbour were generally well down on those seen in the 1980s and 1990s. However, Knots are very mobile between alternative roost sites, particularly those situated within the eastern harbours and on the west Solent, where a variable winter population centred on the Beaulieu Estuary/Pitts Deep area sometimes shows noticeable late winter or early spring increases. For example, a peak of 508 occurred on the Beaulieu Estuary in March 2009, although numbers varied widely with the population in three of the five HBA winters lower than 100. At Hurst–Sowley 530 were present in January 2011. Five-year means of Hampshire WeBS annual maxima indicated a decline in the population of 22% from 1,414 in 1997–2002 to 1,108

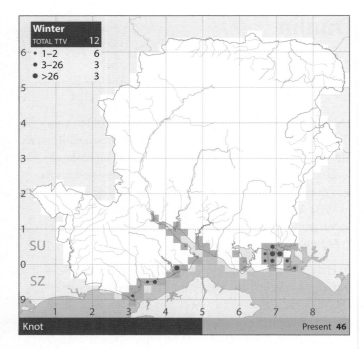

in 2002–07 and remaining at a similar level during the HBA period. The UK population has been relatively stable, declining by 7% from 2001/02–2011/12 (*WeBS 2014*).

A small easterly spring movement through the Solent occurs between mid-April and late May. Between 1971 and 1992 the annual total averaged 40 with a maximum of 120 in 1978 and a day-peak of 102 at Hurst in early May 1981. Autumn counts seldom reached double-figures, although 230 were in the Hurst/Lymington area on September 16th 1962 and 260 in Langstone Harbour on September 14th 1985. Inland records from 1960–1992 totalled just eight individuals with one in February, one in March, three in May and three in September.

Relatively few Knots occurred during HBA spring surveys. The highest count of grounded individuals was 136 between Hurst and Sowley in April 2012. Similarly, diurnal spring passage was also insignificant with a maximum of 50 flying east at Langstone Harbour in early April 2011. The only inland records during 2007–12 all occurred outside the HBA recording periods in September 2011 in the Ibsley area, where one was present between 4th–11th and 18th–22nd with two on 6th/7th. It is now ascertained that Knots

Knot, Normandy, May 2012 – *Marcus Ward*

passing through Hampshire in autumn are from both the north-central Siberian (*C.c. canutus*) and the Greenland and north-east Canadian populations.

Hampshire supports relatively few of the British populations of passage and wintering Knot, where currently the

internationally important site threshold is 4,500 and that of national importance 3,200; a total of close to 240,000 was present in Britain in January 2011 (*WeBS 2012*).

Eddie Wiseman

Sponsored by Steve Copsey

Curlew Sandpiper
Calidris ferruginea

A scarce passage migrant, particularly so in spring; has wintered

The majority of Curlew Sandpipers reaching Britain are autumn passage migrants moving between their Siberian breeding grounds and wintering areas in West Africa. In Hampshire, peak numbers, mainly of juveniles, occur in September. Therefore although passage extends over July-November, most records fell outside the HBA recording seasons. During the 2007–12 period, counts averaged around 72 birds each year. Gatherings were usually in single figures, although there was a remarkable flock of 42 moulting adults in the Keyhaven/Pennington area on August 1st 2009. In addition there was a small number of spring migrants, ranging from one to four per year. There were no reports of wintering birds. All records were from coastal sites, except for singles at Blashford Lakes in September and October 2010.

During the period 1951 to 1992, covered by *BoH*, annual numbers were very variable, ranging from single figures to in excess of 150. It is possible that numbers during the

Curlew Sandpiper, Keyhaven, September 2013 – *David Cuddon*

2007–12 period have declined somewhat, as there has been some loss in formerly attractive sites such as Dibden Bay, Fawley Reclamation and Paulsgrove Reclamation.

John Shillitoe

Pectoral Sandpiper
Calidris melanotos

A rare passage migrant

Pectoral Sandpipers breed in the Arctic from Siberia east to Canada and winter largely in southern South America. In Hampshire they are rare vistors, generally in the autumn, with very occasional spring records, usually in May. Prior to 2007, there had been 75 records in the county in the period since 1950. A further 14 were added during 2007–12 bringing the total to 89. Only three were recorded during the HBA recording periods as follow:

2009: Keyhaven Marsh, May 9th–11th.
2011: Pennington Marsh, May 7th.
2012: Normandy Lagoon, July 29th–31st.

The two May records were unusual, the first in spring since 2004. The other 11 records were all in August–October, all coastal and spread across all years other than 2007.

John Shillitoe

Pectoral Sandpiper, Hayling Island, September 2009 – *Steve Bassett*

Little Stint

Calidris minuta

A scarce passage migrant, mostly in autumn and a very scarce winter visitor

Little Stint occurs in the UK mainly as an autumn migrant between its Arctic breeding and African wintering grounds. Numbers seen in Hampshire vary from year to year depending on breeding success, weather conditions and suitability of local habitat. During 2007–12, most records occurred outside the HBA survey periods with autumn records averaging 27 birds per year, including a maximum flock of eight at Farlington Marshes in September 2008. In addition there were a small number of spring migrants, ranging from zero to four per year. The only wintering birds were singles at Farlington Marshes and around the Beaulieu Estuary in winter 2007/8. Other registrations on the map refer to November migrants.

During the period 1951 to 1992, covered by *BoH*, numbers were very variable, but were possibly a little higher than during the HBA. This is likely to be due, at least in part, to loss of suitable habitat at a number of Hampshire sites, particularly at Dibden Bay where a high count of 60 was made in September 1973.

John Shillitoe

Sponsored by Justin Walker

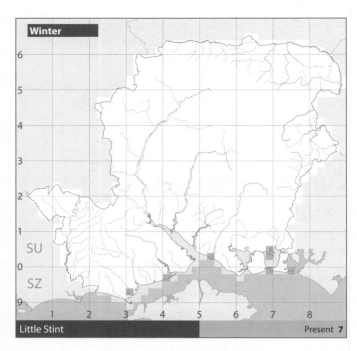

Little Stint, Pennington, September 2011 – *Martin Bennett*

Temminck's Stint

Calidris temminckii

A very scarce passage migrant

The Temminck's Stint breeds in Fennoscandia and northern Russia and very rarely in Britain. It winters largely in tropical west and west-central Africa. Unlike most scarce and rare waders, this species is more likely to be reported in spring than in autumn. Prior to the HBA, there had been 132 records in the county since 1950. A further five were added during the HBA recording period, all in May, with another in August 2011 as follows:

2008: Pennington Marsh, May 6th and 8th.
Farlington Marshes, May 13th–14th.
Farlington Marshes, May 14th.
Normandy Lagoon, May 16th.

2009: Ibsley Water, May 16th.

2011: Farlington Marshes, August 31st.

John Shillitoe

Temmincks Stint, Needs Ore, May 2007 – *Nigel Jones*

Purple Sandpiper

Calidris maritima

A scarce winter visitor and passage migrant

Purple Sandpipers breed on the tundra, moorland and uplands of Arctic and subarctic Eurasia and North America, their range extending southwards to a tiny population in the Scottish highlands. Post-breeding, the birds migrate south but only as far as necessary to find unfrozen coastline where they winter on exposed, rocky shores, a habitat which is very limited in Hampshire.

The species was first recorded in the county at Southsea Castle in December 1939. There were few further records until this site was found to be in regular use from the early 1960s. Numbers there peaked at 32 in the 1981/82 winter and subsequently declined, but Southsea continued to be the most reliably-used site. Small numbers were recorded at other locations, most frequently from the rocky groynes on the shingle beaches in the Milford on Sea/Hurst Castle area until, in the early years of the current millennium, a second regular wintering site was discovered at Barton on Sea, at the western extremity of the Hampshire coastline.

During the HBA period most records were from Southsea and Barton on Sea with regular reports either from, or close to these locations. The birds were often seen on rising and falling tides, although they were not always present. Their whereabouts when absent is uncertain, although they are known to roost on offshore structures in the Solent and also to fly to and from the Isle of Wight. The Barton on Sea birds also move to Mudeford in Dorset and roost on groynes at Chewton Bunny on the county boundary.

Most were reported from late October through to the end of March but records extended into April and May. The later records were sometimes of sizeable groups,

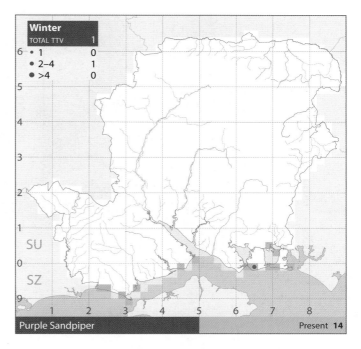

including 25, the highest ever count for the site, at Barton on Sea, on April 6th 2008, and probably indicative of passage along the south coast. Numbers at the two main sites varied from month to month and year to year. The maximum count at Southsea Castle was 20 in December 2008 and March 2012. At Barton on Sea, in addition to the 25 mentioned above, there were 17 in February 2011 and 20 nearby at Chewton Bunny on February 21st and 28th 2012. Elsewhere, there were small clusters of reports from Hurst/Lymington to the east of Barton on Sea and from the shorelines of the eastern harbours, particularly on Hayling Island. These could relate to birds moving to or from the main sites. Occasional records of one or two birds came from other locations along the Solent shore including Lepe and Calshot.

John Shillitoe

Sponsored by Tim Doran

Purple Sandpiper, Southsea Castle, January 2014 – *Martin Bennett*

Common Sandpiper, Blashford Lakes, May 2009 – *Martin Bennett*

Common Sandpiper
Actitis hypoleucos

A moderately common passage migrant; a few regularly winter; has attempted breeding

Although recorded in Hampshire mainly as a passage migrant, the Common Sandpiper appears to have wintered in small numbers throughout the 20th century. It has been recorded from suitable tidal sites, mostly as singles or small parties, apart from occasional larger gatherings usually caused by hard weather (*BoH*). It has always been rare inland during the winter, the majority of records coming from Blashford Lakes.

During the HBA winter period, records of Common Sandpiper came from the tidal stretches of all the main Hampshire rivers, plus the relatively small streams emptying into the eastern harbours. The only inland reports came from the Avon Valley mainly around Blashford Lakes. A small but regular winter population, averaging up to twelve per season, is indicated. The maximum site count was four at Lower Test Marshes in December 2008. Although there has been an extension of range in Britain since the *1981–84 Winter Atlas* (*Bird Atlas 2007–11*), possibly caused by milder winters, this has not been reflected in the Hampshire distribution, birds remaining faithful to traditional sites in the county.

During the summer HBA period, spring passage birds were regularly reported in April and May, with return passage beginning in late June and continuing through July into October and early November. Numbers were, therefore, significantly higher in summer than in winter with the July count averaging 123 over the 2008–12 period. Birds were reported from the wintering areas but also more widely from inland sites, such as Heath Pond (Petersfield), Fleet Pond and Eversley Gravel Pits. Although a pair attempted breeding at Timsbury Gravel Pit in 1978 (*BoH*), they were not successful and no evidence of further attempts has been obtained since.

John Shillitoe

Sponsored by Jennifer Tubbs

Spotted Sandpiper
Actitis macularius

A very rare vagrant

Spotted Sandpipers breed in North America and winter in Central and South America. Prior to the HBA, there had only been one record in Hampshire. This was a long-staying bird at Titchfield Haven from October 4th 1986 to January 12th 1987. Hampshire's second Spotted Sandpiper was recorded during the HBA period on the River Test, near Mottisfont. It was present from November 20th and was last seen on December 17th 2009.

John Shillitoe

Spotted Sandpiper, Christchurch Harbour – *Martin Bennett*

Green Sandpiper

Tringa ochropus

A passage migrant, scarce in spring and moderately common in autumn. Small numbers winter

Prior to the 1960s, Green Sandpiper was known in Hampshire mainly as a double passage migrant with only occasional birds wintering. However, since then, the species has wintered consistently. In the period leading up to the 1986–91 Atlas, it was estimated that, in some years, the winter population exceeded 50 birds with double-figure counts occurring at favoured locations, particularly on the watercress beds in the Itchen Valley (*BoH*). Birds are still recorded along the county's main rivers and their tributaries but their use of watercress beds has declined significantly, probably as a result of changes in the way the beds are managed.

During the HBA winter period, Green Sandpipers were widely reported from both coastal and inland sites, where they favoured still and gently flowing freshwater or brackish habitats. At the coast they were found on scrapes, lagoons and streams behind the tidal walls. Inland, further mineral extraction, particularly in the north-east and Avon Valley, has created new habitat in addition to existing gravel pits, watercress beds, ponds and sewage farms. However, this increase in potential Green Sandpiper habitat does not seem to have made up entirely for the reduction in numbers using watercress beds. The mean of the estimated maximum wintering numbers for the HBA period was 34, with a maximum of 36 in January 2010 and again in January 2011. Reports were mainly of ones or twos but

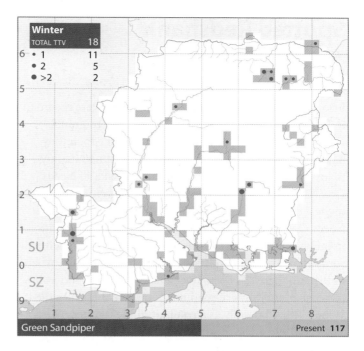

twelve were found during a survey of the Alresford area in cold weather on January 4th 2010.

The Green Sandpiper has an extended passage period which overlaps with the HBA breeding survey at both ends. The first spring migrants usually appear in mid-March. Most have moved through by the end of April with a few seen in May. Return passage, which is heavier, begins in mid-June and extends into October. During the HBA summer period, birds were reported from many of the same sites as those used in winter with the highest count of 17 at Lower Test Marshes on 27th July 2011.

John Shillitoe

Sponsored by Joanna Lowis

Green Sandpiper, Eling Marsh, December 2009 – *Martin Bennett*

189

Spotted Redshank
Tringa erythropus

A scarce and declining winter visitor and passage migrant

Prior to the early 1950s, Spotted Redshanks were recorded in Hampshire mainly as spring and autumn migrants; wintering birds were almost unknown. Since then they have been recorded annually although confined mainly to just two regular sites at Lymington/Hurst and Needs Ore. Numbers vary from year to year but were at their highest prior to the mid-1980s, with peak counts of 25 at Needs Ore in December 1970 and 24 at Lymington/Hurst in January 1981 (*BoH*). Since then numbers have declined somewhat. This is in contrast to the national picture where, in Britain, there has been an extension of range and a slow increase in the wintering population since the 1981–1984 Winter Atlas, possibly as a result of milder winters (*Bird Atlas 2007–11*). The most likely cause of local declines is changes to the particular sites that the birds favour but, with the small numbers involved and year to year variation, it is not possible to draw definite conclusions.

During the five HBA winters, Spotted Redshanks were often found in small flocks, with maxima of 15 at Lymington/Hurst and 11 at Needs Ore in November 2011. In addition a bird was present each winter at Nore Barn near Emsworth. This was thought to be the same individual that first appeared at the site during the 2004/05 winter. It was occasionally joined by a second bird. Elsewhere, single birds were recorded at other coastal sites including Lepe, Titchfield Haven and at Eling and Northam Bridge, both at the north end of Southampton Water. There were also reports from Langstone and Chichester Harbours, which may refer to the Nore Barn birds. Spotted Redshanks have

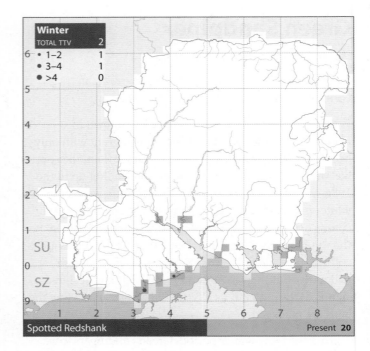

an extended migration period in the autumn, so some birds recorded in early November may have been migrants rather than winterers. Even so, the total of 29 individuals present in the Solent in November 2011 was the highest count made anywhere in the country during the *Bird Atlas 2007–11* winter recording period.

In the summer HBA period, late and early passage birds were regularly reported, with spring birds sometimes in full summer plumage. These reports came mainly from the coastal wintering areas but also inland at Alresford Pond and The Vyne.

John Shillitoe

Sponsored by Peter Milinets-Raby

Spotted Redshank, Emsworth, December 2009 – *Martin Bennett*

Greenshank

Tringa nebularia

A moderately common passage migrant and scarce winter visitor

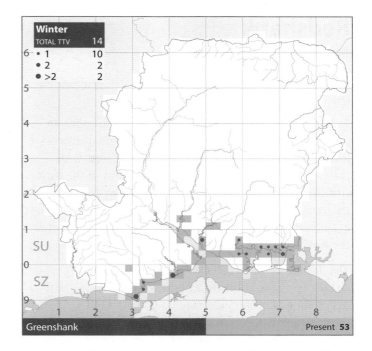

The Greenshank is another wader with an extremely large range and population. It breeds across the Palearctic, including northern Scotland, and winters predominantly in Africa, south Asia and Australasia. Relatively small numbers overwinter in Europe with Britain and Ireland the most northerly outposts in its wintering range.

Although its earlier status in Hampshire is unclear, by the mid-1950s the Greenshank was known to have a small, but regular wintering population in the county. During the late 1970s and early 1980s, the main wintering site was in the Calshot/Fawley area but this was largely abandoned later in the 1980s, with birds then favouring the upper and lower reaches of the River Hamble with smaller numbers in the eastern harbours, in the Beaulieu Estuary and in the Lymington/Hurst area (*BoH*).

During the HBA winter period, Greenshanks were recorded fairly widely along the coast, usually in estuarine but also fresh-water habitats. The HBA winter map is a little deceptive in showing an almost continuous distribution along the coast, as most birds were generally confined to the few traditional areas listed above, where small groups gathered. Over the five HBA winters the average annual total was around 42 with a maximum site count of 11 at Lymington/Hurst in January 2012. Elsewhere high counts included eight at Needs Ore, seven on the upper Hamble around Curbridge and in Langstone/Chichester Harbours, six in Portsmouth Harbour and five on the lower Hamble River at Hook-with-Warsash. These numbers are comparable to those recorded around the time of the first national Winter Atlas in 1981–84 indicating a stable winter population. Apart from the Curbridge birds and a late autumn migrant at Widden Bottom in the New Forest, there were no inland records in the winter period.

Small numbers of spring passage birds were recorded during the first part of the summer HBA period, with larger flocks of return passage birds appearing in July through to October. These birds were widely distributed along the coast, usually at or near the core sites used in winter. The largest gathering was of 48 in Langstone Harbour in August, 2010. There was also a scattering of inland records from the Avon Valley, Winchester Sewage Farm, Alresford Pond, The Vyne, Woolmer Pond and Fleet Pond.

John Shillitoe

Sponsored by the Farlington Ringing Group

Greenshank, Farlington, September 2009 – *Trevor Carpenter*

Redshank

Tringa totanus

A moderately common but declining resident, common passage migrant and winter visitor

In Hampshire, Redshanks breed on coastal marshes, in damp river-side meadows and in the bogs and mires of lowland heaths. In the middle of the 20th century, all these habitats were occupied including many of the rural stretches of the Rivers Itchen, Test and Avon and their tributaries. Breeding was also widespread in the north-east of the county and in the north-west and the south-east of the New Forest.

The decline in the Redshank's breeding range was already apparent at the time of the 1986–91 Atlas and has continued in the years leading up to the HBA. As the accompanying maps show, both the Test and Itchen Valleys have lost their breeding birds and their range in the Avon Valley has decreased. The extent of breeding in the north-east of the county has further declined, as has the distribution in the south-east of the New Forest. The Redshank has disappeared as a breeding bird in the north-west of the Forest. The fall in breeding numbers has, therefore, occurred across all habitats, probably as a result of a combination of causal factors. In the river valleys these include drainage and improvement of agricultural land and a reduction in the level of the water table resulting from water extraction. The losses from heathland are possibly linked to overgrazing, disturbance from increased leisure use and predation. Disturbance and loss of suitable coastal saltmarsh habitat are likely to be behind the reduction of breeding along the coast.

The dramatic contraction in the range of Hampshire's breeding Redshanks is graphically illustrated by the HBA

Change		
Redshank	−128	30	+5

change map, which is based only on probable and proven breeding records in both atlases. The number of tetrads where breeding is considered likely has fallen by 78% since the 1986–91 Atlas. This is consistent with, although higher than, population declines that have taken place nationally. The UK population has fallen by 44% over the period 1995–2012 (*BBS*) and a decline of 62% occurred along UK waterways over the period 1987–2012 (*BirdTrends*).

In winter, Redshank numbers are swelled by visitors from Iceland and northern Europe. Numbers begin to build-up on the coast in July, peak in September/October and then decline as migrants move on to winter farther south. During the winter, they are widely distributed along the coast, with the largest concentrations occurring in the eastern harbours. There are gaps in the distribution on the more rocky foreshores between Gilkicker Point and

Redshank, Blashford Lakes, April 2009 – *Martin Bennett*

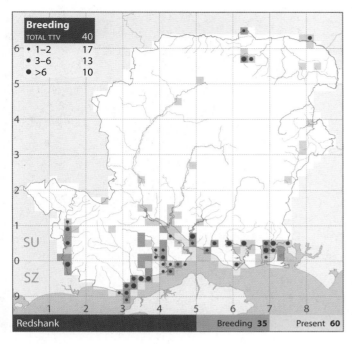

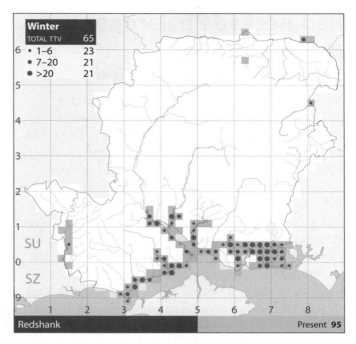

Titchfield Haven, west of the Hamble Estuary and west of Hurst Beach. Birds are also found along the tidal sections of Hampshire's rivers but the only wintering birds found on inland rivers were in the Avon Valley. Otherwise the only inland records were from the north-east and may refer to late or early passage birds. The HBA methodology gives a good representation of the winter distribution and relative abundance of Redshank but a better insight into the actual numbers of birds along the coast comes from WeBS counts. During the HBA winter period, the maximum WeBS count at the main high tide roosts was 2,516 in November 2009. The mean of the maximum monthly counts for the five

winters during the HBA years was almost 2,500. This was similar to the corresponding number for the previous five-year period but down from the time of the *1981–84 Winter Atlas*, when the comparable count for the 1980–85 period was close to 3,500 (*BoH*). The decline appears to be mainly around Southampton Water and may be attributable to loss of suitable feeding and roosting habitat due to industrial development close to the shore.

John Shillitoe

Sponsored by Michael Jaggers

Wood Sandpiper

Tringa glareola

A passage migrant, very scarce in spring and scarce in autumn

For one of the most widespread bird species in the world, with a breeding range extending from eastern Siberia to northern Scotland, Wood Sandpiper is a surprisingly scarce migrant in southern England. It occurs in small numbers in Hampshire on passage between its breeding grounds in Europe and its wintering grounds in sub-Saharan Africa.

During the HBA breeding and winter recording periods, all Wood Sandpipers occurred in the breeding season with 19 spring records (April, May and June) and ten in autumn (July). There were no winter records but larger numbers occurred later in the autumn between the breeding and winter seasons. The peak count in any year during the 2007–12 period was 22 (nine in spring and 13 in autumn) in 2011. Most records were singles with no gatherings of more than two birds. The majority were from coastal sites including Pennington, Needs Ore, Titchfield Haven and Farlington

Wood Sandpiper, Pennington, May 2012 – *Gordon Small*

Marshes, but there was also a scatter of inland sightings from Ibsley North Gravel Pit, Winchester Sewage Farm, and in the north-east at Fleet Pond and gravel pits at Fox Lane (Eversley) and Welshman's Road (Mortimer West End).

John Shillitoe

Red-necked Phalarope

Phalaropus lobatus

A rare passage migrant

An Arctic breeder that reaches the southern limit of its breeding range in the British Isles, the Red-necked Phalarope is a rare autumn passage migrant in Hampshire. It occurs mostly in August–October, therefore outside the HBA period. During 2007–12 (including the autumns before and after the HBA survey), there were seven reports, all of single birds and all at coastal sites. Of these, one was within the HBA winter period. This was seen with two Grey Phalaropes off Hurst Beach, in stormy weather on January 21st 2008. This exceptional record was the first in winter for Hampshire and possibly for the country. The species is known to winter at sea and a Scottish breeding bird has recently been shown to undertake an extraordinary and unique westward migration to winter in the Pacific off the west coast of South America (RSPB 2014).

The 2007–12 records bring the county total to 46 since 1950, averaging less than one bird a year. The seven records over the six year period were, therefore, above the average but probably due to increased observer coverage rather than a real increase in numbers.

John Shillitoe

Red-necked Phalarope, Keyhaven, August 2009 – *Marcus Ward*

Grey Phalarope

Phalaropus fulicarius

A very scarce autumn and early winter visitor, usually occurring after gales

Approximately 29 Grey Phalaropes were reported in Hampshire during 2007–12. Most occurred in September-November therefore overlapping with the HBA winter survey, although the only true winter record was of two storm-driven birds offshore Hurst in January 2008. Most records were of single birds. However, in September 2011, up to four, all juveniles, were reported from the Pennington area. Annual numbers ranged from zero in 2007 up to 17 in 2008. All were at sites on or near the coast apart from a single bird inland at Woolmer Pond in September 2008.

During 1951–92, covered by *BoH*, the annual average number of birds was similar to that during 2007–12, although the much longer period produced some significantly higher annual totals. The maximum was 59 in 1960, which included a storm-driven flock of 18 at Hurst on October 9th.

John Shillitoe

Grey Phalarope, Keyhaven, September 2011 – *Andy Pullen*

Jack Snipe

Lymnocryptes minimus

A scarce, but overlooked winter visitor and passage migrant

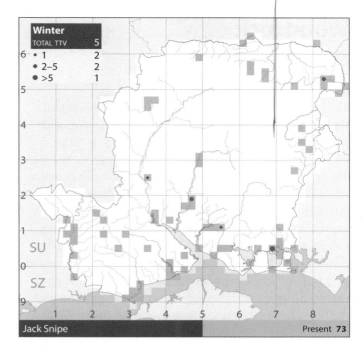

Jack Snipes are almost certainly under-recorded. Their liking for wet, relatively inaccessible habitat and their unobtrusive behaviour makes them difficult to find while their reluctance to fly, even if the observer is almost within touching distance, makes them particularly difficult to count. Even so, the HBA winter map shows them to be widely, if thinly, distributed across Hampshire, occurring on the coast and in the main river valleys, the New Forest and the north-east. In winter, they are generally found in shallow wetlands with areas of short vegetation, although during migration they can also occur on completely different dry heathland habitat, particularly in areas recovering after fires.

During the HBA, most coastal records were from the main estuaries and harbours, with Farlington Marshes, Titchfield Haven, Needs Ore and Keyhaven/Pennington Marshes being favoured locations. Inland, Jack Snipes can occur wherever there is suitable habitat – in flooded meadows, heathland mires and around the edges of ponds and gravel pits. They tend to be faithful to particular sites only leaving them if they ice over, when they probably move to the banks of nearby unfrozen streams and rivers. Reliable sites during the HBA winters included the Avon Valley in the Ibsley/Hucklesbrook area, Itchen Valley Country Park, Lakeside Country Park (Eastleigh) and, in the north of the county, Bourley & Long Valley SSSI.

Given its secretive behaviour and habitat requirements, Jack Snipe is very poorly recorded by WeBS, so trends in distribution and numbers are unknown on both national

and county levels. However, over the five HBA winters, the Hampshire totals averaged 44 with the peak count of 50 in 2009/10. The average is higher than the 32 recorded over the 1970/71–91/92 period but the high count is lower than peaks of 57 and 58 recorded in 1975/76 and 1981/82 respectively (*BoH*). At site level, Farlington Marshes generally produced the highest numbers thanks to occasional organised flush counts. During the 2007–12 period, the maximum of 13 on March 8th 2008 is in the same range as counts of 15 on April 6th 1956 and 13 on October 17th 1990 (all at times of migration). Overall it would seem that there has been little change in the species status over the past several decades.

John Shillitoe

Sponsored by Brian Durham

Jack Snipe, Lakeside, Eastleigh, December 2010 – Robin Pascal

Woodcock

Scolopax rusticola

A common resident and winter visitor

The Eurasian Woodcock is a crepuscular and nocturnal wader that is mainly solitary, and primarily a woodland species. It is a game bird, hunted throughout its range, which stretches from Europe across the Palearctic to Japan. The species is actually a fairly recent colonist as a breeding species in England. Holloway (1996) states that "the establishment of a regular breeding population in Britain and Ireland seems to have taken place in nearly all areas, except Wales and the extreme west, simultaneously in about the 1820s". This expansion appeared to be associated with both new forestry plantations and the creation of coverts for pheasant shooting at that time. More recently the range has contracted, falling by 55% in Britain and Ireland between the 1968–72 and 2007–11 national atlases (*Bird Atlas 2007–11*).

In southern England it is not a common breeding species, being absent from Cornwall and occurring only in small numbers in Devon. In Dorset and Sussex it is found only as a very local breeder. In Hampshire it is primarily a breeding bird of deciduous or mixed forest, most common on the acidic soils of the New Forest, the Thames Basin and the Weald. Together these areas hold the bulk of the breeding population. Smaller numbers occur in the Test Valley and in woodlands on the chalk across the centre of the county. The HBA breeding map shows breeding considered likely in 213 tetrads, a 53% reduction since the 1986–91 Atlas. As with other crepuscular and nocturnal species, there is likely to have been a degree of under-recording in both surveys but the downward trend is clear. Possible causes include increased disturbance through woodland leisure activities, increased browsing of ground cover by deer and drying out of woodlands, but the core breeding areas in Hampshire appear little changed. Further work is required to understand the reasons behind the decline of this cryptic wader.

The Woodcock's breeding biology is interesting in that a number of males will display over a block of woodland in an early evening flight, called roding. The female on the ground draws the attention of a flying male by a tail fan display and, once paired, they stay together until egg laying is complete, when the male will again begin to rode. First clutches are normally completed in late March or early April. Although they are considered single brooded, there is growing evidence that double broods may occur. The males are polygamous, therefore trying to estimate the number of breeding pairs has no true meaning; additionally a significant number of first year males do not appear to rode. That combined with the females' secretive nature makes any interpretation of numbers difficult. However, initial findings by the recently formed New Forest

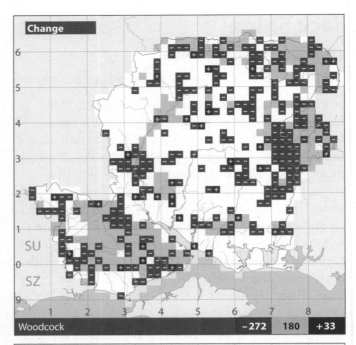

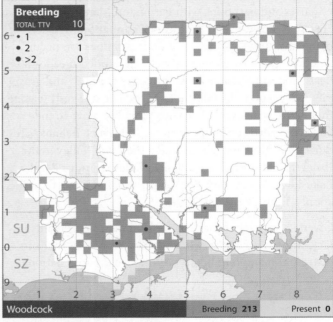

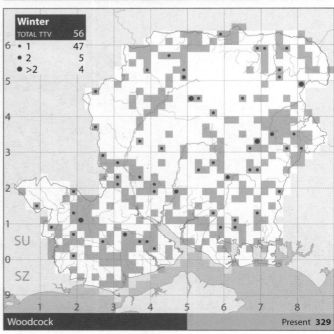

Woodcock Group (NFWG), suggest that the breeding population in the New Forest remains healthy and numbers in winter are higher than previously thought.

Two Woodcock populations occur in Hampshire, the resident breeding population and, in October, an influx of migrants arriving from Fennoscandia and Russia. Britain's resident birds form only about 16% of the total over-wintering population (Hoodless & Powell 2010), with numbers peaking in late December, depending on weather conditions in Europe (hard weather precipitating their movement westwards). Most migrants begin to leave Hampshire in March and all have departed by mid-April. The HBA winter map shows a much wider distribution over the county, compared with the breeding maps. This is to be expected with this large influx utilising a wider area for nocturnal feeding such as pasture, arable fields of newly planted winter wheat and even stubble fields. In hard weather when snow or hard frost makes feeding on soft ground impossible there are often movements to the coast, where hungry Woodcock are forced to feed in the open during the day.

Preliminary nocturnal winter surveys by the NFWG on the New Forest heaths have found that radio tagged birds may travel up to 8 km each night to feeding sites; densities of up to 90 birds per sq. km occur in small, well-defined feeding sites of up to 53 hectares (Hinge 2014). These winter numbers are normally single birds feeding on short heath or grasslands but, as the winter progresses, pairs or even groups of up to six are found together.

Nigel Jones

Sponsored by the New Forest Woodcock Group

Woodcock, New Forest, May 2012 – *Manny Hinge*

Snipe

Gallinago gallinago

A formerly moderately common but currently declining
breeder, common passage migrant and winter visitor

At the beginning of the 20th century *K&M* wrote of the
Snipe "There is happily, no need to specify all the breeding
stations of this bird." At that time it was a common breeder
in suitable wetland habitats in the New Forest, the main
river valleys and other boggy areas around the county.
By 1963, *Cohen* noted a marked decrease as a breeding
species in some areas and by the time of the 1986–91 Atlas,
there were noticeable gaps in its breeding range in the Test
and Itchen Valleys and in the north-east (*BoH*).

The HBA change map shows the continuing and dramatic
decline of the Snipe as a Hampshire breeding species over
the two decades since the 1986–91 Atlas. Over the county
as a whole, there has been a 75% contraction in range.
It has now been lost as a breeding bird in the Test and
Itchen Valleys and from the north-east; likely breeding
occurred in only one tetrad in the Avon Valley, a former
stronghold of the species. The number of tetrads occupied
in the New Forest has reduced by more than 50%. The
range contraction in Hampshire reflects a national decline
in lowland areas. Surveys in England and Wales identified
a decrease of 62% in breeding birds in wet meadows
between 1982 and 2002 (Wilson *et al.* 2005). One of the
likely causes is the drying out of wetland areas resulting
from water extraction, agricultural intensification and river
management but other factors such as a reduction in prey
availability may also be involved.

In Hampshire, the main breeding area is in the mires and
wet grasslands of the New Forest, but even here the HBA
identified only 22 tetrads where breeding was considered
likely. Elsewhere in the county there were only four
tetrads where breeding was considered likely, in the Avon
Valley, the Meon Valley at Warnford and at Woolmer and
Cranmer Ponds in the Weald. The scatter of breeding
season records from the rest of the county refer to passage
birds, lingering winter visitors in spring or exceptionally
early returnees later in the season.

During the winter, Snipe are generally common in suitable
habitat both on the coast and inland. On the coast, they
favour the three eastern harbours, Southampton Water,
the Beaulieu Estuary and the coastal marshes either side
of the Lymington River. They are infrequently found on
the inter-tidal mudflats and saltmarsh, preferring nearby
freshwater-influenced habitats. Inland, they occur in the
meadows along the valleys of the county's main rivers – the
Avon, Test, Itchen and Meon – the wet heaths of the New
Forest and the north-east and around the margins of ponds
and gravel pits. They are rare on the higher chalk downland
where there is limited wetland habitat.

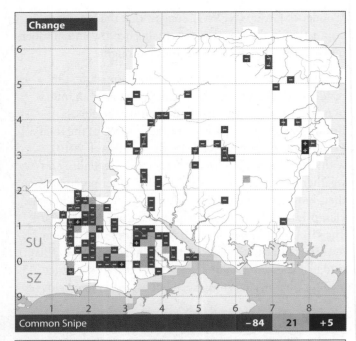

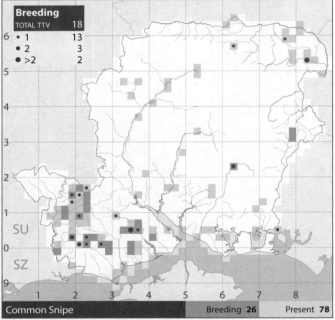

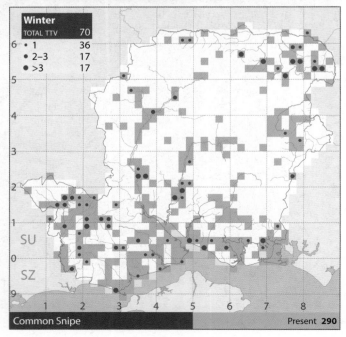

Their cryptic plumage and secretive behaviour makes it inevitable that Snipe are under-recorded, both in terms of distribution and abundance. Accurate counts can usually only be made with an organised flush, which requires several observers, otherwise the highest counts are generally made during WeBS counts or during shoots. Numbers vary from year to year dependent on weather conditions with cold winters or heavy rainfall generally leading to higher counts. During the HBA winters, flocks in excess of 100 were recorded from several coastal sites, including Lymington/Hurst, Lower Test Marshes, Titchfield Haven, Hook-with-Warsash, and Farlington Marshes. Inland, the Avon Valley produced the highest totals with a peak of 220 on the Somerley Estate in January 2011.

The only other inland site to reach 100 was at Hillside Marsh, near Odiham in February 2011.

Although still a common winter visitor to Hampshire, numbers appear to have declined in recent years. In the 1980s, counts of up to 1,000 were made in the Sopley to Hucklesbrook stretch of the Avon Valley and in excess of 200 at several other sites (*BoH*). During the HBA counts of 200 were exceptional. As with several other winter visitors, this reduction might be a result of migrants from north-west Europe stopping short to winter closer to their breeding grounds.

John Shillitoe

Sponsored by Rosemary Cook

Snipe, Titchfield Haven, April 2011 – *John Whichall*; (above) New Forest, April 2010 – *Martin Bennett* (below)

Pomarine Skua

Stercorarius pomarinus

A scarce passage migrant, most frequent in spring; very scarce in summer and rare in winter

The Pomarine Skua breeds on the Arctic tundra and winters in the tropical waters of the Atlantic. On migration most pass to the west of the British Isles and therefore are usually scarce in inshore waters, although numbers vary from year to year. It is a scarce passage migrant along the Hampshire coast occurring more often in spring than in autumn.

During the HBA survey, counts of birds on spring passage, mainly between late April and mid-May, varied between 15 in 2009 and 79 in 2011. For comparison, the highest spring count ever recorded in Hampshire was 113 in 1997. Prior to publication of *BoH* in 1993, there had been a steady increase in the numbers of Pomarine Skuas seen in spring but with counts during the HBA at similar levels to those recorded in the 1980s and 1990s, it appears that this upward trend has plateaued.

Autumn passage, mainly between the end of August and mid-November, was much less marked. The highest annual number recorded in autumn or in winter was 11 in 2008. Of these ten were seen in a group flying west past Hurst

Pomarine Skua, Hill Head, April 2012 – *Bob Marchant*

on September 7th. The remaining bird was seen off Hurst Castle on December 13th. Most sightings were from Hurst Beach with smaller numbers recorded at watch points along the Solent, particularly in the east of the county.

John Jones

Sponsored by Simon Colenutt (of ECOSA Ltd)

Great Skua

Stercorarius skua

A scarce passage migrant

Over half the world's Great Skuas breed in northern Scotland and north-west Ireland with the remainder in Iceland, Norway and the Faroe Islands. They winter in the north Atlantic and are seen in Hampshire mainly as migrants in April/May and August–October, most frequently off the coast at Hurst or from watch points in the eastern Solent and Hayling Island. As with other skuas, the numbers recorded in the county have increased. When *BoH* was published in 1993 it was unusual for the annual count to exceed ten but it is now more typically in the range of 30 to 50.

During 2007–12, numbers recorded on spring passage varied between 21 in 2009 and 176 in 2012, the latter being the highest spring total ever recorded, including at least 81 moving east into the Solent at Hurst Castle on April 25th (Wynn 2012). The maximum number recorded in autumn was 19 in 2011. It is also seen occasionally outside the main migration periods in both summer and winter.

John Jones

Sponsored by Royal Naval Birdwatching Society

Great Skua, Cut Bridge, April 2013– *Alan Lewis*

Arctic Skua
Stercorarius parasiticus
A scarce passage migrant, most frequent in spring; very scarce in summer and rare in winter

The Arctic Skua breeds around the Arctic coast of Europe, Asia and North America, its range extending south to a small and declining breeding population in the north of Scotland. It winters mainly south of the equator, most of the European birds probably off the coasts of southern Africa. It is seen in southern England during spring and autumn migrations, although small numbers occur in summer. A few also over-winter in the northern hemisphere and are occasionally seen off the British coast at this time.

In Hampshire, it is by far the most frequently recorded skua species. Annual numbers have been increasing and are nowadays consistently above a hundred. Most are seen on spring passage in late April/early May, moving east through the Solent. During the HBA breeding season surveys, spring totals varied between 77 in 2009 and 187 in 2012. The latter count was the highest ever and included day counts of 39 on April 25th and 40 on April 30th.

Autumn passage, which is usually lighter, ranged between 27 in 2007 and 46 in 2008. Occasional mid-summer and winter records also occurred.

Arctic Skua, Sandy Point, October 2011 – *Richard Ford*

Inland records are rare but, during the 2007–12 period, there were three involving four birds. The most distant from the coast was seen flying north over Rooksbury Mill, Andover on September 24th 2010.

John Jones

Sponsored by Royal Naval Birdwatching Society

Long-tailed Skua
Stercorarius longicaudus
A very scarce passage migrant also reported twice in winter

The Long-tailed Skua has a circumpolar range breeding as far south as southern Norway. European birds probably winter off Namibia and South Africa but most take a pelagic migration route well away from land. Relatively few are recorded each year off the British coast.

In Hampshire the number of records has increased in recent years, probably because of an increase in sea-watching and improved identification skills. When *BoH* was published, in 1993, there had been just 16 records since the first in 1891. By the end of the HBA period there had been an additional 26, bringing the county total to 42. Of these, 16 were recorded during 2007–12, with seven in 2008 and five in 2010 the two highest totals ever seen in the county. In 2008, all seven occurred as a result of gale-force south-westerlies during the first week of October. Only one bird was recorded in spring during the HBA breeding survey. This was a summer-plumaged adult which flew east past Hurst Beach on May 10th 2010.

John Jones

Sponsored by Royal Naval Birdwatching Society

Long-tailed Skua, Selsey Bill – *Steve Bassett*

Guillemot

Uria aalge

A scarce but increasing visitor and passage migrant

The population of Guillemots breeding in the UK, based on colony counts, increased by 36% between 1986 and 2012 (*SUKB 2013*) continuing the upward trend reported in the *1988–91 Atlas*.

Although Hampshire lacks suitable cliff habitat for nesting, the same upward trend has been apparent in the number of birds seen off the coast. The annual average for 1950–80 was only eight (maximum 28 in 1966) but, during 1981–1992, had increased to 34 (maximum 56 in 1986) (*BoH*). In the following decade, the average was 56 and included the first three-figure count in 2002. The 201 recorded in that year remains the all-time record and was boosted considerably by the 121 counted in January and February.

The ten years from 2003 to 2012, which include the HBA period, had an average of 85 and included five years when counts of 100 or more were made. Year-to-year fluctuations were evident throughout the period (e.g. 110 in 2004 followed by 53 in 2005) and were often the result of variations in wintering numbers and also, to a lesser extent, the strength of spring passage.

The pattern of occurrence across the county has remained the same throughout. As the HBA winter map shows, wintering Guillemots are most evident at the western and eastern extremities of the Solent, with Hurst Beach/ Milford on Sea and Black Point to Hayling Bay providing the lion's share of records. Elsewhere Guillemots are often recorded after winter storms and, in Southampton Water in particular, these birds may make extended stays. During

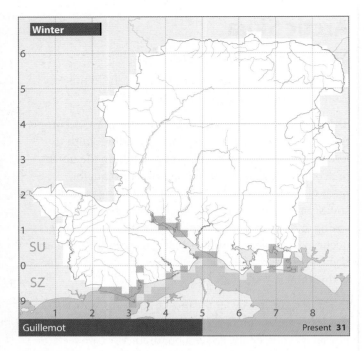

the HBA period the largest concentration of birds in the winter was 39 off Hurst Beach in early 2009 associated with a large fish shoal. Oiled birds accounted for 11 out of 18 birds found dead during the same period.

Spring and autumn passages are variable in response to weather conditions. The Hurst Beach area remains the key site from April through to October and the largest ever spring count was made there on May 14th 2010 when 50 were offshore. Mid-summer records are less-than-annual but during the HBA breeding surveys, 2008 was unusual with an unseasonable eight in July.

Mark Edgeller

Sponsored by Royal Naval Birdwatching Society

Guillemot, Black Point, October 2009 – *Richard Ford*

Razorbill

Alca torda

A scarce but increasing passage migrant and winter visitor

The UK holds around 20% of the world population of Razorbills (JNCC 2014). Most breed in the north and west of Britain, where there are suitable nesting cliffs, with few on the south coast of England. The nearest colony to Hampshire is at Dancing Ledge, Durlston Head in Dorset. At the time of the 1986–91 Atlas, the national population was growing. The upward trend continued through the 1990s but reversed between 2003 and 2010, before resuming again. Consequently, numbers have remained high in the years between the two county atlases. This, coupled with improved observer coverage, has resulted in a major increase in sightings off the Hampshire coast. The average numbers of birds recorded annually over successive time periods are given in *Table 22*.

Most are seen on passage, particularly in autumn, although the highest count during the HBA period was in spring when a record 50 were off Hurst on May 14th 2010. This more than doubled the previous high day-count of 24 at Hayling Bay/ Chichester Harbour in September 2003. High numbers can also occur in the winter, presumably dependent on weather and feeding conditions. During the HBA, 2011 was an exceptional year with 61 seen in January and February.

As can be seen from the accompanying HBA map, in winter Razorbills favour three distinct areas along the

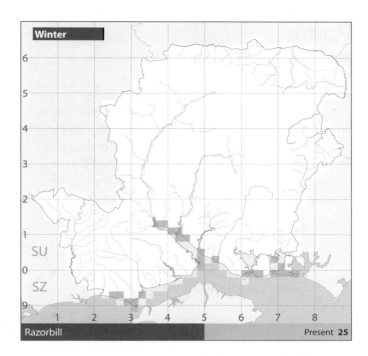

Hampshire coast. Not surprisingly, the two ends of the Solent with access to the open sea are the most reliable with Hurst/Milford on Sea providing the highest number of records in most years. Birds are also seen in winter in Southampton Water, usually following stormy weather or as a result of sickness or injury. During the HBA period only 11 dead birds were reported of which six were oiled.

Mark Edgeller

Sponsored by Royal Naval Birdwatching Society

Period	1950–1980	1981–1992	1993–2002	2003–2011
Average annual count	9	25	35	82
Maximum count/year	29/1957	38/1981	117/2002	167/2011

Table 22 – Razorbill: numbers seen in successive time periods off the Hampshire coast.

Razorbill, Black Point, December 2011 – *Richard Ford*

Puffin

Fratercula arctica

A rare visitor

Puffins are scarce on the English south coast, with only a few pairs continuing to breed in Dorset. They winter at sea so the most likely times to encounter them in Hampshire are in spring or autumn when they are returning to, or dispersing from, their breeding sites. Only six were recorded during the HBA survey periods:

2009: Two off Hurst Beach, April 30th.
2011: Three off Hurst Beach, April 19th.
One found exhausted at the Royal Hampshire County Hospital, Winchester, November 30th. This bird was taken into care but did not survive.

Mark Edgeller

Sponsored by Brian Leach

Puffin, Spitsbergen – *Gordon Small*

Little Auk

Alle alle

A very scarce winter visitor, usually after storms

This species breeds on Arctic islands and winters in the north Atlantic as far south as the UK. It is scarce on the English south coast, usually occurring only after strong northerly gales. In Hampshire, there were sightings in every year from 1992 to 2007, the first of the HBA period and an above average year. Eight were recorded including a single bird picked up alive in Lower Froyle on November 12th. Like the majority of 'wrecked' auks it failed to survive (see also Puffin). Through the remaining four HBA winters, the only other sightings were in 2009 when three were recorded. With exception of the one inland record, the rest were scattered along the Solent, but seen most frequently in the Hurst area, and all fell in the period November 11th to December 9th.

Mark Edgeller

Sponsored by Royal Naval Birdwatching Society

Little Auk, Pennington, December 2009 – *Simon Vale*

Black Guillemot

Cepphus grille

A very rare vagrant

A summer-plumaged bird was seen off Hurst Beach on May 12th 2010. This was only the third record for Hampshire, the previous one being from the same site and just a day earlier on May 11th 1989.

John Eyre

Black Guillemot, Scotland – *Martin Bennett*

Whiskered Tern

Chlidonias hybrida

A rare passage migrant

In the Western Palearctic, Whiskered Terns breed across southern Europe and western Asia. The nearest breeding populations are in central and western France. European birds winter in Africa and occur occasionally in the UK as overshooting spring migrants. It is rare in Hampshire with four, all in April and May, recorded during the HBA period:

2008:   One, east past Hurst Beach and Oxey Marsh, May 6th.
2009:   Two, Testwood Lakes, May 4th.
2011:   One, Stokes Bay, April 14th.

These brought the county total to eleven by the end of 2012.

Mark Edgeller

Whiskered Tern, France – *Andy Swash*

Black Tern

Chlidonias niger

A scarce passage migrant

At the time of the 1986–91 Atlas, Black Tern was considered a moderately common passage migrant in Hampshire with spring movements peaking in early May and averaging 99 birds annually. This was followed by a smaller autumn passage.

It is now regarded as a scarce passage migrant although wide variation between years makes identification of trends uncertain. During the HBA period, spring passage averaged 71 birds with only 13 in 2010 but at least 198 in 2011 including the earliest ever at Lower Test Marshes on April 10th. As with a number of other seabirds in spring, these fluctuations are the result of differences in weather patterns, south-easterly winds with precipitation producing the best up-channel passage through the Solent. Autumn passage was also strong in 2011 with 111 birds recorded between July and October including a record site-count of 49 at Ibsley Water on September 24th.

Mark Edgeller

Black Tern, Blashford Lakes, September 2008 – *Martin Bennett*

Little Tern

Sternula albifrons

A moderately common but declining summer visitor and passage migrant

A national population of 1,927 apparently occupied nests was counted for the Seabird 2000 Survey. There was a general decline in the population after the late 1980s but since 2005 a partial recovery has been noted nationally (JNCC 2014). The fall in numbers coincided with low productivity, which was likely to have contributed to the fall in population as rates of recruitment to the breeding population declined. Human disturbance was the main reason for the poor productivity but predation of eggs and chicks, poor weather and food shortages all played their part.

In Hampshire, breeding has been recorded since the 1930s with numbers peaking at 256 pairs in 1988 during the first Hampshire Atlas. At that time there were three main colonies in the county, at Lymington/Hurst, Beaulieu Estuary and Langstone Harbour. The colony at Beaulieu Estuary declined and disappeared during the 1990s leaving, by the time of the HBA, the protected areas and nature reserves of Lymington/Hurst in the western Solent and Langstone Harbour in the east as the only extant breeding colonies. At both sites there have been significant decreases since the 1986–91 Atlas. During the HBA this decline accelerated (contrary to the national situation) and the number of pairs more than halved over the five breeding seasons 2008–2012 (see *Table 23*).

The number of fledged young was generally very low during this period. Since both sites are protected, human disturbance is not likely to be the problem it is nationally; instead predation and adverse weather at key periods of the breeding cycle appear to be limiting productivity. The low

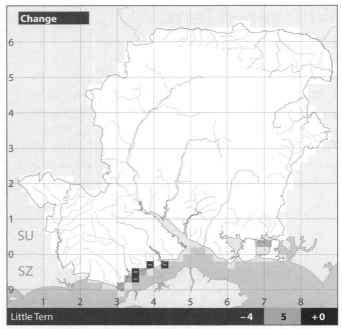

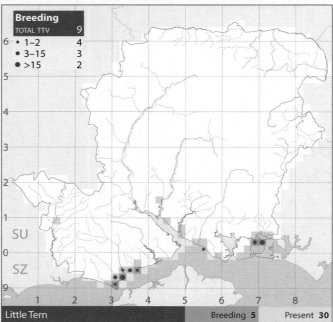

Little Tern, Hayling Oysterbeds, May 2007 – *Jason Crook*

Year	2008	2009	2010	2011	2012
Langstone Harbour	47/0	45/5	61/47	47/1	40/0
Lymington/Hurst	43/1	30	28/16	4	4
Total number of pairs	90	75	89	51	44

Table 23 – Little Tern: number of pairs/fledged young (where counts available).

breeding productivity was reversed briefly in 2010 when at least 63 young were raised. In Langstone Harbour this success was attributed to the absence of corvid and Fox predation, no damaging surge tides and an adequate food supply.

This is an opportunistic species; in the past breeding has been confirmed in Portsmouth Harbour in 1971 and suspected on the Hamble Estuary in four years between 1982 and 1991 but, despite widespread coastal records each year, there has been no further evidence of breeding away from protected areas.

Little Terns will continue to face a range of issues and if the recent rate of decline continues there is a real risk that this charismatic seabird will become extinct as a breeding species in Hampshire. Measures to prevent that happening are already being taken but further steps may be necessary to halt and reverse the downward trend.

Outside the breeding season, the Little Tern occurs as a passage migrant. Total numbers recorded in spring, usually passing east through the Solent, have declined from an average of 239 during 1971–92 (*BoH*) to 181 during the HBA period. The declining local breeding population has also resulted in lower numbers being seen in late summer/ early autumn. During the HBA period, the maximum count was 140 adults at Black Point, Hayling Island, on July 13th 2008. Numbers fell subsequently but, by August 15th, the flock held 46 birds including 16 juveniles, indicative of the passage of birds fledged outside Hampshire.

Mark Edgeller

Sponsored by Michael Creighton

Little Tern, Keyhaven, May 2010 – *Simon Ingram*

Sandwich Tern

Sterna sandvicensis

A moderately common summer visitor and passage migrant with a small number now wintering

Sandwich Terns breed in scattered colonies around the British coast, their locations dependent on the availability of suitable nesting habitat. This species exhibits the most erratic population trends and distribution of any breeding seabird in the UK. The national population was approximately 12,500 apparently occupied nests as measured by the Seabird 2000 survey, but fluctuations occur from year to year because of large variations in the proportion of mature birds attempting to breed and mass movements between colonies (JNCC 2014).

These variations are evident in the Hampshire population. First recorded breeding in the county in 1954 at Hurst/ Lymington, colonisation then occurred at the Beaulieu Estuary in 1959 and Langstone Harbour in 1983. Beaulieu Estuary was the most favoured site throughout the 1980s in terms of regularity of use and numbers of pairs but the colony was last occupied in 2004 when 96 pairs failed to raise any young due to Fox predation and nests being flooded by heavy rain and high tides.

Colonies are still present in Langstone Harbour and the Hurst/Lymington area. The number of breeding pairs peaked at 428 in 2006 but was much lower during the five HBA breeding seasons with just 154 in 2012, the lowest since 1971 (see *Table 24*).

The number of young fledged was variable during the HBA period with continuing predation by Foxes, gulls and corvids together with poor weather identified as key factors reducing productivity. In 2010, when there was little evidence of any of these hazards, the resulting number of fledged young was high (see also Little Tern).

Congregations of adults away from known breeding sites, for example 43 at Langdown on June 25th 2009, have led to speculation that there may be an undiscovered colony

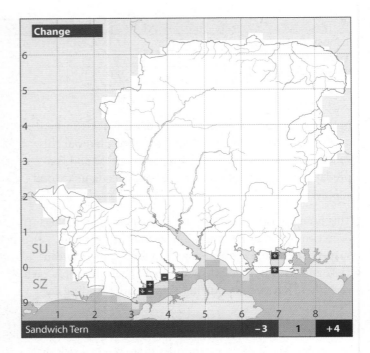

along an inaccessible part of the coast. Unfortunately no firm evidence for this was obtained during the HBA period and these may simply be failed breeders or non-breeding birds.

Inland records are less than annual, occurring occasionally during spring passage. During the HBA period birds were seen at Ibsley Water in 2010 and 2012 and at Fleet Pond in 2010 and 2011. All records were in April.

Although the wintering range of this species extends as far south as South Africa, small but increasing numbers are recorded in Hampshire during the winter months (see *Table 25*). The accompanying winter map shows records at Hurst, Southampton Water and the eastern harbours during the HBA period with the latter site producing the highest numbers. The count of at least 25 in late 2010 occurred immediately after a summer when good numbers of fledged young were produced in the county, although this may have been a coincidence.

Mark Edgeller

Sponsored by Peter Milinets-Raby

Year	2008	2009	2010	2011	2012
Langstone Harbour	130/32	153/21	205/112	181/11	46/0
Hurst/Lymington	67/28	67	60+	96	106/2
Total number of pairs	197/60	220	265	277	154/2

Table 24 – Sandwich Tern: number of pairs/fledged young (where counts available).

Winter	2007/08	2008/09	2009/10	2010/11	2011/12
Birds	2	9	14	25–30	17

Table 25 – Sandwich Tern: numbers recorded during the HBA winters.

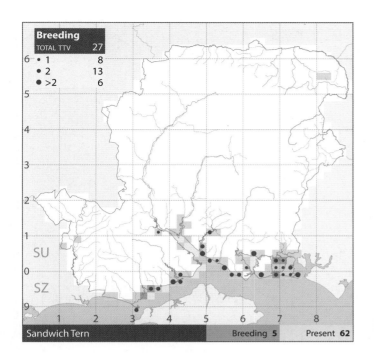

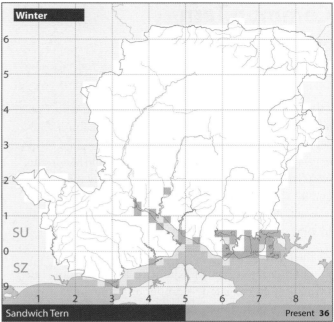

Sandwich Tern, Hayling Oysterbeds, August 2011 – *Richard Ford*

Common Tern

Sterna hirundo

A moderately common summer visitor and common passage migrant

Common Tern is the best known British tern with 11,800 apparently occupied nests counted in the Seabird 2002 survey (*APEP3*). Breeding in Hampshire was first recorded in 1948 and within a decade was well established in the western Solent, with 78 pairs in the Hurst/Lymington area and 48 at Needs Ore on the Beaulieu Estuary in 1957. The first inland breeding was recorded at Blashford Lakes in 1967.

As the HBA breeding map shows, it continues as a predominantly coastal breeder with colonies from Hurst/Lymington to Langstone Harbour and confirmed breeding at only two inland sites, Blashford Lakes and Fleet Pond. During the HBA period the total number of pairs varied little from the average of 408 during the 2008–11 breeding seasons but fell sharply in 2012. The total of 243 pairs in 2012 was the lowest since 211 in 2000 (*Table 26*).

At the Hayling Oysterbeds (West Hayling Local Nature Reserve) numbers have increased significantly in the decade since the colony was established in 2002. The relatively high productivity here (e.g. almost one young per pair in 2010) is partly a result of the implementation of conservation measures. These include shingle recharge, vegetation control and a rat eradication programme. Other coastal colonies have had mixed fortunes in the period between the two atlases. Poor weather and predation by gulls have been cited as the main factors limiting fledging (e.g. in 2011 and 2012).

At Blashford Lakes productivity was particularly high with 2·7 young per pair in 2010 and averaging 2·3 over the 2009–12 period. The successes have been attributed to the mesh-sided rafts with chick shelters to deter predators as well as the plentiful food supply.

The breeding season map also includes a wide scatter of records which are likely to be passage birds, non-breeders and wanderers from nearby colonies.

The most significant changes between atlases, as shown on the change map, were the collapse of the colony at Needs Ore and the establishment of two new ones, at Hayling Oysterbeds and at a second inland site, Fleet Pond. Since the former site is in the same tetrad as the Langstone Harbour colony, it does not appear as a gain on the HBA map. In 1986 numbers at Needs Ore peaked at 375 pairs but had decreased to 60 pairs, all of which failed, in 2004. Breeding has not been recorded since. The increase at other colonies can, in part, be explained by the movement of birds away from here. Numbers at Fleet Pond may increase further due to the recent creation of a number of artificial islands and the presence of several other colonies nearby

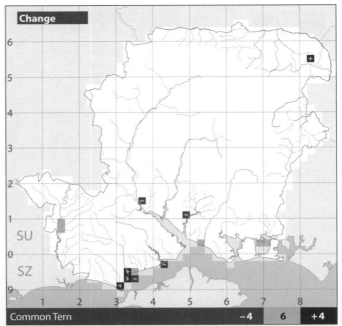

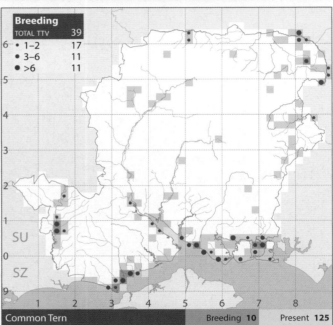

in neighbouring counties, although management of the habitat on the islands will be critical.

Common Terns have occasionally bred elsewhere in the county including two pairs at Eling Great Marsh in 1986 and single pairs at Hamble Country Park in 1986–88. Since these records coincided with the 1986–91 Atlas, the sites show as losses on the HBA change map.

Large post-breeding flocks build up at some coastal sites from late July with the nocturnal roost in Langstone Harbour regularly reaching four figures in August. These gatherings, which contain both local and migrant birds, decline rapidly in September. Small numbers continue to be seen through October and occasionally in November which account for the few HBA winter records.

Mark Edgeller

Sponsored by Jenny Jones

Year	2008	2009	2010	2011	2012
West Hayling LNR	41/18	59/47	86/84	135/27	18/23
Langstone Harbour Islands	108/11	89/8	81/7	57/0	74/23
Titchfield Haven	9	14	21	24	25/13
Hurst/Lymington	223	253	209	145	95
Blashford Lakes	15	17/30	17/46	18/42	22/50
Fleet Pond	1/1	2/3	2/3	3/2	9/0
Total number of pairs	397	434	416	383	243

Table 26 – Common Tern: number of pairs/fledged young (where counts available).

Common Tern, Blashford Lakes, August 2011 – *Andrew Madgwick*

Roseate Tern

Sterna dougallii

A very scarce passage migrant which occasionally breeds

Roseate Tern is a rare and declining breeding species in the British Isles with the vast majority of pairs found at just three colonies in Northumberland, Dublin and Wexford. European birds migrate to West Africa and ringing recoveries suggest that the coast off Ghana is the principle wintering area (*Migration Atlas*).

The first record of a pair of Roseate Terns nesting in Hampshire was in 1957 with a further 57 pairs recorded at three sites up to 2006. Of these, 20 laid eggs whilst the rest were present in colonies of other terns with no evidence of breeding. The only definite proof of successful fledging came in 1998 when a single pair raised one young at one site and two flying juveniles were seen at another although it is not known whether the latter were reared locally.

There was no evidence of breeding during the HBA and the only records of birds in tern colonies were singles in May to July 2008 and June to August 2012.

During the HBA period, excluding 2008, between five and fourteen were recorded annually on spring passage through the Solent with most sightings in the first half of May. Exceptionally, 27 were seen in 2008 including a record day count of 16 past Stokes Bay on April 29th. Two birds noted at Hurst Beach and Stokes Bay on April 17th 2011 were the earliest ever recorded in the county.

The post-breeding period is characterised by sightings at Hill Head/Titchfield Haven and birds flying into Langstone Harbour to roost with occasional records from elsewhere along the coast. Numbers during the HBA were typically

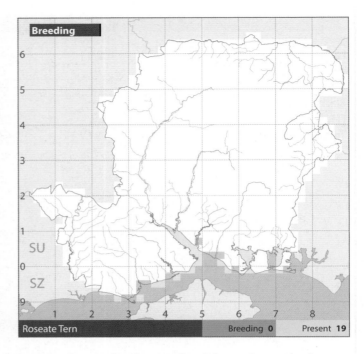

Roseate Tern   Breeding 0   Present 19

between four and eight, mostly adults, with a peak of ten in 2011.

Nationally there was a 50% decline in breeding numbers between 1988 and 2011 and Seabird 2000 recorded 52 pairs in Great Britain and 738 in Ireland. Hunting in the wintering grounds is thought to be the main cause of this large decrease (Cabot 1996). This decline, along with local problems such as flooding, disturbance and predation, as well as remoteness from the main colonies make it unlikely that Roseate Tern will ever be anything other than a scarce and irregular breeder in Hampshire.

Mark Edgeller

Sponsored by John Norton

Roseate Tern, Titchfield, August 2007 – *Nigel Jones*

Arctic Tern

Sterna paradisaea
A scarce passage migrant

This, the most numerous of the British breeding terns, is not a common bird in Hampshire. The pattern of occurrence has changed little between atlases. Peak spring passage is recorded between mid-April and late May with few seen between June and early August. There is a lighter passage, mainly of juveniles, from late August to mid-October, with a handful of records through to early November.

The majority of records during the HBA period came from the well-watched coastal spots of Hurst Beach, Stokes Bay/ Hill Head and Sandy Point. There was also a scatter of records from inland waters across the county, including Ibsley Water, Rooksbury Mill and Alresford, Fleet and Tundry Ponds.

Numbers vary from year to year, probably determined by weather patterns during migration periods. The record count of 277 during spring migration occurred in 2006 and was followed during the HBA period with annual totals ranging from 41 to 204. The spring of 2008 was exceptional with more birds seen inland than on the coast. Numbers moving at Fleet Pond on April 23rd probably exceeded 100 and included a group of 77, the largest flock yet recorded in the county. 2012 was also a good year with 171 moving east along the coast between April 14th and May 1st.

The only other significant event during the HBA period was the autumn passage in 2011 when 91 birds were noted, a record count which included 13 inland.

Mark Edgeller

Sponsored by Royal Naval Birdwatching Society

Arctic Tern, Sturt Pond, September 2011 – *Martin Bennett* (above); Sturt Pond, September 2011 – *Linda Fuller* (below)

Kittiwake

Rissa tridactyla

A passage migrant and winter visitor

The Kittiwake is one of the world's most abundant seabirds and Britain's most numerous breeding gull, although numbers have declined in recent years. It nests colonially on cliffs around the British coast with by far the largest numbers in Scotland and north-east England. In winter the birds desert their colonies to spend the time at sea, mostly out of sight of land unless driven inshore by gales.

It is usually scarce in Hampshire with the nearest breeding populations in Dorset and East Sussex where appropriate cliff nesting habitat exists. In spring between mid-March and early June there is evidence of eastward passage along the Hampshire coast, but the numbers counted during this period usually total less than a hundred, dependent on weather conditions. An exceptional count was made on the afternoon of April 8th 2005 when 829 moved west past Hurst Castle after a period of stormy weather but, during the HBA period, the highest spring count was 60 off Hurst on May 19th 2012.

Few are seen during summer and there is no marked autumn passage but numbers generally increase in winter with influxes occurring after gales. High counts during the HBA winter recording period involved a flock of 152 west at Hurst on November 11th 2007 and 113 heading north-eastwards at Sandy Point on November 8th 2010. The latter count followed strong south-westerly winds.

Inland records are rare. During the HBA period individuals were recorded at Ibsley Water (on three occasions), Testwood Lakes, Winchester Sewage Farm and Fleet Pond. Given the intermittent occurrence of this species and variable levels of sea-watching, trends over time are difficult to identify but overall its status in the county seems to be much the same now as at the time of the first national Winter Atlas in 1981–84.

John Jones

Sponsored by Royal Naval Birdwatching Society

Kittiwake, Titchfield Haven, March 2014 – *Tom Bickerton*

Little Gull

Hydrocoloeus minutus

A scarce visitor recorded in all months but most numerous in spring and autumn

The Little Gull is most frequently recorded in Hampshire on passage between its breeding grounds around the Baltic and north-west Russia and wintering grounds in the Atlantic, south to North Africa. It does not breed in Britain although it has attempted to do so and its range has expanded westwards into Scandinavia and the Netherlands. This spread, together with the growth in bird-watching activity, may explain the upward trend in the numbers seen in Hampshire prior to the 1986–91 Atlas (*BoH*) although its status has changed relatively little since then.

During the HBA it was recorded mainly between late March and late May while on eastward migration through the Solent. Fewer were seen in autumn on return passage. The numbers logged in spring varied widely from year to year ranging from 37 in 2009 to 193 in 2011. Most were recorded from coastal watch-points, particularly at the western end of the Solent, although smaller numbers of off-passage birds occurred at both coastal and inland sites. The latter were usually at large water bodies such as Ibsley Water, Fleet Pond and Alresford Pond.

Usually few are seen either in summer or winter although exceptional numbers can occur along the coast following gales. During the HBA winter period, 103 were recorded heading westwards at Hurst Castle on November 30th 2009. Some Little Gulls over-winter in the seas around the British Isles and therefore find their way to the British coastline during strong on-shore winds.

John Jones

Little Gull, Pennington Marsh, May 2012 – *Steve Bassett*

Little Gull, Pennington Marsh, May 2012 – *Gordon Small*

Laughing Gull

Larus atricilla

A very rare vagrant

A second-summer Laughing Gull was photographed at Testwood Lakes on May 24th 2009. This was only the second occurrence of this very rare American vagrant in Hampshire following the first in the Gosport area from November 5th to December 11th 2005.

John Jones

Laughing Gull, Testwood Lakes, May 2009 – *Ian Pibworth*

Black-headed Gull
Chroicocephalus ridibundus
A numerous resident, passage migrant and winter visitor

The Black-headed Gull breeds across northern Europe from where most of Britain's overwintering population of around 2·2 million individuals migrate; in winter it is the most numerous gull present in the country. By contrast the British breeding population derived from the last national seabird census in 1998–2002 is much lower at around 130,000 pairs (*APEP3*).

Black-headed Gulls nest colonially with most colonies in Hampshire located on coastal saltmarsh or islands. Although they breed from Dorset to Kent, Hampshire has the highest breeding population on the English south coast and holds a significant proportion of the national breeding population. Total breeding pairs have varied from year to year falling to as low as 11,000 in 2005. The highest number breeding during the HBA period was 14,458 pairs in 2010, similar to numbers in 1991 at the time of the previous atlas. The most significant change since then has been in the distribution of colonies across the county. *Table 27* shows where the colonies were in 1991 and 2010.

At the time of the 1986–91 Atlas there were only two significant colonies, both in the west Solent and both having their origins in the early 20th century. The one at Pylewell-Keyhaven was relatively stable but the Needs Ore colony was in decline, its nesting population having fallen from around 21,000 pairs in the early 1970s. In 2005, 328 pairs nested there but they did not do so again until 2012, when 350 pairs returned only for all their nests to be lost to tidal flooding. The Needs Ore colony was largely replaced by the colonisation of new sites in the east Solent. In 1991 there was already a small colony at Langstone Harbour which subsequently grew as Needs Ore declined. Other small colonies were established at Titchfield Haven and West Hayling and in 2007 Black-headed Gulls started nesting at Hook-with-Warsash at the mouth of the River Hamble and at the inland site of Ibsley Water in the Avon Valley. The Hook-with-Warsash colony has so far not prospered while numbers at Ibsley have grown annually. In 2012 five pairs nested on newly-created islands at Fleet Pond in the north of the county but no young survived.

Breeding success is often compromised by the tidal flooding of nests and by disturbance and predation by Foxes and avian predators. Langstone Harbour has been particularly vulnerable to both of these pressures and in some years there have been high losses of young. The wet summer of 2012 resulted in particularly low breeding success as storm-driven high tides washed out the majority of nests at Pylewell–Keyhaven and Langstone/West Hayling. Tidal flooding was one of the problems faced by the Needs Ore colony and, with further sea level rise inevitable, it is likely to become a more serious problem for coastal colonies in the future.

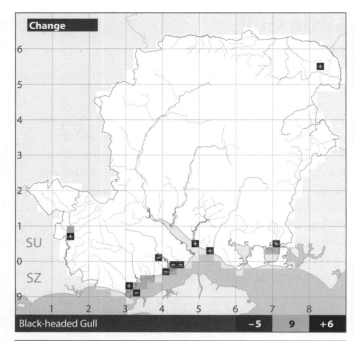

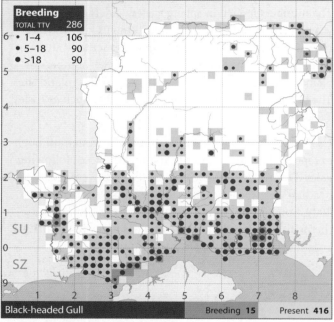

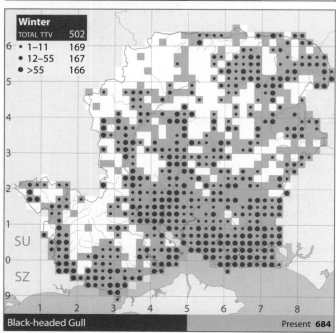

The coastal locations of breeding colonies tends to concentrate the summer distribution to the southern half of the county but during the winter months they are more widely distributed, with a significant presence in the north. The largest gatherings occur at roost sites and, as at the time of the 1986–91 Atlas, the biggest of these are to be found in Southampton Water, Portsmouth Harbour and Langstone Harbour. More recently a large inland roost has also developed at Ibsley Water. Complete roost counts are rarely made and are not available for the HBA period although maximum counts for Ibsley Water exceeded 6,000 at this time. For the county as a whole the most recent roost count was in January 2004 as part of the national winter gull survey, when 40,400 individuals were counted (Shillitoe 2007). This compares with 46,443 counted in January 1993 soon after the previous atlas.

During the day Black-headed Gulls range widely over the county in search of food. Large numbers can often be seen on farmland, particularly at pig farms or, in late summer, hawking for flying ants. Twenty years ago, council rubbish tips were a focus for large gatherings but, with virtually

First year of nesting	Black-headed Gull nesting colonies	Pairs	
		1991	2010
1905	Pylewell-Keyhaven	6,000	7,738
1909	Needs Ore Beaulieu Estuary	8,726	0
1978	Langstone Harbour	6	5,023
2002	Titchfield Haven	0	1,055
2003	West Hayling	0	461
2007	Hook-with-Warsash	0	1
2007	Ibsley Water	0	180
Total		14,732	14,458

Table 27 – Black headed Gull colonies in Hampshire.

all of them now closed, this source of food is no longer available. During the HBA period there were numerous records of winter aggregations of 1,000–2,000 birds at coastal locations as well as inland on farmland. While birds from the east Solent roosts move inland over the chalk downs to feed, many of those in the Avon Valley are from Christchurch Harbour.

John Jones

Sponsored by Sarah Harvey

Black-headed Gull,
Hayling Island, March 2006
– Richard Ford

Mediterranean Gull

Larus melanocephalus

A moderately common and increasing summer visitor and passage migrant; scarce in winter

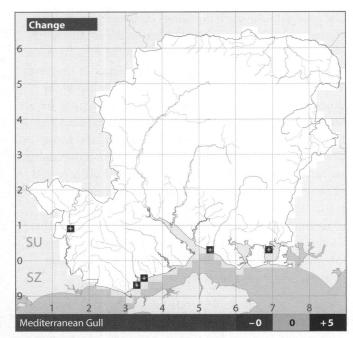

The majority of the world population of Mediterranean Gulls breeds around the Black Sea and it was not until the middle of the 20th century that the species' range expanded across Western Europe. It first bred in Hampshire at Needs Ore in 1968, this being the first breeding record for Britain. Since then it has spread more widely. In 2010 the national breeding population was around 1,000 pairs, with the majority in Hampshire, Sussex and Kent (*RBBP* 2012). Increasing numbers spend the winter in Britain with 1,800 individuals being estimated from data available during the period 2004–2009 (*APEP3*).

The Hampshire breeding population has increased significantly since the 1986–91 Atlas. At that time the species was described in *BoH* as a scarce but regular visitor, which occasionally bred. Single pairs nested in some years, usually unsuccessfully, at the then extant Black-headed Gull colony at Needs Ore. Breeding continued intermittently there until 2005, but in 1998 14 pairs nested on the RSPB islands in Langstone Harbour. By the time of the HBA, this colony had grown to become the largest in the country, with 498 pairs nesting in 2011, although numbers fell to only 58 pairs in 2012 when weather conditions were particularly unfavourable. As the accompanying maps show, other Hampshire breeding sites during the HBA period, although all with far fewer nesting pairs than at Langstone Harbour, were along the west Solent off Lymington, at Titchfield Haven and at Ibsley Water. Breeding at Ibsley Water first occurred in 2011, the first inland nesting of Mediterranean Gull in Hampshire. The total Hampshire breeding population in 2011 amounted to 520 pairs, which was about half of the national total.

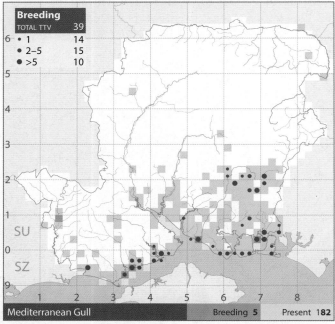

Nesting habitat is similar to that of Black-headed Gulls, the two species sometimes nesting in mixed colonies. Like Black-headed Gull and some tern colonies they are vulnerable to tidal flooding and predation resulting in low breeding success in some years. For instance in 2011 the 498 pairs that nested at Langstone Harbour failed to produce any young due to a combination of tidal flooding and Fox predation. By contrast the 400 pairs that nested in 2010 managed to raise 218 young.

In winter the distribution is mainly coastal with few inland sightings. Numbers tend to be low until February when they start to build up. Peak annual counts occur in the west Solent at this time of year and are typically in the 200–300 range, though the highest during the HBA period was over 800 including a record site count of 585 at Badminston Gravel Pit (near Fawley) on April 4th 2009. In summer the distribution is again mainly coastal but with

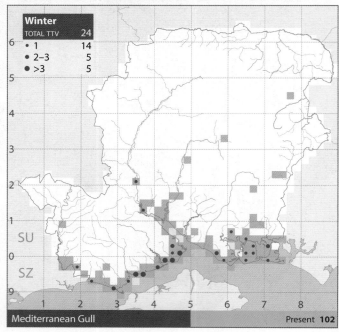

more incursions inland than during the winter period. The highest inland numbers occur on the South Downs due to feeding movements by birds nesting at Langstone Harbour. During the HBA period the highest aggregations found over the downs were in early April and after mid-June. There are usually large post-breeding gatherings at the coast, the highest of these during 2007–12 being 626 near Titchfield Haven on September 19th 2010. Numbers then gradually decline into winter.

Sightings of 74 colour-ringed birds at Badminston Gravel Pit, mainly in 2009, identified their origins as 40 ringed in Belgium, 15 in France, 11 in Germany, three in Hungary, four in Poland and one in Britain, confirming the continuing westward spread of birds from the Continent. As expected given the increased national presence of this species over the last twenty years it was found to be more prevalent in Hampshire during the HBA survey. At the time of the 1986–91 Atlas about 50 were recorded each year and maximum numbers seen together at any one time were in single figures. At that time the highest numbers were seen in Langstone Harbour with occasional sightings elsewhere along the coast. Gatherings of over a hundred are now frequent and can occur anywhere along the Hampshire coastline.

John Jones

Sponsored by Royal Naval Birdwatching Society

Mediterranean Gull, (with Black-headed Gull (left)) Sturt Pond, September 2011 – *Martin Bennett*

Mediterranean Gulls (with Sandwich Terns), Normandy Marsh, May 2012 – *Marcus Ward*

Common Gull

Larus canus

A common winter visitor and passage migrant; small numbers summer and one or two pairs attempt breeding annually

The Common Gull breeds across northern Eurasia and north-west North America where it is known as the Mew Gull. Post-breeding, European birds migrate westwards or south-westwards reaching as far south as the Atlantic coast of North Africa but with significant numbers over-wintering in Britain. More than 90% of the British breeding population, which numbers around 48,000 pairs, nests in Scotland and most of these over-winter in Britain and Ireland. The estimated over-wintering population in Britain totals about 700,000 individuals (*APEP3*) the majority of which are immigrants from the Continental breeding population.

Nationally, there are few breeding sites in southern England (*Bird Atlas 2007–11*); one of these is in the west Solent. The first evidence of breeding there was in 1991 when two pairs nested, albeit unsuccessfully, in Black-headed Gull colonies. Breeding was attempted again the following year and has been, intermittently, in the years since, but the outcomes were either unknown or failures. During the HBA period a pair nested in 2008 and pairs were present in 2009, 2010 and 2012 but there was no evidence of successful breeding. The species cannot therefore be considered an established breeder. Although the HBA maps show widespread presence during the breeding season, most records refer to migrants and few actually spend the summer in the county.

The build-up of the over-wintering population begins around mid-July as birds dispersing from their breeding grounds start to arrive in the county. By mid-winter they are common, remaining so until their early April departure. At the time of the 1986–91 Atlas there had already been a marked decline in the size of the over-wintering population, with counts at the principal roost sites of Langstone and Portsmouth Harbours much below their 1950s levels when up to 10,000 regularly roosted in Langstone Harbour. The evidence of recent years is that the decline has continued, with lower roost counts in the two harbours and smaller feeding flocks inland. The most recent total count for Hampshire, which was made in January 2004 during the 2003–05 national winter gull survey, was 2,090, a significant decline from the total of 5,061 during the previous survey in January 1993 (Shillitoe 2007). At the time of the 1986–91 Atlas, flocks of 500 or more were widespread on the South Downs. In recent years feeding flocks of this size have become much less frequent.

The HBA survey confirmed the traditional winter pattern of a greater prevalence in the east of the county both in terms of distribution and abundance. Though present along the west Solent, it occurs in much lower numbers although several hundred can roost inland at Ibsley Water, in the

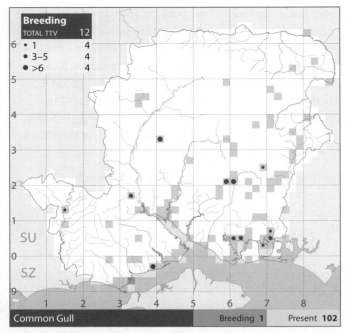

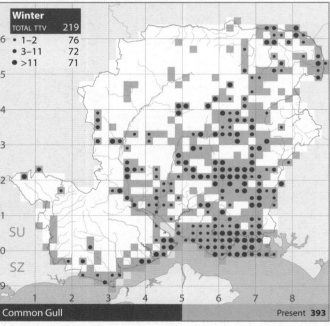

far west of the county. This occurs mainly during times of extremely cold weather and the lack of TTV counts for the Avon Valley demonstrates that it is generally uncommon here. Another inland site, Alresford Pond in the east of the county, also attracts large numbers with the highest count during the 2007–12 period of 500 on October 14th 2007. This site tends to be used by gulls feeding in the area during the day prior to flying to the coast to roost.

In spring Common Gulls that have over-wintered elsewhere can often be seen moving north across the county or eastwards along the Solent heading back towards their breeding grounds. Birds grounded during these movements are responsible for most of the records shown on the HBA breeding map.

John Jones

Sponsored by Alison Hogan

Common Gull, Sturt Pond, March 2014 – *Steve Bassett*

Ring-billed Gull

Larus delawarensis

A very scarce visitor

This North American visitor was first identified in Britain in 1973. It occurred in Hampshire for the first time in 1977 and has been seen annually since 1981 except in 1991. During the HBA period, many records referred to the same individual which was originally seen as an adult at Walpole Park, Gosport in November 2003 and returned to the same location each winter, completing its ninth season by the end of the Atlas in the 2011/12 winter. There were an additional six records during 2007–12:

2009: A second-winter at Ibsley Water on October 11th.
      A first-winter at Ibsley Water on November 6th.

2010: A second-summer at Sopley on September 10th.
      An adult at Ibsley Water on November 7th.

2011: A first-winter at Ibsley Water on January 22nd.
      An adult at Eastoke on September 4th.

These brought the total recorded in the county to 39 by the end of 2012.

John Jones

Sponsored by Ian Calderwood

Ring-billed Gull, Gosport, January 2010 – *Steve Copsey*

Lesser Black-backed Gull
Larus fuscus

A common visitor which occurs in all months; a small number breeds

The British breeding population, all of which are of the subspecies *graellsii,* amounted to around 110,000 pairs at the time of the last full national seabird survey in 1998–2002 (*Seabird 2000*) but the population is thought to have declined since then. Most coastal breeding colonies are in the north and west of Britain with the closest large colonies to Hampshire in the Bristol Channel.

At the time of the 1986–91 Atlas, Lesser Black-backed Gulls did not breed in Hampshire but in 2001 at least four pairs nested successfully on roof-top sites in Southampton and Eastleigh. Since then the Southampton colonies have grown to around 30 pairs while only two pairs were found nesting at Eastleigh during the HBA survey. Single pairs were also found breeding at three sites around Portsmouth, at Lymington/Hurst and at at three sites well inland, one near Andover, one in Aldershot and one at Ibsley Water in the Avon Valley. All nests so far have been on roof-tops except for one or two on islands off Lymington/Hurst, in Langstone Harbour and at Ibsley Water. With their increasing presence in the county there is every prospect that the breeding population will continue to increase. Their arrival as a breeding species was not unexpected given the general increase in breeding range in south-east England; they are now present in most 10 km coastal squares from Dorset through to the Thames Estuary (*Bird Atlas 2007–11*). There is also a large inland breeding presence in neighbouring Wiltshire, which did not exist at the time of the 1986–91 Atlas and may, at least in part, be the result of dispersal from the Bristol Channel colonies.

In the summer they are now more numerous and more widespread in the county than at the time of the previous atlas and have a significant inland presence, particularly around Andover and in the Avon and Test Valleys. They occur in all summer months and while this might be partly associated with their increased regional breeding presence it also reflects spring passage in April and autumn dispersal. The largest aggregations occur after mid-June as birds dispersing from their breeding colonies move into the county. By autumn Hampshire is host to large influxes of birds.

Numbers in the county in autumn and winter have increased significantly since the 1986–91 Atlas with by far the highest numbers occurring between September and November, when birds are attracted to post-harvest autumn cultivation on cereal fields. By the mid-1990s unprecedented numbers began roosting each autumn at Ibsley Water in the Avon Valley and the annual influx continued to grow both there and at Fox Lane Gravel Pit, Eversley. There were record counts at both sites during the 2007–12 period with 10,000,

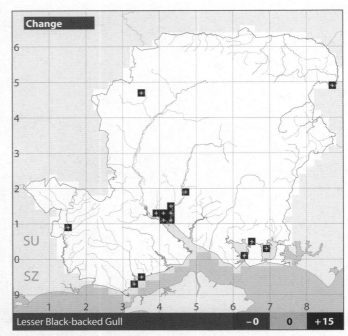

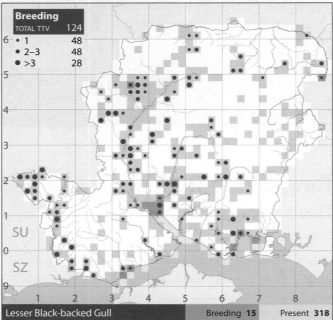

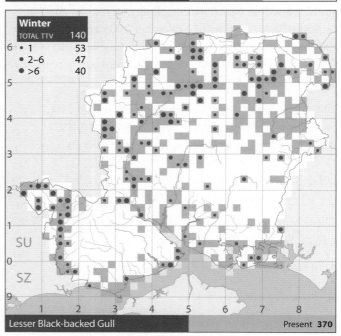

Lesser Black-backed Gull (with Black-headed Gulls), Titchfield, June 2013 – *John Whichall* (above);
Sturt Pond, March 2014 – *Steve Bassett* (below)

a county record, at Ibsley Water in September 2009, and 3,100, a site record, at Fox Lane in both October 2009 and 2011. By the end of November, as the weather turns colder, the majority departs southwards on migration. At the time of the 1986–91 Atlas autumn passage through the county was much less marked with peak annual counts of a few hundreds.

While large numbers of British Lesser Black-backed Gulls migrate to wintering grounds along the Atlantic coasts of France, Iberia and West Africa, the proportion that does so has been falling for several decades as the population has become steadily less migratory. Over-winterers from British colonies are augmented by immigrants from Iceland and northern Europe, leading to an estimated total British wintering population of around 120,000 individuals (*APEP3*). While Hampshire hosts large numbers on passage, the total remaining in the county beyond November is much lower. The majority of those that stay tend to roost at

Ibsley Water. During the 1990s a large roost developed in Southampton Water of birds which fed inland during the day. This was deserted prior to the HBA with the birds most probably switching to Ibsley Water. Numbers in the north-east were much reduced following closure of Bramshill and Wrecclesham rubbish tips although some continue to roost at Eversley. During the HBA winters they were found in more than a third of the county's tetrads and were more widespread in the north and along the Avon Valley than at the coast. This is probably due in large measure to the early winter concentrations at Ibsley and Eversley as well as to visitors from roosts in adjoining counties. Most of the larger flocks are seen in these areas in autumn and early winter with such sightings less frequent from January until the eventual return passage through the county in spring.

John Jones

Sponsored by Mike Wildish

Herring Gull
Larus argentatus

A common winter visitor and passage migrant with a small but increasing breeding population and moderate numbers summering

The majority of this, the most common of the large British gulls, breeds in the north and west of the country. There are relatively small numbers in the south, although they do breed in all counties along the south coast. The national breeding population was declining at the time of the 1986–91 Atlas and the downward trend continued. By the time of Seabird 2000, the nation-wide breeding survey carried out in 1998–2002, the British population amounted to around 130,000 pairs (*APEP3*) but it is known to have declined further since then (JNCC 2014).

In Hampshire, following the first record of a pair nesting at Needs Ore in 1938, small numbers bred intermittently on shingle, saltings and in fields along the coast. By the time of the 1986–91 Atlas, the county's breeding population was about 15 pairs but in 1989 two pairs nested on roofs in Southampton and by 1991, at the end of the Atlas period, breeding was also occurring on the top of tanks and pipe-runs in Fawley Refinery. Since then, the number nesting on buildings has been increasing rapidly and now forms by far the largest part of the total. By the end of the HBA, the county's breeding population had grown to at least 120 pairs, of which 91 were nesting on roofs in Southampton. The breeding range had also increased with nesting in 27 tetrads compared with only seven at the time of the previous atlas. The Southampton population has been surveyed several times in recent years (Jones 2010) and has shown year-on-year growth, which has continued beyond the end of the HBA period. In 2013 the count was 154 pairs, out of a county total of around 180 pairs. The big increase was mainly due to a previously unrecorded population in the eastern docks. The largest concentrations occur on warehouse and factory roofs along the Itchen Estuary and around the docks, with others in the centre of the city. The majority of nest sites outside Southampton are also on man-made structures although a few pairs continue to breed in natural habitat at Lymington/Hurst and Titchfield Haven. The increase in Hampshire is part of a general upward trend in south-east England due, in large part, to the increased prevalence of roof-nesting.

Around 730,000 Herring Gulls over-winter in Britain (*APEP3*). In Hampshire, numbers build up in autumn as birds disperse both from breeding colonies in the UK and the Continent. The winter distribution is heavily biased towards the coast and the main river systems as birds from the coastal roosts tend to move inland along the river valleys to forage. As at the time of the 1986–91 Atlas, the county's main roosts are still in Southampton Water, Langstone Harbour and Portsmouth Harbour, but there

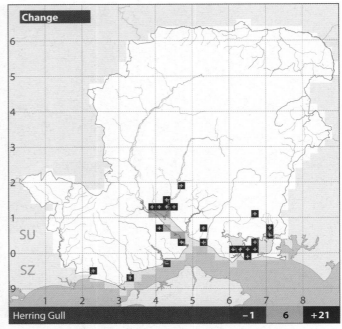

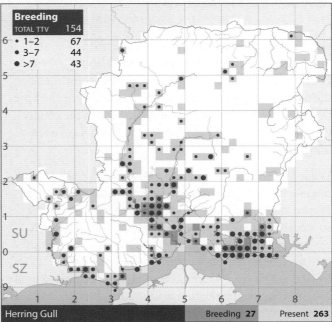

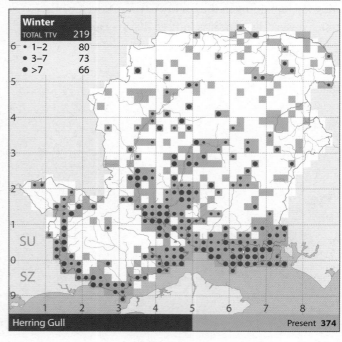

Herring Gull, Blashford Lakes, October 2007 – *Martin Bennett* (above); Hayling Island, February 2009 – *Steve Bassett* (below)

is now an inland roost at Ibsley Water that has developed in the interim. This roost is used by gulls from Dorset and Wiltshire as well as from Hampshire. There have been no recent comprehensive roost counts to give an accurate measure of the total winter population. The last complete winter roost census of January 2004 arrived at a total of 2,023 (Shillitoe 2007). During the HBA period the highest count at a coastal roost site was 1,400 at Eling/Redbridge (Southampton Water) in February 2012 and the highest inland was 1,000 at Ibsley Water in December 2009. At the time of the previous atlas large, sometimes four-figure gatherings, were often found at council rubbish tips some of which were located close to the coast. Since these were closed, such large feeding flocks have occurred less frequently and those found on farmland in more recent times are now typically in the 200 to 300 range. In the north-east, large numbers were at Bramshill Rubbish Tip in the 1990s including a maximum count of 1,500 on January 8th 1997. The maximum count in the area this millenium is 70.

Summer distribution shows a similar pattern to winter but is sparser both at the coast and inland which is consistent with the much lower population.

John Jones

Sponsored by Huw Morgan

Great Black-backed Gull

Larus marinus

A moderately common winter visitor and passage migrant; small but increasing numbers breed

The Great Black-backed Gull is essentially a North Atlantic species, breeding from the north-east coast of North America, through southern Greenland and Iceland to Scandanavia and north-west Russia and encompassing the British Isles. Its European wintering range extends down the coasts as far south as the Bay of Biscay. The majority of the British breeding population of 17,000 pairs (*APEP3*) occurs on the north and west coasts with 85% of the total in Scotland. While many of the British, Icelandic and Greenland birds disperse relatively short distances after breeding, those of Norway and Russia tend to migrate southwards and westwards, many of them arriving in Britain in the autumn. There are an estimated 76,000 individuals over-wintering in Britain (*APEP3*).

Up to the time of the 1986–91 Atlas this species was not a regular breeder in Hampshire although single pairs had nested occasionally at Pennington Marsh and the Beaulieu Estuary. During the Atlas period, breeding occurred in Langstone Harbour and, immediately afterwards in 1992, on a wooden tower off Fawley. In 1995 the county's first roof-nesting pair was found in Southampton Docks. Since then a small but growing breeding population has established itself, which, during the HBA period, reached a total of 17 pairs in 14 tetrads. The roof-top sites in Southampton, with seven pairs, and at Lymington, Calmore, Portsmouth and Fareham, with a pair each, may offer the best prospects for future growth in the breeding population. However, they also nest in small numbers at sites in traditional natural habitat along the west Solent coast around Lymington and the Beaulieu Estuary. The increased breeding presence in Hampshire over the two decades since the previous atlas is part of a general breeding range expansion along the south coast of England. At the time of the previous atlas they were established as breeders along the south-west peninsula as far east as Dorset and the Isle of Wight but with no presence to the east of Hampshire. There are now small numbers that nest along the coast as far as Kent (*Bird Atlas 2007–11*).

Great Black-backed Gulls are most numerous in Hampshire during the winter when migrants from northern Europe and birds dispersing from British colonies are present. However, they have become significantly less common than at the time of the 1986–91 Atlas, when 200–300 could be seen regularly in Portsmouth and Langstone Harbours and large aggregations were often present in Southampton Water. A feature at that time was the presence of large numbers feeding at council refuse tips which have since been closed. The largest gathering ever recorded in the

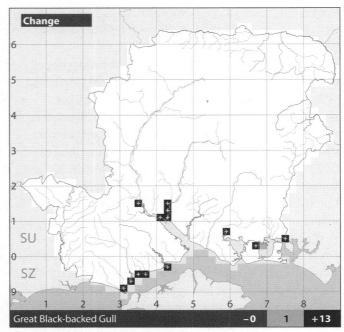

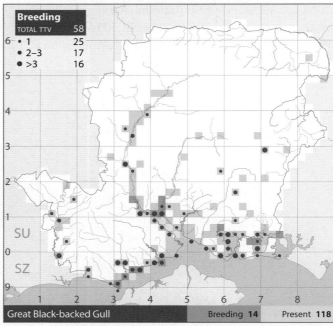

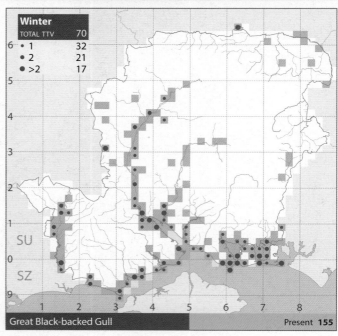

county was 1,329 on January 16th 1999 in Portsmouth Harbour, where the close proximity of the now-closed Paulsgrove refuse tip was a major attraction. During 2007–12 there were few three-figure counts, which suggests a significant decline in autumn and winter numbers. The highest counts during the HBA period were of 200 at East Hayling on December 19th 2008 and 182 at Langstone Harbour on December 13th 2008.

As the HBA map shows, during winter the species is present along the whole of the Hampshire coastline. Inland it occurs in small numbers mainly along the Avon, Itchen and Test Valleys with an erratic presence in the north-east that is presumably due to incursions of birds from roosts in neighbouring counties. It was formerly regular in winter at Bramshill Rubbish Tip, with a maximum count of 75 on

December 30th 1994. Since the tip was closed in the late 1990s, there has been only one double-figure count of 13 at Fleet Pond on January 6th 2002 and in some winters the species is not recorded at all. In summer the distribution is similar but more thinly spread with flocks of non-breeders often seen at the coast. During the HBA breeding season survey, the largest of these was 119 on the RSPB Langstone Harbour Islands on June 5th 2008. Elsewhere notable counts included 101 on the Beaulieu Estuary on May 5th 2008 and 80 at Badminston Common (near Calshot) on July 1st 2010. Inland numbers were far lower with most records, as in winter, coming from the main river valleys.

John Jones

Sponsored by Chris Packham

Great Black-backed Gull, Bunny Meadows, August 2013 – *Mike Crutch*

Yellow-legged Gull
Larus michahellis

Scarce visitor, recorded in all months; has bred in mixed pairings with other large gull species

The Yellow-legged Gull was not recorded in Britain until the middle of the 20th century. Its core breeding range is around the Mediterranean and it was formerly considered to be a race of Herring Gull until, in 2005, it was recognised as a separate species actually more closely related to Lesser Black-backed Gull. In Hampshire, the first was at Langstone Harbour in 1957. It gradually became more numerous but, even by the time of the 1986–91 Atlas, was still scarce. Numbers continued to increase and, although still localised, by the time of the HBA, it was being recorded more widely across the county. It was present in greater numbers in the autumn and winter than at other times of the year probably due to post-breeding dispersal of birds into northern and western Europe.

Until 2012 the highest numbers were concentrated at a few specific sites. At the time of the 1986–91 Atlas most were seen at Eling/Lower Test, where birds started to arrive in July and reached a peak in September. This continued to be the case for several years with a record number of 178 there in September 2007, immediately prior to the start of the HBA. Subsequently numbers at this site declined until, by 2012, they were no higher than at any other location. Yellow-legged Gulls can now be seen throughout the year but in quite low numbers and still slightly more numerous in the autumn and winter. They are seen most frequently along the east Solent, in and around Southampton, at Blashford Lakes and in the north-east particularly at Fleet Pond, Blackbushe and gravel pits around Eversley.

Yellow-legged Gull, Hook Spit, July 2010 – *Bob Marchant*

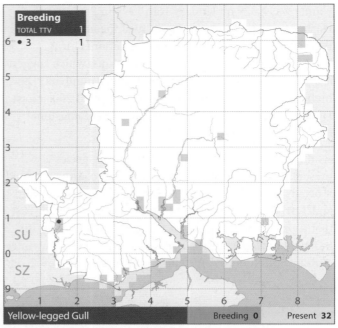

Breeding
TOTAL TTV 1
● 3   1
Yellow-legged Gull   Breeding 0   Present 32

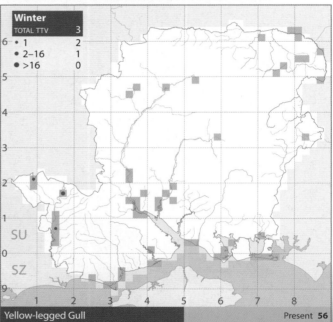

Winter
TOTAL TTV 3
● 1   2
● 2–16   1
● >16   0
Yellow-legged Gull   Present 56

The species first bred in Britain in 1995 but has still not established a stable breeding population. There are only a few breeding records each year, most involving mixed pairings with either Lesser Black-backed or Herring Gulls. So far the only nesting by pure pairs in the country has been in Dorset. In Hampshire the first recorded incidence of breeding was in 2003 when a mixed pairing with a Lesser Black-backed Gull raised three young in Southampton. Since then there has been a small number of other breeding records, all from Southampton on roof-tops or other man-made structures, and all involving mixed pairs, some with Herring Gull. If numbers continue to grow, it is likley that breeding between a pure pair will occur in the near future.

John Jones

Yellow-legged Gull, Middlebere – *Martin Bennett*

Caspian Gull
Larus cachinnans
A very scarce autumn and winter visitor

This species did not feature in the 1986–91 Atlas as it had not been identified in Hampshire, or indeed in Britain, at that time. Also it was then considered to be a race of Herring Gull, not being recognised as a separate species until 2007. Its main breeding range is from the Black Sea to central Asia but in recent times it has spread to Poland and eastern Germany and has become a frequent visitor to north-west Europe. First recorded in Britain in 1995, it occurs mainly as a winter visitor and there have been no records of it breeding here.

Caspian Gull, Ibsley, January 2009 – *Richard Ford* (both images)

It was first recorded in Hampshire in 1997 since when there had been records of 36 individuals to the end of 2012. During the HBA period it is probable that no more than seven were recorded in the county, although distinguishing between individuals introduces uncertainty. For example, at Ibsley Water, a single adult, assumed the same individual, was seen in the four winters 2008/9–2011/12. There was also a second-winter bird there in October/November 2010. Other records, all of single birds, are listed below:

2010: A first–winter at Keyhaven, March 14th.
2011: An adult at Redbridge, January 5th to 8th.
      A first–summer at Lower Test Marshes, June 1st to 15th (the only summer record).
      A third–winter at Lymington, December 29th.
2012: A first–winter at Fox Lane Gravel Pit, Eversley, January 16th.

John Jones

Glaucous Gull

Larus hyperboreus

A very scarce visitor, usually in winter

The Glaucous Gull breeds around the Arctic Circle, in the Atlantic south to Iceland and Greenland. In winter it ranges as far south as the North Sea with the English south coast being at the southern limit of its normal wintering range. Numbers in Britain vary from winter to winter with influxes tending to follow periods of northerly or north-westerly gales.

In Hampshire it does not occur every year. During the five winters of the HBA it was seen in only three, during which eight individuals were recorded. Of these, six occurred in the winter of 2008/09, when there were also large numbers elsewhere in the country. All were recorded at the coast. Since the *1981–84 Winter Atlas* this species has been a less frequent visitor to Hampshire. In the decade to the winter of 1990/91 it occurred in every year with a total of 56 recorded, whereas in the decade to 2011/12 it occurred in only six winters with a total of 11. The likely reason for the decline is the closure of several rubbish tips in the county

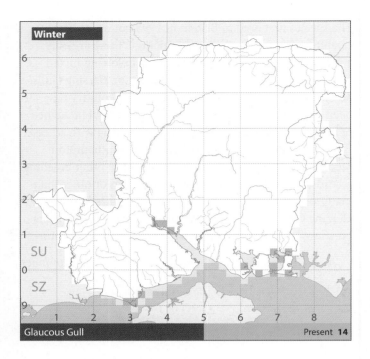

which formerly provided attractive feeding grounds for this and other gull species.

John Jones

Glaucous Gull, Southsea, January 2009 – *Darren Evans*

Iceland Gull

Larus glaucoides

A very scarce visitor, usually in winter

Despite its name, this species breeds in Greenland and parts of Canada but not in Iceland. It winters around the North Atlantic coast, the east Greenland population mainly in Iceland, the Faroe Islands, Scandinavia and the British Isles. Numbers reaching Britain are generally small but vary from year to year with more occurring following north-westerly gales. It is generally very scarce in southern England.

In Hampshire, it is seen in small numbers in most years, usually in January-March, although it has been recorded in every month. During the HBA period it occurred annually but no more than 17 individuals were recorded. This total included a count of nine in the 2011/12 winter when there was an unusually large influx into Britain and was the highest annual number since early 1984 when at least 12 were seen. While most records are from the coast they occasionally also occur inland, with Ibsley Water hosting five individuals during the HBA period. One was also seen at Winchester Sewage Farm between March 28th and April 2nd 2012 but does not appear on the accompanying map because it fell outside the winter recording period. Also in 2012, a

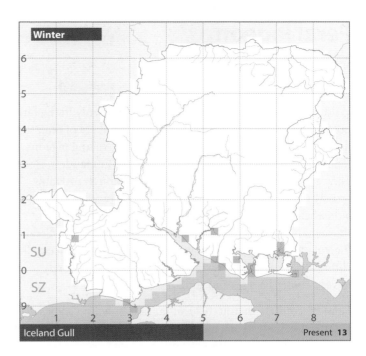

second-summer bird in Portsmouth Harbour on June 4th (and July 4th) was the first June record for Hampshire.

Based on the frequency of annual records the status of this species in the county does not appear to have changed since the *1981–84 Winter Atlas*.

John Jones

Iceland Gull, Bedhampton Quay, March 2012 – *Richard Ford*

Feral Pigeon

Columba livia

A common resident

Wild 'pure' Rock Doves now breed in Britain only in the far north and west but there are substantial numbers of once-domesticated, escaped, semi-captive and ex-racing pigeons (and their descendants) at large in lowland England. They are common birds in Hampshire, although probably grossly under-reported given their 'plastic' reputation. Nonetheless, few bird species are of greater concern to those managing urban areas, the preferred habitat for Feral Pigeons. Here they exploit habitat as close to their ancestral cliffs as they can find – niches in high buildings, church towers, under bridges and similar sites.

Feral Pigeons are distinctly local in their breeding across Hampshire, with strong and unsurprising concentrations around Southampton, Portsmouth, Gosport, Fareham, Aldershot, Andover and all other sizeable towns. They are present in more than a third of tetrads, but there appear to have been some distinct losses since the 1986–91 Atlas. During the HBA period, breeding was considered likely in 374 tetrads compared with 414 in the previous Atlas, a range reduction of about 11%. Although this is consistent with a 20% reduction in the English population over the 1995–2010 period (*BBS*), it may present an over-pessimistic picture, because some of the losses relate only to possible breeding records in the earlier atlas. Even so, the maps show notable range losses in the southern New Forest, around Lymington, Sway and New Milton, on the western chalk around Martin and Damerham, in the Stockbridge area and across much of eastern Hampshire.

Population control measures by public and private bodies in towns might be responsible for some local declines but it seems probable that increased competition from Woodpigeons (also see the Collared Dove account), which have increasingly taken to urban and suburban habitats, is at least as important. Either way, Feral Pigeon is not widely regarded as a species of conservation concern, or even of great interest to birders or to the general public!

The winter distribution maps mirror the breeding maps closely. Although Feral Pigeons are more widely noted on agricultural land at this season, notably in the north-east of the county, the highest numbers and densities remain those found in the conurbations. Counts of more than 400 are regularly made at sites such as Gosport, Fareham, central Southampton and Millbrook.

Simon Woolley

Sponsored by Mike Wildish

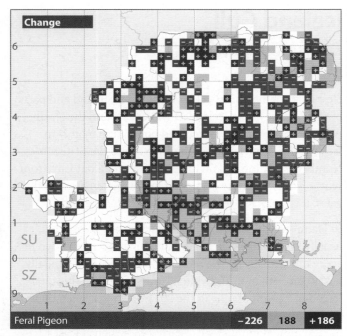

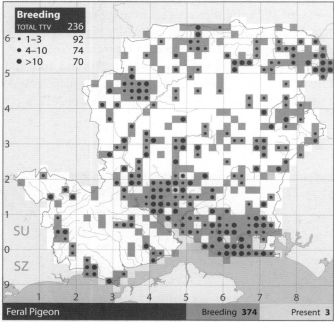

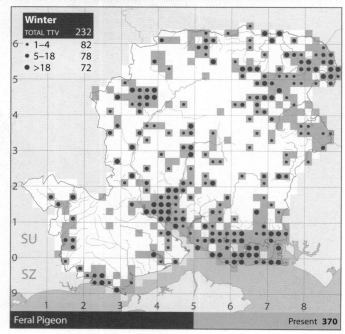

Feral Pigeon, Basingstoke, September 2015 – *Robert Still* (above); Hayling Island, November 2008 – *Richard Ford* (below);

Stock Dove

Columba oenas

A numerous resident and winter visitor

In the breeding season Stock Doves are common and widespread in suitable habitat with mature trees. Although many remain resident in their wooded habitats throughout the year, they are more conspicuous in open, agricultural areas in winter. Some breed in more built-up areas, often using cavities in buildings to nest.

In Hampshire, Stock Doves are widespread and quite evenly distributed, with breeding considered likely in about 80% of tetrads, but their abundance during the breeding season is much less even. There are significant concentrations in the New Forest (although even here there are noticeable gaps), the woodlands north and east of Southampton, and the area between Stockbridge and Andover, but there are obvious 'holes' across the high chalk and in other predominantly agricultural regions. Since the 1986–91 Atlas Stock Doves have apparently colonised some urban areas of Southampton while, surprisingly, other areas around Basingstoke and in the far west around Fordingbridge appear to have lost their breeding birds. Overall, the pattern is of little net change. It seems likely that the Hampshire population has returned to levels at least close to those recorded prior to the decline associated with organochlorine seed dressings in the 1950s and 1960s, also benefiting from being removed from the quarry species list in 1982.

Fewer tetrads hold Stock Doves in the winter than in the breeding season. The pattern of occurrence shows greater concentration, a result of many woodland areas being partly or wholly vacated, and probably mostly local movements into farmland areas for feeding. Winter flocks in excess of 50 are rare, and only 88 numbering over 100 have been found since the 1986–91 Atlas, the largest being 600 at Beaulieu on February 2nd 2008.

It is probable but unproven that immigrants, either from elsewhere in Britain, or even overseas, further supplement the winter population. Such autumn migration was noted as long ago as 1773 (White 1789) and quantified in southern England from 1945 (Denby Wilkinson 1950) but *The Migration Atlas* notes a marked decline in recoveries of overseas-bred Stock Doves in recent decades. In Hampshire, there is a distinct but usually light autumn movement detected. Regular watching at Fleet Pond until 2000 produced hundreds in October and November every year and increased interest in visible migration since about 2005 has resulted in more high counts, notably in 2005 when 1,500 were recorded moving south and south-west in November, and in 2010, when 3,100 were logged moving in a similar direction, including 1,174 at Barton on Sea on November 16th alone. It is likely that many more are missed, particularly inland, and are probably subsumed in

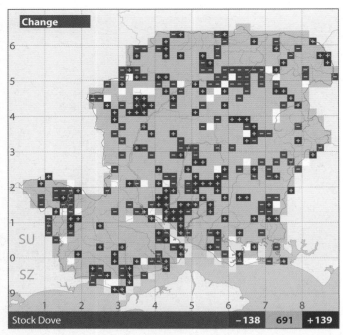

Stock Dove   −138   691   +139

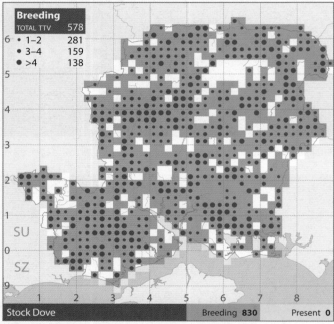

Breeding
TOTAL TTV 578
- 1–2   281
- 3–4   159
- >4   138

Stock Dove   Breeding 830   Present 0

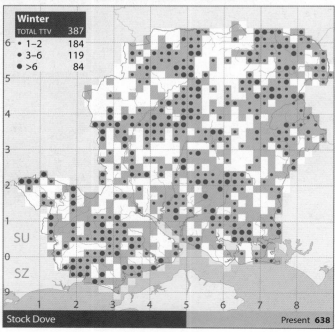

Winter
TOTAL TTV 387
- 1–2   184
- 3–6   119
- >6   84

Stock Dove   Present 638

the much larger Woodpigeon movements of the season. It is noteworthy that much larger westerly autumn movements are detected most years in neighbouring Dorset.

Spring passage is light or largely undetected, although semi-regular gatherings of scores to the low hundreds sometimes occur on chalkland agricultural sites as late as mid-May.

Simon Woolley

Stock Dove, Titchfield Haven, July 2011 – *John Whichall*

Sponsored by John Moon

Woodpigeon
Columba palumbus
An abundant resident, passage migrant and winter visitor

Woodpigeons are amongst the most numerous and conspicuous of Hampshire's birds; by virtue of their physical size, they make up the largest proportion of the county's avian biomass of any species other than released Pheasants. As noted in *BoH*, Woodpigeons have benefited from the switch to autumn-sown cereals, since the availability of food for squabs the following years is earlier and longer-lasting. Also significant is the continued growth in Oil-seed Rape and similar brassicas, crops which provide excellent winter feeding for the species.

Following a period of decline in the mid-20th century, Woodpigeons experienced a period of rapid population growth, increasing by some 75% across the UK between 1986 and 2011 (*BBS*). The growth was less dramatic in the south-east than in some other regions but populations in Hampshire are probably now as high as they have ever been. Based on the estimated population of 60,000 breeding pairs in the county at the time of the 1986–91 Atlas, Hampshire probably now holds somewhere in the region of 90,000 pairs, and thus perhaps close to a quarter of a million birds by the end of the breeding season.

While traditionally associated with rural and especially agricultural habitats, the numbers using urban and suburban areas for breeding and feeding has increased substantially in recent years. As recently as 1995, around 60% of gardens reported the presence of the species; by 2012 that figure stood at 90% (GBW). The increased presence of Woodpigeons in gardens may well account for the recent slight decline in Feral Pigeons and Collared Doves (see accounts).

Virtually every tetrad in Hampshire holds Woodpigeons year round. They are common everywhere but breed at highest densities in the farmland of central and northern Hampshire, and the very far west of the county. While still common, Woodpigeons are thinner on the ground as breeders in the New Forest, presumably as a function of poorer local food sources rather than lack of habitat.

During the winter large flocks can be found almost anywhere in the farmed areas of the county. Flocks well into four figures are common, the largest reported during the HBA period being 10,000 at Gander Down on November 5th 2007, notably at the peak season for apparent movements (see below). Some also use the New Forest, presumably as a safe roosting area rather than a prime feeding site.

While British Woodpigeons are essentially sedentary (*Migration Atlas*), the question of whether Hampshire experiences net immigration, or indeed receives any non-local Woodpigeons at all, in autumn and winter remains

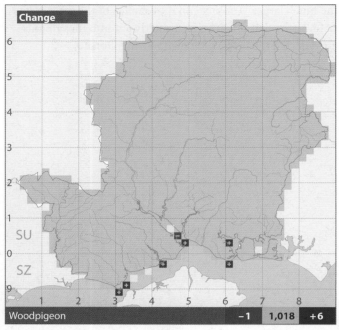

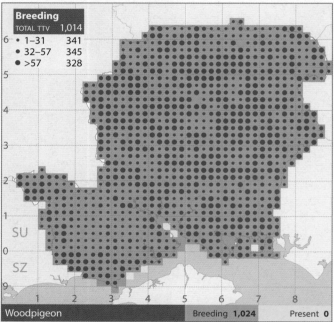

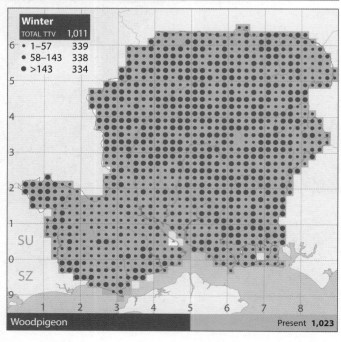

an open one. This is despite well-known and sometimes enormous apparent movements of birds, especially in early November. While there are substantial year-to-year fluctuations, massive flocks of Woodpigeons moving mostly between west and south-west are an established feature of clear, cold mornings at this time of year, and this is not a wholly new phenomenon (White 1789, Lack and Ridpath 1955). During the HBA period, almost 920,000 were reported 'migrating' in this fashion. The peak year was 2010, when some 395,000 were noted, including a huge 59,250 west at Barton on Sea on November 16th, 60% of them in just 20 minutes! Similar (and usually even larger) movements are recorded annually in Dorset and, generally smaller ones, in Sussex, suggesting some kind of 'funnelling' of Woodpigeons to points south and west. Large movements are recorded as far west as Cornwall, where thousands are logged flying west and south-west out to sea in November. Among the things we do not know are: whether these are British birds, or Continental immigrants; where they are headed; whether all our breeding Woodpigeons are sedentary and whether any of the apparent migrants spend the winter with us. Ringing recoveries do not support a foreign component to our grounded wintering birds, but the overflying birds might be from farther afield. But if so, by what route do they return from their unknown wintering grounds in the spring?

So in summary, despite it being among our most familiar and abundant species, there remains a good deal to learn about the ubiquitous Woodpigeon.

Simon Woolley

Sponsored by Dominic Reynolds

Woodpigeon, New Forest, December 2012 – *Martin Bennett*

Collared Dove

Streptopelia decaocto

A numerous resident and passage migrant

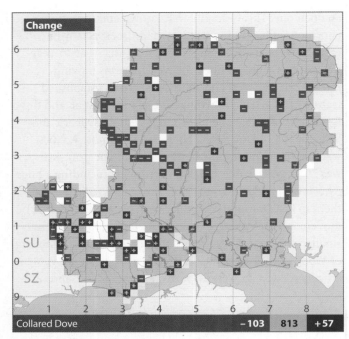

Following the establishment of the species as a breeder in Hampshire in the 1960s, the Collared Dove's range and numbers increased rapidly, such that 89% of tetrads were occupied at the time of the 1986–91 Atlas. The only regions of the county lacking Collared Doves during this period were parts of the New Forest. The species remains almost ubiquitous but recent indications suggest a decline accompanied by a small but distinct contraction in range.

The HBA results show that 85% of tetrads are now occupied in the breeding season, with some of the highest densities in the suburban areas of Portsmouth, Southampton and other towns. As in 1986–91, large swathes of the New Forest remain unoccupied. The change map shows some telling signs of decline in more rural areas. Collared Doves are now thin on the ground in the far west of the county's chalk (north-west of Fordingbridge) and distinct gaps in distribution have opened up on the chalk around Porton Down and west of Winchester. It is possible that 'cleaner' and more intensive farming in these areas accounts for the loss of Collared Doves, as with so many other species of farmland birds.

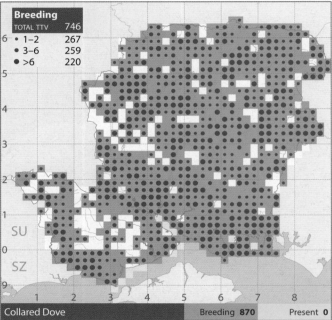

The winter distribution map shows little difference from the breeding map, indicating that our Collared Doves are mostly sedentary. There is little indication that winter numbers are swelled by immigrants; only just over 300 have been observed (apparently) migrating in autumn since *BoH*, despite the recent interest in visible migration recording.

Collared Doves became so widespread and common that routine (non-Atlas) reporting rates have declined to a very low level. Larger gatherings continue to catch birders' attention, however. Since *BoH*, the mean number of flocks of 100+ birds reported each year is 1·65, although the figures for 1992–2001 and 2002–12 are 2·5 and 0·7 respectively, consistent with a decline, at least in large gatherings. In 1996, 400 were at Warblington on October 6th, while in 2012 82 in a Petersfield garden on December 22nd, was the only count to exceed 50. No gathering of 100+ has been found since 2009. Less winter stubble and spilled grain may account for this shift, although a wider national decline has been detected recently, notably in gardens (*GBW*). In south-east England, *BBS* data indicated a 9% drop in population between 2006 and 2011. The BTO suggests one factor behind the downward trend may be competition from increasing Woodpigeon numbers. It is also possible that Collared Doves might be more susceptible to trichomonosis than Woodpigeons and that the rise in the disease might be having a disproportionate effect on the Collared Dove population (Toms 2010).

Simon Woolley

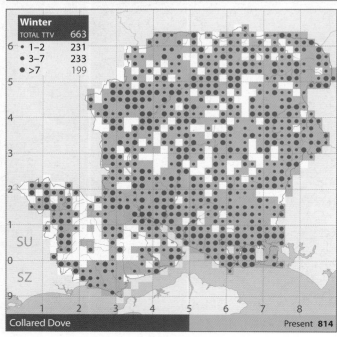

Sponsored by Mike Wildish

Collared Dove, Basingstoke, July 2015 – *Robert Still* (above); New Forest, April 2009 – *Martin Bennett* (below)

Turtle Dove
Streptopelia turtur
A scarce and declining summer visitor and passage migrant

This account makes very depressing reading. Turtle Doves were once familiar and almost abundant in Hampshire. *Cohen* quotes estimates of 100+ pairs on 4,000 acres near Fordingbridge and 20–50 pairs on 1,000 acres near Micheldever in the early 1950s. Today, they are on the verge of extirpation as breeders, and almost unknown as migrants.

Following the 1986–91 Atlas, Clark & Eyre (*BoH*) gave what was probably, even then, an optimistic county population estimate of 1200–2400 pairs. This was based on records with some degree of breeding evidence from 575 tetrads during the Atlas period. Subsequently, the annual totals of breeding records were much lower, amounting to only 40 post-Atlas in 1993. The obvious cause for concern led to greater observer effort and recording. The result was that breeding registrations increased to 90 by 1997, remaining at about that level until 2004. Local extirpations were reported almost every year and a further, steeper decline began from 2005.

Numbers continued to drop through the HBA period, despite continuing and more widespread surveillance for the Atlas fieldwork. The HBA distribution/abundance and change maps confirm the dire situation. Moreover, given that these are five-year composite maps and include as likely breeding many records without confirmation of breeding, they almost certainly present an optimistic picture of the actual range of Turtle Dove in the county. Putting these uncertainties aside, the bottom line is that 75% fewer tetrads hold Turtle Doves today than in 1986–91. Over two decades, whole meta-populations have been fragmented to the point of near extinction.

The species has been lost from almost all 'ordinary countryside' sites, and even at such former strongholds as Noar Hill just one or two pairs now survive. Botley Wood, which held over a dozen pairs a decade ago, had none at all by 2011. Only Martin Down has retained anything like a viable population, with a recent peak of 12 pairs on the old CBC survey area in 2011, bizarrely up from nine the year before, and seven the year before that! Few remaining sites appear to be suitable for the survival of the species as a breeder, the areas around Martin Down and Stockbridge being possible exceptions. But, even there, chance events and a likely lack of re-colonisation make extirpation possible.

The Hampshire data reflect the national trends depressingly well. *BBS* data indicate a linear 90% decline in the UK and south-east populations since the early 1990s (and the species is now too rare to be well-monitored by *BBS*). Agricultural intensification is likely the main cause, mostly through loss of weed seeds as a result of increased herbicide use. The reduction in food supply has led to a shortened breeding period and fewer nesting attempts. Other factors at play, to an unknown extent, include wintering habitat

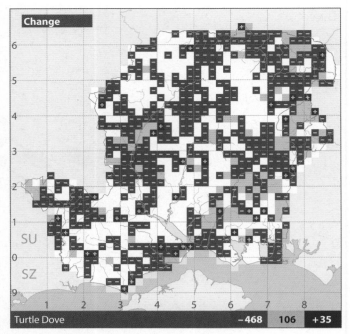

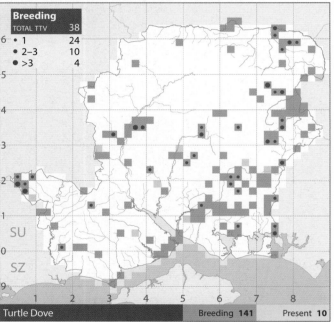

degradation and hunting pressures during migration through the Mediterranean basin.

The parlous state of the Hampshire and wider British population of Turtle Doves is further confirmed by the decline in numbers of passage migrants. Very few are now recorded away from breeding sites in spring, and single-figure totals in autumn have been the norm since 2007. In 2009, for the first time on record, not one Turtle Dove was seen in Hampshire after the end of August. Very occasionally, Turtle Doves have been found in winter in the county, but none was found at this season during the HBA period.

Once a quintessential part of the summer scene, Turtle Doves are now rare, still declining, and quite likely on the verge of disappearance as a regular sight in the county.

Simon Woolley

Sponsored by David Crossley

Turtle Dove, Martin Down, June 2010 – *Martin Bennett* (above): Headley Down, July 2013 – *John Whichall* (below)

Cuckoo
Cuculus canorus
A moderately common summer visitor

Cuckoos are probably the most widely-known of all the heralds of spring, at least by ear, and the song of the male remains a frequent and welcome sound across much of the county in April and May. The species is most abundant and widespread in the New Forest, with up to ten males recorded in some tetrads. While most frequently encountered in wooded areas, it is likely that the commonest host species for egg-laying is the Meadow Pipit, which of course nests on the open heaths and grassland (although see account for current status).

Cuckoos are also relatively frequent in the east and north-east of the county, especially on the Thames Basin and Wealden Heaths and in the wooded hangars of the Wealden scarp, where the second major host species, the Dunnock, is common. The HBA tetrad maps also show quite clearly, if subtly, relative abundance along the major river valleys of the Test, Itchen and Meon where one of the major target host species is doubtless the Reed Warbler.

Cuckoos have declined seriously in Britain in recent years. A 76% decline has been estimated for England between 1967 and 2011 (*BirdTrends*), with a 63% fall in the south-east during 1995–2012 (*BBS*). The decline has been reflected in Hampshire, the 1986–91 Atlas producing records in 911 tetrads, whereas the accompanying HBA map sees birds in just 681 – a fall of 25%. The number of tetrads in which breeding was considered likely fell by the same percentage. As noted above, the decline has been most marked in the open, 'ordinary' countryside away from the river valleys or other more specialised habitats.

Hypotheses to explain this alarming collapse fall into three categories: degradation of wintering habitat in Africa, the

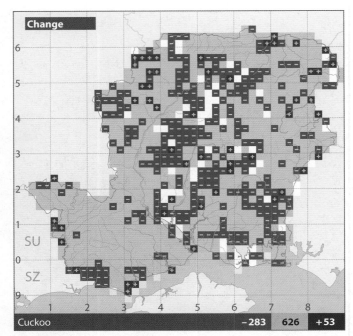

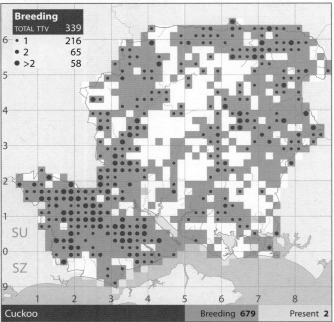

Cuckoo, New Forest, October 2010 – *Martin Bennett*

Cuckoo, New Forest, May 2009 – *Martin Bennett* (right); with
Meadow Pipit, New Forest, June 2010 – *Martin Bennett* (below)

severe decline of macro-moths (and thus their caterpillars,
an important summer and autumn food source for
Cuckoos) in Europe, and possible changing timings of host
species nesting attempts (Douglas *et al.* 2010).

The latter might favour Cuckoos which use Reed Warblers
as against those which parasitize resident species such
as Dunnock. Interestingly, recent research in central and
north-east Europe (Fuisz & de Kort, 2007; Moksnes *et
al.* 2011) suggest that Cuckoos using different habitats
(and thus host species) are sufficiently divergent in their
egg morphology, genetics and voice to represent effective
'races'; it may even be that two or more crypto-species are
in fact involved.

Simon Woolley

Sponsored by Sarah White

Barn Owl
Tyto alba
A moderately common resident

Found on every continent except Antarctica with a global range in excess of 63,000,000 sq. km, the Barn Owl has the most cosmopolitan distribution of any owl species. In the UK, the population has probably suffered significant changes brought about, initially, by changes in land use. The widespread clearance of forests enabled the species to expand across the country from its former strongholds in the open areas along coasts, rivers, marshes and fens. Coupled with the development of agriculture, this created an environment rich with prey items in which the species could flourish. These improving fortunes continued into the early 19th century, during which the Barn Owl population is likely to have reached its peak. Since then a succession of severe winters, periods of agricultural depression, the effects of organochlorine pollution and rapid habitat change have contributed to the population decline to its current level of around 4,000 pairs (Eaton *et al.* 2009).

In contrast to some other counties, the Hampshire population has fared reasonably well, even during the most recent period of decline. The National Census of Barn Owls, carried out in 1932, reported Hampshire's breeding population as 351 pairs (Blaker 1933). By the time of the second national survey in 1985, the county held the third highest density of Barn Owls in England although, by then, this amounted to only 145 pairs (Shawyer 1987). There is evidence of a more recent national increase (*BirdTrends*) and this is reflected by a net increase of 20% in occupied tetrads in the HBA. This increase has also been accompanied by a significant change in distribution, with both gains (more than two-thirds of currently occupied tetrads are in new locations) and losses (more than 60% of formerly occupied tetrads no longer hold records).

Across the county, gains since the 1986–91 Atlas are most apparent in areas where there are extensive targeted nest box schemes; the three areas with the most notable gains (the north-western downs and north and north-east Hampshire) hold a total of more than 250 nest boxes. While much of the Hampshire landscape can be considered broadly suitable for Barn Owls, the provision of nest boxes significantly improves the chances of recording both their presence and nesting. It is perhaps not too surprising then that the species appears to have greatly increased in these areas. The increase in nest boxes across the county is further highlighted by the county ringing totals for the species, which have increased from 53 in 1986–91 to 303 in 2008–12. Further gains are to be expected in future surveys since current schemes monitor more than 400 nest boxes across the county.

Some areas have apparently suffered losses. These are particularly noticeable in the southern and eastern New

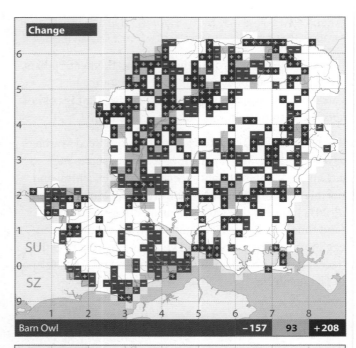

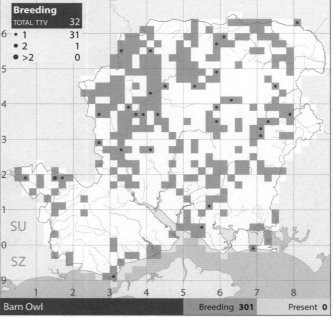

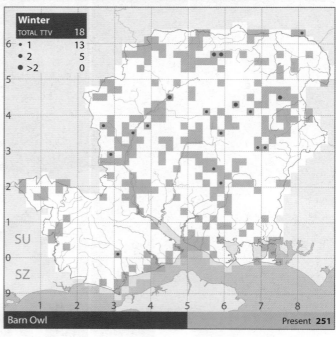

Forest, around Basingstoke (SU65) and near Romsey (SU22/32). Identification of their causes is difficult. While it is tempting to ascribe them to habitat change/loss, there appears to have been little in the way of substantial loss of habitat between the two survey periods and the implementation of agri-environment schemes will generally have improved habitat quality and suitability since 1986–91. There may be other factors, such as increased competition or predation by other raptors, but there is no direct evidence for this. Perhaps the main cause of these apparent losses relates to under-recording and to changes in nest box monitoring in certain areas.

The winter distribution of Barn Owls broadly follows that of the summer, although 41% of occupied tetrads were different from those occupied during the breeding season. This is likely to be a combination of young birds attempting to establish territories away from their natal area, the expansion of adult territories during winter, and the recording of adult birds on territory that were missed during the breeding season. The overall reduction in number of tetrads in which the species is recorded during winter reflects a reduction in activity of Barn Owls to conserve energy. Similarly, a lack of dependent young and the need to make regular visits to the nest location also combine to make Barn Owls less apparent during this period.

Matt Stevens

Sponsored by Brian Sharkey

Barn Owl, Hayling Island, February 2009 – *Richard Ford*

Little Owl
Athene noctua
A moderately common but decreasing resident

Hampshire was in the vanguard of the introduction of Little Owls into Britain. In the second half of the 19th century, Edmund Meade-Waldo is reported to have released specimens into the New Forest (*K&M*). It is not known how successful this initiative was but his well-documented releases at Stonewall Park near Edenbridge in Kent, between 1874 and 1900, resulted in a flourishing population that soon expanded into surrounding counties (Lever 2009). The Hampshire population was well established by the 1920s (*Cohen*) and continued to grow, albeit with fluctuations, up to the time of the 1986–91 Atlas survey. At that time Little Owls were found in 52% of Hampshire tetrads. In *BoH* it was, justifiably, described as a common resident. The picture emerging from the HBA is quite different. As the breeding and change maps show, the number of tetrads in which it was found has fallen from 531 in 1986–91 to 253 in 2008–12. Although the species remains widespread across the county, its range determined by the number of occupied tetrads, is less than half of what it was 20 years ago.

For a species that is more active by night than by day, there is always the possibility that under-recording could have contributed to the observed range reduction. However, the decline seen in Hampshire is consistent with national results which show a continuous downward trend in population from 1986 to date (*BirdTrends*). *Bird Atlas 2007–11* shows that the decline has been particularly marked in western and southern counties of Britain.

The reasons for the decline are unknown but, as a predominantly farmland species, it may be that agricultural intensification is involved. Invertebrates form a large part of the Little Owl's diet and are particularly important as food for their young (*BWP*). Insecticides, herbicides and other agricultural chemicals that reduce the number and diversity of invertebrates could be having a negative effect.

Little Owls remain on territory throughout the year so it is no surprise that the HBA winter map shows a similar distribution to that during the breeding season. However, fewer occupied tetrads were recorded, suggesting that birds are harder to find in winter than in summer. This may be because they are less vocal and active during the short winter days.

John Eyre

Sponsored by Di Mitchell

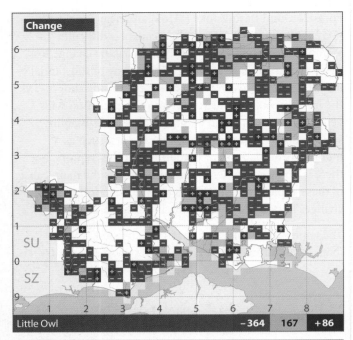

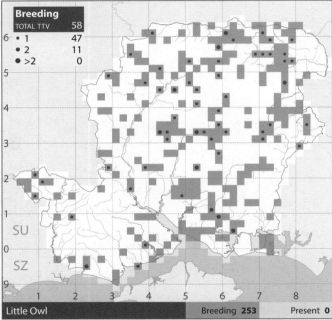

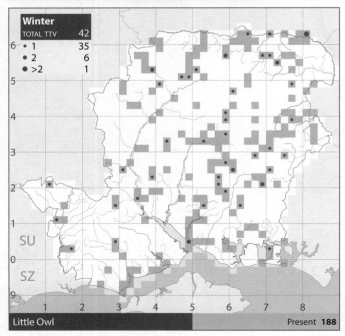

Little Owl, Near Winchester, April 2010 – *Martin Bennett*

Little Owl, Hayling Island, July 2011 – *Richard Ford*

Little Owl,
Near Winchester,
April 2010 –

Martin Bennett

Tawny Owl

Strix aluco

A common resident

The Tawny Owl is the most common owl in Britain although it is far more frequently heard than seen. As the HBA maps show, it is widespread across Hampshire where it occurs at the greatest densities in mature broadleaved woodland. It is also found in many other locations where there are suitable trees to provide nest sites, including farmland, parkland, churchyards and large gardens. It will also breed in mixed and coniferous woodland using old bird nests and squirrel dreys as nest sites where tree holes are not available and will readily take to suitable nest boxes. In Hampshire, it is at its lowest densities on the intensely cultivated farmland in the centre and north-west of the county and in densely populated conurbations such as Portsmouth and Gosport.

The HBA change map shows both gains and losses since the 1986–91 Atlas but with a small net range reduction of less than 5%. This is consistent with the national picture where a downward trend has been identified by both the annual CBC/BBS monitoring scheme (*BirdTrends*) and *Bird Atlas 2007–11* but is at odds with the results of targeted national surveys carried out in 1989 and 1995. In Hampshire, these showed a big population increase between the surveys, albeit at a small number of sites (Sharkey 2007). However, Tawny Owls are difficult birds to survey. Atlas methodology in particular, is not ideal for locating a species which is strictly nocturnal and secretive. Although attempts were made towards the end of the HBA to improve coverage, there remains a likelihood of them being overlooked in some areas.

As would be expected for a sedentary species, the Tawny Owl's winter distribution, as shown by the HBA winter map, mirrors that of the breeding season although the number of occupied tetrads was substantially lower in winter than in summer. This is counterintuitive both because Tawny Owls are particularly vocal during the winter and also because the adults drive their offspring out of their natal territories in the autumn, so it might be expected that more tetrads would be occupied post-breeding. However, many of the apparent losses were in the less populated areas of the county such as the extensive central and north-western agricultural areas and the New Forest, which again points to the results being affected by a lack of coverage.

Despite the uncertainties, the HBA results indicate that Tawny Owl remains a common and widespread Hampshire resident. If any real change in distribution has occurred over the past two decades it has been relatively small. Given the continuing availability of suitable habitat, and discounting the possible impacts of long term environmental change, it is likely that this situation will continue.

John Eyre

Sponsored by Brian Durham

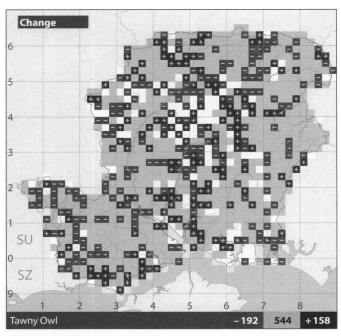

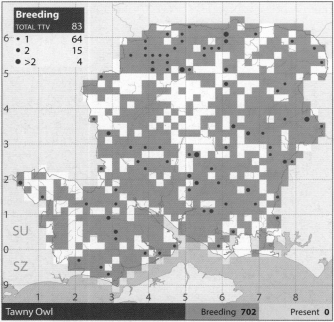

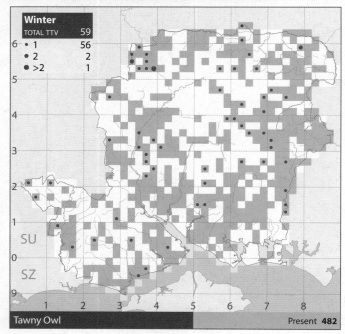

Tawny Owl, New Forest, March 2011 – *Martin Bennett*

Long-eared Owl

Asio otus

A scarce resident, passage migrant and winter visitor

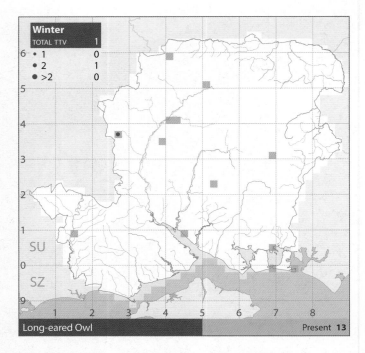

This secretive and enigmatic species is seen infrequently in Hampshire. Despite having a circumpolar distribution, it is relatively scarce in Britain and particularly so in Hampshire and neighbouring southern counties. This was not always the case. In 1905 *K&M* described it as common in suitable districts, including the New Forest, the Avon Valley and elsewhere in the county but by the mid-20th century it had suffered a major decline. *Cohen* (1963) acknowledged that the paucity of records made it impossible to accurately assess the status of the species. That situation remains true today although the indications are that numbers have declined still further over the past 50 years.

The initial decline of the Long-eared Owl has coincided with an increase in its larger and more aggressive congener, the Tawny Owl. The two species share similar habitat and food requirements, so it is possible that the latter has out-competed the former (Mikkola 1983). However, more recently, the decrease in Tawny Owl numbers has not led to a reversal in the Long-eared Owl's downward trend so it is likely that other factors are involved.

During the HBA survey, breeding was proved in only three Hampshire tetrads and considered likely in a fourth. All were in the north of the county. They have not been mapped here to maintain site-security. There were only two other records during the breeding season, one in the far west at Damerham and one in the north-east near Fleet. These numbers should be compared with the 1986–91 Atlas when there were nine likely breeding and six possible breeding records.

Long-eared Owls are seen more frequently during the winter when the resident population is supplemented by incoming visitors from Scandinavia and other parts of northern Europe. The species is semi-irruptive so numbers vary from year to year. During the 2007–12 HBA winters there was no major irruption, the winter map showing a thin scatter of records across the county with most on the chalk and a concentration on the coast in the south-east.

John Eyre

Sponsored by Barry Stalker

Long-eared Owl, Kingsley, January 2006 – *Richard Ford*

Short-eared Owl

Asio flammeus

A scarce but regular winter visitor and passage migrant that occasionally breeds

The Short-eared Owl has a surprisingly large world range occurring on every continent other than Antarctica and Australasia. In the UK, it breeds primarily in upland areas, particularly in northern England and Scotland, and much less frequently in the lowlands. In winter the UK population is swelled by immigrants from northern Europe with numbers varying from year to year dependent on weather conditions and prey availability closer to home.

In Hampshire the first incoming migrants are usually seen in late August/early September with numbers peaking in October. During the HBA period, wintering birds were recorded predominantly from the coast or the chalk with only a scatter of sightings elsewhere. The peak counts for each of the HBA winters, together with the month and year of occurrence, are given in *Table 28*.

The variability in annual numbers makes comparison with early periods difficult, but the 2011/12 winter was a good one by recent standards. Site counts of five were made at Tidgrove Warren and Bransbury Common, and four at Martin Down and the Broadlands Estate.

Most wintering birds have departed by the end of March but passage continues through April and into May. Occasionally birds remain into mid-summer, as in 2012 when there were records from Pennington/Keyhaven Marshes until July 5th and Farlington Marshes until July 31st.

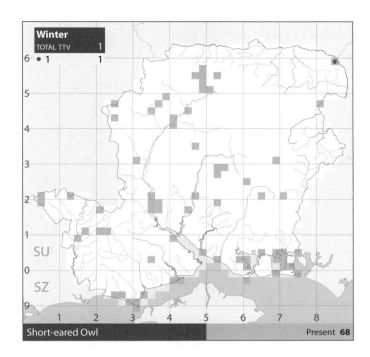

Winter	2007/08	2008/09	2009/10	2010/11	2011/12
Peak count	21	13	6	15	35
Month	Feb 2008	Nov 2008	Jan/Feb 2010	Nov 2010	Dec 2011

Table 28 – Short-eared Owl: number of wintering birds.

Although Short-eared Owls have bred in Hampshire on several occasions, most recently during the 1986–91 Atlas in 1989, there has been no indication of breeding in the county since then.

John Eyre

Sponsored by Hugh & James Tomlinson

Short-eared Owl, Martin Down, December 2010 – *Martin Bennett*

Nightjar

Caprimulgus europaeus

A moderately common summer visitor and passage migrant

The Nightjar has long been one of Hampshire's 'special' birds. In the second half of the 18th century Gilbert White knew it sufficiently well in the Selborne area to consider writing a paper to the Royal Society to "advance some particulars concerning that peculiar, migratory, nocturnal bird". Although its range has contracted over the intervening years, Hampshire remains the number-one county for Nightjars in Britain. Based on the counts of territorial males made during the most recent country-wide survey in 2004, the county holds around 19% of the national total (Conway *et al.* 2007).

As ground-nesters, Nightjars prefer areas of well-drained, essentially open land with cover such as Bracken, heather or scrub in which to nest and scattered trees to use as song posts. In Hampshire, these conditions are found on heathland and forest clear-fells or young plantations, particularly on the sandy soils in the south and north-east of the county. As the HBA breeding map shows, the distribution of Nightjars is closely allied to heathland with the main populations in the New Forest, the Thames Basin and the Wealden Heaths. Smaller but significant populations also occur in Ringwood Forest and the areas around Romsey and Wickham. Numbers on the chalk are much lower and usually dependent on transient habitat created by woodland clearance or new forestry plantations.

As a crepuscular species, the Nightjar is difficult to survey, particularly in the large and, in parts, secluded area of the New Forest. For this reason, the HBA results have been supplemented with those from a dedicated New Forest Nightjar survey carried out by the RPS Group in 2013. We are grateful to the NFNPA for permission to incorporate these results into the HBA breeding and change maps. For the county as a whole, the maps show gains and losses relative to the 1986–91 Atlas with a net contraction of just seven tetrads. On balance, the majority of the losses appear to have occurred in the south-west, in Ringwood Forest and the borders of the New Forest. Some of these have probably resulted from the re-growth of forestry clear-fells making the habitat unsuitable.

Despite the apparent small decrease in range, the population of Hampshire's Nightjars is undoubtedly higher than it was 20 years ago. Following the 1986–91 survey the county population was estimated at 530 territorial males (*BoH*). This was confirmed by the 1992 national survey with a count of 514 territories (Morris *et al.* 1994). In 2004 the national survey indicated a 52% growth with a count of 781. Based on the HBA results supplemented by the RPS New Forest survey, the population in 2012/13 is estimated to be 790 territories (comprising 550 in the New Forest, 25 in Ringwood Forest, 175 in the north-east and 40 elsewhere). This is very close to the 2004 count. Given fluctuations from year to year, the data support the general impression that Nightjar numbers are stable and have probably plateaued following the earlier growth. Thankfully Hampshire's "peculiar, migratory, nocturnal bird" is thriving, in contrast to many other sub-Saharan migrants such as Turtle Dove and Cuckoo whose populations have undergone major declines in recent decades.

John Eyre

Sponsored by Mike Crutch

Nightjar, New Forest, August 2014 – *Martin Bennett*

Change

6

5

SU
1

SZ
0

9

1   2   3   4   5   6   7   8

Nightjar   − 45   147   + 40

Breeding
TOTAL TTV   6
• 1   5
• 2–7   1
• >7   0

6

5

4

3

SU
1

SZ
0

9

1   2   3   4   5   6   7   8

Nightjar   Breeding 187   Present 9

Nightjar, Alresford, September 2009 – *Jacquie Frampton* (above left); Ocean Village, Southampton, May 2011 – *Elaine Mallion* (above right); New Forest, May 2008 – *Martin Bennett* (below)

253

Swift

Apus apus

A numerous but declining summer visitor and passage migrant

Swifts are amongst the latest of our long distance migrants to return to their breeding grounds. Their arrival, usually beginning in the second half of April and peaking in May, is a welcome sign that summer is on the way. As the HBA breeding map shows, the species is widespread with the largest breeding numbers occurring in towns and villages where older buildings provide suitable nest sites.

The Swift is not an easy species to survey. Obtaining breeding evidence is difficult because there are many non-breeding birds in the population; they range over wide areas and, although their low-level screaming display flights are usually a good indication of nearby breeding, they can be difficult to watch back to nest sites in built-up areas. Even so, in the 1986–91 Atlas, Swifts were confirmed or found to be probably breeding in 432 tetrads. By comparison, the equivalent number in the HBA was just 161 tetrads, a reduction of 63%. The accompanying HBA breeding and change maps were derived using the BCL approach. Although this produced lower numbers because probable breeding records based on observation of a pair were discounted, the resulting trend remained the same. BCL numbers fell from 351 tetrads in 1986–91 to 128 in 2008–12, a reduction of 64%. While it is likely that many nest sites will have been overlooked and the Swift continues to breed more widely than shown in the breeding distribution map, it is clear that its range has contracted significantly over the previous two decades.

The downward trend is consistent with national *BBS* data which show a 38% range reduction in the UK over the period 1995–2010. As a result, in 2009 Swift was moved from the green to the amber list of Birds of Conservation Concern (Eaton *et al.* 2009). There may be a number of factors behind the decline but one of the main issues is thought to be the loss of suitable nest sites as a result of house refurbishment and the demolition of old buildings.

Although the breeding population has undoubtedly declined, Swifts can still be seen in large numbers in Hampshire. During the summer, gatherings of several hundred are often recorded over water or arable fields, particularly when adverse weather conditions force them to feed at lower levels. Four-figure counts are infrequent but during the HBA period, an unprecedented 4,111 moved west over Testwood Lakes during a four hour period on June 24th 2012. The previous high count was 2,300 at the same site on July 10th 2000. Such movements generally occur ahead of advancing weather fronts.

John Eyre

Sponsored by Winchester College in memory of Cameron Bespolka

Swift, Old Basing, July 2015 – *Robert Still*

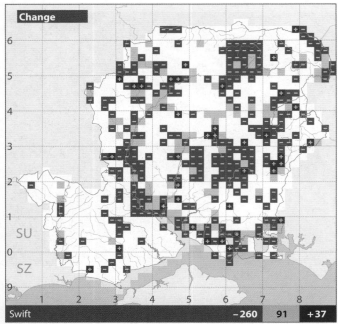

Change

Swift   − 260   91   + 37

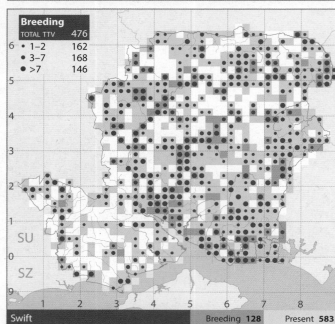

Breeding
TOTAL TTV 476
● 1–2   162
● 3–7   168
● >7   146

Swift   Breeding **128**   Present **583**

Swift, Woolmer, July 2009 – *Richard Ford*

Alpine Swift

Apus melba

A rare vagrant

Alpine Swifts breed in mountains from southern Europe to the Himalaya. They wander widely on migration but are rare in the UK. Prior to the HBA, there had been just ten records in Hampshire of which seven were post-1950. A further three were added during the 2007–12 period as follows:

2010:   Fleet Pond, March 31st and April 3rd.
2012:   Havant, March 29th.
        Needs Ore, June 30th.

John Eyre

Alpine Swift, Fleet Pond, April 2010 – *Ian Williamson*

Kingfisher, New Forest, May 2010 – *Martin Bennett*

Kingfisher

Alcedo atthis

A moderately common resident

Appropriately for the species which is the logo of HOS, the Kingfisher is widespread in Hampshire. Its distribution is closely allied to the courses of the main rivers, their tributaries and other waterways. For such a strikingly coloured bird, it can be unobtrusive and easily missed but is often detected by its call and a flash of iridescent blue as it streaks low along a watercourse through its extended territory. This makes it a difficult species to pin down to a particular breeding site. As a result, some birds will have undoubtedly been overlooked while others will have been counted in non-breeding locations. These factors may have contributed to the large number of gains and losses shown on the HBA change map. Of the 232 tetrads where breeding was considered likely in the 1986–91 Atlas, exactly half, 116, have apparently been lost while 95 new tetrads have been gained, a net loss of 21 tetrads. A reduction in breeding range and population is consistent with the findings of *Bird Atlas 2007–11*, which shows a range contraction across most of southern England over the past 20 years, and *BBS* data, which show a 26% reduction in the English population over the period 1995–2010.

The pattern of the range changes in Hampshire between atlases is striking. There appear to have been major reductions in the Basingstoke area and also in the upper Avon Valley with increases in the Itchen valley. The reasons for these shifts are unknown but Kingfishers are susceptible to a number of environmental threats. They suffer heavy losses in hard winters while wet summers, such as the one experienced in 2012, can lead to nests being flooded. They are also vulnerable to pollution of watercourses by industrial chemicals and agricultural run-off and to predation, particularly by cats and mink. The availability of suitable nest sites is another key factor which can determine whether an area is occupied or deserted.

The HBA maps show similar distributions in winter and in the breeding season but with a noticeable increase in the occupation of coastal tetrads in winter. This is to be expected because, after the breeding season, the juveniles disperse, many of them to the coast. The adults remain on territory throughout the year except in the coldest months when their feeding areas may become frozen. Under such circumstances they too are forced to move to areas with open water.

John Eyre

Sponsored by David Thelwell

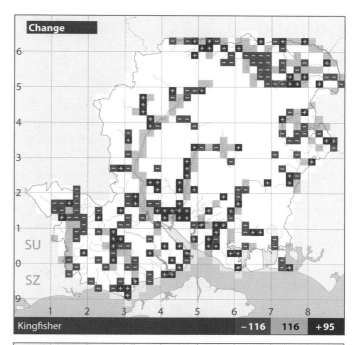

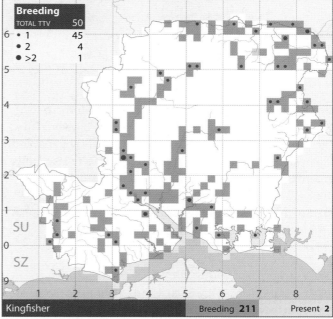

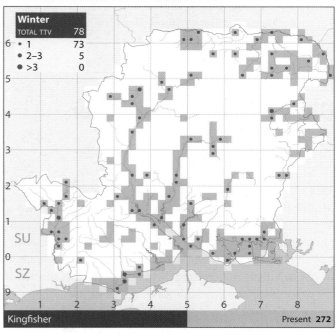

257

Hoopoe

Upupa epops

A very scarce visitor; has bred but not since 1959

During the 2007–12 period, 25 Hoopoes were seen in Hampshire, including four in spring 2007 prior to the start of the HBA. Annual numbers varied between one in 2009 and seven in 2011. The majority of the records (21) were in spring. While this is consistent with migrants overshooting their breeding grounds in southern Europe or drifting off course on their way to more northerly Continental sites, the records were scattered across the county and did not show a prevalence for the coast.

The annual numbers and seasonal pattern do not appear to have changed since the 1986–91 Atlas (*BoH*) although one found near Broxhead Common on October 31st 2007,

Hoopoe, New Forest, May 2010 – *Martin Bennett*

which stayed in the area until at least January 14th 2008, provided a very unusual winter record.

John Eyre

Bee-eater

Merops apiaster

A rare vagrant

Bee-eaters breed from southern Europe and Morocco to Kazakhstan (and also in South Africa). They have bred in the UK (including on the Isle of Wight in 2014) but never in Hampshire. Prior to the HBA period, there were 13 county records, all post 1950. A further 11 were added during the 2007–12 period, although the first of these pre-dated the start of the HBA recording period. 2008 was an exceptional year with seven individuals including a party of five. All records are given below:

2007: Sandy Point, August 9th.
2008: Cadman's Pool, five on May 11th. These birds remained in the area for a few days and were probably seen flying north on May 14th.
Beaulieu Road/Denny Wood, May 23rd.
West Hayling, July 14th.

Bee-eater, Spain – *Martin Bennett*

2012: Lower Test Marshes, May 5th.
South Hayling, May 17th.
Titchfield Haven, July 28th/29th.

John Eyre

Sponsored by Simon Colenutt (of ECOSA Ltd)

Blue-cheeked Bee-eater

Merops persicus

A very rare vagrant

This attractive species breeds in North Africa and the Middle East from eastern Turkey to Kazakhstan and India. The first for Hampshire and ninth for Britain was seen and photographed at Needs Ore on June 21st 2009. A bee-eater was also seen at the same site on June 23rd but the views were inadequate to determine whether it was this species or the more familiar *M. apiaster* of southern Europe.

John Eyre

Blue-cheeked Bee-eater, Needs Ore Point, June 2009
– *Caroline and Alan Dawson*

Wryneck
Jynx torquilla

A very scarce passage migrant which formerly bred

The Wryneck has a very large breeding range extending across the temperate regions of Eurasia from Spain to China, but numbers in west and central Europe have been on a long-term downward trend, the reasons for which are unclear. The species is now virtually extinct as a breeder in the UK with only one record of probable breeding in Scotland during *Bird Atlas 2007–11*.

Wrynecks last bred in Hampshire in 1975. Their decline prior to then and their subsequent status as passage migrants have been documented in *BoH*. During the 2007–12 period, the species was seen in every year (*Table 29*),

Year	2007	2008	2009	2010	2011	2012
Spring	0	0	2	2	2	5
Autumn	12	10	4	10	9	7
Total	12	10	6	12	11	12

Table 29 – Wrynecks recorded in Hampshire 2007–12.

mostly in September and October, and therefore outside the HBA recording periods.

Annual numbers may have increased slightly over the past two decades but whether this is real or a result of better observer coverage is not clear. With the ongoing withdrawal of the population from Western Europe, it seems unlikely that we will see Wryneck return to breed in Hampshire in the foreseeable future.

John Eyre

Sponsored by Martin Bennett

Wryneck, Pennington,
September 2011 – *Martin Bennett*

Green Woodpecker

Picus viridis

A common resident

In Britain, Green Woodpeckers occur at their greatest densities in south-east England (*Bird Atlas 2007–11*). Their far-carrying and distinctive laugh-like call is a well-known sound in the Hampshire countryside. This, coupled with the habit of visiting garden lawns, playing fields and parks in search of ants, their main food source, makes this a conspicuous and familiar species in the county.

They are widespread across Hampshire, with breeding considered likely in more than 90% of the county's tetrads. They are particularly common in the New Forest and on the north-east heaths where the combination of scattered trees and an abundance of ants provide ideal habitat. Counts during the HBA period found the highest densities in these areas with a maximum of six territories per sq. km on Longmoor Inclosure in the Wealden Heaths SPA. They are also common in the main river valleys but more thinly spread across the intensively-cultivated areas on the chalk. In less disturbed downland areas, such as Porton Down, numbers are higher, suggesting that the absence of arable farming provides more suitable conditions, probably by allowing ant colonies to develop undisturbed and retaining generally higher densities of soil invertebrates.

Nationally, Green Woodpecker numbers increased markedly through the second half of the 20th century. *BBS* data show a continuing growth of 38% in south-east England over the 17 year period from 1995 to 2011. The HBA change map confirms a corresponding range increase in Hampshire between the two atlases with notable infilling of occupied tetrads on the central chalk and around Portsmouth. The reason for the population growth is not clear but is probably associated with the long run of comparatively mild winters from the mid-1980s onwards. For such a specialised feeder, largely dependent on ants and other soil invertebrates, heavy snowfall and frozen ground must make feeding difficult. This vulnerability to cold winters is consistent with recent *BBS* data, which show that the population in south-east England declined in 2009, 2010 and 2011, three years with unusually harsh winters in the region.

Adult Green Woodpeckers are sedentary, so it is to be expected that the HBA winter map shows a distribution very similar to that in summer with the highest densities again in the non-agricultural areas. Post-breeding dispersal of immatures might be expected to result in a wider distribution in winter than during the breeding season but this is not apparent from the HBA results. The most likely reason for this is that, despite their size and colour, they can be less easy to find in winter than in summer when their call draws immediate attention to their presence.

John Eyre

Sponsored by Betty Hansell

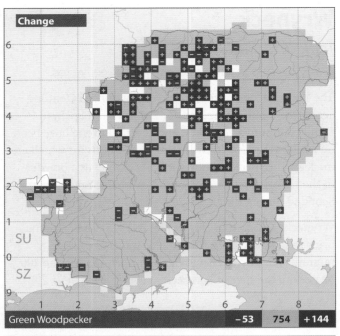

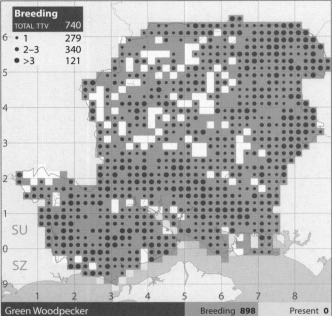

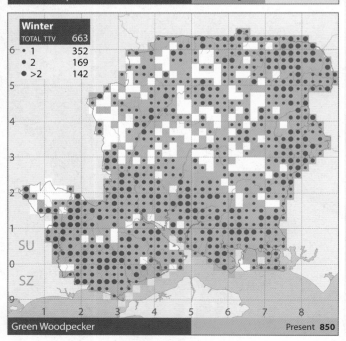

Green Woodpecker, New Forest, November 2010 – *Martin Bennett* (above); New Forest, August 2014 – *Martin Bennett* (below)

Great Spotted Woodpecker,
New Forest, May 2010.
— Martin Bennett.

Great Spotted Woodpecker

Dendrocopos major

A common resident

During a period when many of our native woodland and farmland birds have declined, the Great Spotted Woodpecker has bucked the trend. Over the past 50 years, its national population has multiplied and its range has expanded. In the UK, its population increased fivefold between 1967 and 2011 (*BirdTrends*) and, during the current Atlas period, it colonised Ireland. A number of factors may have contributed to its success including the increased availability of nest sites resulting from Dutch elm disease and reduced competition for those sites from the declining number of Starlings.

The status of the species in Hampshire is consistent with the national picture. At the beginning of the 20th Century, Great Spotted Woodpeckers were "nowhere common" (*K&M*) but numbers increased dramatically, particularly in the second half of the century. Today it is by far the commonest of our resident woodpeckers, occurring wherever there are trees big enough to provide suitable nest sites. This includes not only well-wooded countryside and rural areas but also urban parks and gardens.

Although it was already common in Hampshire by the time of the 1986–91 Atlas, its breeding range has continued to expand over the past twenty years. The HBA breeding season maps show that it is now found in over 93% of tetrads, up from 85% in 1986–91. The range expansion has occurred mainly on the chalk. Only a few gaps remain, notably in the most urbanised areas of Portsmouth and Gosport and, at the other extreme, in the wide open spaces of Martin Down. While confirmation of breeding was lower in the current atlas, Great Spotted Woodpecker is a largely sedentary species, so its presence in a tetrad during the summer would most probably be indicative of breeding. The accompanying breeding and change maps have been produced on that basis. The highest densities were found in the New Forest and north-east with lower numbers across the agricultural heartland of the county.

Not surprisingly, the winter map shows a similar distribution to that in summer with an even higher number of occupied tetrads. This may be because birds are more easily seen when the trees are bare. It is also likely that they wander more widely in search of food and regularly visit garden feeders during the winter. Taken together, the winter and summer maps show that Great Spotted Woodpecker can now be found almost everywhere in the county.

John Eyre

Sponsored by Nigel Allen

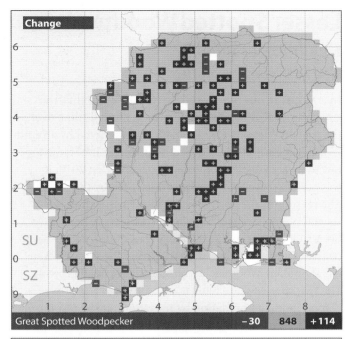

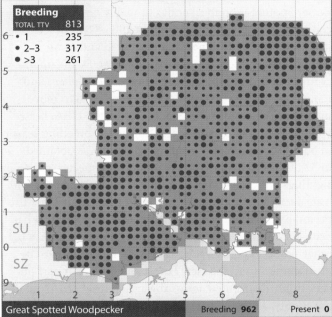

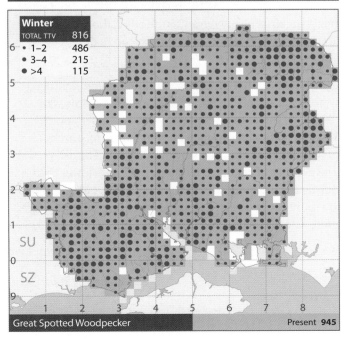

Lesser Spotted Woodpecker
Dendrocopos minor
A scarce and declining resident

In contrast to our other resident woodpeckers this, the smallest of the three, has undergone a rapid decline over the past 30 years. Its UK population plummeted by around 75% between 1980 and 2000, at which time it became too low to be accurately monitored by the *BBS*. In 2010, it was added to the list of species monitored by the RBBP. The reason for the decline is not known and although several possible causes have been considered, most have been ruled out as unlikely (Fuller *et al.* 2005). It may be no coincidence that it has occurred during the period when Great Spotted Woodpecker numbers have been growing. The two species share habitat and, although not proven, competition and predation by the latter may be responsible, at least in part, for the demise of its smaller relative

Lesser Spotted Woodpecker has probably never been common in Hampshire although in 1905 *K&M* described it as "certainly more generally distributed and more plentiful than" Great Spotted Woodpecker. By the middle of the 20th century this order had reversed (*Cohen*) and the fortunes of the two species have continued to move in opposite directions ever since. During the HBA, Lesser Spotted Woodpecker was found during the breeding season in only 150 tetrads. No breeding evidence was obtained in 37 of these but, since this is a sedentary species, most sightings are likely to be indicative of nearby breeding and have been included as such on the breeding map. Over the period between the two Hampshire breeding atlases it has been lost from 246 tetrads and found in 68 new ones, a net range reduction of 178 tetrads or 54%. It continues to be most numerous in the New Forest and the north-east but very thinly distributed across the agricultural heartland of the county. As the change map shows, it has declined in all areas. No counts during the breeding season located more than two birds in any tetrad so the population estimate of 700 pairs in *BoH* is now probably far too high.

Not surprisingly, the winter map shows a similar distribution to that in summer although some sightings were in tetrads where no breeding season records were obtained. This is to be expected because Lesser Spotted Woodpeckers range more widely in winter in search of food, often in the company of other small birds. The number of occupied tetrads, at 111, was lower than during the breeding season but this may be because they are more easily detected in the early spring when they are more actively calling and drumming.

John Eyre

Sponsored by Robert Pearl

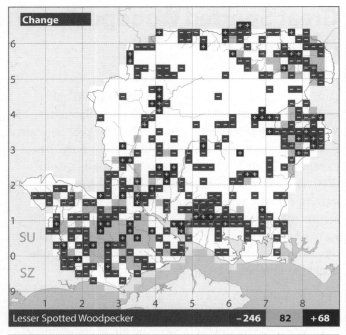

Lesser Spotted Woodpecker — Change: −246 | 82 | +68

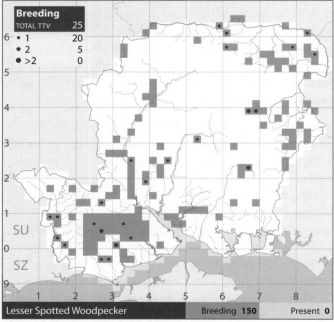

Breeding — TOTAL TTV 25
• 1   20
• 2   5
• >2   0

Lesser Spotted Woodpecker — Breeding 150   Present 0

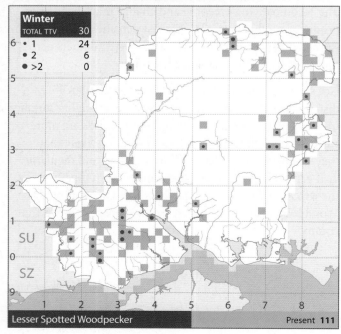

Winter — TOTAL TTV 30
• 1   24
• 2   6
• >2   0

Lesser Spotted Woodpecker — Present 111

Lesser Spotted Woodpecker,
New Forest, March 2015
– *Mike Darling* (above);
Blashford Lakes, April 2008
– *Martin Bennett* (left)

Kestrel

Falco tinnunculus

A common resident, passage migrant and winter visitor

Although the Kestrel remains common and widespread across Britain it has suffered a large fall in numbers, with *Bird Atlas 2007–11* highlighting a 44% population decline since 1970. Reductions in England have been less marked with a fall of 21% over the 1995–2012 period (*BirdTrends*).

In Hampshire the species is found in a variety of habitats including open farmland containing hedgerows, trees and small woods, downland, coastal marsh and in urban areas. It does not like large wooded areas and, although found on heaths, has never been common in the New Forest, probably due to high grazing pressure which precludes an abundance of small mammals. It is a relatively sedentary species being found in similar numbers in both the breeding season and during the winter, although observational evidence and ringing data confirm that some passage and movement in and out of the county do occur.

The HBA change map highlights a 6% range reduction with a net loss of 52 tetrads compared with the 1986–91 Atlas. Gains and losses were approximately balanced across much of the county but with noticeably more losses in and around the New Forest. It may be coincidence but this area forms the core for the county's Goshawk population, which has been implicated in the decline of the Kestrel population elsewhere in the UK (Petty *et al.* 2003). That said, *BBS* results shows that Kestrel numbers have declined

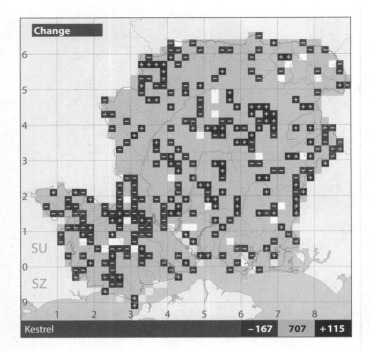

Kestrel   −167   707   +115

more generally across south-east England, including much of our mainly farmed landscape, probably due to changes in agricultural practice and widespread use of rodenticides. Competition for prey with a massively increased Buzzard population could also be a contributing factor.

The Kestrel remains a widespread species in Hampshire, still being found in every 10 km square, but is far less abundant than it once was.

Andy Page

Sponsored by Archie Simpson

Kestrel, Pennington, July 2012 – *Martin Bennett*

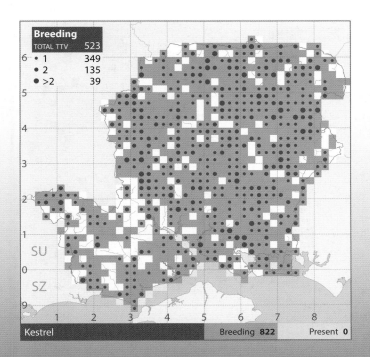

Breeding
TOTAL TTV 523

•	1	349
•	2	135
•	>2	39

Kestrel　　　　　　　　　　　　Breeding **822**　　Present **0**

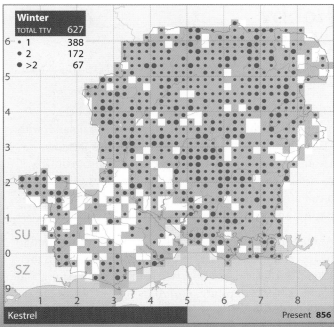

Winter
TOTAL TTV 627

•	1	388
•	2	172
•	>2	67

Kestrel　　　　　　　　　　　　　　　　　Present **856**

Kestrel, Fordingbridge, October 2010 – *Martin Bennett*

Hobby

Falco subbuteo

A moderately common summer visitor and passage migrant

This dashing migrant falcon has traditionally been associated with the heathlands of southern England, with Hampshire's New Forest, Thames Basin and Wealden Heaths being particular strongholds. It is also regularly recorded along the river valleys and we now know that it can also be encountered across much of the county's farmed and wooded landscape.

At the time of the 1988–91 Atlas, the Hobby was found to be spreading northwards in the UK. Compared with the 1968–72 Atlas, it had also made gains, even in stronghold counties like Hampshire. *Bird Atlas 2007–11* showed further consolidation of range in southern England and additional expansion in the north and west.

In Hampshire the HBA breeding distribution map shows the species to be widespread across the county with its presence noted in 403 tetrads, a significant increase over the 216 tetrads in the 1986–91 Atlas. In contrast, the change map shows an apparent reduction in tetrads where breeding was considered likely from 115 to 75, with many of the losses concentrated in the south-west, particularly in the New Forest. In both cases the numbers are based only on probable and confirmed breeding records so this decline could reflect the lack of breeding evidence apparent across the HBA data. However, Hobbies range widely while hunting and are notoriously difficult to prove breeding. They can be particularly inconspicuous until noisy young indicate their presence in August, beyond the end of the Atlas survey period (although all appropriate records beyond the end of the HBA breeding season were incorporated into the breeding maps). Given these uncertainties, great caution is needed when interpreting the survey results.

That said, there is a perception amongst some observers that Hobbies are less easily seen in the New Forest now than they once were, with some regular breeding areas apparently vacated in recent years and even some local declines. Day-flying heathland moths, once a key food source for Hobbies, are far less common than they were at the time of the 1986–91 Atlas, a recent Butterfly Conservation report showing a massive 40% decline in abundance of many of our macro-moth species (Fox *et al.* 2013). The presence of increasing numbers of Goshawks at many of the Hobby's core New Forest sites may also be a factor affecting site occupation. This, coupled with recent drops in hirundine numbers, which are an important food source for the species during the fledging period, may explain some of these perceptions and could lie behind a small but real decline.

The most recent comprehensive study of Hobbies in the Forest, carried out in 1981 and 1982, found between 12

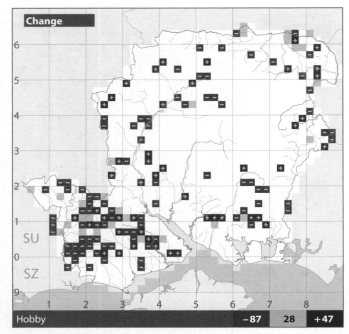

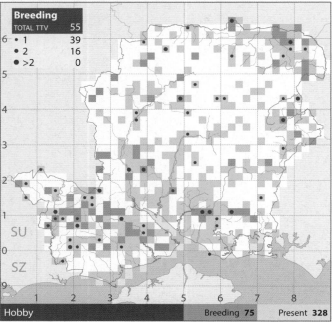

and 16 pairs and, as far back as 1954, the population was estimated at around 12 pairs (Parr 1985). With around twenty New Forest sites having held breeding Hobbies since that study and a cursory survey undertaken during 2012 and 2013 finding a minimum of ten sites occupied (A. Page & S. Curry unpublished), this suggests that the present breeding population may not be too dissimilar from those previous studies. A further comprehensive survey of breeding Hobbies in the New Forest is needed to properly address these uncertainties.

Away from the New Forest and south-west of the county, the HBA maps show a more balanced picture of gains and losses. Overall, the widespread distribution of sightings across the county suggests a sizeable and healthy population.

Andy Page

Sponsored by Geoff Rapley

Red-footed Falcon

Falco vespertinus

A rare non-breeding summer visitor and passage migrant

The Red-footed Falcon is a scarce and irregular visitor to Hampshire. During the 2007–12 period it occurred only in 2008 and 2010.

During 2008 at least five individuals were recorded in the county, the first since 2005. Nearly all sightings came from the New Forest, with the Beaulieu Road Station/Shatterford area a favoured site. A first-summer female was at Ridley Plain on May 10th and an adult male was at Beaulieu Road on May 13th, where it was joined by a first-summer male on the 23rd. At least one was present there until June 1st. A first-summer male was at Holm Hill near Brockenhurst from May 13th–15th. Outside the New Forest, a first-summer male was seen heading north over Ibsley Water in the Avon Valley on May 18th and a female in the Itchen Valley on September 20th was only the third ever autumn record.

In 2010, a juvenile at Hawkhill Inclosure in the New Forest on October 10th brought the number of autumn records to four and the county total since 1950 to 55.

Andy Page

Sponsored by Martin Bennett

Red-footed Falcon, New Forest, May 2008 – *Mike Darling*

Peregrine
Falco peregrinus

A scarce but increasing breeder, winter visitor and passage migrant

Although regularly nesting in neighbouring counties, the only historic record of Peregrines breeding in Hampshire is of a pair that nested in heather at the base of a Scots Pine on a west Hampshire heath in 1928. The species only started to breed regularly in the county in 1993. Until this time it was mainly a winter visitor from September to March. Organised killing of Peregrines during World War II had reduced the population in many places and, after the war, the side effects of organochlorine pesticides caused a further, more serious decline by increasing nest failure and adult mortality.

After decades of challenge the species started to recover following the banning of DDT in the 1980s; breeding recommenced in Dorset and Sussex. Sightings in Hampshire grew in line with this expansion and in 1993 a pair nested on the chimney of Fawley Power Station. A pair has since nested annually at this site without a break. In 1995 a nest was built on a pylon near to Marchwood and was subsequently used for nine years in succession. A nest box was installed on Sway Tower in 2000, but the pair continually failed to rear chicks. Over time more pylon nests were occupied, particularly on the small ledge that is part of the design on the tension towers, placed where the pylon line changes direction. Other pylons are used, but usually only when an unoccupied corvid nest is available as a platform.

By the start of the HBA period there were nine pairs nesting on a variety of structures and in 2008 the first of two quarry sites was used. The number of pairs nesting in 2009–12 totalled 9, 11, 11 and 10, although it is likely that a number of nests were not detected.

Unfortunately the failure rate on pylons and some other man-made structures is considerably higher than on more natural cliff-type sites. Pylons and open roof-tops are often quite susceptible to the effects of bad weather and human disturbance. In a number of counties the local Peregrines have benefited from the erection of nest boxes and, with natural sites being at a premium, counties such as Hampshire can do a lot to encourage Peregrines. Following the HBA, the placing of two new nest boxes in Winchester and Southampton in 2013 resulted in immediate success, and a total of 14 pairs attempted to breed in the county. This included seven pairs within 2 km of Southampton Water – all nesting on man-made structures.

Most adult Peregrines remain in their nesting territories throughout the year. Sub-adults remain with their parents into their first winter but are chased away at the beginning of the new breeding season. Peregrines are more widely distributed outside the breeding season than during

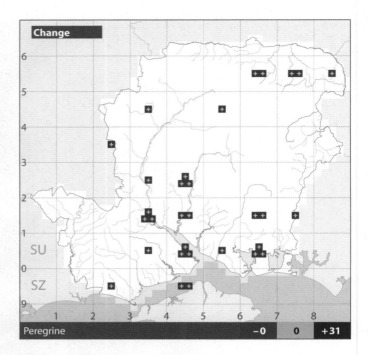

it and the HBA winter map shows that many of these birds frequent the coast. This is no surprise given the concentrations of suitable prey such as wildfowl and waders to be found there. Farther inland there were many sightings from areas of farmland and downland. These birds often use buildings, pylons, towers and other structures as their vantage points from which to spot passing prey, particularly Feral Pigeons.

The Peregrine is still regarded as being of conservation concern in both a European and a UK context but after having suffered at the hands of man for many years, this top predator is now benefiting from human intervention. Even so, for security reasons the HBA breeding map does not distinguish between breeding and presence tetrads, and the change map has been plotted at 10 sq. km resolution.

Keith Betton

Sponsored by Janet & Richard Jacobs

Peregrine, New Forest, August 2010– *Martin Bennett*

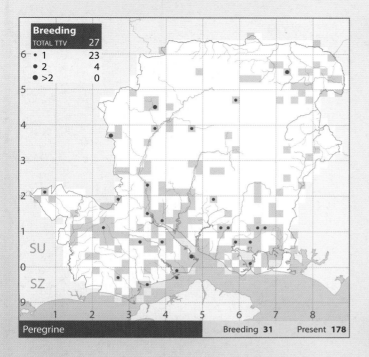

Breeding
TOTAL TTV 27
- 1   23
- 2   4
- >2   0

Peregrine   Breeding **31**   Present **178**

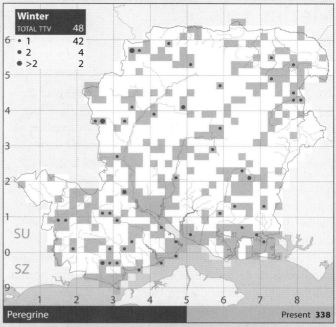

Winter
TOTAL TTV 48
- 1   42
- 2   4
- >2   2

Peregrine   Present **338**

Peregrine, Winchester, May 2015 – *Richard Jacobs*

271

Merlin

Falco columbarius

A scarce winter visitor and passage migrant

The Merlin is a breeding species of heather moorland in Scotland, northern England, Wales and Devon, but does not breed on the heaths of Hampshire. It is the smallest of our falcons and feeds on small passerines, particularly the pipits, larks and chats associated with its breeding habitat.

Bird Atlas 2007–11 shows a mixed picture of gains and losses for Britain. There has been a further reduction in the Merlin breeding population of south-west England on top of losses noted in the *1988–91 Atlas*. Elsewhere there has been some range expansion but overall breeding numbers have declined over recent years. In winter Merlin numbers are supplemented by Continental visitors, particularly from Iceland.

In Hampshire the Merlin is a scarce and easily overlooked winter visitor and passage migrant. It is regularly recorded along the coastal strip where small passerines are often more abundant in times of harsh weather and where the regular presence of birdwatchers ensures the submission of these sightings. The species is also seen in the New Forest particularly in the north, and along the river valleys and chalk downland zones of the county as can be seen from the HBA map.

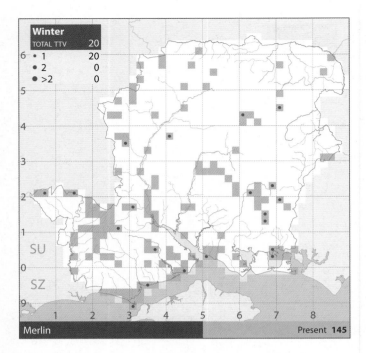

Returning birds first appear in the county around the end of August/early September and some stay through to the end of April when some coastal passage is often noted as well. Annual numbers in the county fluctuate from month to month but no more than 20–30 individuals are thought to be involved.

Andy Page

Sponsored by Ade Parker

Merlin, Sandy Point, September 2010 – *Andy Johnson*

Ring-necked Parakeet
Psittacula krameri
A very scarce and possibly only transitory resident and visitor

Since the first Hampshire record in 1972, there has been an expectation that colonisation by this fast-increasing species was inevitable and probably imminent. However, records have increased only very slowly in recent years and there is still no confirmed breeding record for the county. During the HBA, records came from 25 scattered tetrads occurring in both summer and winter, although only four locations were common to both seasons. No meaningful pattern on either timing or location has yet emerged, although more birds are seen in the east and along the coastal strip than elsewhere. While it is probable that these originate from the burgeoning populations in Surrey, Greater London and Kent, it is possible that some are local escapees. Regular records in the Lymington area may refer to the same individuals cropping up from time to time.

Colonisation of Surrey from the west London strongholds has been quite spectacular in recent years and birds now breed no more than 20 km from the Hampshire border. Whether the range expansion will be sustained in the years ahead remains to be seen. The next Hampshire Atlas will document either colonisation or continuing perplexity as to why it has not happened yet!

Simon Woolley

Ring-necked Parakeet, Brockenhurst, November 2013 – *Paul Brock*

Golden Oriole
Oriolus oriolus
A rare passage migrant; has bred

The Golden Oriole breeds across Europe, absent only from more northern latitudes. In the UK there is a very small breeding population at Lakenheath Fen in Suffolk and occasional breeding has occurred in Hampshire, most recently in 1987. Between 1950 and 2007 there were 57 records; a further five were added over the HBA period as follows:

2008: Burley, May 15th/16th.
2009: Eyeworth Pond, May 10th.
      Plastow Green, June 5th.
2011: New Forest, May 15th.
2012: Slufters Inclosure, May 15th.

John Eyre

Sponsored by Alan Snook

Golden Oriole, Pennington, April 2013 – *David Cuddon*

Great Grey Shrike
Lanius excubitor
A very scarce winter visitor and passage migrant

Small numbers of this northern breeding species winter in Hampshire every year. Most occur in the New Forest with additional, but less regular, birds recorded at heathland sites in the north-east. There are also occasional records from coastal sites and areas of farmland and downland, but these are usually either early or late in the winter suggesting that they are passage birds. Most records are of lone individuals, with occasionally two together. The birds normally depart in April.

HBA records from the New Forest suggest that in the five winters 2007/08–2011/12 there were four, four, two, four and three territories respectively. In each year the first birds arrived in October, however often there was only one reported regularly for several weeks, with others seeming to appear in December. Similarly birds were sometimes not reported for a month or more, often to reappear again in January or February.

Great Grey Shrikes can be frustrating birds to study. They hunt for flying insects, small mammals and birds and, despite their tendency to perch up on obvious bushes and small trees, they frequently vanish from sight for long periods. It is known that individual birds may frequent more than one feeding area and may travel 2 km or more across suitable habitat. With such a large feeding territory each bird may maintain several larders of stored food. It is therefore conceivable that a single bird may frequent several areas and give the impression that more than one is present. Although the accompanying map suggests presence across a large section of the New Forest, during the HBA period the birds generally favoured six areas:

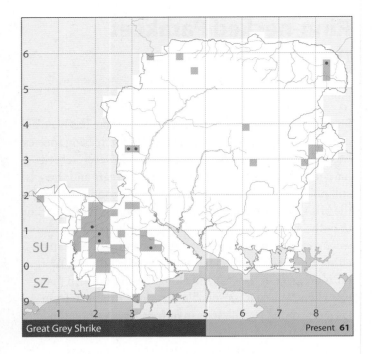

Great Grey Shrike — Present **61**

- Leaden Hall/Black Gutter Bottom/Ashley Walk.
- Latchmore Bottom/Ogdens Purlieu/Hampton Ridge.
- Handy Cross Plain/Buckherd Bottom/Broomy Plain/ Ocknell Plain.
- Bratley Plain/Backley Plain/Ridley Plain.
- Beaulieu Road/Bishops Dyke/Pig Bush.
- Vales Moor/Cranes Moor/Holmsley.

Other nearby areas that held birds on numerous dates included Holm Hill, Ibsley Common, Acres Down, Half Moon Common, Furzley Common and Rhinefield Walk.

In three of the HBA winters a bird was seen at Woolmer Forest on at least one date. Although birds clearly winter here in some years, access problems to the military site make recording difficult. This site may also be used on passage too.

Great Grey Shrike,
New Forest, March 2014
– *Martin Bennett*

Recent analysis of the UK wintering population shows that numbers have declined since the *1981–84 Winter Atlas* (Fraser & Ryan 1995). This trend is supported by HOS data, which show that on average there were larger numbers in the 1960s and 1970s. Numbers reached a low point in 1985/86, with only two in the New Forest and none located elsewhere in the county. The breeding populations over most of north-west and central Europe have declined markedly since the 1960s. It is thought that most birds visiting the UK originate in Scandinavia, particularly Norway.

Keith Betton

Sponsored by Adam Parsonage

Woodchat Shrike

Lanius senator

A very rare vagrant

There were two records during the HBA period, bringing the county total to eight:

2012:   A probable first summer female, Keyhaven, May 12th/13th.

A probable first-summer male, Martin Down, May 20th/21st.

John Eyre

Woodchat Shrike, Martin Down, May 2012 – *Alan Lewis*

Red-backed Shrike

Lanius collurio

A very scarce passage migrant

The Red-backed Shrike was lost as a Hampshire breeding species in the years leading up to the 1986–91 Atlas. Its last known breeding attempt was near Overton in 1984 when a pair successfully raised two young (*BoH*). Subsequently it has become a very scarce spring and autumn migrant. During 2007–12 there were records in all years other than 2011 but only one, in July 2012, fell into the HBA recording periods. All records for 2007–12 are given below bringing the county total to 56 since the last breeding in 1984:

2007:   Normandy Marsh, a female on June 9th.
Yateley Common, a male on June 20th.
Mill Rythe, Hayling Island, a juvenile from September 1st–14th.

2008:   Pennington Marsh, a juvenile from September 27th–October 11th.

2009:   Lower Pennington Lane, a Juvenile on August 16th.
West Hayling, a juvenile on August 18th.

2010:   Southampton West Docks, a juvenile on September 8th.
IBM Lake, an adult on September 10th.

2012:   Cheriton Mill, a male on July 26th.

John Eyre

Sponsored by Martin Bennett

Red-backed Shrike, Hayling Island, August 2009 – *Steve Copsey*

Magpie

Pica pica

A numerous resident

As with most other corvids, the Magpie is a highly adaptable and successful species. It is an opportunistic, omnivorous feeder which has benefited greatly from the increase in domestic waste and road-kills resulting from urban spread and growth of traffic. This, coupled with lower levels of persecution and improved breeding success, combined to bring about a doubling of the national population over the period leading up to the 1986–91 Hampshire Atlas. Since then, numbers have stabilised with only minor changes in the English population over the 1995–2012 period (*BirdTrends*). This suggests that numbers may now have reached an all-time-high plateau level.

The HBA breeding maps show that the species is widespread across the county. During the survey, breeding was considered likely in 93% of tetrads with 20% having more than 12 birds present, although these counts do not differentiate between breeding and non-breeding birds. Those tetrads with the highest densities are clustered around urban areas, particularly Southampton, Fareham and Havant in the south and Aldershot, Farnborough and Basingstoke in the north. The few gaps in its distribution are most noticeable on the Downs in the centre and north of the county, where Magpies are probably still controlled by gamekeepers, and in the New Forest.

The change map shows the breeding distribution has remained broadly similar to that at the time of the previous atlas although the gaps currently showing in the New Forest are a new and surprising feature (see also Jackdaw and Jay). There is still some culling of Magpies in the Forest and there is evidence from remains found at Goshawk nests that this top predator, which is increasing in numbers, includes them, along with many other bird species, in its prey.

The Magpie is a sedentary species with adult pairs often remaining on their territories throughout the year. However, in winter, post-breeding dispersal of first-year birds results in a more widespread distribution than in summer. In winter, as the HBA map shows, Magpies were found in almost every tetrad with counts of more than eight birds in almost a third of them. In common with the breeding distribution, the tetrads with the highest densities were clustered around urban areas. Magpies often roost communally in the winter and large pre-roost gatherings are often reported; Fishlake Meadows and Fleet Pond are examples of areas where such roosts regularly occur.

Richard Carpenter

Sponsored by John & Kay Shillitoe

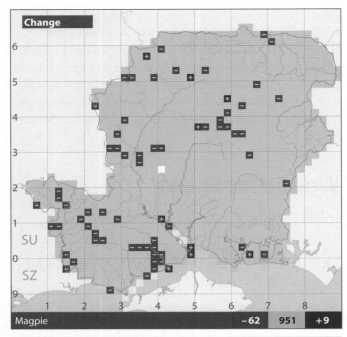

Change | Magpie | −62 | 951 | +9

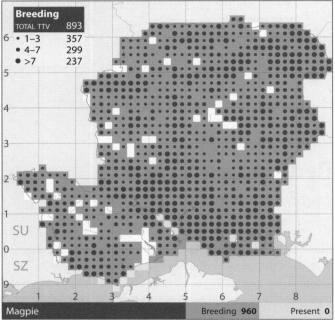

Breeding
TOTAL TTV 893
• 1–3 357
• 4–7 299
• >7 237
Magpie | Breeding 960 | Present 0

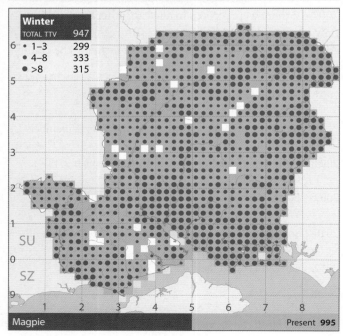

Winter
TOTAL TTV 947
• 1–3 299
• 4–8 333
• >8 315
Magpie | Present 995

Magpie, Blashford Lakes, June 2011 – *Martin Bennett* (above) Hayling Island, September 2011 – *Andy Johnson* (below)

Jay
Garrulus glandarius
A numerous resident and passage migrant

Although less common than most other members of the crow family, the Jay is a widespread and successful species. The national population has fluctuated but, overall, has remained stable showing no long term upward or downward trend (*BirdTrends*). Following the 1986–91 Atlas, it was noted that there was no evidence to suggest a different picture in Hampshire (*BoH*).

The HBA breeding maps show that the species remains widespread across the county. It is found predominantly in broadleaved woodland but also occurs in mixed and conifer plantations, wooded farmland, parks and gardens. It is most common in the north-east and south-west but patchily distributed across the chalk. Breeding was considered likely in 83% of tetrads. Those tetrads with the highest densities are in woodland in the north-east and east of the county with concentrations in the Forest of Bere and some parts of the New Forest. Absence is most noticeable on the New Forest heaths, in some extensively farmed and downland areas, and in the south-east around Havant and Hayling Island.

The change map shows that the breeding distribution has remained broadly similar to that during the 1986–91 Atlas. Overall there has apparently been a small range contraction of around 8% which, coincidentally, matches the population decline in south-east England over the 1995–2011 period as measured by the *BBS*. The gaps which have appeared in the New Forest are a new and surprising feature (see also Magpie). As with Magpies, there is still some culling of Jays in the Forest and also evidence that the rapidly increasing population of Goshawks may prey on them. However, for the county as a whole, over the period between atlases it would seem that the no major change in the status of the species has occurred. In general, the population has remained stable and given continuing low levels of persecution and more urban tree planting this situation is likely to persist into the future.

The Jay is a highly sedentary species with adult pairs often remaining on their territories throughout the year. However, even though first-year birds do not generally move very far, post-breeding dispersal does result in a more widespread distribution in winter than in summer. Winter numbers in some years are also supplemented by autumnal irruptions and movements following food shortages, especially failure of the acorn crop in northern Britain and the near Continent. No such irruption occurred during the Atlas period although one followed immediately after the fieldwork was finished in the autumn of 2012. In winter, as the HBA map shows, Jays were found in over 91% of tetrads with their distribution and relative densities being broadly similar to those found during the breeding season.

Richard Carpenter

Sponsored by Rachel Hodgkinson

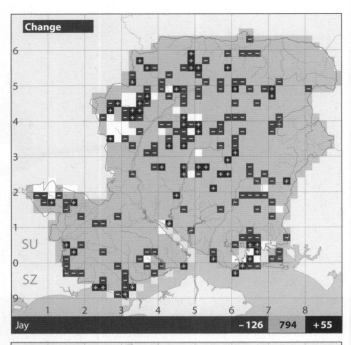

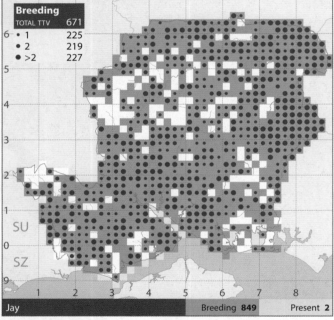

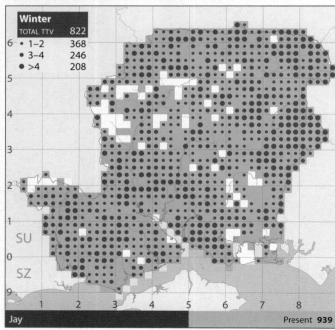

Jay, New Forest, January 2013 – *Martin Bennett* (above); New Forest, October 2008 (below)

Jackdaw

Corvus monedula

A numerous resident

Like other members of the corvid family, the Jackdaw, the smallest of the tribe, is a highly adaptable and successful species. It is at home in both rural and built-up areas wherever there are suitable nest sites and adequate food supplies. It generally has little difficulty finding either, able to nest in holes in trees or cavities in buildings and, being omnivorous, able to eat a wide variety of both vegetable and animal material. In fact increasing food availability, particularly in urban areas, may explain the Jackdaw's improved breeding performance and increasing population. Over the 1967–2011 period, numbers in England more than doubled with the growth rate getting steeper in recent years (*BirdTrends*).

The HBA breeding maps show that the species is widespread and common across Hampshire with breeding considered likely in 94% of tetrads. Numbers are fairly evenly spread with the higher densities tending to be in the north-east and south-west and generally lower in the south. The largest gap in its breeding distribution is in the conurbation around Portsmouth Harbour. There is also a scatter of unoccupied tetrads elsewhere, particularly on the chalk and in open areas of the New Forest, where there may be a lack of suitable nesting sites.

The change map shows that, in keeping with an increasing population, the breeding distribution has expanded slightly since the 1986–91 Atlas. An additional 33 tetrads have been occupied with noticeable infilling in the south, particularly along the north coast of Southampton Water, and in the east. A few tetrads have apparently been vacated, including a cluster in the New Forest.

The Jackdaw is a gregarious species, often nesting in colonies and, in autumn and winter, congregating in feeding flocks and large communal roosts. The feeding flocks sometimes associate with other corvids and move opportunistically in search of food. In agricultural areas flocks occur on grassland, arable fields and stubble; in urban areas on playing fields, waste ground and rubbish tips, wherever there is food. During the HBA winter surveys, Jackdaws were found in 95% of Hampshire tetrads with TTV counts of 12 or more in almost 60% of them. Four-figure counts of feeding and roost flocks are made occasionally. During the HBA period, the species was well recorded in 2008 with counts of 1,900 at Appleshaw on January 14th, 1,550 at Somerley Estate on December 21st, 1,300 at Lakeside on January 17th, 1,300 leaving roost at Itchen Valley Country Park on December 21st and 1,000 at Greywell on December 29th.

Richard Carpenter

Sponsored by Geoff Rapley

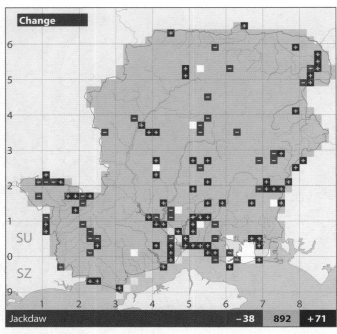

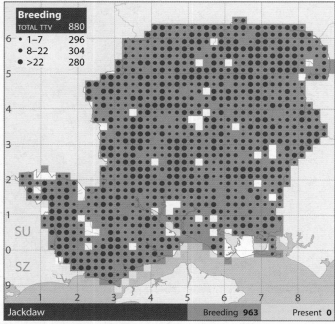

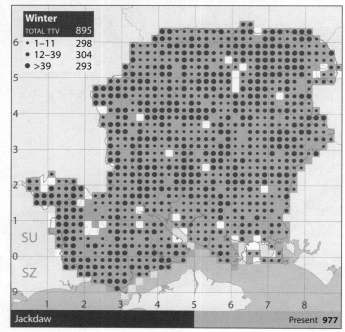

Jackdaw, New Forest, February 2010 – *Martin Bennett* (above); Jackdaw, New Forest, June 2015 – *Martin Bennett* (below)

Rook

Corvus frugilegus

A numerous resident and probable winter visitor

The Rook, a widespread and familiar British corvid, shares the family characteristics as an intelligent, adaptable and successful species. However, in contrast to other common family members, it is almost entirely restricted to agricultural areas and its UK population has declined in recent years. Following an increase of around 40% between 1975 and 1996, numbers began to fall. By 2012, they were some 20% lower than at their peak at the turn of the century (*BirdTrends*). The picture varies across the country with increases in some lowland areas and declines particularly in the Scottish uplands (*Bird Atlas 2007–11*). The reasons for the ups and downs are not known but are most likely connected to changes in farming practices, particularly the reduction in mixed farming, conversion of pasture to arable and less spring tillage, reducing the size and quality of suitable feeding areas. An increase in sheep husbandry in some areas may have provided an offsetting benefit.

In Hampshire, the HBA breeding map shows Rooks present in 83% of county tetrads but considered likely to be breeding in just under 50%. While proof of breeding is relatively easy to obtain for a species that nests in conspicuous, tree-top colonies, many Atlas records were submitted without any breeding evidence or in the possible and probable breeding categories. Some of the probable categories were considered insufficient to merit likely breeding status, so only records of nest building and above are included as such on the map.

The species is most numerous on the agricultural areas in the centre and north of the county, and in the main river valleys. There are significant gaps in breeding distribution in urban areas such as Southampton and Portsmouth, and on heathland in the New Forest, Thames Basin and the Weald. Large rookeries are located in the Itchen and Test Valleys but the biggest reported during the HBA period was near Middle Wallop, which contained 230 pairs in 2010. Also, despite their general absence from urban areas, in 2006 a small rookery was established in Hoglands Park in central Southampton and contained 23 nests in 2012, the final year of the Atlas.

Although the breeding distribution has remained broadly unchanged from the time of the 1986–91 Atlas, the change map indicates a surprisingly large range contraction of around 13%. While it is known that some traditional rookeries have been destroyed or abandoned, new rookeries have also been established elsewhere. The apparent range reduction may be an artefact of the methodology used here to compare the two Atlases but is of sufficient magnitude to merit a separate species-specific survey.

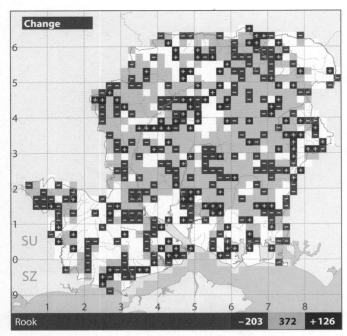

Change

Rook — -203 | 372 | +126

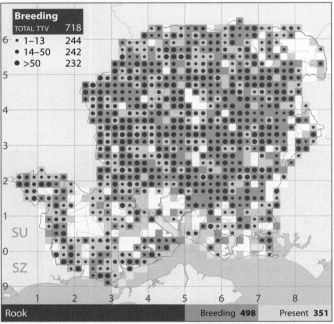

Breeding
TOTAL TTV 718
• 1–13   244
• 14–50 242
• >50   232

Rook — Breeding 498 | Present 351

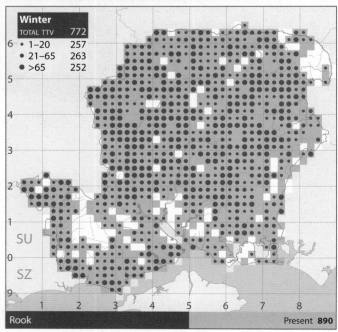

Winter
TOTAL TTV 772
• 1–20   257
• 21–65 263
• >65   252

Rook — Present 890

Rook, New Forest, September 2013 – *Martin Bennett* (right);
New Forest, March 2013 – *Martin Bennett* (below)

In winter Rooks tend to congregate in large feeding flocks and roost communally, often with other corvids. The flocks move opportunistically to pasture and arable, sometimes covering appreciable distances to find good feeding areas. As the HBA map shows, distribution in winter remains similar to that during the breeding season although slightly more tetrads are occupied, probably as a result of mobile flocks rather than numbers being swelled by winter visitors. Some movement within Britain and from the Continent does occur (*Migration Atlas*) but there is little evidence to suggest that large numbers of immigrants reach Hampshire.

Richard Carpenter

Sponsored by John Jones

Carrion Crow

Corvus corone

A numerous resident

The Carrion Crow is a widespread and successful species. It is one of a select few farmland birds that has expanded both its UK range and numbers since the 1968–72 Atlas. Other corvids, including Raven, Magpie and Jackdaw, are also doing well, possibly due in part to lower levels of persecution by gamekeepers, farmers and members of the public. However, the Carrion Crow is an adaptable species, able to utilise a wide range of habitats, including towns and cities, and to exploit a variety of food sources. The latter comprise grain and vegetable matter, urban food waste, road-kills and other carrion as well as live prey such as invertebrates, fledglings and larger quarry including adult birds and mammals. Evidence suggests that increased food availability has led to an improvement in breeding success and it is this that has driven their population increase (BirdTrends).

The HBA breeding map shows that the species is widespread and common across Hampshire. Breeding was considered likely in more than 99% of tetrads, with all but one of the few unoccupied squares on the coast and largely devoid of suitable habitat. The exceptional Crow-less tetrad, SU42C, west of Hursley, merits close attention to determine what makes this location so different from the rest of the county!

It is a conspicuous species so it is no surprise that breeding season TTV counts located more than ten individuals in roughly a third of tetrads with the highest densities generally in the south and east rather than in the agricultural areas of the north and west. Counts in excess of 100 were not uncommon. The old adage that a large black bird on its own is a Crow whereas similar birds in a flock are Rooks is clearly no longer sound advice!

The change map shows that the breeding distribution has expanded to fill the gaps existing at the time of the 1986–91 Hampshire Atlas, which were mostly on the chalk in the north-west of the county. The fact that many of these gaps were in agricultural areas containing plenty of suitable habitat tends to support the suggestion that high levels of persecution in these areas may have been responsible for their earlier absence.

The Carrion Crow is a sedentary species with adult pairs often remaining on their territories throughout the year. However, in winter, post-breeding dispersal of first-year birds results in higher numbers in some areas than in summer. Large flocks can be found particularly on the Solent shore at Brownwich/Chilling and along Southampton Water at Weston Shore. There are also large communal roosts at this time of year. Since the winter flocks contain many first year birds, which don't breed in their second calendar year, the flocks can persist into the spring of the following year, leading to the high numbers encountered during the

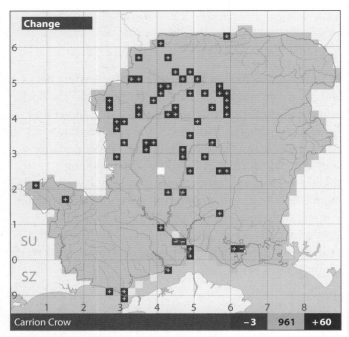

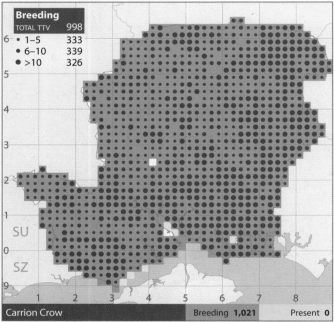

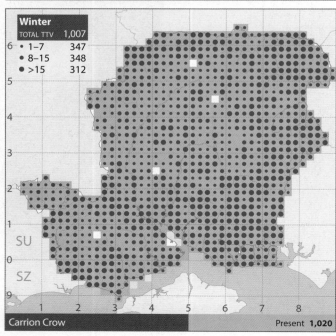

breeding season. As the HBA winter map shows, Carrion Crows were found in almost every Hampshire tetrad with counts of more than 15 birds in roughly a third of them and high counts sometimes exceeding 200.

Richard Carpenter

Sponsored by Mike Wildish

Carrion Crow, New Forest, October 2009 – *Martin Bennett*

Raven

Corvus corax

A scarce but increasing resident

The Raven was evidently quite widespread in Hampshire until the middle of the 19th century but a combination of persecution and the progressive switch from sheep husbandry to cereal cultivation was no doubt the cause of a rapid decline (D.E. Glue *in litt.*), with the last nesting recorded in 1887 (*K&M*). There were few records for the first half of the 20th century but, in the period between 1951 and 1992, Ravens were recorded in 22 years involving a total of 33 individuals, mostly from the south-west of the county (*BoH*). The frequency of sightings increased rapidly during the 1990s, with a total of eight 'bird-months' in 1992–94, 69 in 1995–98, 52 in 1999 alone, 91 in 2000, 127 in 2001 and 258 in 2002. In the last year, a pair bred successfully on a pylon in Ringwood Forest, which was 50 m into Dorset.

Breeding was confirmed in Hampshire for the first time in 2003, when a pair raised three young in Cholderton Park, although the actual nest site was not located. In the following year, a pair fledged four young from a pylon nest at Fryern Court near Fordingbridge, the Cholderton pair was again successful and a pair was seen with a begging juvenile at Leckford. In 2008, the first year of the HBA breeding survey, 14 nests were found and pairs or family parties were noted at a further 23 locations.

During the five years of the HBA, breeding was considered likely in 53 tetrads, with presence recorded in a further 387. Records submitted to HOS for this period indicated breeding at more than 40 locations, with known nest sites comprising 14 in a variety of softwoods including Scots Pine, Douglas Fir and cedars, nine on pylons and one on a building. For this species, likely breeding has been based only on confirmed records and probable records at a level of N (visiting probable nest site) or above. While some of the records of likely breeding in adjacent tetrads possibly referred to the same pair, some records of presence possibly included pairs on territory or displaying which could have involved additional pairs. Whatever the interpretation, the results depict a rapid spread and growth in the Hampshire population since the recommencement of breeding. The species is breeding across the county although there is still room for expansion, for example in the central agricultural area, in the east from Petersfield northwards and in the coastal strip between Southampton and Hayling Island. It remains to be seen how long it will take for some of these gaps to be filled.

The HBA winter map is broadly similar to the summer one. Established pairs presumably remain on their territories throughout the year while juveniles and sub-adult birds disperse and may form loose aggregations. Groups of up to six were frequently recorded but higher numbers included a gathering attracted to food put out for the wintering White-

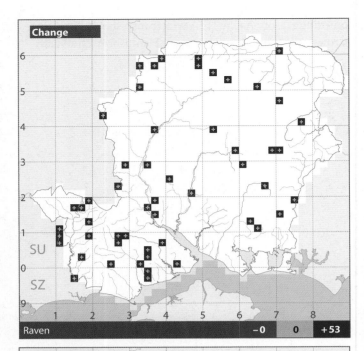

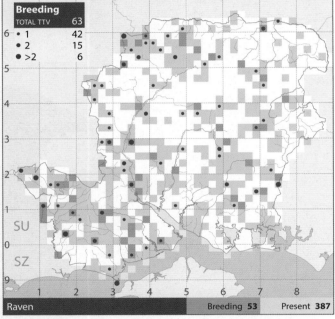

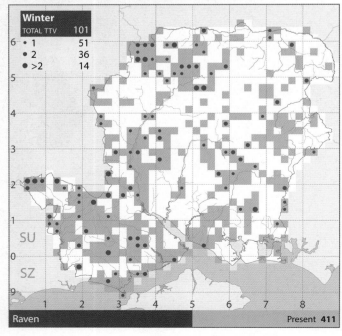

tailed Eagle at Cholderton in 2007/08, which peaked at 26 on January 20th, 15 flying south-east over Hasley Inclosure in the New Forest on February 14th 2009, 21 at Pilot Hill which flew south-east to roost on December 26th 2009 and 15 at Old Winchester Hill on February 18th 2012. By far the largest numbers were attracted to pig fields in the Tidpit Down area in spring 2012 where 105 were counted on May 13th. These were presumably mostly non-breeding birds and give an indication of the potential for future increase.

John Clark

Sponsored by Barrie Roberts

Raven, New Forest, July 2012 – *Martin Bennett*

Goldcrest

Regulus regulus

A numerous resident, passage migrant and winter visitor

The Goldcrest is widely distributed across Europe, North Africa, the Middle East and into Southeast Asia. It is widespread and common across the UK, predominantly in conifers but also in mixed deciduous woodland, especially where Holly and Ivy are present. It can also be found at lower densities in a range of urban environments, particularly in gardens and parks.

As can be seen from the HBA breeding distribution maps, the Goldcrest's range in Hampshire has remained stable when compared to the 1986–91 Atlas, despite the run of cold winters between 2008/09 and 2010/11. This, the smallest of our resident birds, is known to suffer high mortality during sustained periods of cold weather. In the UK, it was badly hit by the very cold winters in the early 1960s and has undergone a roller-coaster recovery since then (*BirdTrends*). However, survey work in 46 sq. km of New Forest woodland between 2009 and 2011 recorded a 58% overall increase of singing males, despite the survey period coinciding with the coldest winters since 1987 (see *Figure xix*). This suggests that the dense woodland cover of the New Forest, coupled with its southern location, may provide a level of protection against harsh winter weather enabling insectivorous species such as Goldcrest to survive and flourish (Ward & Wynn 2013).

The county population is augmented from early autumn onwards by incoming migrants, some of which may overwinter. As the HBA maps show, the species' range is slightly larger in winter, when it can be found in a wider range of habitats particularly on the coast. Migrants occur regularly along the coastal fringe, often associating with roving tit flocks, and occasionally occurring in significant numbers when conditions produce a fall. Recent high counts have included 47 grounded birds at Hook-with-Warsash on October 9th 2000 and 44 at Titchfield Haven on October 5th 2004. During the HBA period, 2008 produced the highest numbers with a peak count of 25 at Sinah on October 17th. Ringing data suggest that these incomers originate primarily from north-west Europe, although some also come from farther north in the UK. Examples of long-distance recoveries in Hampshire made during the HBA period include a bird ringed at Cokaifagne, Liege, Belgium on October 16th 2007 and controlled 30 days later in Fareham, a distance of 507 km, and a first-year male, ringed in Castrum, the Netherlands on October 15th 2010, controlled on Southampton Common on November 10th, a distance of 452 km. More recently, although post-Atlas, an individual ringed at Heysham, Lancashire on October 1st 2012 was controlled 12 days later in Embley Wood.

Marcus Ward

Sponsored by Rachel Hodgkinson

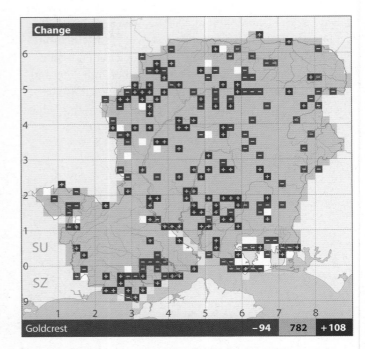

Goldcrest | −94 | 782 | +108

Goldcrest, New Forest, March 2012 – *Martin Bennett*

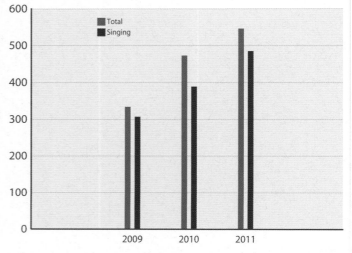

Figure xix – Goldcrest numbers in 46 sq. km of New Forest woodland.

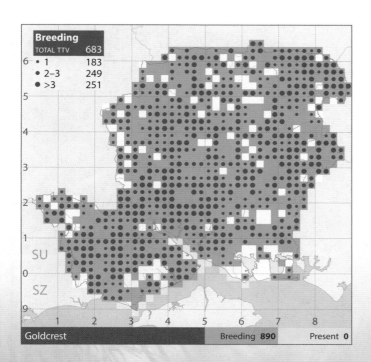

Breeding
TOTAL TTV 683

•	1	183
•	2–3	249
●	>3	251

Goldcrest · Breeding **890** · Present **0**

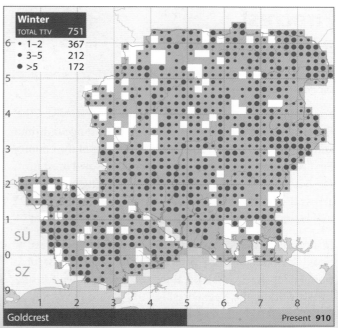

Winter
TOTAL TTV 751

•	1–2	367
•	3–5	212
●	>5	172

Goldcrest · Present **910**

Goldcrest,
New Forest, February 2012
– *Martin Bennett*

Firecrest

Regulus ignicapilla

A moderately common and increasing resident and passage migrant

Found across temperate Europe and north-west Africa, the Firecrest is on the north-westerly edge of its range in Britain, and is restricted mainly to the south and east of the country. First confirmed breeding in the UK in the New Forest in 1962, it has now established itself as a breeding resident across the county with numbers rapidly increasing (*Figure xx*). Hampshire remains a UK stronghold for the species.

In a countrywide context, the RBBP report for 2011 gave a total UK population of 758 territories, of which 415 were from Hampshire (54%). Breaking the figures down further, survey work in the New Forest in 2011 (Ward & Wynn 2013) found 255 Firecrest territories (34% of the total UK population) highlighting the importance of both the New Forest and the county as a whole for Firecrests in the UK.

Males return to their territories and start singing from late February. They can be found breeding in a variety of woodland habitats though they show a preference for 'soft' conifer species such as Douglas Fir and Norway Spruce. In a study in the New Forest between 2009 and 2011 (Ward & Wynn unpublished) 83% of Firecrest territories in 2009 were in soft conifer tree species; for 2010 the figure was 67% and in 2011 it was 60%. Beech and oak woodland with an understory of Holly is also important breeding habitat, in particular where Ivy is present. Territories were

Firecrest, Sandy Point, November 2008 – *Richard Ford*

Number of territories

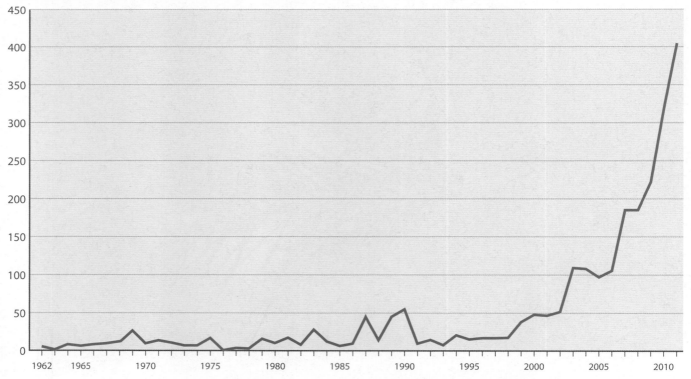

Figure xx – Firecrest territories in Hampshire 1961–2011.

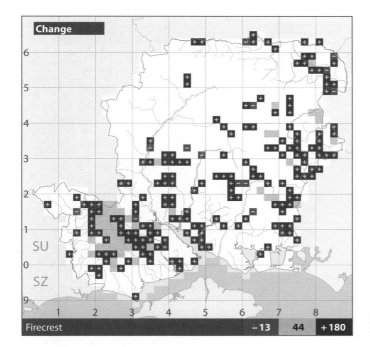

Change

Firecrest — 13 | 44 | +180

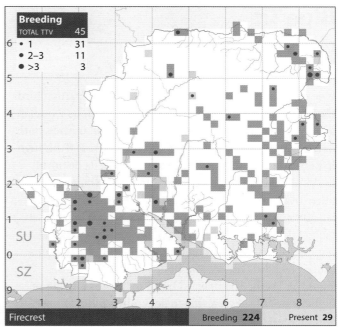

Breeding
TOTAL TTV 45
• 1   31
• 2–3   11
● >3   3

Firecrest   Breeding **224**   Present **29**

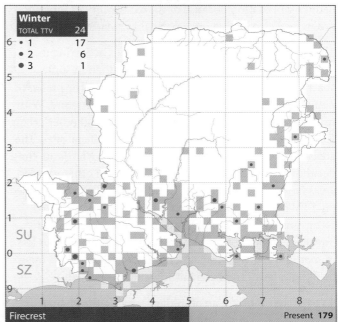

Winter
TOTAL TTV 24
• 1   17
• 2   6
● 3   1

Firecrest   Present **179**

also found in Yew, birch, Scots Pine and willow. Although most records are from woodland blocks containing their favoured habitat, the species is now widespread across the county, occurring even in isolated conifers in parks and gardens. Colour-ringing studies in the New Forest found high breeding site fidelity.

Post-breeding, most Firecrests disperse from their breeding grounds. The bulk of the population, mainly females and juveniles, departs in late June and early July. However, colour-ringing evidence suggests that males in the New Forest remain on territory well into November and are back on territory from February (Ward & Wynn 2013), confirming that at least part of the population is semi-resident. The increasing number of records from the coast and heat-pockets such as parks and gardens further suggests that many individuals move only a short distance during the coldest period of the winter. Counts in mid-November 2012 revealed a total of 35 individuals on Southampton Common. Results from a colour-ringing scheme on the Common suggest that a proportion of the birds ringed are resident whilst some are over-wintering individuals.

As the breeding distribution maps show, the New Forest and surrounding areas remain the stronghold of the species in Hampshire. The densest populations outside the Forest occur in forestry plantations on the Thames Basin and Wealden Heaths as well as the wooded sections of the South Downs centred on Queen Elizabeth Country Park. However, north-west Hampshire remains sparsely populated, probably reflecting the largely cultivated nature of the region. Peak breeding abundance still occurs in the tetrad where the first breeding attempt was made in 1962 with a total of 41 territories in 2011.

Marcus Ward

Sponsored by John & Kay Shillitoe

Firecrest,
New Forest, June 2011
– Martin Bennett

Blue Tit

Cyanistes caeruleus

An abundant resident and passage migrant

One of the most common and familiar of our garden birds, the preferred habitat of the Blue Tit is deciduous woodland but it can occur wherever there are trees and bushes, both in the countryside and throughout urban areas. Although in pairs during the breeding season, Blue Tits occur in flocks at other times of the year, often in association with other tit species and various small birds. Their main food is adult and larval insects and spiders, with fruit and seeds being taken outside the breeding season. The national population has been increasing, albeit with fluctuations caused by hard winters and poor breeding seasons, since the 1960s. The upward trend may be as a result of higher rates of survival due to generally milder winters and increased garden feeding. Reduced levels of egg and fledgling predation because of the availability of more nest boxes may also be playing a part (*BirdTrends*).

The HBA breeding map shows the species occurring in virtually every tetrad in the county other than in some coastal areas where suitable habitat is lacking. The preferred nest site is a hole or cavity in a tree or other structure. With many more nest-boxes available in gardens and other urban areas there is an increasing availability of artificial sites. The areas with the greatest abundance of breeding birds are the deciduous woodlands of the New Forest and other wooded areas in the south, north and north-east of the county. Based on TTV counts, approximately a third of all tetrads held 18 or more birds, with high counts of up to 50 obtained during one hour counts in prime habitat. The species is less numerous on the central agricultural belt where large open fields with fewer trees provide less suitable habitat.

As expected for such an abundant species, the change map shows no significant change in breeding distribution between the 1986–91 Atlas and the HBA period. Although, based on *BBS* results the Blue Tit population in south-east England increased by 12% between 1995 and 2011, at tetrad resolution, the range is not affected.

The HBA winter map shows that outside the breeding season, Blue Tits are found throughout the county, the areas with the greatest concentrations of birds being broadly similar to those in the breeding season. This to be expected since the species is largely sedentary although local populations are sometimes augmented by post-breeding dispersal, especially of juveniles, and by immigrants from farther afield in autumn and winter. Numbers recorded during TTV counts were slightly higher than in summer with approximately a third of tetrads holding 24 or more birds and a maximum of 86 in a one hour count.

Richard Carpenter

Sponsored by David Murdoch

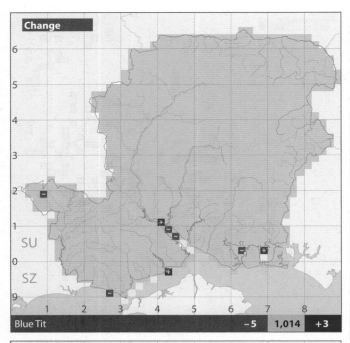

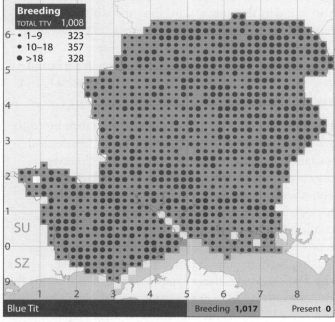

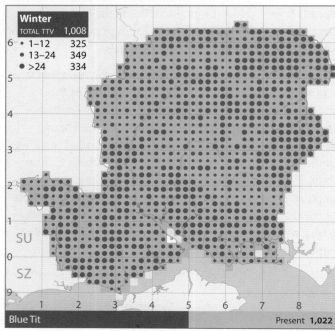

Blue Tit, Blashford Lakes, February 2009 – *Martin Bennett*

Great Tit

Parus major

An abundant resident

This, the largest UK member of the tit family, shares both habits and habitat with the previous species, the Blue Tit. They occupy the same locations, nest in holes, have similar diets, join mixed flocks in winter and are common and familiar garden birds. Given the similarities, it is perhaps not surprising that the Great Tit's national population has increased in parallel with that of the Blue Tit, showing an even stronger upward trend since the severe weather of 1962/63. In England, numbers doubled between 1968 and 2011 (*BirdTrends*) although it is still outnumbered by its smaller relative.

The HBA breeding map shows the species occurring throughout the county, present in virtually all tetrads other than those on the coast where suitable habitat is lacking. While the Great Tit's natural breeding habitat is in deciduous woodland, parkland and gardens, where a hole or cavity in a tree provides a nest site, they will also occupy suitable cavities in man-made structures and take readily to nest boxes. With many more boxes now available in small gardens and other urban areas, they are almost equally at home in the town as in the country. Breeding season TTV counts recorded 66% of occupied tetrads holding at least seven birds although the areas with the greatest abundance continue to be the deciduous woodlands of the New Forest, the Forest of Bere and woodlands in the north and east of the county. Numbers in some densely urban areas and on the more open agricultural chalkland are generally lower.

The change map shows no difference in breeding range between the 1986–91 Atlas and the HBA. This is hardly surprising given close to 100% tetrad occupancy and the increase in population between the two surveys.

Adult Great Tits are sedentary often remaining on territory throughout the winter. There is some post-breeding dispersal, particularly by juveniles. The species moves in flocks with other tits and small birds and is found frequently in gardens and built-up areas often attracted by the now plentiful feeders. Many adult birds only join the flocks if local food becomes scarce. Predictably, the HBA winter map shows the same distribution as in the breeding season. Areas with the greatest concentration of birds in winter are also broadly similar to those in the breeding season, although winter TTV counts recorded higher densities with 66% of occupied tetrads holding at least nine birds. Parties of up to 30, and occasionally higher, are recorded most years.

There is little evidence of large-scale migration to or from the county with ringing data indicating that most movements are local. Long distance movements are rare,

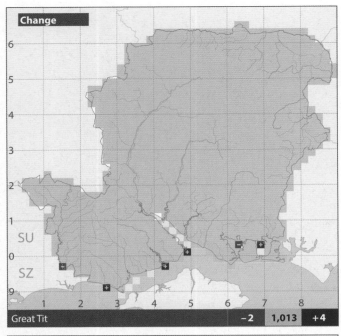

Change

Great Tit   − 2   1,013   + 4

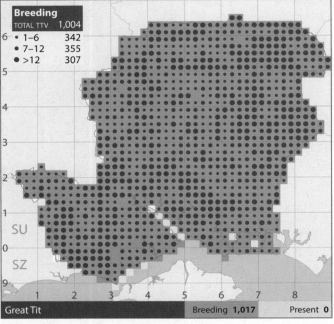

Breeding
TOTAL TTV 1,004
• 1–6   342
• 7–12   355
• >12   307

Great Tit   Breeding **1,017**   Present **0**

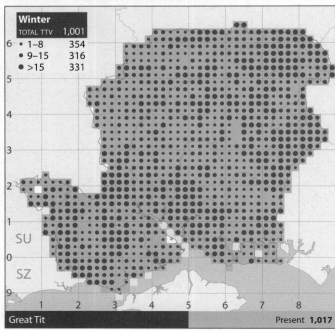

Winter
TOTAL TTV 1,001
• 1–8   354
• 9–15   316
• >15   331

Great Tit   Present **1,017**

Great Tit, Sandy Point, January 2011 – *Andy Johnson* (right);
New Forest, November 2008 – *Martin Bennett* (below)

although the record for a Hampshire-ringed bird is 370 km:
a first-year female ringed in Hartley Mauditt, Alton on
March 9th 2003 was caught by a ringer in Haverthwaite,
Cumbria on October 1st 2007. It is possible that the
increase in garden feeders may have reduced the need for
cold-weather movements induced by food shortages.

Richard Carpenter

Sponsored by Geoffrey Farwell

Coal Tit

Periparus ater

A numerous resident

The preferred habitat of the Coal Tit is coniferous woodland but it is also found in deciduous and mixed woodland, parkland and gardens especially where there are conifers; its breeding and winter distributions reflect this. It is not as numerous or gregarious as the Blue and Great Tit and, because it often feeds higher in trees, is not so easily seen. It nests in a hole in a tree, wall or bank and occasionally in the ground; conifers are usually in the vicinity of the site. Its main food is adult and larval insects, spiders and seeds, especially spruce when available.

Nationally, the population has been stable since the 1970s (*BirdTrends*) particularly in the south-east of England (*BBS*). In Hampshire, the HBA breeding map shows the species occurring throughout the county. Areas with the greatest abundance of breeding birds are the New Forest and woodland in the north-east of the county. There are gaps on large areas of farmland and downland, and along the south-east coastal belt.

The HBA change map shows the breeding distribution has remained basically unchanged since the 1986–91 Atlas. Overall, there has been a small net range loss of around 5%. While this could be real, it could also reflect differences in coverage between the two surveys. It might be expected that the planting of more native and ornamental conifers coupled with an increased number of bird feeders in gardens would have had a positive effect on both breeding range and survival but, overall, this does not appear to be the case.

The HBA winter map shows that the winter distribution of the Coal Tit mirrors that in the breeding season. This is to be expected since the species is largely sedentary with some post-breeding dispersal as birds join mixed feeding flocks ranging through suitable woodland. Ringing recoveries suggest that numbers may increase in autumn as local birds are augmented by longer-distance movements possibly caused by population pressure. In winter the Coal Tit is found throughout the county where there is suitable habitat although, as with breeding records, there are few tetrads with birds present in the south-east coastal belt.

Richard Carpenter

Sponsored by Helen Demopoulos

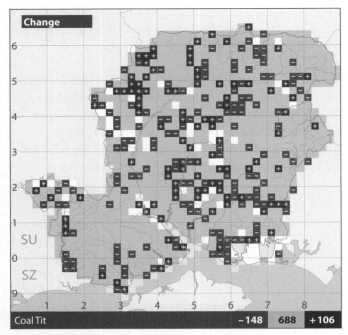

Coal Tit — Change — − 148 | 688 | + 106

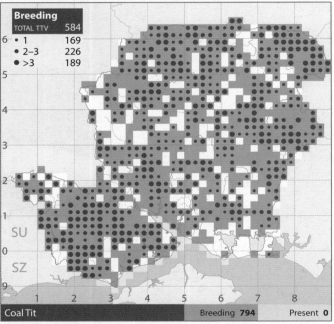

Coal Tit — Breeding
TOTAL TTV 584
• 1 — 169
• 2–3 — 226
• >3 — 189
Breeding 794 — Present 0

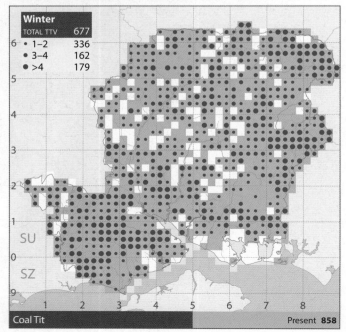

Coal Tit — Winter
TOTAL TTV 677
• 1–2 — 336
• 3–4 — 162
• >4 — 179
Present 858

Coal Tit, New Forest, January 2009 – *Martin Bennett* (above); New Forest, October 2012 – *Martin Bennett* (below)

Willow Tit
Poecile montanus
A declining and scarce resident

Formerly a moderately common and widespread species in Hampshire, in recent years Willow Tit numbers have declined and its range has shrunk dramatically. The HBA change map indicates an 82% range contraction since the 1986–91 Atlas. This is consistent with a decline in the national population of 89% between 1986 and 2011 (*BirdTrends*). The fall began in the mid-1970s and, while it has been easy to chart the reduction, it has been more difficult to explain why it has occurred.

Apart from the possibility of confusion with the very similar Marsh Tit, one of the challenges in assessing the numbers of this species is that they can be inconspicuous and densities are often low. Their breeding season starts early and the main song period is in March. By mid-April the need for the birds to sing is reduced and so it would seem very likely that breeding pairs were overlooked during the HBA fieldwork. Also due to their low densities, the birds are often not stimulated to sing, as they do not often encounter rivals. Furthermore, many of the woods that Willow Tits occupy are strictly private and may not have been visited during the Atlas fieldwork.

As the HBA breeding map shows, in Hampshire Willow Tits are thinly spread and mainly restricted to a narrow belt across the chalk. Coppiced woodlands around Faccombe and Netherton in the north-west and near Dummer to the south-west of Basingstoke remain reliable sites, although many of these areas offer very limited public access. A number of other woods still hold breeding birds, albeit at low densities, and it is likely that more remain to be found. A concerted effort is now being made to locate them. Away from the known centres of population the species is exceedingly rare. Occasional records from the New Forest are believed to refer to Marsh Tits which are more suited to its mature woodland structure.

Most of the available research on Willow Tit ecology is based on birds in Scandinavia where coniferous forests are often their preferred habitat. There are no detailed studies published on the territory requirements of Willow Tit in Britain which is a different subspecies and generally favours young damp woodland with suitable dead wood for nesting, particularly Alder or Silver Birch (Broughton 2009).

It is possible that climate change has affected the distribution of Willow Tits but, while the population across southern England has declined, the species' range has not extended farther north. As with the Marsh Tit, another possible cause is the impact of significantly higher deer numbers on habitats such as coppiced woodland, their browsing of young shoots resulting in the failure of

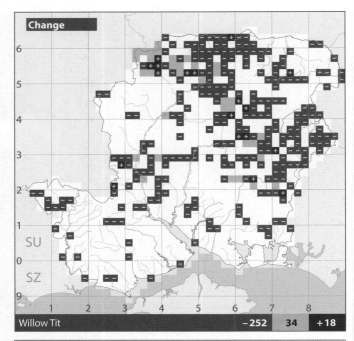

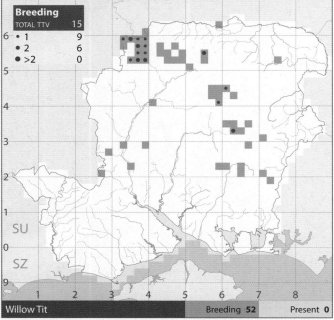

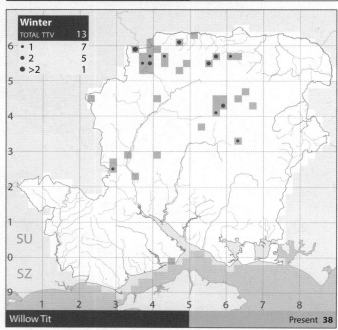

the coppice to regenerate. Other theories for the decline include predation by Great Spotted Woodpeckers and nest-site competition from more assertive species such as the Great Tit or Blue Tit (Lewis *et al.* 2007). The Willow Tit is a single-brooded species and so a predation event can result in total breeding failure for that year.

More research into the UK Willow Tit population is needed if we are to understand why the decline has occurred and whether any intervention by conservation organisations can reverse the trend. HOS and the HIWWT have joined forces to survey the species and to identify key areas where breeding success may be increased through the use of nest boxes. Initial results from fieldwork in early 2014 suggest that the species is in a number of woods that are well away from the public gaze. If there is a species that deserves more of our attention then the Willow Tit is certainly a strong candidate.

Keith Betton

Sponsored by Barry Stalker

Willow Tit, Dummer, February 2012 – *Barry Stalker*

Marsh Tit

Poecile palustris

A locally common but declining resident

The preferred habitat of the Marsh Tit is broadleaved woodland, although they can also be found in parks, gardens, wooded farmland and other areas containing mature trees with a well-developed understorey. Like other members of the tit family, this species nests in holes, mainly in trees, feeding on invertebrates during the summer and seeds at other times of the year. These requirements are similar to Blue Tit and Great Tit but, in contrast to them, its UK population has been in decline since the 1960s. Numbers fell by 73% between 1967 and 2011 (*BirdTrends*) and consequently it is on the red list of Birds of Conservation Concern.

In Hampshire, the HBA breeding map shows it to be widespread, particularly in the New Forest and the north-west. Elsewhere it is more scattered with large sections of the county apparently devoid of birds. Breeding was considered likely in just under half of the county's tetrads. Since the species is sedentary, it is probable that the vast majority of breeding season records reflect nearby breeding. Most records were of just one or two individuals. Some of the areas with the greatest abundance of breeding birds are the central New Forest, woodland in the Hurstbourne Tarrant area, Micheldever Wood, Alice Holt Forest and Woolmer Forest.

The change map shows a mixture of gains and losses but with a net range contraction of 21% since the 1986–91 Atlas. The overall picture is one of withdrawal from substantial parts of the county, particularly in the north-east, south-east and Andover areas. The losses have expanded pre-existing gaps in the species' range, particularly in the north-east and in a broad swathe extending from the south-east coast north-west to the Wiltshire border. The situation in Hampshire is therefore consistent with the national trend.

The most probable cause of decline is thought to be a reduction in habitat quality resulting from a decrease in woodland management and over-browsing by the escalating deer population, both factors leading to degradation of the

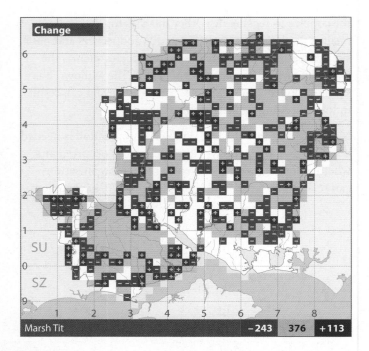

Marsh Tit   − 243   376   + 113

forest understory. Lack of management results in closure of woodland canopies allowing less light to reach the forest floor, while deer browse directly on the shrub layer. Marsh Tits are known to prefer sections of woodland with more understorey cover (Carpenter 2008, Carpenter *et al.* 2010). As with the Willow Tit, there are other possible causes of decline including nest predation, for example by Grey Squirrels or Great Spotted Woodpeckers, or failure to compete for available nest sites against dominant species such as the Blue Tit. However, there is little evidence to support either of these mechanisms (Siriwardena 2006).

The HBA maps shows a similar but wider distribution in winter than during the breeding season. Consistent with its sedentary nature, ringing returns indicate that most Marsh Tits generally move only over short distances from their natal areas, but post-breeding dispersal and movements in search of food presumably account for the expansion in winter range. Birds are increasingly visiting gardens and feeding stations and, in time, this may have a positive effect on the species' distribution and survival.

Richard Carpenter

Sponsored by Wilf Simcox

Marsh Tit, New Forest, March 2011– *Martin Bennett*

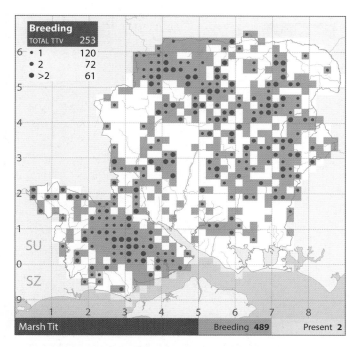

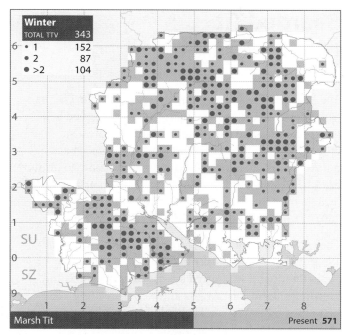

Breeding		
TOTAL TTV	253	
• 1		120
• 2		72
● >2		61

Winter		
TOTAL TTV	343	
• 1		152
• 2		87
● >2		104

Marsh Tit — Breeding **489** — Present **2**

Marsh Tit — Present **571**

Marsh Tit, Eyeworth Pond, January 2009 – *Richard Ford*

Bearded Tit
Panurus biarmicus
A scarce resident, passage migrant and winter visitor

The Bearded Tit is not a common species in the UK. Its dependence on extensive areas of *Phragmites* reed bed limits its range and distribution. Numbers are also reduced by hard winters, although they bounce back quickly thanks to a long breeding season with two or more broods. Despite this constraint, its British range increased by 82% over the four decades between the 1968–72 and 2007–11 national atlases (*Bird Atlas 2007–11*).

The colonisation of Hampshire began in the winter of 1964/65 following influxes into the county from the Netherlands and supported by dispersal from existing breeding sites in East Anglia and Kent. Breeding was first reported in 1966 at Titchfield Haven with additional colonies established at Farlington Marshes in 1984, Keyhaven in 1989 and Lymington in 1992. As the HBA breeding and change maps show, further expansion has occurred over the past two decades with a new colony at Needs Ore and extensions at Keyhaven/Lymington and Lower Test Marshes. The last of these sites qualifies as a likely breeding site because of records during both winter and breeding seasons, although confirmation of breeding was not obtained during the HBA period.

In winter, Hampshire's Bearded Tits are mainly found in, or close to, their breeding areas. Some post-breeding dispersal occurs, mainly in September and October, to a few other local reed-bed sites. During the 1960s and 1970s, the period in which the county was colonised, large influxes occurred into south-east England following irruptive movements from a huge breeding population on the Dutch polders. Ringing returns confirmed that birds reaching Hampshire originated in the Netherlands or sites in East Anglia and Kent. Some of these immigrants reached inland sites such as Alresford and Fleet Ponds and occasionally overwintered there but none remained to breed and these movements have now stopped. During the HBA period, the only winter records of Bearded Tits away from known or likely breeding sites were of one at Fishlake Meadows in December 2008, and one or two at Blashford Lakes in December 2010. The most likely reason for this change in behaviour is the loss of the temporary habitat created by construction of the Dutch polders, but it also appears that the birds breeding in south-east England have lost their wanderlust and become more sedentary.

Given the limited extent of reed beds it is unlikely that Bearded Tits will ever be common in Hampshire but it is possible that, with mild winters and good breeding seasons, local movements might lead to further range expansion including colonisation of suitable inland sites.

Richard Carpenter

Sponsored by John Walton

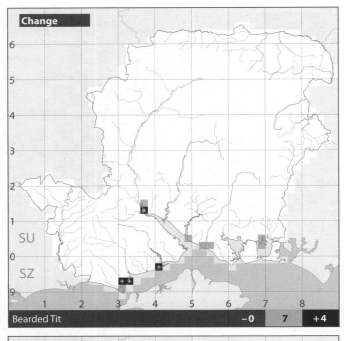

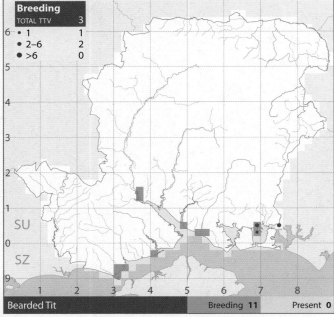

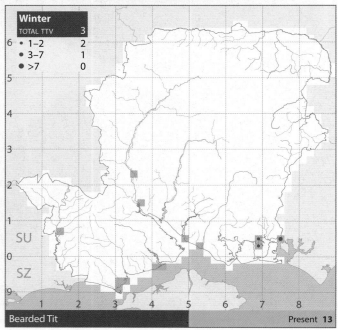

Bearded Tit,
Keyhaven, September 2009 –
Alan Lewis

303

Woodlark
Lullula arborea
A moderately common resident and passage migrant

The Woodlark is a species of the temperate and Mediterranean regions of the Western Palearctic. It reaches the north-westerly edge of its range in Britain, where it is restricted mainly to the warmer southern counties. Historically, while the national population and range have fluctuated, Hampshire has always remained an important stronghold. In the first national survey carried out in 1986 after a period of decline, the population totalled just 241 pairs, of which 92 (38%) were in the county. Over the following decades, the population recovered. The most recent national survey in 2006 showed substantial growth with 347–379 territories located in Hampshire alone (Eyre 2007). This represented about 20% of the national recorded total (Conway *et al.* 2009).

Woodlarks breed in areas of well-drained, friable soil, with patches of grass, heather or other short vegetation for nesting, bare ground or sparse ground-cover for feeding and scattered trees or other elevated perches for use as look-outs and song posts. These conditions are found on Hampshire's heathlands and, as the breeding map shows, the New Forest, Wealden Heaths and Thames Basin Heaths provide the main centres of the breeding population. In the period between the two Hampshire atlases all three areas have been classified as heathland SPAs, in part to protect this species.

Although most of Hampshire's Woodlarks continue to breed on heathland, they are not restricted to this habitat. In the 1950s many bred on the chalk agricultural belt across the centre of the county. This latter population declined, possibly as a result of changes to agricultural subsidies that led to a drop in the amount of rough grassland. The myxomatosis epidemic of 1954/55 could also have had an effect by depleting the Rabbit population allowing habitat to become overgrown and unsuitable. Numbers were further reduced and almost eliminated by the hard winters in 1961/62 and 1962/63. By the time of the first Hampshire atlas in 1986–91, the few remaining non-heathland birds were found mainly on horticultural land and tree nurseries particularly in the Romsey area. In recent years, perhaps aided by heathland management and mild winters, the county population has grown and spread back onto agricultural land. In the 2006 survey around 14% of territories were found on farmland and horticultural sites, primarily on stubble, set-aside and fallow areas. The expansion is shown clearly by the change and breeding maps, which confirm that the species now occurs across the county. Between the two Hampshire atlases, Woodlarks have colonised an additional 121 tetrads many of these on agricultural land.

At first sight, the distribution maps suggest that the range of Woodlarks in winter is similar to that during the breeding season but this is not actually the case. Most of

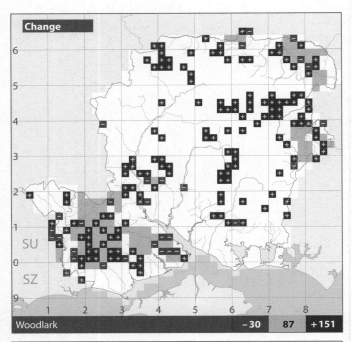

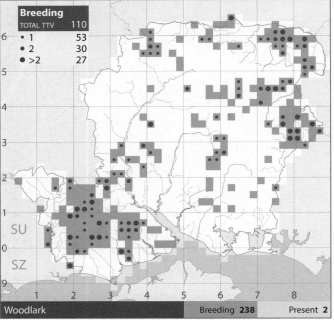

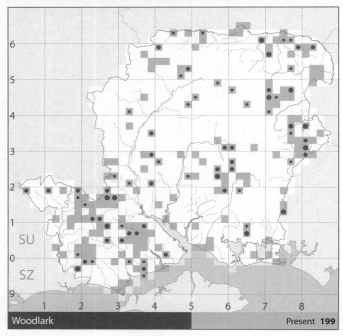

the birds leave the heathlands during the coldest months but return to establish territories in the late winter/early spring. The majority of the winter atlas records therefore refer to February sightings of birds back on their breeding grounds. Considering that the population following a successful breeding season probably exceeds 2,000 individuals, relatively few are seen during the winter which is perhaps not that surprising if they spread over large areas of agricultural land. A few regular flocks occur, for example at Hundred Acres, Wickham, on fields in the Bisterne/ Kingston area and on Portsdown Hill, with occasional smaller numbers seen elsewhere, usually on agricultural land. During the HBA period, the maximum count at any one location was 33 at Portsdown Hill on January 1st 2010. Interestingly, these birds did not intermingle with a neighbouring flock of Skylarks. Although autumn movements are noted regularly at both inland and coastal sites (*HBR*), and hard weather movements also occur, there is no direct evidence of emigration out of the country. However, given that there have been recoveries of birds colour-ringed in Thetford, Norfolk from as far afield as St. Marys on the Isles of Scilly and closer to home, of one ringed on Hankley Common, Surrey at Wick, Christchurch Harbour, Dorset, it seems likely that some Hampshire birds may also move outside the county.

John Eyre

Sponsored by John Eyre

Woodlark, New Forest, May 2008 – *Martin Bennett* (above); New Forest, May 2015 – *Martin Bennett* (below)

305

Skylark
Alauda arvensis
A numerous resident, passage migrant and winter visitor

The Skylark is a bird of open countryside, familiar and appreciated more on account of its emotive song than its dull, brown, streaky plumage. *K&M* describe it as a very common resident in all parts of Hampshire. It remains widespread, particularly across the county's agricultural heartland. It also occurs on coastal marsh, heathland, wasteland and other areas of rough grassland which provide suitable feeding and nesting habitat.

However, as a bird that has long been associated with the peace and tranquillity of the British countryside, the Skylark's changing fortunes give a stark indication of the alterations taking place in that environment. Monitoring has shown a 62% decline in its English population between 1967 and 2011 (*BirdTrends*) most probably as a result of agricultural intensification. In particular, changes in grassland management have reduced the number of possible breeding attempts and additionally, the switch to autumn cereals may also have reduced overwinter survival.

In Hampshire, the HBA breeding maps show that Skylarks occur at the greatest densities on the chalk and are generally less common on the acid soils of the Hampshire and Thames Basins and the Weald. The change map indicates a 14% range reduction since the 1986–91 Atlas with the losses concentrated particularly in the south-west and north-east. As their population has fallen, it appears that Skylarks have deserted marginal habitats in the New Forest and Thames Basin and Wealden Heaths. A major hole has also opened up in the range east of Southampton. This change in distribution is shared with other seed-eating farmland birds, particularly the Yellowhammer, which has deserted the same areas over the past few decades.

In winter, the county's resident birds are joined by immigrants from farther north in Britain and Continental Europe. The number of incomers is likely to depend on weather conditions both in Britain and on the European mainland. During the HBA period, heavy snowfall on January 5th/6th 2010 resulted in widespread movements noted particularly on the coast. Examples of movements and grounded flocks at this time included 6,845 moving east in two hours at Titchfield Haven on January 6th and 2,200 at Avon Causeway on January 9th. Despite the higher numbers, the Skylark's winter range in Hampshire is more concentrated than during the breeding season. The HBA winter map shows an overall range reduction of almost 10% relative to the breeding season. Withdrawal from marginal breeding areas to better winter feeding areas on farmland may explain the contraction.

John Eyre

Sponsored by Roger Dickey

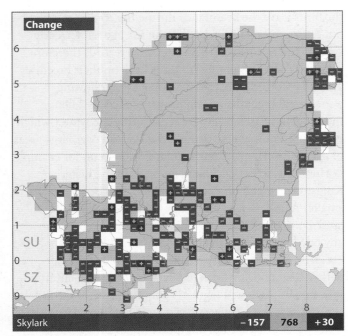

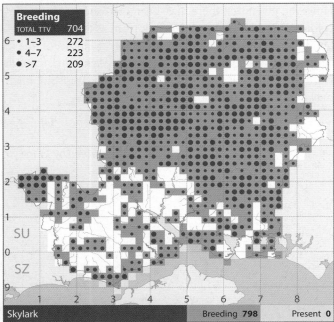

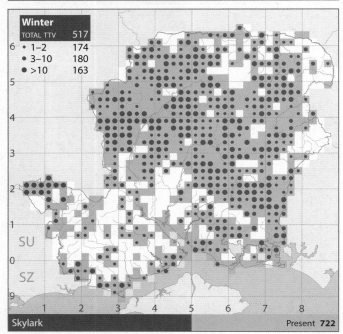

Skylark, New Forest, October 2010 – *Martin Bennett*

Shore Lark

Eremophila alpestris

A rare late autumn migrant and winter visitor

Prior to the HBA period, the last record of Shore Lark in Hampshire was in October 2003. During the HBA (including records outside the breeding and winter surveys) an additional five birds were recorded, with an exceptional total of four in 2009:

2009:   Pennington Marsh, two, October 13th.
          Sandy Point, one, November 5th.
          Needs Ore, one, November 17th–19th.
2012:   West Hayling, one, January 15th–February 17th.

These bring the total number of Shore Larks recorded in the county to 45 since the first in 1955.

John Eyre

Shore Lark, Hayling Oyster Beds, January 2012 – *Richard Ford*

Short-toed Lark

Calandrella brachydactyla

Very rare vagrant

Given the proximity of its nearest breeding areas in France, this is a surprisingly rare visitor to Hampshire. During the HBA only one, just the second for the county, was found at Normandy Lagoon on May 18th 2010. It spent the day in the area but could not be relocated the following day. The previous county record was at Calshot and Ower from October 9th to 19th 1983.

John Eyre

Short-toed Lark, Normandy Marsh, May 2010 – *Simon Ingram*

Sand Martin

Riparia riparia

A common breeding summer visitor and numerous passage migrant

Sand Martins are among the earliest heralds of spring, regularly appearing in the first week of March, although local breeders are not usually on territory until early April. They breed in riverbanks and in some sandy sea-cliffs but in Hampshire are almost wholly confined to sand and gravel pits, sometimes in still-working sites; in recent years increasing numbers have successfully used artificial colonies.

Severe population crashes occurred in 1969, 1984 and 1991, most likely because of drought in the West African wintering grounds of the species. The crashes were followed by rapid rebounds but the population suffered a further and longer decline through the late 1990s until 2003 when it began to grow again. Overall, despite the fluctuations, numbers have held up at national level, *BBS* results showing that the UK population increased by 20% between 1995 and 2012 (*BirdTrends*). However, *Bird Atlas 2007–11* indicates that while northern and Irish populations have grown, numbers in south-east England have declined. There has been no recent count of the Hampshire population, so a comprehensive survey of nests at the county's active colonies would provide a valuable benchmark.

The accompanying maps show a reduction in the number of tetrads where breeding was proven from 23 at the time of the 1986–91 Atlas to 18 during the HBA, although both figures probably overestimate the number of active colonies in any one year. In part, this is because some colonies extend across tetrad boundaries but the species is also extremely local in its breeding habits, and very fickle

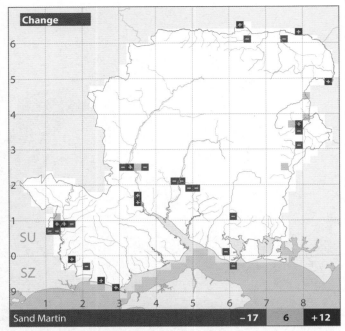

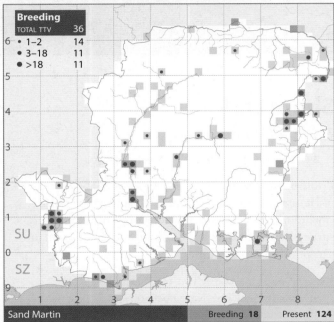

Sand Martin, Blashford Lakes, June 2010 – *Martin Bennett*

Sand Martin, Blashford Lakes, April 2010 – *Martin Bennett*

and even nomadic. Long-established colonies are regularly deserted, despite no apparent habitat change, and new opportunities are readily taken up. Consequently, over the extended period of the Atlas surveys, some colonies may have been deserted and new ones established, again resulting in an oversestimate of colonies in any given year. Comparison of the breeding tetrads in 1986–91 and 2008–12 shows that only six were common to both periods. Previously occupied sites in the Test, lower Itchen and upper Meon Valleys were deserted as sand and gravel extraction ceased. At other sites, notably Testwood Lakes and Blashford Lakes, the provision of artificial nesting banks has been highly successful, with three-figure nest counts at both sites during the HBA period. It is possible that almost half of the county's Sand Martins are now dependent on such provision.

Few Hampshire species of comparable familiarity and abundance are so highly concentrated into so few breeding sites, and it must be a matter of some concern that Sand Martins are so vulnerable to what might seem insignificant changes in habitat. It is to be hoped that management of working mineral extraction sites remains sympathetic to the species and that consideration is given to Sand Martins when decommissioning of quarries takes place.

Simon Woolley

Sponsored by David Robison

Red-rumped Swallow

Cecropis daurica

A rare vagrant

The Red-rumped Swallow is extending its breeding range northward in Europe. At the time of the 1986–91 Atlas there had been just one record in Hampshire but by the end of 2012 there had been 12 including six during the HBA period as follows:

2009: Rooksbury Mill, Andover, April 21st.
       Lakeside Country Park, Eastleigh, May 23rd.
       Swiveltown Lane, Portsdown Hill, June 2nd.
2010: Portchester Castle, May 5th.
       Nursling, May 12th.
2011: Sandy Point, July 10th.

Simon Woolley

Red-rumped Swallow, Spain – *Martin Bennett*

Swallow

Hirundo rustica

A numerous summer visitor and abundant passage migrant

Thankfully, in contrast to some other summer migrants, Swallows remain common, widespread and familiar birds in Hampshire, from their first arrival in late March, sometimes right through until early November. They migrate to and from southern Africa, where their population is occasionally impacted by the failure of rains and droughts. They are especially conspicuous in Hampshire during migration periods, which are extended. Large numbers are often noted in the first week of May, typically at inland sites, and from mid-August, when large gatherings may be found inland and sometimes at coastal roost sites. Although the latter have become rarer and smaller, in season upwards of 20,000 per day have been recorded coasting along the Solent.

The HBA breeding maps show Swallows to be almost ubiquitous across the county, with breeding likely in close to 92% of tetrads. They breed in a variety of rural, suburban and even urban locations. This pattern is repeated across the country. Swallows are described in *Bird Atlas 2007–11* as having the most extensive distribution of any summer migrant bird. In Hampshire, they are absent from very densely populated areas such as parts of Southampton, Portsmouth and the Aldershot/Farnborough area. There are also significant gaps in breeding distribution on the high chalk and other intensively farmed districts, in parts of the New Forest and in some coastal tetrads. In all these areas nest sites and/or feeding opportunities

are presumably rare. Swallows habitually nest in a wide variety of man-made structures, from sheds to barns and outbuildings; the loss of farm buildings and the 'sealing' and even conversion of more ramshackle ones, has been connected with local declines in this species elsewhere. It is also possible that changes in farming practices, particularly conversion from livestock to arable farming, has resulted in poorer feeding opportunities and the loss of birds from some agricultural areas.

It is remarkable just how similar the current breeding map is to that in the 1986–91 Atlas (*BoH*). The HBA change map shows gains in the south-west, losses on the high chalk, and a mixture of the two in the north-east but, overall, the picture remains basically unchanged.

Nationally, there was formerly quite severe concern that the Swallow was in long-term decline but recent data have revealed a more subtle picture. The population in England fluctuates but increased by 43% between 1995 and 2011 (*BirdTrends*). There have indeed been declines in the east of Britain, but they have been more than compensated for by an increase in the west. Hampshire appears to lie at the fulcrum of this see-saw, and no significant change in population seems to have occurred in the county.

There were no records of Swallows overwintering during the HBA period but several of departing migrants in November and two of early returnees in February. One of the latter at Calmore, Totton on February 23rd 2009 was the earliest ever recorded in the county.

Simon Woolley

Sponsored by Ruth Croger

Swallow, New Forest, May 2009 – *Martin Bennett*

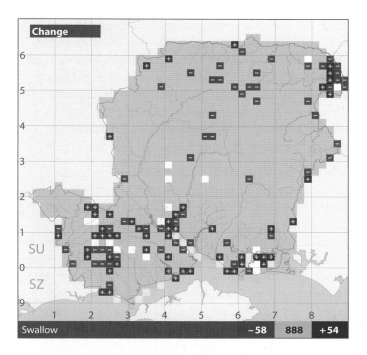

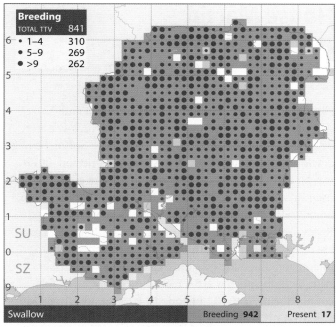

Swallow, Needs Ore, May 2009 – *Nigel Jones*

House Martin
Delichon urbicum

A numerous but declining summer visitor and abundant passage migrant

House Martins are among the most common and conspicuous of the summer migrants, arriving over an extended period from mid-March into May. Spring passage is seldom spectacular but, during the HBA period, 2012 was an exceptional year with two four-figure counts of migrants. At least 1,000 were watched in off the sea in an hour at Hill Head on 29th April and there were 2,000 at Ibsley Water on May 15th. Autumn migration gatherings are often substantial, with large numbers moving both inland and along the coast in September and October. Although outside the HBA recording periods, notable counts during 2007–12 included 14,200 east in three hours at Barton on Sea on September 23rd 2008, some 10,000 north-west over Hook-with-Warsash in just 25 minutes on September 13th 2009 and over 10,000 per hour past Hurst on September 16th 2011. These movements are spectacular yet, despite the numbers involved, this is a species in trouble.

Sadly, the House Martin is another familiar bird whose breeding population has declined seriously in recent years. BTO data indicate a 69% decline in England since 1967, with a 27% drop in 1995–2012 alone (*BirdTrends*). *Bird Atlas 2007–11* indicates that the steepest English declines have occurred in the south-east with Hampshire, while not suffering the largest fall, included in this. HBA results show that the number of tetrads where breeding is considered likely has declined by 30% since the 1986–91 Atlas.

There has been a severe thinning out in the south-west of the county, especially in the New Forest (although the species was never a common breeder there), but also right across the county, with contraction of range in both rural and built-up areas. Particularly notable is the apparent disappearance of the species as a breeder from large swathes of suburban Southampton and Portsmouth, a change perhaps unimaginable a generation ago.

Whether the decline is due to habitat or other changes here in Britain, or farther afield, is unclear. For such a common bird, surprisingly little is known about its requirements in its winter quarters in Africa. However, there is little evidence to suggest that problems there or on migration underlie the decline. Across Britain, more northerly populations have held up or even increased in recent years, suggesting a possible response to climate change, but it seems likely that the reduced availability of flying insects may also be involved. Other factors such as increased use of plastic soffits, and perhaps even drier springs making mud for nest-building less accessible, cannot be ruled out. The species is certainly (in the BTO's words) extraordinarily difficult to monitor accurately given its habit of nesting in loose, mobile colonies, often in urban areas. Moreover, the general lack of breeding evidence may have led to an underestimate of the actual level of breeding, although the method of assessing likely breeding used here should have minimised this error. However, despite the uncertainties, there is no mistaking the signal in both the Hampshire and national data that the species is in serious decline.

Simon Woolley

Sponsored by Ann Hale

House Martin, Alresford, June 2015 – *Hilary Cornford*

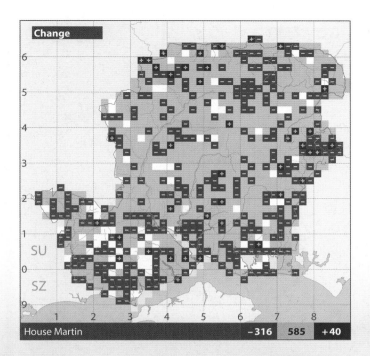

Change

6
5
4
3
2
1
SU
0
SZ
9

1   2   3   4   5   6   7   8

House Martin   −316   585   +40

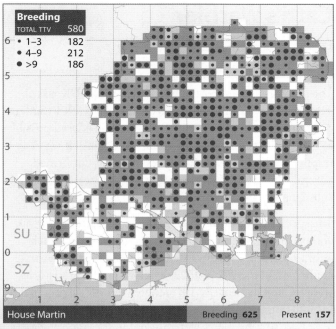

Breeding
TOTAL TTV   580
• 1–3   182
• 4–9   212
● >9   186

6
5
4
3
2
1
SU
0
SZ
9

1   2   3   4   5   6   7   8

House Martin   Breeding 625   Present 157

House Martin, Blashford Lakes, September 2013 – *Martin Bennett*

313

Cetti's Warbler
Cettia cetti
A moderately common resident

The first Cetti's Warbler to be recorded in the UK was at Titchfield Haven from March 4th–April 10th 1961 (Suffern & Ferguson-Lees 1964). Initially, it was considered possibly to be a Moustached Warbler and it wasn't until it was trapped on March 19th that its identity was confirmed. Several heated letters discussing the events were published subsequently (*British Birds* 58: 225–227, 516–520).

The species breeds low down in dense vegetation, comprising a mixture of reeds, bushes and shrubs such as bramble, and usually close to water. Breeding was first confirmed in the UK in 1973, when around 15 territories were located in Kent. By 1976, there were 80 singing males in eight counties including one in Hampshire. In 1978, at least four singing males were present in the Avon Valley and one was at Kingsworthy. In the following year breeding was confirmed on the Avon at Bickton, where there were four territories, and was strongly suspected at Ellingham Lake (Blashford) and also at Alresford Pond.

During the 1986–91 Atlas survey, Cetti's Warblers were located in 62 Hampshire tetrads, largely confined to the Avon, Test and upper Itchen Valleys and the coastal strip, particularly in the Keyhaven area and between Warsash and Gosport. A full breeding survey in 1990 located 125–127 singing males including 40 at Titchfield Haven, 17 at Lower Test Marshes and 28 in the Avon Valley. Following severe weather in early 1991, the population was estimated to have fallen by around 50%, but the next national survey in 1996 produced a county total of 136–148 singing males. This included 46–53 at Titchfield Haven, eight at Lower Test Marshes, 23–24 in the Avon Valley, 18–20 in the Test Valley and 18–20 in the Itchen Valley, including 10–12 at Alresford Pond. Expansion followed over the next decade, with the species spreading to unoccupied stretches of the Test and Itchen Valleys, the coastal strip between Needs Ore and Calshot, and suitable sites around the perimeter of Langstone Harbour. A full survey was not undertaken during this period but maxima from important areas included 55 at Titchfield Haven and 12 at the Alver Valley near Gosport in 2000, 39 in the Avon Valley in 2001, 38 at Lower Test Marshes in 2002, 52–61 in the Itchen Valley in 2002–03 (Cloyne 2007), and 14 at Farlington Marshes and 11 between Keyhaven and Lymington in 2004. These records suggest a total well in excess of 200 singing males in the early years of the new millennium, although the population was hit by a cold spell of weather in early 2006.

The HBA breeding map shows strong occupation of the three main river valleys and sections of the coast with suitable habitat. These areas largely escaped the severe weather in the 2008/09 winter but this was not the case in early 2010, when all the main river valleys suffered a

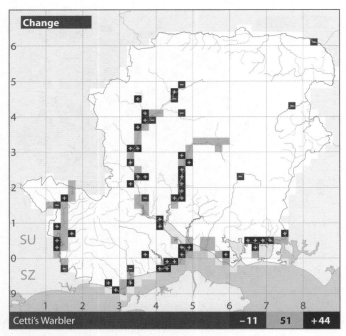

Cetti's Warbler   −11   51   +44

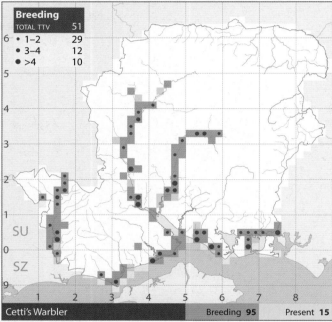

Breeding
TOTAL TTV 51
- 1–2   29
- 3–4   12
- >4   10

Cetti's Warbler   Breeding 95   Present 15

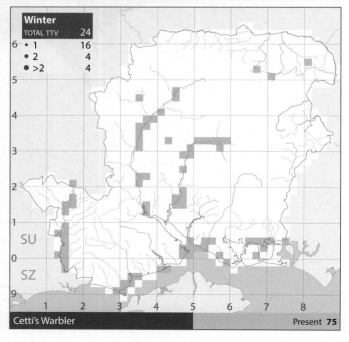

Winter
TOTAL TTV 24
- 1   16
- 2   4
- >2   4

Cetti's Warbler   Present 75

prolonged spell of below-average temperatures. Despite this the population was estimated to be at a record level of 250–275 singing males in 2010, with increases noted at the two most consistently covered sites – Titchfield Haven up from 29 to 32 and Lower Test Marshes up from 27 to 35. Other counts included minimum totals of 36, 30 and 26 territories in the Avon, Test and Itchen Valleys. The consolidation since the 1986–91 Atlas is shown by the change map which confirms the range extensions described above.

As would be expected, the HBA winter map shows a distribution broadly similar to that in summer, although it is unrecorded in some tetrads in the breeding range,

presumably reflecting the greater difficulty in detecting it during the colder winter months. There were also records of singles in the north-east at The Mill Field, Basing on February 10th 2010, Springhead, Greywell from November 6th 2010–January 30th 2011 and Fleet Pond on January 29th 2012. Despite the wealth of suitable habitat available in this part of the county, Cetti's Warbler has, as yet, been unable to colonise the area despite the proximity of a breeding population in the Kennet Valley in Berkshire.

John Clark

Sponsored by John Goodspeed

Cetti's Warbler, Fordingbridge, June 2012 – *Martin Bennett*

Long-tailed Tit
Aegithalos caudatus
A numerous resident

The preferred habitat of the Long-tailed Tit is woodland, hedgerows, scrub, parks and gardens. The bottle-like nests, constructed by weaving gossamer and hair to create a flexible ball of feathers, moss and lichen, are usually built in thorny bushes or scrub. Although in discrete pairs during the breeding season, at other times of the year birds form flocks, sometime quite large and often in association with other tits and small birds. They feed mainly on adult and larval insects and spiders, although they will take seeds and berries in winter and are increasingly common visitors to garden feeders.

Like other small passerines, they suffer high mortality in severe winters. For example, *BBS* monitoring showed a 17% fall in the English population following record low temperatures and heavy snow-fall in November/December 2010. However, despite their vulnerability, the run of generally mild winters over the past two decades has allowed their population to increase, so that this is now a common and successful species. The overall population trend remains positive (*BirdTrends*).

The HBA breeding map shows the species occurring throughout the county with breeding considered likely in 91% of tetrads. There are some apparent gaps in distribution on the chalk, on the heaths of the New Forest and in large urban areas such as Portsmouth and Southampton, although some of these may be due to inadequate coverage. Areas with the greatest abundance of breeding birds are those with the largest amount of suitable habitat, particularly along the main river valleys and in the north-east of the county.

The change map shows a small increase in breeding range between the 1986–91 Atlas and the HBA. While this is consistent with the growth in population over the period, there are also some surprising losses, particularly in the New Forest. Unless this is due to under-recording, it suggests that there may have been loss of suitable scrub habitat in some parts of the Forest. This might have occurred as a result of over-grazing, burning or other forms of clearance.

The HBA maps show that the species is more widespread in winter but its distribution remains similar to that during the breeding season. Although it is largely sedentary, there is some post-breeding dispersal and the birds range more widely within their winter flocks. They occur more frequently in winter in gardens and parks, even in built-up areas. Although most remain close to their breeding territories, there are occasional longer distance ringing recoveries of up to 50 km.

Richard Carpenter

Sponsored by Dan Hoare

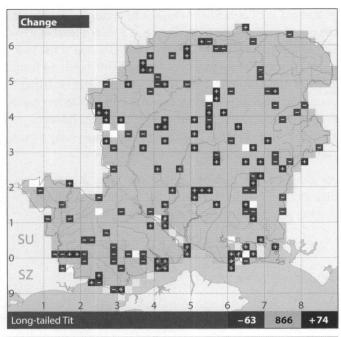

Change

Long-tailed Tit — −63 | 866 | +74

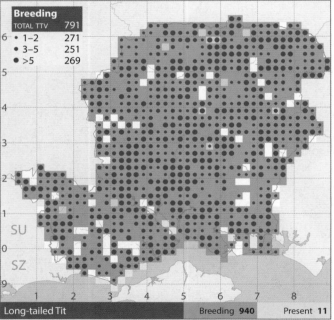

Breeding
TOTAL TTV 791
- 1–2   271
- 3–5   251
- >5   269

Long-tailed Tit — Breeding **940**   Present **11**

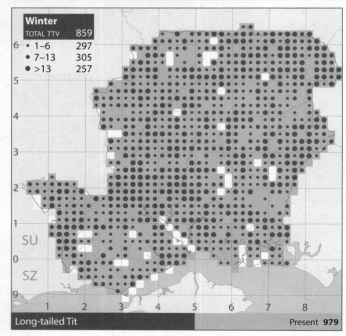

Winter
TOTAL TTV 859
- 1–6   297
- 7–13   305
- >13   257

Long-tailed Tit — Present **979**

Long-tailed Tit, New Forest, December 2012 – *Martin Bennett* (both images)

Wood Warbler

Phylloscopus sibilatrix

A local and declining summer visitor and passage migrant

The Wood Warbler's global range encompasses the whole of Europe, excluding Spain, and extends into parts of central Asia. Recent surveys indicate that the species is declining throughout the western part of its range but is stable in the east (*Bird Atlas 2007–11*). The cause of this decline is thought to be related, at least in part, to climate and land use changes in the wintering quarters in the humid zone of tropical West Africa. Along with many other trans-Saharan migrants the species is undergoing a slow long-term decline, although numbers can fluctuate on a yearly basis. In Britain, it is mainly found in deciduous woods, particularly those of Sessile Oak, in the uplands of the north and west. During the 1970s and 1980s the national population was deemed to be stable or even slightly increasing. However, since then, although there has been little change in the occupied range, a notable decline in abundance has occurred in many areas. The species' conservation status has been raised to red, the highest level of concern, in response to this decrease.

In Hampshire, as a breeding bird the Wood Warbler is now almost totally confined to the New Forest. It requires mature broadleaved woodland, especially oak and Beech, with a sparse understorey and ground layer. This habitat is plentiful in the New Forest but scarce throughout the rest of the county. Suitable areas are found only in small pockets, mainly in the east and north-east, and therefore represent a major limiting factor on their distribution. The HBA breeding maps clearly show the importance of the New Forest for the species. This has always been the stronghold within the county and, at the time of the 1986–91 Atlas, was estimated to hold up to 450 territorial males. During the HBA period, annual surveys of a 46 sq. km block of woodland west of Lyndhurst were carried out (Ward & Wynn 2013). These resulted in counts of 104 singing males in 2009, 87 in 2010, and 115 in 2011, with concentrations around Holm Hill and Highland Water Inclosures. Based on these counts, the total New Forest population was estimated to be 200–250 territorial males (M. Ward *in litt.*) although numbers appear to have fallen further since then.

The change map, which is based only on probable and proven breeding records in both atlases, shows a net 76% range loss. The causes of this major decline are unclear but, in addition to possible detrimental changes in the wintering area, the increase in deer populations and a wide variety of predators are also perceived as having a negative effect on this ground-nesting species. Nevertheless, the population in the New Forest continues to be the most significant in southern England.

In the rest of the county the Wood Warbler is now only an occasional and sporadic breeder. Up until the early

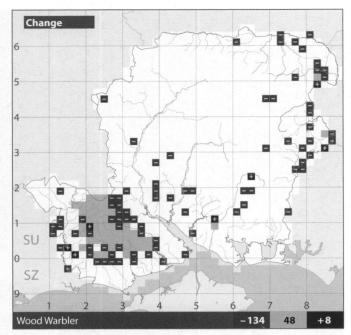

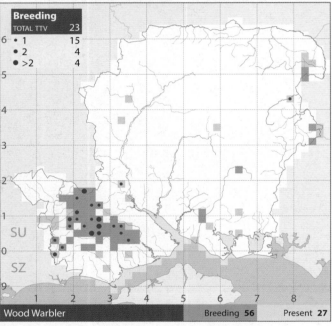

1990s small numbers could be still found scattered across the county although few sites were occupied on an annual basis. Only two locations, Waggoners Wells and the Bourley & Long Valley areas, consistently held breeding birds. Since then, the species has almost disappeared even from these sites. There are occasional records of singing males but these birds hold territory for only a few days, before apparently moving on. It is possible that breeding pairs are occasionally overlooked in seldom-visited woodlands in the county. The only confirmed breeding during the HBA project away from the New Forest was of single pairs feeding young in the nest at Ludshott Common in both 2010 and 2012 although, based on the criteria used, breeding was considered likely at a few additional sites.

Keith Wills

Sponsored by Andy Broadhurst

Wood Warbler,
New Forest, May 2012 –
Martin Bennett

Chiffchaff
Phylloscopus collybita

A common summer visitor and passage migrant, which also winters in small numbers

The Chiffchaff has an enormous global range extending across most of Europe and northern Asia and involving several different subspecies. Although there have been local decreases, most countries indicate that populations are stable or slightly increasing. During the 1960s and 1970s the British population suffered a decline but since then has grown significantly. Indications are that this upward trend is still continuing throughout its British range. *Bird Atlas 2007–11* has shown that the greatest increase has been in the Midlands but the densest populations remain in the south of the country, including Hampshire. The increase is most probably linked to the fact that the majority of British Chiffchaffs do not cross the Sahara to winter, only travelling as far as south-west Europe and North Africa. Therefore, they do not suffer the rigours of crossing the desert, or endure the difficulties of finding food in the Sahel, factors that appear to be a cause of declines in many other migrants.

As a breeding bird, the Chiffchaff is common and widespread in Hampshire. It is found predominantly in broadleaved woodland. Providing there is sufficient undergrowth for nesting, it can be found in small copses, large gardens and hedgerows containing mature trees, as well as in larger woodlands. Along with Blackcap, it is one of the two most numerous warblers breeding in the county.

Compared to the 1986–91 Atlas, the HBA breeding maps show that there has been a small increase in range between the two surveys. There has been some infilling, particularly on the chalk, with a net increase of 32 tetrads. Comparison of abundance is difficult to quantify, but the species has undoubtedly increased in numbers during the intervening period. The densest populations are in the major river valleys and in the east and north-east of Hampshire. Indicative counts of singing males/breeding pairs received during the survey period from river valley sites include 68 at Itchen Valley Country Park, 33 at Lower Test Marshes, and 30 at Titchfield Haven. Not surprisingly, the species is common in parts of the New Forest, although densities vary depending on the suitability of the habitat. A survey of a 46 sq. km block of woodland west of Lyndhurst counted 125 singing males in 2011 (Ward & Wynn 2013). The apparently lower numbers present across the centre of the county may be an indication of less wooded habitat in the open, agricultural landscape of the chalk downland.

The first report of a Chiffchaff wintering in Hampshire was in January 1952. Since then, small but gradually increasing numbers have regularly over-wintered. Around 100 individuals are now recorded most years, although its

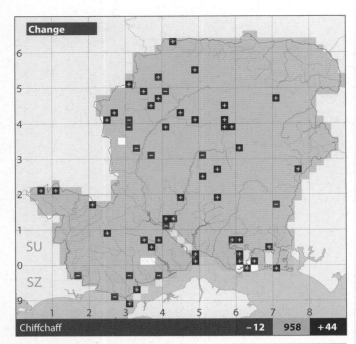

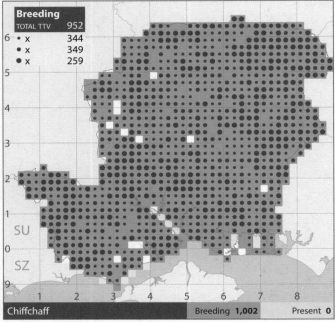

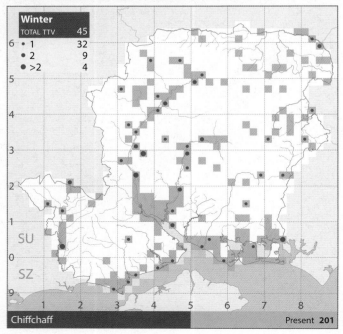

Chiffchaff, New Forest, April 2014 – *Martin Bennett*

presence in 201 tetrads over the HBA period suggests that the actual population may be considerably higher. It seems likely that many of these birds are not of British origin but come from elsewhere in the species' range, presumably Scandinavia and Russia (*Migration Atlas*). Unlike the Blackcap, another now-regular over-wintering warbler, the Chiffchaff depends primarily on insects for its diet. The vast majority are therefore found close to water where they search for food in vegetation alongside rivers, around lakes, ponds, and gravel pits, and especially in the vicinity of sewage farms. Double-figure counts are sometimes made at the latter sites but during very hard weather they can disappear entirely. In this situation it is unclear whether they move to warmer climes or succumb to the conditions.

The dependence on water is clear from the HBA winter map, with the distinct majority of occupied tetrads being from the coast and the main river valleys. During the HBA survey period maximum winter counts included 16 at Eastleigh Sewage Farm and 12 at Darby Green adjacent to Sandhurst Sewage Farm in Berkshire.

During winter, there are increasing reports of Chiffchaffs of one or more of the eastern races, notably of the form *tristis*, colloquially known as Siberian Chiffchaff. During the survey period individuals were recorded from several sites in the county, all close to water.

Keith Wills

Sponsored by Betty Hansell

Iberian Chiffchaff

Phylloscopus ibericus

A very rare vagrant

Until recently this species was considered a race of Chiffchaff *P. collybita*. It was given full species status early in the new millennium and appeared on the 7th edition of the BOU checklist in 2006. Identification depends critically on assessment of its song. During the HBA period the first for Hampshire was present at New Copse Inclosure in the New Forest from at least May 10th to 17th 2009. Recordings of its song were analysed and found to contain diagnostic notes of *P. ibericus* not within the repertoire of *P. collybita*.

Keith Wills

Iberian Chiffchaff, New Forest, May 2009 – *Nigel Jones*

Willow Warbler
Phylloscopus trochilus
A common but declining summer visitor and passage migrant

The Willow Warbler is widespread in Hampshire, found on woodland edges and in all kinds of scrub habitat. Highest densities occur on heathland where there is an abundance of birch scrub, but it is also found in suitable habitat on downland, in young conifer plantations and on farmland with suitable hedgerows and trees.

It has been well-documented that there has been a drastic decline in numbers during the last 25 years. At the time of the 1986–91 Atlas, Clark & Eyre described the species as being easily our most common warbler (*BoH*). Sadly, this is no longer the case, with the populations of Blackcap, Chiffchaff, and possibly Whitethroat now exceeding that of Willow Warbler in the county. During the HBA project the species was recorded in only 69% of the county's tetrads compared to 96% at the time of the previous Atlas, and the density of birds present in individual tetrads has declined to an even greater extent. This crash in numbers has occurred throughout southern and eastern England, with a 71% fall in the south-east between 1995 and 2011 (*BBS*). In contrast, numbers in northern England, Wales and Scotland are stable and in the far north of Scotland are even increasing. The decline in southern England is linked to a decrease in breeding productivity, perhaps due to a reduction in habitat quality and subsequent lack of insect food. British Willow Warblers winter in Africa south of the Sahara and pressures during migration and in the winter quarters may also have contributed to the decline. However, the increasing population farther north suggests that climate change may be the key factor. The species has an enormous global range that includes the whole of the northern Palearctic. It remains an abundant species throughout much of this range but is deemed to be gradually decreasing in numbers overall.

As indicated by the HBA breeding maps, despite the decline, Willow Warbler remains a common and widespread visitor to Hampshire, particularly to the New Forest and north/ north-east. However, compared to the 1986–91 survey it is noticeable that there are many more gaps in distribution. It has been lost from many downland and farmland areas across a wide central belt of the county, presumably now occurring only at sites where optimum habitat can still be found. An example of the decline is illustrated by the fact that during the HBA survey only four territories were found at Martin Down compared with 63 back in 1981. It can be discerned from both the distribution and abundance data that the Test Valley is one of the few remaining locations in the central area where the species still occurs in any numbers.

In Hampshire, the Willow Warbler appears to be becoming increasingly dependent on heathland habitat. Fortunately, it

Willow Warbler, Martin Down, April 2014 – *Martin Bennett*

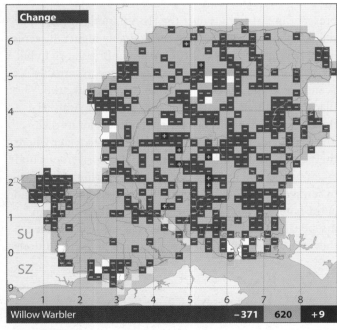

Change — Willow Warbler — −371 | 620 | +9

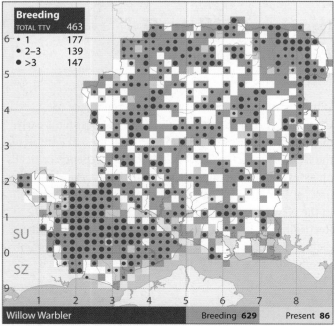

Breeding
TOTAL TTV 463
- 1 — 177
- 2–3 — 139
- >3 — 147

Willow Warbler — Breeding **629** — Present **86**

still remains common in the New Forest and on the Thames Basin and Wealden Heath SPAs, particularly those sites that have plentiful birch scrub. Counts from the north-eastern heaths include 32 singing males at Ludshott Common in 2011, 30 at Longmoor Inclosure in 2008 and 15 at Blackbushe in 2011. In the New Forest it still occurs in some wooded areas as well as on the heathland, and also in young plantations. During the HBA survey period a maximum total of 124 singing males was located in a 46 sq. km block of woodland west of Lyndhurst (Ward & Wynn 2013). Conversely,

and again showing how much the species has declined numerically, the numbers of singing males at Roydon Woods decreased from 62 in 1990 to just four in 2009.

Although there have been occasional records of Willow Warblers in Hampshire during the winter months none were recorded during the HBA survey period.

Keith Wills

Sponsored by Janet Dedman

Pallas's Warbler

Phylloscopus proregulus

A very rare vagrant

Prior to the HBA period there had been only four records of this attractive Siberian warbler in Hampshire, with the last at Lymington on January 15th 2005. By the end of the survey, the number had doubled, thanks to an unprecedented year in 2008 when three were recorded. All records during the 2007–12 period are given below:

2008: Totton, a male March 1st–April 3rd.
Sandy Point Nature Reserve, a male on May 8th.
Bramley, north Hampshire, December 28th.
2011: Sandy Point, October 24th/25th.

Keith Wills

Sponsored in memory of Tim Lawman

Pallas's Warbler, Eversley, January 2013 – *Dave Perrett*

Yellow-browed Warbler

Phylloscopus inornatus

A rare visitor, most frequent in autumn, but recorded in every month from September to April

This is an abundant species which breeds predominantly in north and central Asia and migrates south to winter in south-east Asia. Its range extends westwards just into eastern Europe. The expansion of this western population in recent years probably explains why the numbers seen on migration and wintering in the UK have also increased. During the 2007–12 period there were 32 records in Hampshire, equalling the number recorded prior to 2007 following the first in 1959. Most were recorded on the coast as autumn migrants, so outside the HBA breeding and winter survey periods. Wintering birds, all singles, were seen as follows (the first two before the HBA survey began):

2007: Hawley Meadows, Blackwater, December 2006–March 16th.
Rooksbury Mill, February 5th–March 25th.
2008: Newlands Farm, Fareham, December 12th–21st.
2009: Vokes Park, Southampton, February 6th.
2012: Brownwich Lane, Titchfield, February 26th.

Yellow-browed Warbler, Titchfield Haven, October 2011 – *Trevor Codlin*

Keith Wills

Sponsored by Damian Offer

Blackcap

Sylvia atricapilla

A common summer visitor and passage migrant, which also winters in small numbers

As a breeding bird, the Blackcap is common and widespread in Hampshire. Along with Chiffchaff, it is one of the two most numerous warblers breeding in the county. It occurs predominantly in broadleaved woodland and providing there is a sufficient shrub layer for nesting, it can be found in small copses, large gardens, and hedgerows, as well as in larger wooded areas.

The population of Blackcaps has increased significantly since the 1970s, not just in Hampshire but throughout its British range. *Bird Atlas 2007–11* has shown that the greatest increase has been in southern England, including Hampshire, and in a broad band up through the west Midlands, Wales, and on into south-west Scotland. However, the densest populations remain in the south and east of the country. The majority of British Blackcaps do not cross the Sahara to winter, only travelling as far as south-west Europe and North Africa. Like the Chiffchaff, they therefore avoid the inevitable hazards of crossing the desert and wintering in the drought-prone Sahel region. Although this advantage is unlikely to have led to the observed population increase, the relatively short migration, coupled with warmer springs, may have advanced the breeding season and increased productivity (*BirdTrends*). The species has a large global range extending across most of Europe and western Asia. Reports from many of the countries where it occurs indicate that numbers are slowly increasing.

Compared to the 1986–91 Atlas, the HBA breeding maps show that there has been little change in distribution within the county. The species was recorded in 98% of tetrads with breeding considered likely in most of them. There are a few apparent gaps, for example in some built-up areas such as Portsmouth, and, curiously, in a small area of the New Forest, the latter possibly being due to under-recording rather than an actual absence. Comparison of abundance is difficult but the species has undoubtedly increased in numbers over the past two decades. The densest populations appear to be along the River Itchen between Winchester and Eastleigh, and in the east and north-east of Hampshire, particularly in the vicinity of Alton. The species is common in the wooded parts of the New Forest, as indicated by 163 singing males being counted in a 46 sq. km block of woodland west of Lyndhurst in 2009 – rising to 233 in 2011 (Ward & Wynn 2013). Other counts of singing males/breeding pairs received during the HBA period included 63 at Itchen Valley Country Park and 29 at both Lower Test Marshes and Titchfield Haven.

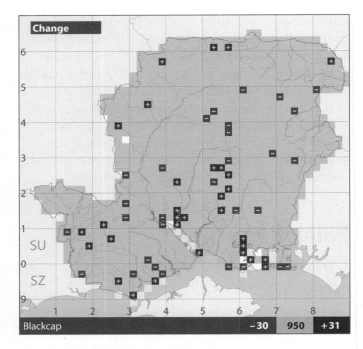

The first report of a Blackcap wintering in Hampshire appears to date from the late 19th century but occurrences remained rare right up until the 1970s. Since then there has been a significant increase in numbers over-wintering in the county. The vast majority of these are found in observers' gardens and it is no coincidence that the HBA winter distribution map correlates strongly with built-up areas – Southampton, Eastleigh, Andover, Basingstoke and Alton, for example, are all clearly demarcated on the map. Very few are recorded in the more rural countryside. The attraction of gardens can be linked to a readily available food supply at bird-tables. During the winter Blackcaps partake of a wide variety of food including various berries, fruit, fat-bars, peanut cake and even more exotic items such as the icing on Christmas cake. They are often dominant at feeding sites, aggressively chasing off other species.

It is difficult to determine the actual numbers present in the county during the winter. During the HBA period the highest total number recorded was 140 from 82 sites in the first two months of 2010. The true total, taking into account under-recording and the change-over of birds at individual sites, is likely to be much higher. Up to five are regularly recorded together at various favoured localities. Ringing recoveries have shown that Hampshire-bred Blackcaps do not stay in the county during the winter but leave for warmer climes. It is actually Continental birds, particularly from Germany and Belgium, which cross the English Channel to spend the winter here.

Keith Wills

Sponsored by Glynne Evans

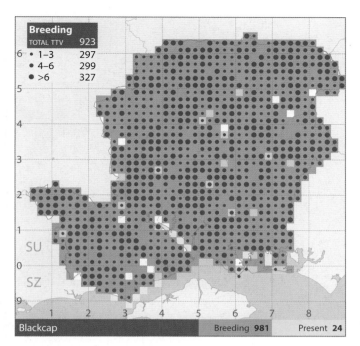

Breeding

TOTAL TTV 923

- 1–3   297
- 4–6   299
- >6   327

Blackcap   Breeding **981**   Present **24**

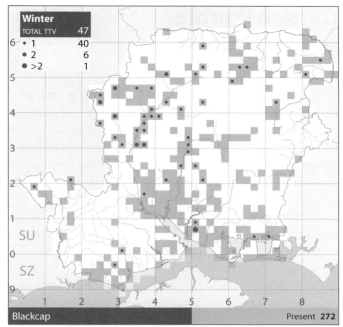

Winter

TOTAL TTV 47

- 1   40
- 2   6
- >2   1

Blackcap   Present **272**

Blackcap, Blashford Lakes, April 2011 – *Martin Bennett*

Garden Warbler

Sylvia borin

A common summer visitor and passage migrant

The Garden Warbler is widespread in Hampshire, mainly occurring in dense scrub in open broadleaved woodland and along woodland and heathland edges. It also occurs in young conifer plantations providing that there is a sufficient under-storey of brambles and other vegetation. Along with many other trans-Saharan migrants the Garden Warbler is thought to be in a slow long-term decline, although numbers can fluctuate on a yearly basis. The population in England has decreased by 23% over the 1967–2011 period (*BirdTrends*) with larger declines in the south and east (*Bird Atlas 2007–11*). Studies throughout the species' global range, which encompasses the whole of Europe, would also indicate that there is a general decline in numbers.

The HBA breeding map shows that the Garden Warbler remains a common visitor to Hampshire, being recorded in around half of the county's tetrads. While the species continues to be distributed across the county, there does appear to have been a general contraction in breeding range compared to the 1986–91 Atlas. Birds were located in only 520 tetrads during the HBA compared to 718 in the earlier survey. There may have been a degree of under-recording during both Atlas surveys. The species is difficult to observe in its favoured scrub habitat and has always been one of the least reported of the warblers. This is probably due to it often being misidentified because its song is similar to the Blackcap's, the commoner species. Furthermore, the reduced level of breeding evidence during the HBA makes it difficult to differentiate between breeding birds and migrants so the change map may overstate the apparent decline in breeding range.

The Garden Warbler has always been scarce on the chalk downland but during the 1986–91 survey there were still many localities where the species could be found (although not always proved breeding). The results of the HBA show that breeding is no longer considered likely at many of these chalkland sites, particularly on the higher ground and including Martin Down. The species can now only be found in numbers in the river valleys that pass through the area. Even here, although still frequent along the River Test, there are fewer seen along the River Itchen, especially the section between Winchester and Southampton. This may well be due to the lack of suitable habitat as a result of the general 'tidying up' of the countryside.

The Garden Warbler also appears to have always been a localised breeder along the coast. During the current survey there has been a further contraction in range from the coastal fringe, particularly in the west, with breeding considered likely only in the Beaulieu Estuary, Calshot and Titchfield Haven areas and in a few scattered tetrads elsewhere. There also appears to have been a decrease in

Garden Warbler, Blashford Lakes, April 2014 – *Steve Bassett*

the south of the New Forest but elsewhere in the Forest numbers have been maintained. For example, a total of 36 singing males was located in a survey of a 46 sq. km block of mixed woodland west of Lyndhurst during 2009, although numbers decreased in the following years (Ward & Wynn 2013).

On a more positive note, the status of the species appears to have changed little during the last two decades in the north-eastern quadrant of the county, where it is still present in good numbers. In this area it favours suitable scrubby habitat around the many gravel pits along the Blackwater Valley, in the Thames Basin and Wealden Heath SPAs and in woodland areas such as Alice Holt Forest and Binswood. It is encouraging that it is also still frequently found on farmland in this area, notably to the north of Basingstoke and south of Alton.

Owing to the skulking habits of this species, obtaining actual proof of breeding is difficult. Confirmed breeding was reported from only 42 tetrads although it was considered likely in almost half of the county's total. Most of the occupied tetrads contained only one to three singing males. Double-figure counts from single sites are highly unusual but during the HBA period there were 13 singing males in the Ivy Lake area of the Blashford complex in 2008 and 12 at Blackbushe in 2012.

The only winter record during the HBA survey period was of a single bird seen and photographed at Rooksbury Mill on November 6th 2008.

Keith Wills

Sponsored by Ian Cox

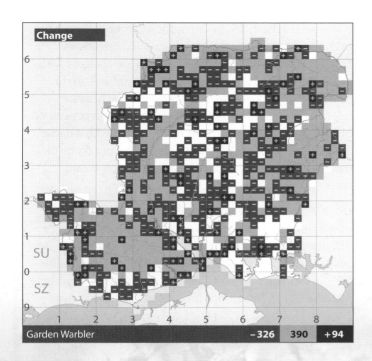

Change

6
5
4
3
1
SU
0
SZ
9

1 2 3 4 5 6 7 8

Garden Warbler — 326 390 +94

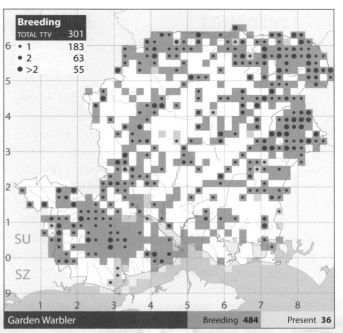

Breeding

TOTAL TTV 301
• 1 183
• 2 63
• >2 55

6
5
4
3
2
1
SU
0
SZ
9

1 2 3 4 5 6 7 8

Garden Warbler Breeding 484 Present 36

Garden Warbler, Blashford Lakes, July 2009 – *Martin Bennett*

Whitethroat

Sylvia communis

A common summer visitor and passage migrant

As a summer visitor from sub-Saharan Africa, the number of Whitethroats reaching Britain can fluctuate from year to year. In the late 1960s there was a well-documented population crash that affected not just Hampshire but the whole of the country. This was linked to drought conditions in the wintering quarters in the Sahel region of Africa, a factor that continues to have a major effect on the species today. National indices (*BirdTrends*) show that since the crash, there has been a slow recovery. The overall national trend is of a gradual increase in numbers, although they are still thought to be less than half of pre-1968 levels. When compared to the 1988–91 Atlas survey, *Bird Atlas 2007–11* shows that numbers have increased throughout most of its range in lowland England, including Hampshire, and also in northern England and lowland Scotland. The species' extensive global range includes the whole of Europe, extending into central Asia, with most countries indicating that breeding numbers are being maintained.

As indicated by the HBA breeding map, the Whitethroat is widespread and common in Hampshire. It is found in hedgerows and brush with adjacent thick ground cover. It occurs at the highest densities on ungrazed heathland where there is mature gorse and invading birch scrub, but it is commonly found in farmland where there are long-established hedges, downland, rough waste and marginal land, and along the river valleys and coast where suitable scrub habitat prevails. The HBA change map shows that,

compared to the 1986–91 Atlas, there has been very little overall change in the number of occupied territories. However, the county-wide distribution has changed with a decrease in the New Forest and some infilling on the chalk. The decline in the New Forest may be because intense grazing of the heathland prevents the regeneration of mature gorse and emergent birch habitat with a dense under-layer that the species prefers. This is in contrast to the heaths on the Thames Basin and Western Weald, where the species continues to be abundant.

Double-figure counts of singing males/breeding pairs during the HBA period came from many localities. The densest populations are found on some of the heathland sites in the Thames Basin and Wealden Heath SPAs, including Ludshott Common (maximum 37 singing males in 2011), Longmoor Inclosure (27 in 2011) and Hazeley Heath (22 in 2011). However, the largest count from a single site during the survey period was 45 at Itchen Valley Country Park in 2011. Coastal sites with significant populations include Titchfield Haven (36 in 2010), and the Normandy/Oxey Marsh area (25 in 2009). Suitable habitat on downland can also hold reasonable numbers, including sites such as Butser Hill (14 in 2011), and the Martin Down CBC area (13 in 2010).

Although there have been occasional records of Whitethroats wintering in Hampshire, none were recorded during the HBA winter survey period.

Keith Wills

Sponsored by Alf Smallbone

Whitethroat, New Forest, September 2010 – *Martin Bennett*

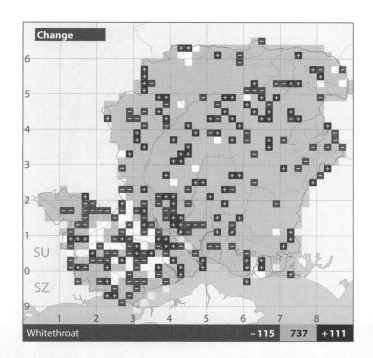

Change

6
5
4
3
2
1
SU
0
SZ
9

1 2 3 4 5 6 7 8

Whitethroat — 115 | 737 | +111

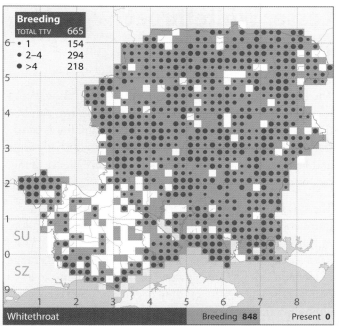

Breeding

TOTAL TTV 665

• 1   154
• 2–4   294
• >4   218

6
5
4
3
2
1
SU
0
SZ
9

1 2 3 4 5 6 7 8

Whitethroat — Breeding **848** | Present **0**

Whitethroat, New Forest, April 2011 – *Martin Bennett*

Lesser Whitethroat

Sylvia curruca

An uncommon summer visitor and passage migrant

The Lesser Whitethroat is widespread in Hampshire, being found in mature hedgerows and dense, overgrown scrub throughout the county. It is nowhere common but is most frequently found on downland with well-established scrub and bushes, and on farmland where there are plenty of tall, old, uncut hedges.

The species is known to experience fluctuations in numbers. At the time of the 1986–91 Atlas, the population in Hampshire was relatively high but since then there has been a decline both in the county and throughout its range in lowland Britain. This downward trend reached a low point in the late 1990s and then began a gradual recovery, although numbers are still not back up to earlier levels. Relative to the previous Atlas there has been a notable contraction of the species' range in the county, with only around 56% of the tetrads being occupied during the HBA compared to the 1986–91 survey. This decline is not specific to one area, affecting the whole county although the south-west, in particular, appears to have been badly affected. The species generally avoids heathland habitat, so it has never been common in the New Forest but it also seems to have disappeared from most of the Avon Valley and from the majority of the downland on the border with Dorset and Wiltshire, although it is still present at Martin Down. It has also largely disappeared from the well-watched north-east of the county where, during the 1986–91 survey, it was frequently encountered in farmland north of Basingstoke and along the Blackwater Valley and its associated gravel pits.

Lesser Whitethroat has a massive global range, encompassing most of Europe excluding the south-west, and vast swathes of Asia. The species is believed to be maintaining, or even increasing, its numbers in many countries; in certain areas it is the commonest warbler encountered. It is unusual among Hampshire's warblers in that it winters in north-east Africa. In Britain it is at the western extremity of its European range and is therefore more likely to experience population fluctuations than elsewhere.

It should also be noted that the species is very easily overlooked. It has a distinctive, but subdued rattle of a song, which may not be familiar to some observers. Also, the song period is rather short and, because of these combined factors, there may be some under-recording during the surveys. Many reports are for one date only. This may be because the record is from a farmland or downland site which is not re-visited by the observer for

Lesser Whitethroat, Blashford Lakes, August 2008 – *Martin Bennett*

a number of weeks, by which time the bird has probably gone silent and cannot be relocated due to its skulking behaviour. Although not apparent from the breeding map, there was a concentration of confirmed breeding evidence from coastal localities, such as Keyhaven/Pennington Marshes, Titchfield Haven and Farlington Marshes. This is no doubt due to the fact that there is not only suitable habitat at these sites but also because the localities are frequented by many observers, therefore providing more opportunities to obtain proof of breeding. Elsewhere many records may relate to migrants that take up temporary territory before moving on again. This makes confirmation of breeding difficult and comparison of numbers and distribution between surveys subject to major uncertainty. While there has undoubtedly been a contraction in the species' range in Hampshire, the scale of the change may be lower than shown on the change map. At the vast majority of sites where the species was recorded during the HBA survey, only one to three singing males/pairs were present. However, there were nine singing males at Itchen Valley Country Park in 2010, seven at Martin Down in 2008 and 2010, seven in the Lymington/Hurst area in 2009 and six at Portsdown Hill in 2008.

The Lesser Whitethroat is known to over-winter in Britain occasionally, and there have been several previous records in Hampshire. During the HBA period there was one, possibly of the eastern race *halimodendri*, at Barton on Sea on November 19th 2008, and one at Bursledon from January 23rd to March 7th 2010.

Keith Wills

Sponsored by John Hale

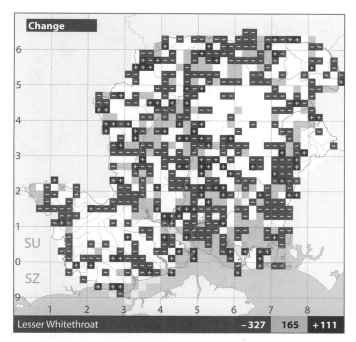

Change

6
5
4
3
SU
0
SZ
9

1 2 3 4 5 6 7 8

Lesser Whitethroat   − 327   165   + 111

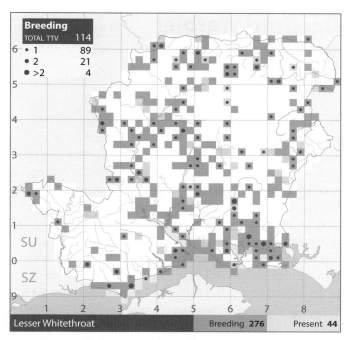

Breeding

TOTAL TTV	114
• 1	89
• 2	21
● >2	4

6
5
4
3
SU
0
SZ
9

1 2 3 4 5 6 7 8

Lesser Whitethroat   Breeding **276**   Present **44**

Lesser Whitethroat, Blashford Lakes, August 2009 – *Martin Bennett*

331

Dartford Warbler

Sylvia undata

A moderately common resident largely confined to
lowland heath and coastal scrub

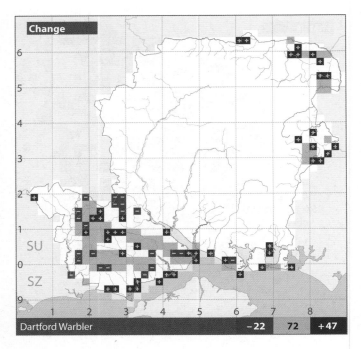

The Dartford Warbler is one of Hampshire's iconic birds.
Largely confined to lowland heath with a mixture of
mature heather and medium height gorse, it is subject to
periodic fluctuations in its population due to the ravages of
severe winter weather. The species was described by John
Latham from a pair shot at Bexley Heath, near Dartford,
in Kent, in 1773. Yet it was not known to Hampshire's
first ornithologist, Gilbert White (1720–93), although he
regularly visited Woolmer Forest, one of its present day
haunts. It seems probable that the frequent severe winters
in the second half of the 18th century had exterminated the
species in Hampshire, thus accounting for White's lack of
sightings. Although the first nest was found by Montagu in
Devon in 1806, it is difficult to ascertain when it was first
recorded in Hampshire. *K&M* document a specimen taken
at Woolmer in 1847 but give no earlier information for the
New Forest.

The first breeding season of the HBA coincided with a high
population level for the species. On the Thames Basin and
Wealden Heaths in the north-east of the county, numbers
reached their highest ever recorded level in 2003–2005
and were only slightly lower in 2008 (Clark 2011a).
Severe weather in the following two winters (2008/09
and 2009/10) decimated the population in this area,
although numbers held up better in the New Forest where
the extent and duration of snow cover was much less.
Thus the summer atlas map largely reflects the position in
2008, with registrations in 61 New Forest tetrads, 27 on the
Thames Basin and Wealden Heaths, a handful on isolated
heaths at Barton in the south-west, Badminston near
Fawley, Silchester and Tadley in the north and at coastal
locations, where the species occurs in heather or low scrub
with a mixture of bramble and gorse. There was also a
report of a singing male, possibly accompanied by another
bird, at Martin Down in June 2010.

The HBA change map shows a strong increase with a net
gain of 25 tetrads (+27%) compared with the 1986–91
Atlas. However, this masks some local differences. In the
New Forest, there were registrations in 18 fewer tetrads.
Surveys of the forest in 1988 (at the time of the first tetrad
atlas), 1994 and 2006 produced totals of 454, approximately
560 and approximately 440 territories respectively.
The trend since 2006 is unclear. In one 4 sq. km study area
in the south-east of the Forest, which held 13 territories
in that year, totals have fluctuated between 16 and 20 up
to 2011 (E.J. Wiseman *in litt.*), which suggests a stable
population. However, data from the monthly New Forest
Winter Bird Survey show that the maximum February/
March totals in 2008–12 were 105, 82, 83, 28 and 28

(K.F. Betton *in litt.*), suggesting a decline. Given that the
population levels in 1988 and 2006 were similar, and that
mild weather prevailed until 2008, it seems likely that the
species has been missed in some tetrads. Nonetheless, its
absence from the National Trust-owned Bramshaw group
of commons, where it was present in five tetrads in 1986–
91, may be due to this being marginal habitat, with plenty
of mature gorse but little mature heather (G.C. Evans,
pers. comm.).

On the Thames Basin and Wealden Heaths registrations
were up from 13 tetrads in the 1986–91 Atlas to 27 in the
HBA. The peak population level recorded during the first
atlas was 31 pairs at five sites in 1990. This had increased to
an estimated 271 pairs at 22 sites in 2008 but fell back to 50
and then 29 pairs following severe winters in 2008/09 and
2009/10.

The winter atlas map shows a broadly similar distribution,
as expected for a resident species. However, there are more
registrations at coastal sites, some of which have held
breeding birds in the past. Inland, there are registrations
well away from known breeding sites on downland at Long
Down (December 2007), Ashley Warren (January 2008)
and Portsdown Hill (November 2009), and at Great Covert
Wood (November 2008), Kingston in the Avon Valley
(January 2010), Pauncefoot Hill near Romsey (November
2010) and Newtown (December 2010). These probably
represent juvenile dispersal.

John Clark

Sponsored by John Clark

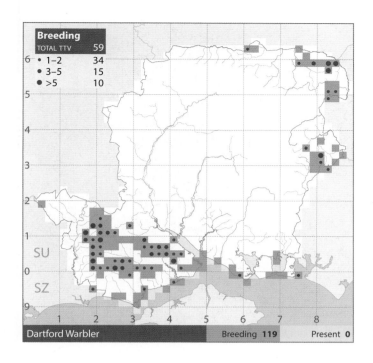

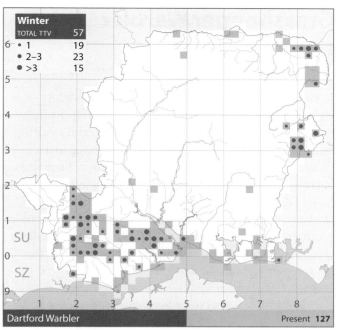

Dartford Warbler,
New Forest, January 2014
– *Martin Bennett*

Grasshopper Warbler
Locustella naevia
A scarce summer visitor and passage migrant

In Hampshire, the Grasshopper Warbler is nowadays most closely associated with marshy areas in river valleys that contain a lush growth of low vegetation and small bushes. In former times it was far more catholic in its choice of habitat, being found in young conifer plantations, heathland and on downland. The species suffered a major fall in population during the late 1970s and 1980s throughout the whole of Britain but particularly marked in southern counties of England (*1988–91 Atlas*). Reasons for this drop are unclear but are thought to be linked to the on-going drought in the Sahel region of Africa where Britain's Grasshopper Warblers spend the winter. Nationally there is also some evidence that removal of scrub and consequent lack of suitable breeding habitat has contributed to the decline but this seems unlikely to apply in Hampshire where there appears to be plenty of suitable habitat still available. The species has a very large global range incorporating most of temperate Europe and extending into central Asia. Throughout the region numbers appear to be slowly declining, although it is reported as being stable in some countries.

At the time of the 1986–91 Atlas there were fewer than 20 pairs being reported annually in Hampshire. Since then, numbers have remained at a low ebb, reaching their nadir at the start of the HBA breeding survey in 2008 when only nine singing males were located. However, since then there has been some cause for optimism with a sudden increase in the numbers of reeling birds reported, to 35 in 2010 (the highest count since the late 1980s) and 27 in 2011. This trend is supported by data from elsewhere in the country, with a general improvement in overall numbers since a low point in the early years of the 21st century.

From the HBA maps, it can be seen that most of Hampshire's breeding Grasshopper Warblers are now found at a handful of sites in the Test and Itchen Valleys and at Titchfield Haven. The change map shows a substantial range contraction since the previous survey but this needs to be treated with caution. Almost all Grasshopper Warblers are located by their distinctive reeling song and, because of their tendency of singing at dawn and dusk, it is possible that some birds are missed. Conversely, many singing individuals are migrants passing through the county, which makes it possible to over-estimate the numbers staying to breed. For this latter reason, the change map compares only likely breeding during the HBA with probable plus proven breeding records from the 1986–91 Atlas. On this basis, the range has contracted from 36 occupied tetrads in 1986–91 to just 14 during the HBA. Based on comparison of just the proven and probable breeding records in both atlases the range reduction is even greater – from 36 tetrads in 1986–91 to just 10 during the HBA period.

Grasshopper Warbler, Winchester, May 2010 – *Keith Maycock*

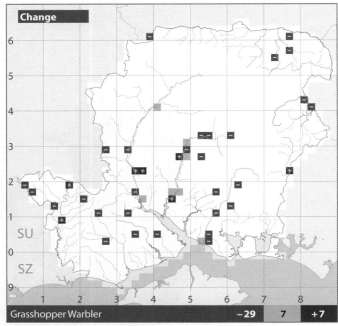

Grasshopper Warbler   −29   7   +7

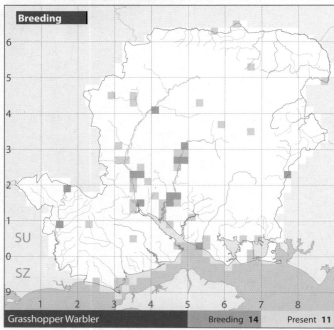

Grasshopper Warbler   Breeding 14   Present 11

During the HBA period, vast swathes of the north and east of the county had no records at all and there were only a few scattered reports from the New Forest and other sites in the south-west. Even in the river valleys there has been a reduction in localities at which the species was recorded. The most favoured sites are currently being utilised almost annually. These include Itchen Valley Country Park, along the River Itchen at Winchester, Lower Test Marshes and Fishlake Meadows, Romsey. The last of these provided the maximum site count during the survey period of five reeling males in 2011. However, owing to its unobtrusive behaviour, obtaining confirmation of breeding is extremely difficult, with the only proof during the survey period coming from Lower Test Marshes and Titchfield Haven.

Keith Wills

Sponsored in memory of Terence Hampton

Savi's Warbler

Locustella luscinioides

A rare summer visitor and very rare autumn passage migrant

This species breeds across southern Europe into Asia and winters in Africa. It is on the western extremity of its range in the UK and rare in Hampshire. The first for the county was a territorial male at Titchfield Haven in 1969. This was followed by further records from the same site between 1976 and 1983 with a maximum of six singing males and one pair confirmed breeding in 1978. Breeding occurred again in 1979 and 1982 and an unmated male was present in 1987, although the record was not submitted to the 1986–91 Atlas. Unmated males were also at Titchfield Haven in 1998 (Duffin 2003) and 2004.

During the HBA period there were two records, as follows:

2009: A male held territory at Fishlake Meadows from May 1st–June 27th.

2011: A singing male was at Titchfield Haven on April 15th and 24th.

These brought the county total to 34.

John Eyre

Savi's Warbler, Fishlake Meadows, May 2009 – *Nigel Jones*

Icterine Warbler

Hippolais icterina

A rare passage migrant

A singing male at Sandy Point on May 13th 2009 was the tenth for the county. This was the first since 1996 and the first May record, the previous nine being between June and October.

Keith Wills

Icterine Warbler, Sandy Point, May 2009 – *Richard Ford*

Sedge Warbler

Acrocephalus schoenobaenus
A common but local summer visitor and passage migrant

The Sedge Warbler is widespread in Hampshire but usually restricted to scrub and bushy habitat adjacent to rivers and other water bodies. The species favours localities with low, dense vegetation with scattered small bushes, such as water meadows and around the drier margins of *Phragmites* reed beds. Therefore, numbers are concentrated along the main river valleys and at some coastal wetland sites. As with many trans-Saharan migrants the species is enduring a slow decline in population due to the on-going drought in the Sahel region of Africa, where most of Britain's Sedge Warblers over-winter. The species has a very large global distribution that includes most of Europe eastwards to the Urals and the decline in Britain is supported by data received from elsewhere in its range. However, populations are prone to cyclical fluctuations, probably linked to variations in winter survival.

As indicated by the HBA breeding map, the Sedge Warbler remains a common visitor in Hampshire where there is suitable habitat. The map plainly shows the affinity of the species to wetland sites, with the Rivers Avon, Test, and Itchen being clearly demarcated, as well as some of the major coastal sites such as Titchfield Haven and Farlington Marshes.

With regard to the change in the species' status within Hampshire, based on the methodology adopted here, there has been a 37% reduction in the number of tetrads where breeding was considered likely during the HBA when compared to the previous survey. However, this may overestimate the decline because it includes tetrads in 1986–91 where breeding was considered possible but not probable or proven. However, if the comparison is made only on the basis of probable and proven breeding records in both atlases, the resulting decline is even larger at around 46%, which illustrates the problem of lack of breeding evidence. Ignoring breeding evidence altogether and comparing presence in 1986–91 with presence during the HBA still produces a range reduction of 20%. This loss is most noticeable at coastal sites in the western half of the county. During the 1986–91 survey, breeding was considered likely in more than twenty tetrads between Keyhaven Marsh and Calshot and continuing up the west side of Southampton Water. During the HBA there were only eight records of likely breeding along this stretch of coastline and none of these was confirmed. With the exception of 15 singing males at Calshot in May 2011 only single-figure counts were made at these sites. Fortunately, the species is still found at several coastal localities in the eastern half of the county but even here it appears to have been lost from former haunts around Gosport and Fareham and on Hayling Island. The largest numbers can be found at Titchfield Haven where, during the current survey, annual

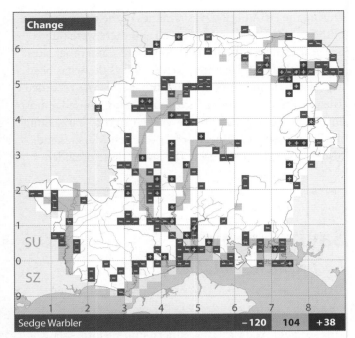

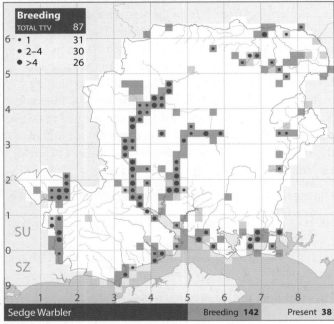

counts varied between 26 and 42 singing males/breeding pairs, thus illustrating the year-to-year fluctuations that can occur. However, the overall continuing decline is shown by the fact that as recently as 1989 there was a minimum of 89 territories at this site. At least 20 pairs can also be found at Farlington Marshes although very few counts are received from this well-watched locality.

Another part of the county where Sedge Warbler has declined is in the north-east. Although never abundant in this area, during the 1986–91 survey the species could be found in small numbers at Fleet Pond, along the Rivers Blackwater and Whitewater and parts of the Basingstoke Canal. It is now mainly just a migrant through the area, with the only regular breeding site now being Stratfield Saye, where up to eight territories can be found, plus sporadic breeding at other localities such as Woolmer Pond and Springhead, Greywell.

Fortunately, the species is still common in the main river valleys, although there has no doubt been a decrease in overall numbers. Important localities include Itchen Valley Country Park (37 territories in 2011), Lower Test Marshes (37 territories in 2010) and Fishlake Meadows, Romsey (45 territories in 2011). The short-term trend during the HBA period at all these sites was one of increase, being another illustration of the variability in numbers from year to year. Significant numbers can also be found along the length of the Avon Valley mainly alongside the actual river but also at Blashford Lakes. Owing to the difficulty of access to many privately owned sections along all the main river valleys, it is difficult to evaluate how many pairs are actually on territory, but survey work during the HBA period would indicate that the species is still present in good numbers.

Keith Wills

Sponsored by Colin Bates

Sedge Warbler, Pennington, September 2008 – *Mike Duffy*

Sedge Warbler, Titchfield Haven, May 2014 – *Mike Crutch*

337

Reed Warbler

Acrocephalus scirpaceus

A common but local summer visitor and passage migrant

The Reed Warbler is widespread in Hampshire but restricted to its favoured *Phragmites* reed bed habitat. It can therefore be found along all the main river valleys, in the major coastal reed beds, around the margins of suitable lakes and flooded gravel pits and in reed-filled ditches. It is one of the few trans-Saharan migrants that seems to be maintaining breeding numbers, or perhaps even slightly increasing. The species' global range includes the whole of Europe, extending into central Asia, with most countries indicating that breeding numbers are being maintained or increasing. Studies support the theory that the Reed Warbler has benefited from climate change, with warmer summers extending the breeding season, allowing many pairs to raise two broods. Also, it does not appear to be under any undue pressure in its wintering quarters; most British Reed Warblers winter in West Africa south of the Sahel zone.

In Hampshire, as indicated by the HBA breeding maps, the Reed Warbler remains a common visitor in suitable habitat. The maps show the dependence of the species on reed beds, with the Rivers Avon, Test, and Itchen being clearly demarcated, together with the major coastal sites such as Keyhaven/Pennington Marshes, Titchfield Haven and Farlington Marshes and many gravel pits in the north-east.

Compared to the 1986–91 Atlas there has been little change in the species' distribution pattern, although there has been a 24% growth in the number of occupied tetrads. This has resulted, in large part, from the creation of new gravel pits. Examples include the Blashford Lakes complex in the Avon Valley and Eversley Gravel Pits/Moor Green Lakes on the county boundary with Berkshire. Less obvious is the change in breeding numbers at individual sites.

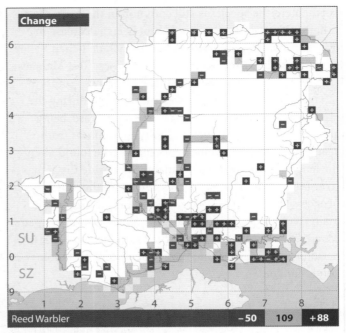

Change

Reed Warbler — −50 | 109 | +88

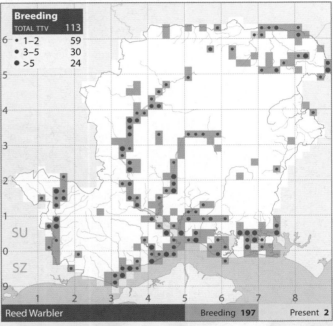

Breeding
TOTAL TTV 113
- 1–2   59
- 3–5   30
- >5   24

Reed Warbler — Breeding **197**   Present **2**

Reed Warbler, Fordingbridge, June 2012 – *Martin Bennett*

Reed Warbler, Blashford Lakes, August 2010 – *Martin Bennett*

This is largely due to the natural waxing and waning of reed beds. For example, at Fleet Pond numbers dropped from 80 territories in 1981 to 40 in the late 1980s and have subsequently decreased further to an average of around 25 during the HBA period. The decline has been in direct correlation with the major reduction in the area of reed beds at this site due to increased siltation from inflowing streams.

Not surprisingly, owing to the difficulty of surveying in a habitat such as reed bed, obtaining accurate numbers at the major sites is no easy task. The largest colony is at Titchfield Haven where a peak count of 130 singing males/pairs was obtained in 2010; this compares favourably with the estimated 100 pairs in 1988. Other important localities include Lower Test Marshes (82 pairs in 2008), Blashford Lakes (50 pairs in 2008) and Fishlake Meadows,

Romsey (39 in 2010). Large numbers are also present at Farlington Marshes and Keyhaven/Pennington Marshes but no definitive counts have been received for these sites. Significant numbers can also be found in the valleys of the River Test and River Itchen but, owing to the difficulty of access to many privately owned sections along these rivers, including the large reed bed at Alresford Pond, it has not been possible to gain an accurate estimate of how many pairs are actually present.

The only record during the HBA winter period was of a presumed late migrant seen at Pennington Marsh on November 23rd 2010.

Keith Wills

Sponsored by Colin Bates

Marsh Warbler

Acrocephalus palustris

A rare summer visitor and autumn passage migrant

Although common and widespread in Europe, Marsh Warbler reaches the western limit of its breeding range in the UK and is now a rare breeder restricted mainly to the east coast. It has never been common in Hampshire, even though the first documented record of its occurrence in the country was from Alresford Pond in 1863. There had been just 27 records prior to 2007 and three more were added over the period to 2012. Only one of these fell into the HBA recording windows; all are given below:

2007: Titchfield Haven, a juvenile/first-winter on September 2nd.

2010: Titchfield Haven, a juvenile trapped and ringed on September 4th and re-trapped the following day.

2012: Ibsley Bridge, a singing male from June 5th–9th.

Keith Wills

Sponsored by Justin Walker

Marsh Warbler, Harbridge, June 2012 – *Martin Bennett*

Waxwing

Bombycilla garrulus

A rare winter visitor, sometimes occurring in large numbers

The Waxwing is arguably our most photogenic native bird and we are fortunate that its periodic invasions to Hampshire have become more frequent in the new millennium, thus affording birders plenty of opportunities to experience its tame behaviour at close quarters. Clark (2007) described an invasion of 2,000 or more Waxwings into Hampshire in the winter of 2004/05, which was the largest ever recorded in the county at that time. The species was recorded during all five winters of the HBA atlas, with 220 in 2008/09, the third largest total ever, an estimated 3,000 in 2010/11, the most ever (Clark 2013), and totals between one and three in each of the other three winters.

The HBA winter map thus principally shows the combined sightings in the two winters 2008/09 and 2010/11. In the first of these two seasons, Waxwings were recorded between November 19th and April 9th with the largest concentrations in December at Lordshill (maximum 12) and Gosport (maximum 32), in January at Bursledon/Locks Heath/Whiteley (maximum 34), Cheesefoot Head (maximum 25) and Bordon (maximum 14) and in February at Farlington (maximum 19) and Titchfield Common (maximum 12). There were few thereafter apart from a group of up to 20 in Locks Heath between April 3rd and 9th. In 2010/11, there were records between

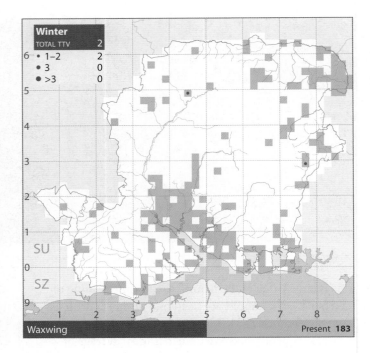

November 10th and April 30th. The two areas with the highest density of sightings and highest numbers were from Romsey and Totton south-eastwards to Fareham and Gosport, and in the north-east of the county around Aldershot, Farnborough, Fleet and Yateley. The only other areas with three-figure flocks were Basingstoke/Chineham and Greywell/Odiham, with smaller numbers in Alton, Andover, the Havant/Hayling Island/Waterlooville area, Lymington, New Milton, Petersfield, Ringwood and Winchester. The largest flock recorded was of 773 at North

Waxwing, Romsey, December 2010 – *Martin Bennett*

Camp Station, on the Hampshire/Surrey border, on January 14th 2011, counted from a digital photograph. Other flocks to exceed 200 were of 259 around Beverley and Rimington Gardens in Romsey on January 7th and an estimated 300 in the Totton/Ashurst area on January 26th. Most had departed by mid-March but daily records continued until April 12th and a further 69 were recorded until the end of the month, including 40 which were drinking at a puddle at Meon Valley Golf Course on the final day.

The favoured food sources were Rowan and other berries such as cotoneaster. The map shows a strong correlation with built-up areas, since the largest sources of red berries were around trading estates, retail parks, supermarket car parks and housing estates. Records from rural areas often involved birds pausing briefly in a suitable berry-laden hedgerow or fruit tree, but rosehips near Thatcher's Copse, Brownwich attracted a group of up to 51 and Sturmer Pippin apples in a garden at Lower Froyle proved irresistible to up to 25, with both flocks being sustained for almost two weeks in January and February 2011.

John Clark

Sponsored by Christine Colgrave

Waxwing, Romsey, December 2010 – *Martin Bennett*

Nuthatch

Sitta europaea

A numerous resident

The UK Nuthatch population was already on an upward trend at the time of the 1988–91 Atlas and its rate of growth has continued, even accelerated, over the past 20 years (*BirdTrends*). The species' range has expanded into northern England and southern Scotland and, in south-east England, its population increased by 54% over the period 1995–2012 (*BBS*). The causes of growth appear to be linked to an increase in breeding success with more fledglings per breeding attempt and lower nest failure rates.

This species inhabits woodland, parks and large gardens where it utilises mature trees, both deciduous and coniferous, for nest sites and feeding. During the winter it feeds on nuts and seeds and is increasingly visiting garden feeders when natural food may be in short supply. In fact the long run of relatively mild winters during the inter-atlas period coupled with increasing availability of garden feeders may be additional factors underlying its population growth. In Hampshire, the Nuthatch is widely distributed with breeding considered likely in 84% of county tetrads. The most densely populated areas include the New Forest, the south-west, the north and the north-east. It is more thinly spread on the chalk and is absent from the open, relatively treeless spaces west of Andover and around Martin Down. It is also scarce in the south-east coastal zone, in particular Hayling Island and the urban areas of Portsmouth and Gosport which lack extensive woodland.

As expected for a species that was already widespread at the time of the 1986–91 Atlas, there has been little change in distribution since that time with a continuing breeding presence in 761 tetrads and a small net range increase of 24 tetrads or just under 3%. The Nuthatch is largely sedentary; the winter map demonstrates this, with a presence in almost the same number of tetrads as in summer and an essentially identical distribution.

Graham Osborne

Sponsored by Paul Hope

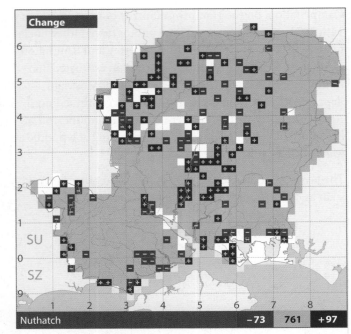

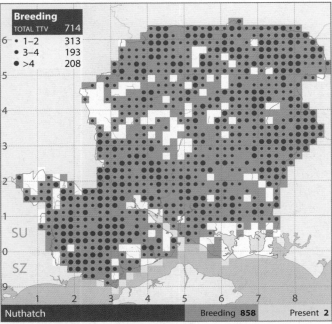

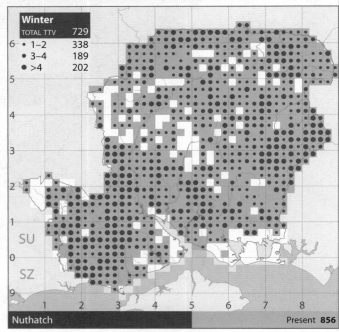

Treecreeper
Certhia familiaris
A numerous resident

Treecreepers are unobtrusive birds occurring mainly in broadleaved woodland but also in mixed woodland, parks, gardens and other habitats wherever there are mature trees to provide suitable nest sites. They are generally sedentary but some post-breeding dispersal occurs and in autumn and winter they may join mixed-species feeding flocks, ranging more widely, though typically staying close to their natal sites. Consequently all records of this species during the breeding season have been taken as indicative of likely breeding.

The HBA breeding map shows Treecreepers to be distributed throughout Hampshire, most commonly in the New Forest and the north/north-east, but more thinly spread on the open chalkland and in the densely urban south-east coastal region. This distribution mirrors that found during the 1986–91 Atlas, but there is an unexpected indication of a contraction in range. The change map shows a 19% reduction in the number of occupied tetrads with losses scattered across the county but particularly on the chalk north-west of Winchester and along the coast. The BTO's population index shows a fall in UK numbers of 18% over the 25 year period 1985–2009 but a recovery from 2010 onwards (*BirdTrends*). The HBA recording period spanned the low point so some reduction in population might be expected, although *BBS* counts in Hampshire have shown steadily increasing numbers in recent years. Another possible explanation of the apparent range reduction is inconsistency in the level of recording between the two surveys. This species is easily missed. Its high-pitched call and song are not audible to all observers and its camouflaged plumage and habit of creeping up the trunks of high trees makes it difficult to see. Where populations are low, Treecreepers will not be easy to find so a degree of under-recording must be expected.

The most densely populated areas are the New Forest and other heavily wooded sites across the county. Surveys of a 46 sq. km block of New Forest woodland between May 1st and July 1st in 2009, 2010 and 2011 found 156, 154 and 148 birds respectively (Ward & Wynn 2013).

Not surprisingly, the number of occupied tetrads and distribution of Treecreepers in winter were very similar to those during the breeding season. Although some tetrads which were unoccupied in summer held birds in winter and *vice versa,* the population gaps in the north-west and south-east were common to both seasons. Further investigation of whether these are real or an indication of under-recording would be worthwhile.

Graham Osborne

Sponsored by Sandy Baker

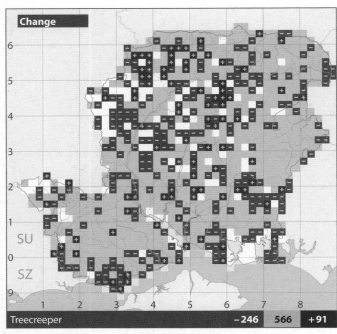

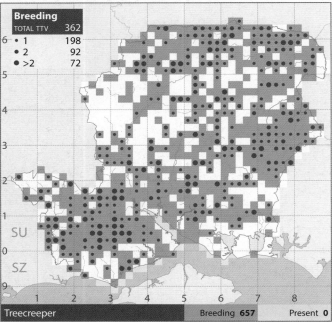

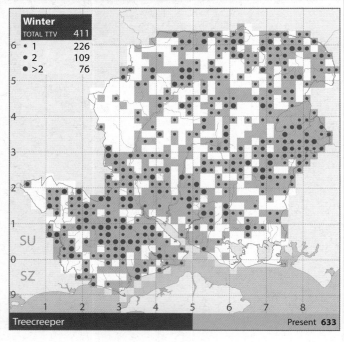

Treecreeper,
New Forest, October 2012
– Martin Bennett

Wren

Troglodytes troglodytes

An abundant resident

This species is exceptionally common in the UK. It is the nation's most common breeding bird, accounting for roughly 10% of the country's total breeding bird population with an estimated 8·6 million territories in 2009 (*APEP3*),

Wrens are susceptible to harsh winters so numbers tend to fluctuate from year to year. The population was hard hit by the very cold winter in 1962/63 but has subsequently recovered with numbers in England being some 63% higher in 2011 than they were in 1967 (*BirdTrends*). Recent data suggest there has been a moderate decrease in southern England, probably due to the succession of colder than normal winters but, being double brooded, the population can recover quickly.

With a presence in 99% of all Hampshire tetrads, the species has not changed its range since the 1986–91 Atlas. It breeds in a wide variety of habitats including woodland, parks, gardens, scrubland and heathland, indeed almost anywhere where there is dense undergrowth or other opportunities to nest. Its loud song and distinctive call draw attention so, despite its small size and skulking nature, it is easily detected. Breeding densities can be high with almost one third of occupied tetrads recording 15 or more birds during summer TTV counts. It is most common in the north-east, the east, the New Forest and the lower valleys of the major rivers. Densities are lower on the higher ground of the South Downs and central chalkland belt. Site counts during the HBA period demonstrated the effect of harsh winters and also how local these can be. In 2008 there were 140 territories at Longmoor Inclosure and 139 at Lower Test Marshes. In 2009, after the hard intervening winter, the corresponding counts were 99 and 86. After a second hard winter in 2009/10 numbers

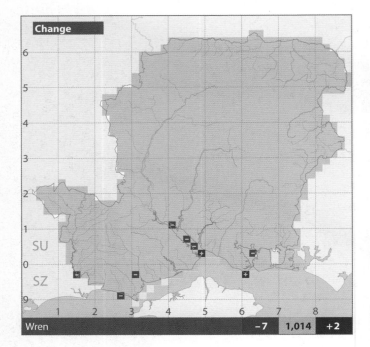

at Longmoor dropped further to just 47 territories but at Lower Test recovered slightly to 95.

The Wren's winter range and abundance pattern are very similar to those during the breeding season, as expected for what is essentially a sedentary species. Some local movement occurs as young birds seek territories or move to communal reed-bed roosts. This species is well known for its habit of collective roosting and may for instance pack into nestboxes, squirrel's dreys and old nests in an effort to keep warm. Ringing data also show some longer movements both into and out of the county. Wrens remain insectivorous in winter; they prefer to feed in cover and are thus rarely seen at bird tables even in very harsh conditions. Due to their susceptibility to cold weather, it is possible that a warming climate will be of benefit to this species.

Graham Osborne

Sponsored by Ralph Sambrook

Wren, New Forest, November 2009 – *Martin Bennett*

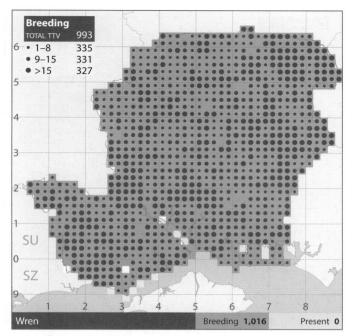

Breeding

TOTAL TTV	993
• 1–8	335
• 9–15	331
● >15	327

Wren — Breeding **1,016** — Present **0**

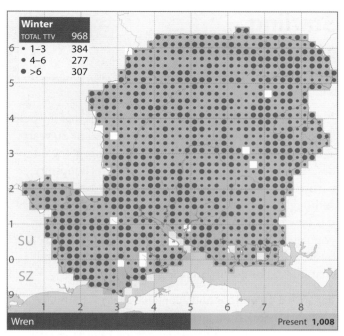

Winter

TOTAL TTV	968
• 1–3	384
• 4–6	277
● >6	307

Wren — Present **1,008**

Wren, New Forest, October 2012 – *Martin Bennett*

Starling

Sturnus vulgaris

An abundant but declining resident, passage migrant and winter visitor

"So much material is available on this species that it would almost make a book by itself." This is how, some 50 years ago, Cohen began his account of the Starling, going on to describe the vast numbers that occurred in Hampshire, particularly in winter but also as resident breeding birds. Although it remains a widespread and familiar species, it is now far less common than it was then. The English population has been declining since the 1970s, falling by 80% between 1986 and 2011, and the current trend continues to be downward (*BirdTrends*).

For such a ubiquitous and adaptable species, found in habitats ranging from farmland to the inner-city, able to nest in mature woodland and natural cavities as well as around buildings and man-made sites and to feed in farmland or in urban parks and gardens, it is surprising that it has been unable to cope with the ecological changes affecting its environment. However, evidence suggests that, in common with many other species, it is changes in farming practices, particularly grassland management, that underlie its demise. A decrease in winter survival of first-year birds best explains the decline, although increased use of pesticides could have affected food supply during the breeding season. The urban population may also be declining as modern building techniques reduce the availability of nest sites.

At the time of the 1986–91 Atlas, Hampshire Starling numbers were already declining and this trend has continued. Even so, the HBA breeding map shows that it remains widespread with breeding considered likely in 80% of the county's tetrads. Those tetrads with the highest densities are in the urban areas in the south and north-east with the species more thinly spread across the agricultural expanses on the chalk.

The change map illustrates that, compared to 1986–91, the breeding range has contracted by around 18% with some significant gaps opening up in the distribution. These are mainly in rural areas on the downs and in the north-western part of the New Forest.

The local breeding population is largely sedentary with territory-holders remaining on their breeding sites throughout the year. However, post-breeding dispersal of first-year birds and influxes of immigrants result in a more widespread distribution in winter than in summer. The HBA winter map shows presence in 87% of tetrads with numbers of individual birds significantly higher than during the breeding season. Although large flocks can still be found, particularly along the coast, there are no longer any of the big spectacular roosts that were a feature of the pre-1970s. The highest winter roost count during

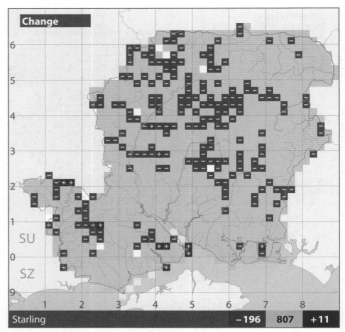

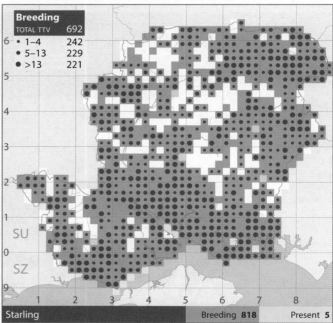

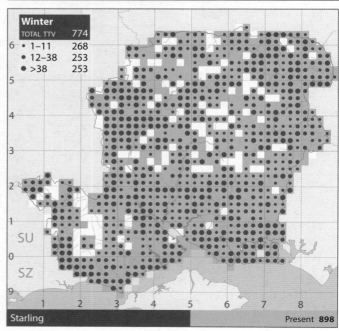

Starling, New Forest, January 2012 – *Martin Bennett*

the HBA period was 20,000 at Avon Water in December 2010. Away from this site, the only other five-figure counts were estimated upper limits of 10,000 at Alresford Pond in December 2007 and at Kentsboro in November 2009. Four figure counts are now scarce while three-figure flocks are still relatively common.

Incoming migrants arrive in Hampshire between late September and the end of November with diurnal movements noted at both coastal and inland sites. Numbers peak in November and it is then that four-figure counts of grounded flocks are sometimes made, especially following severe weather. During 2007, the first year of HBA winter survey, high counts included 2,500 at Keyhaven on November 6th with 2,000 at Ibsley on 20th, Moody's Down on 22nd and Thruxton on 25th.

Given the Starling's proven ability to survive and flourish in close proximity to people, it will be interesting to see what the future holds for this opportunistic and adaptable species.

Richard Carpenter

Sponsored by Jeremy Peters

Rose-coloured Starling

Pastor roseus

A scarce vagrant

The Rose-coloured Starling is a bird of steppe and open agricultural land, breeding in temperate regions of Eastern Europe and Asia. It is an irruptive species sometimes moving well outside its core range into Western Europe. In Hampshire, during the 2007–12 period, six birds were recorded, mainly in autumn. Only one occurred during the HBA breeding and winter seasons, the bird at Hordle in 2012 bridging both seasons. All records are given below and brought the county total to 23:

2007: Oxey Marsh, an adult on June 10th.
        Pennington Marsh, a juvenile September 23rd–28th.

2010: Lepe, a juvenile October 20th–26th.

2011: Lower Pennington Lane, a juvenile on October 2nd/3rd.

2012: Hordle, a first–summer first reported on February 29th had been in the area for three weeks and remained until at least April 16th.
        Northney, a juvenile on September 28th/29th.

Rose-coloured Starling, Hordle, March 2012 – *Andy Johnson*

Richard Carpenter

Ring Ouzel

Turdus torquatas

A scarce passage migrant

The Ring Ouzel, uniquely among Britain's breeding thrushes, is a summer visitor and Hampshire can claim a special place in confirming its migratory status. In 1768 Gilbert White, in a letter to Thomas Pennant FRS, questioned whether the Ring Ouzels seen around Selborne that autumn were British breeding birds moving south. He reasoned that if these birds should be the Ring Ouzels "of the north of England, then here is a migration disclosed within our kingdom never before remarked". A few months later he learned that Ring Ouzels in the Derbyshire Peak District deserted their breeding grounds in autumn to return the following spring, so in January 1769 he wrote again to Pennant that "this information seems to throw some light on my new migration". In fact, as we now know, the Ring Ouzel is a double passage migrant through Hampshire and birds probably include a mix of both British and Fennoscandian breeders.

Spring passage peaks in mid-April and therefore falls within the HBA breeding season survey. During the 2008–12 period, migrants were noted in about 3% of all Hampshire tetrads. A particularly strong spring passage occurred in 2011 with a minimum of 28 birds recorded, including seven at Butser Hill on April 16th. Return passage, which is usually heavier, begins in September and peaks in October, therefore falling between the HBA breeding and winter season surveys. During the 2007–11 autumns, 2010 was a good year with approximately 67 individuals recorded between September 15th and December 1st. Winter records are rare and during the HBA winter periods only five birds were recorded, four in November and one in December. Birds have occasionally over-wintered although not during the HBA period.

On its UK breeding grounds, the Ring Ouzel has been in rapid decline over the past 30 years and the species is now red-listed. The reasons for the fall in numbers are not fully understood but a reduction of suitable habitat, increased disturbance and the effects of climate change on a montane species may all be contributory factors. This reduction does not appear to have lowered the number of passage birds recorded in Hampshire. Although variations occur from year to year, on average higher numbers have been recorded in recent years. Whether this represents greater observer effort or a real increase is unclear.

Favoured sites include Beacon Hill (Burghclere) and Old Winchester Hill, whilst in the New Forest Leaden Hall and Latchmore Bottom are responsible for the most records. Records are also received each year from south coast sites such as Farlington Marshes, Portsdown Hill, Brownwich and Keyhaven.

Graham Osborne

Sponsored by Ade Parker

Ring Ouzel, Funtley, October 2009 – *Trevor Codlin*

Fieldfare

Turdus pilaris

An abundant winter visitor and passage migrant

Although a few Fieldfares breed in Scotland, the vast majority of our wintering birds are immigrants from Fennoscandia. Birds arrive in Hampshire from October onwards but numbers usually do not build up significantly until the end of the month. Timing and numbers are dependent on weather conditions and the availability of food – the size of the berry crop – in northern Europe. Furthermore, hard weather in the UK can result in large internal movements of birds moving south in search of milder conditions. This means that the numbers in the county vary considerably from year to year and from month to month.

Fieldfares are gregarious and are usually found in flocks, often mixed with Redwings, our other migrant wintering thrush. They are very much a bird of rural locations, typically feeding on farmland hedgerows or in woodland wherever there is a good supply of berries. When the berry crops are exhausted they move onto fields and other grassland areas where they feed on invertebrates. They are not usually found in gardens unless the weather is very harsh, and generally shun large urban areas. The HBA winter distribution map shows that, although they were found in 92% of the county's tetrads during the course of the survey, the highest densities occurred in the west and north, with lower numbers around the heavily populated areas on the south coast.

TTV counts of more than 50 were made in 233 tetrads. Three-figure counts are not uncommon and flocks of 500–1,000 occur in most winters. During the five winters of the HBA survey the only grounded flock of 1,000 was at

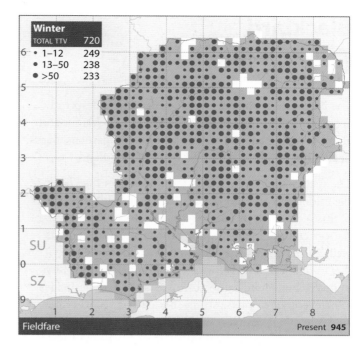

Leckford Golf Course on January 31st 2011. Movements included 1,680 west at Winters Down, Warnford on October 18th 2007 and 1,490 east past Titchfield Haven on January 10th 2010 although historically much larger movements have occurred. The record count was an estimated 30,000 moving south-east at Gilkicker Point on December 31st 1961.

Return migration begins in late February and continues throughout March. Most have gone by the end of the month with the last usually departing by mid-April. During the HBA breeding season surveys occasional sizeable flocks were recorded, including a maximum of 200 at Old Winchester Hill on April 6th 2008.

Graham Osborne

Sponsored by Eldeg Lukes

Fieldfare, New Forest, December 2010 – *Martin Bennett*

351

Blackbird

Turdus merula

An abundant resident, passage migrant and winter visitor

The Blackbird is one the most familiar and widespread species in Hampshire. It is not particularly discriminating about breeding habitat and can be found in gardens, parks, heathland, farmland and most types of woodland.

The species underwent a long term decline in the UK up to the mid-1990s and was amber-listed as a result. The causes of this seem to be correlated with a fall in adult survival but agricultural intensification probably played a part as well. The latter may have resulted in a loss of nest sites due to removal of hedgerows and to reduced availability of invertebrate food caused by increased use of pesticides. Whatever the reasons, a strong, but partial, recovery has subsequently taken place and the species was restored to the green list in 2002. Much of the increase has been in Wales, north-west England and southern Scotland but the English population increased by 19% between 1995 and 2011. This is one of the most common breeding birds in the UK with an estimated population in excess of 5 million pairs.

During the HBA breeding survey, Blackbirds were found in more than 99% of all tetrads, absent mainly only from those containing very little dry land! Breeding densities can be quite high with TTV counts of more than 23 birds found in almost a third of Hampshire tetrads. The highest breeding densities were found in the western New Forest, the lower Test Valley and the north-east. They have a long breeding season stretching from March through to August and may have multiple broods.

In winter, Blackbirds were again recorded in almost all tetrads. The areas of highest abundance were the western New Forest, the lower Test Valley, the north-east and around Petersfield. The lowest densities were in the

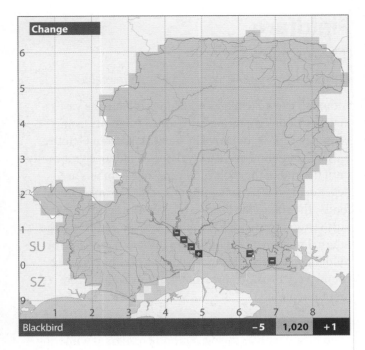

Blackbird — Change — Blackbird — −5 | 1,020 | +1

eastern New Forest, the extreme north-west and the high ground in the centre of the county. The winter abundance map has a very similar appearance to the summer map, although this masks some changes. It is believed that most British birds do not move far in winter but numbers are boosted by immigrants from Scandinavia and elsewhere in Continental Europe. In extreme weather British birds may move a short distance west and south pursuing milder conditions.

In winter Blackbirds eat invertebrates whenever they can find them, above all earthworms, but they will also take a lot of fruit, especially haws, Ivy and Rowan, and visit garden feeding stations. Blackbirds do not form large flocks in winter but often roost communally.

Graham Osborne

Sponsored by Jonathan Stokes

Blackbird, New Forest, November 2010 – *Martin Bennett*

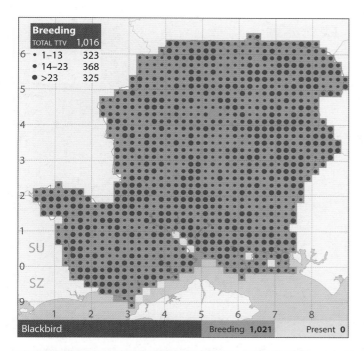

Breeding
TOTAL TTV 1,016
- 1–13   323
- 14–23   368
- >23   325

Blackbird   Breeding **1,021**   Present **0**

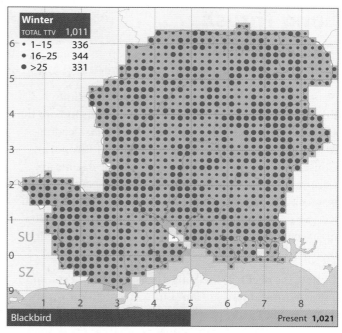

Winter
TOTAL TTV 1,011
- 1–15   336
- 16–25   344
- >25   331

Blackbird   Present **1,021**

Blackbird, Chandlers Ford, March 2012 – *Steve Bassett*

Song Thrush

Turdus philomelos

A numerous resident, passage migrant and winter visitor

Nationally, Song Thrushes suffered a major decline through the 1970s and 1980s. The populations in both the UK and England fell by over 50% (*BirdTrends*) leading to the species being placed on the red list of Birds of Conservation Concern. The reasons for the decline are uncertain but, as with many other resident passerines, may be attributed largely to agricultural intensification which led to a decrease in juvenile survival. Changes in forestry management and a reduction in the shrub layer through increased browsing by deer may also be important.

Despite the declines, the Song Thrush remains a common and widespread bird in Hampshire. It is well-known and appreciated by most people thanks to its powerful attractive song and its habit of using stones as anvils to break snail shells. Like its relative and our commonest resident thrush, the Blackbird, it breeds in a wide variety of habitats including woodland, parks and gardens. During the HBA breeding survey, it was present, and likely to be breeding, in 97% of all the county's tetrads. There has been little change in its distribution since the 1986–91 Atlas, with a small number of both gains and losses. The latter involve several coastal tetrads where there is little suitable habitat, and the heavily urbanised areas of Portsmouth and Fareham.

The areas of greatest breeding abundance are the New Forest, the lower Test Valley and the north-east, with fewer birds in the agricultural belt across the centre of the county. Almost one third of the tetrads registered TTV counts of more than five birds although BBS counts typically record counts of around four per kilometre square. Densities are never very high even in suitable habitat because this species has relatively large territories.

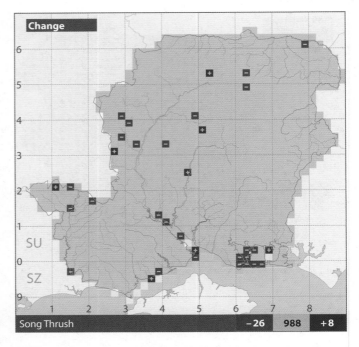

Although most of our Song Thrushes are sedentary there is some dispersal of juveniles as well as immigration into, and passage through, the county in autumn. Not surprisingly for such a widely distributed species, the HBA winter and summer maps are almost identical. Unlike Redwings and Fieldfares, Song Thrushes do not typically flock in big numbers and are comparatively uncommon on farmland. Cold weather movements are less marked than for the winter thrushes as well, although south coast sites sometimes see influxes which are probably a result of birds crossing the channel primarily from the Netherlands and Belgium. The county population may also be augmented by birds moving from farther north in Britain, particularly in response to cold weather.

Graham Osborne

Sponsored by Kevin & Alison Fuller

Song Thrush, New Forest, December 2009 – *Martin Bennett*

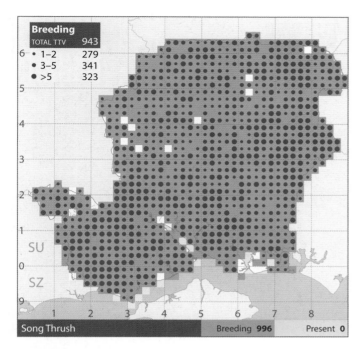

Breeding
TOTAL TTV	943
• 1–2	279
• 3–5	341
● >5	323

Song Thrush — Breeding **996** — Present **0**

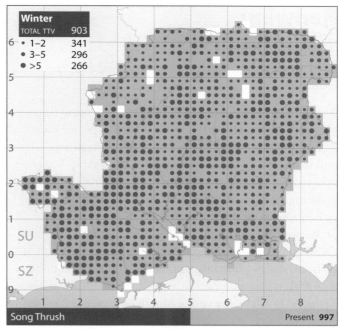

Winter
TOTAL TTV	903
• 1–2	341
• 3–5	296
● >5	266

Song Thrush — Present **997**

Song Thrush, Hayling Island, January 2010 – *Richard Ford*

Redwing

Turdus iliacus

A numerous to abundant winter visitor and passage migrant

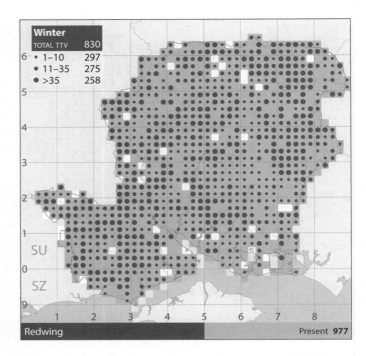

Winter	
TOTAL TTV	830
• 1–10	297
• 11–35	275
• >35	258

Redwing — Present **977**

The Redwing is the smallest of our regularly occurring thrushes. It is an attractive and distinctive species with a creamy white eye-stripe and rusty red underwings and flanks. Small numbers breed in Scotland but otherwise it is a common winter visitor to the UK, those reaching Hampshire arriving from breeding grounds in Fennoscandia. The first birds usually arrive in late September but significant numbers are not recorded until October. On clear nights, their thin "tseep" call can often be heard overhead as migrant flocks arrive in the county, a clear sign that autumn has arrived. Most birds will have departed north by the end of March but some linger into April and rarely into May. These late-leavers accounted for around ten records per year on average during the HBA breeding season surveys.

They have very similar habitat preferences to Fieldfares, the two species often being found together in sizeable mixed feeding flocks on farmland and open grassland. When they first arrive in the autumn they feed on fruit and berries, particularly Hawthorn, Ivy, Rowan and Holly. Although they are quite shy, during hard weather they will visit suburban gardens where they feed on the berries of ornamental shrubs and fallen apples. As the berry crop is depleted they switch to feeding on soil invertebrates and, when the ground is frozen, will move on in search of warmer conditions.

This is a numerous and widespread species. During the HBA winter survey, Redwings were found in 95% of all tetrads with the highest densities in the New Forest, the north-east heaths and the Test Valley. They occurred in lower numbers along the coast, particularly in the densely urban areas of the south-east, and on the higher ground of the South Downs. Numbers reaching Hampshire depend on weather conditions on the near Continent and farther north in the UK and thus can vary significantly from year to year. During periods of frost and snow large movements, both into and out of the county, can occur.

During the five HBA winters, the summed counts of grounded flocks typically peaked in the 5,000–6,000 range with the highest site count of 1,000 at Cadnam Common in December 2011. Roosts, regularly containing up to a few hundred birds, form in woodland scrub but in November 2009 exceptionally high numbers were found at one roost in the New Forest. On 22nd/23rd, 60,000 Redwings were estimated roosting at Broomy Lodge Inclosure. By mid-December most birds had departed. The following year, also in late November, more than 15,000 were found roosting at Long Beech Inclosure, just a short distance from Broomy Lodge. These numbers are unprecedented in Hampshire and the UK (Clark 2011).

Graham Osborne

Sponsored by Sue Hiley

Redwing, New Forest, December 2009 – *Martin Bennett*

Redwing,
New Forest,
November 2010 –
Martin Bennett

Mistle Thrush

Turdus viscivorus

A common but declining resident and passage migrant

The Mistle Thrush, the largest of our regularly occurring thrushes, is a familiar bird in Hampshire. It favours open woodland, heathland, farmland, parks and large gardens where the presence of mature trees for use as song posts and nest sites is a prerequisite. Its habit of singing from the top of trees in mid-winter is responsible for its old country name of Stormcock and its far-carrying song, coupled with its size and rattling call, draw attention to its presence.

As the summer HBA map shows, it is widely distributed throughout the county with likely breeding in 83% of tetrads. However, the change map confirms that it is less widespread today than it was 20 years ago, its range having contracted by 14% over the past two decades. Like our other resident thrushes, the Mistle Thrush population in the UK has declined, falling by over 60% since the 1970s, particularly on farmland. The decline has been marked in south-east England where *BBS* data show numbers falling by 59% over the 18 year period 1995–2012. The species is now amber-listed. The reasons for the decline are uncertain but, as with Song Thrush and other resident passerines, may be due to reduced juvenile survival probably associated with agricultural intensification.

The highest breeding densities in Hampshire are in the New Forest and the Test Valley. Elsewhere numbers are less concentrated with a scatter of vacant tetrads across the county, particularly in densely urban areas, such as Southampton, Gosport, Portsmouth and Basingstoke, and

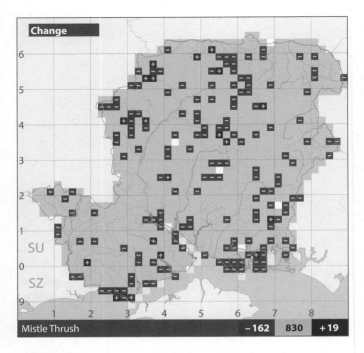

Mistle Thrush   – 162   830   +19

on the more intensely cultivated and largely treeless areas on the chalk. However, this species is an early breeder with song peaking in February/March, prior to the beginning of the HBA summer recording period, and declining thereafter. It also has a comparatively large territory, so where birds are thin on the ground some under-recording is to be expected.

Mistle Thrushes form post-breeding flocks. The highest count during the HBA breeding season period was 60 on Cadnam Common on July 14th 2011, although 75 at Sandy Ridge in the New Forest on October 22nd 2007 was the highest during 2007–11. The flocks disperse from October onwards and, during the winter, adults often defend feeding

Mistle Thrush, New Forest, March 2013 – *Martin Bennett*

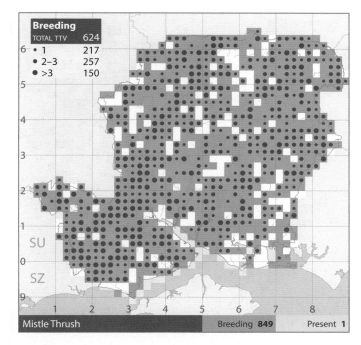

Breeding
TOTAL TTV 624
- 1   217
- 2–3   257
- >3   150

Mistle Thrush   Breeding **849**   Present **1**

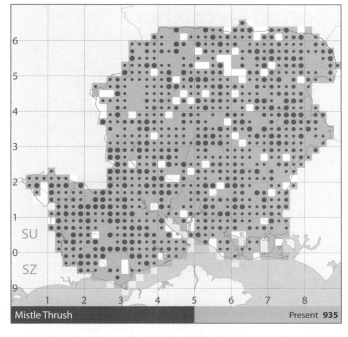

Mistle Thrush   Present **935**

territories, associating in numbers with other thrush species only during mild weather. At these times they are more likely to be found in grazed pasture where there is an abundance of invertebrate food compared to woodland habitat. The highest count during the HBA winter period was an exceptional 65 feeding appropriately on mistletoe berries at Avington Park on February 6th 2012. The adult population is largely sedentary and, although a small

number of birds may arrive from outside the county, the winter distribution is very similar to that in summer. The number of occupied tetrads is higher during the winter, possibly as a result of birds moving locally in search of food.

Graham Osborne

Sponsored by Christopher Jones

Mistle Thrush, New Forest, October 2009 – *Martin Bennett*

Spotted Flycatcher
Muscicapa striata
A moderately common but declining summer visitor and passage migrant

This is one of the latest of the summer visitors to arrive, with the first usually seen in Hampshire in the last week of April and the main arrival not until the middle of May. Departure is in August/September with a few stragglers lingering into early October. Their preferred habitat is deciduous woodland, parks and gardens where they nest on a ledge or in a suitable open cavity, often in creepers and sometimes in close proximity to people. They are relatively quiet low-profile birds but can be conspicuous when they repeatedly sally forth from a high prominent perch to catch flying insects.

Spotted Flycatchers have suffered a prolonged and significant decline throughout most of the UK beginning in the 1960s and continuing to date (*BirdTrends*). The population has fallen by around 90% over that period, with the fastest rate of decline coinciding with the 1986–91 Atlas period. The species is now red-listed. The reasons are not fully understood but smaller average clutch sizes and lower post-fledging survival, both factors possibly caused by reduced availability of flying insects, may have played their part. It is also possible that conditions on their wintering grounds in West Africa or along migration routes may be involved.

In Hampshire, the HBA survey found the species to remain widely distributed with breeding considered likely in 394 tetrads or 38% of the total. The change map suggests that this is less than half the number in the 1986–91 Atlas but this may over-estimate the scale of the decline by including possible breeding records in the earlier Atlas. An alternative comparison is between the probable and proven breeding records in the two atlases. This results in a larger range reduction of 42% but this may be due to lack of breeding evidence in the later survey. Due to the unobtrusive nature of the bird, its quiet unfamiliar song and the numbers that nest in private gardens, there is likely to have been an element of under-recording in both atlases, but the contraction in the species' range, as shown in the accompanying map, is obvious. The losses are spread across the entire county with major gaps in distribution opening up, particularly in the south-east and on the chalk. The New Forest remains its county stronghold. A survey of 46 sq. km of New Forest woodland in 2009, 2010 and 2011 found 21, 22 and 24 territories respectively (Ward & Wynn 2013). Over the county as a whole, TTV counts recorded no more than two birds in 88% of tetrads in which Spotted Flycatchers were found. Away from the New Forest, the lower Test Valley and some parts of the north of the county still hold reasonable numbers, but the species is now almost totally absent in the south-east and is very sparsely distributed in much of the central belt.

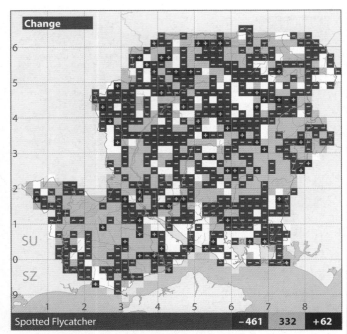

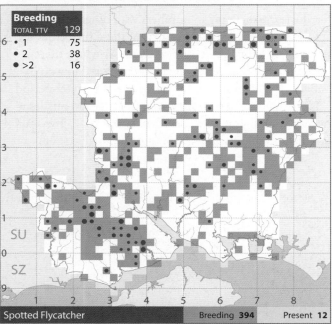

Spotted Flycatcher numbers can still be relatively high during autumn migration both on the coast and inland. Historical high counts include 60+ at Anton Lakes on August 16th 1978 and 53 at Old Winchester Hill with 51 at Beacon Hill, Warnford on August 20th 1989 (*BoH*). As recently as 2001, there were 45 at Old Winchester Hill on August 25th but during the HBA years, 2007–12, the highest count was 20 at Fritham in the New Forest on August 14th 2011. This was most probably a post-breeding, pre-migration gathering, and peak site counts during migration were lower ranging from eight in 2007 and 2010 to 12 in 2009 and 2012.

Graham Osborne

Sponsored by Keith Wills

Spotted Flycatcher, New Forest, June 2011 – *Martin Bennett*

Robin

Erithacus rubecula

An abundant resident, passage migrant and winter visitor

Thanks to its tameness, particularly around gardeners, and its association with Christmas, the Robin is one of the most familiar British birds. It has a very large breeding population estimated to be around 6 million pairs in Great Britain (*APEP3*). There has been a marked increase since the 1980s, with a 57% rise in the English population between 1986 and 2011, numbers prior to this having been reduced by a succession of cold winters. Conditions through the 1990s and early years of the new millennium were comparatively mild allowing the population to grow but cold winters in 2008/09, 2009/10 and 2010/11 brought a sharp reversal to the upward trend (*BirdTrends*).

In Hampshire, Robins are widespread and common across the entire county. During the HBA breeding survey they were found in 99% of tetrads, the few gaps being almost entirely in coastal tetrads lacking suitable habitat. With these removed the range increases to close to 100%. Sadly for the inhabitants of Nether Wallop, the one tetrad in the county apparently lacking this much-loved species lies south-west of the village!

Robins are well known for their catholic choice of nest sites. They will nest in any suitable cavity, ranging from natural recesses in creepers, banks or tree stumps, to man-made constructions such as in sheds, nest boxes or in bizarre

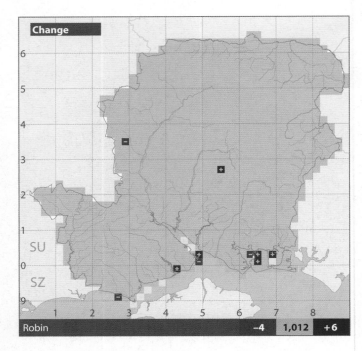

Robin   -4   1,012   +6

artefacts such as discarded pots and pans. Their choice of habitat covers all types of wooded country, including parks, gardens and farmland. This is reflected in the breeding density map, which shows the highest numbers in well-wooded areas such as the Thames Basin, the Weald, the lower river valleys and Hampshire Basin including the New Forest. Numbers are lower on the high, more open arable farmland through the centre and north-west. In favourable habitat breeding densities can be quite high with almost a third of tetrads having TTV counts of more than 16 birds.

Robin, New Forest, January 2013 – *Martin Bennett*

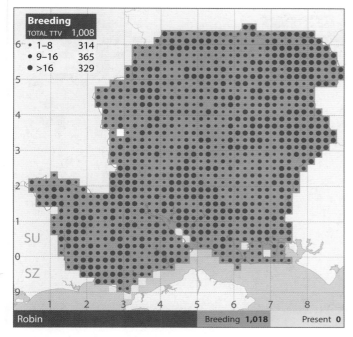

Breeding		
TOTAL TTV		1,008
•	1–8	314
•	9–16	365
•	>16	329

Robin · Breeding **1,018** · Present **0**

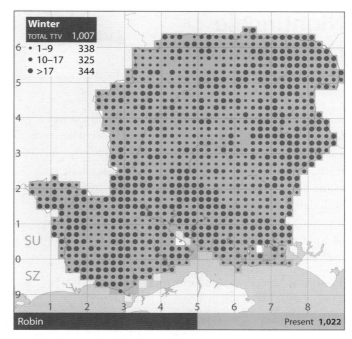

Winter		
TOTAL TTV		1,007
•	1–9	338
•	10–17	325
•	>17	344

Robin · Present **1,022**

Not surprisingly, for such a common resident, the HBA winter map shows a very similar profile to that in summer, both in terms of range and abundance although, happily, the people of Nether Wallop are not devoid of Robins at Christmas time. The local population is essentially sedentary although numbers in winter are bolstered by immigrants, mainly from Scandinavia. Since Continental Robins are generally less tame than British birds, they are less likely to be seen in our gardens preferring instead to remain in woodland. Both males and females of the local population establish winter feeding territories. For the male this is usually the same as the breeding territory but for the female may be a short distance away. The territories are aggressively defended and birds are rarely seen together in large numbers. Robins are vulnerable to severe winter weather and will sometimes move in search of food or milder conditions. At this time garden bird tables can make a big difference, since Robins will take a variety of foods including seeds and particularly fatty foods such as cheese and bacon rind.

Graham Osborne

Sponsored by Ralph Sambrook

Robin, New Forest, January 2010 – *Martin Bennett*

Nightingale
Luscinia megarhynchos

An uncommon passage migrant and increasingly scarce breeder

To most people the Nightingale is undoubtedly more famous for its song than its appearance. Those who see it are often surprised at how plain and drab this powerful and iconic songster is. Even catching a glimpse is challenging, as the birds favour areas of open woodland and scrub with dense undergrowth from which they rarely emerge. It is also becoming more difficult to locate a bird in the first place, as Hampshire's Nightingales have undergone a prolonged period of decline.

The species breeds across Europe into Asia and North Africa but is at the north-westerly limit of its range in Britain where there has been a dramatic fall in its population. The BTO has estimated a 91% drop between 1967 and 2007 (Holt *et al.* 2012), second only to the Tree Sparrow in the scale of the decline. The causes most probably relate to problems both in this country and the wintering grounds in sub-Saharan Africa. The huge increase in deer numbers, coupled with lack of woodland management in England, is believed to have had a significant effect because this has reduced the amount of thick understorey that this species requires for nesting. In Africa, changes in climate or land-use in the humid tropics are driving declines in many long-distance migrants, including the Nightingale, possibly both through habitat loss and migratory constraints (Ockendon *et al.* 2012). As the national range has contracted, Nightingales appear to be becoming increasingly concentrated into south-east England, with counties elsewhere, particularly in the south-west including Hampshire, Dorset and Somerset, seeing the largest falls (*Bird Atlas 2007–11*).

The decline in Hampshire began in the 1950s and has continued to date. At the time of the 1986–91 Atlas, the county population was estimated at 240–360 pairs (*BoH*). The number of territories located during the 1999 national survey was 105–123 and during the repeat survey in 2012 dropped down to 61–65. The fall in numbers is consistent with the contraction in range graphically illustrated by the HBA maps. These suggest that since the 1986–91 Atlas, there have been losses from a net 183 tetrads, an overall range reduction of 76%. However, these numbers must be treated with caution because, in this case, they include possible breeders in both atlases. Furthermore, Nightingales are not easy birds to survey. They are opportunistic, often occupying nesting sites for short periods, so the composite pictures painted by both atlases may overestimate the annual range. The counter argument, that sites covered early in the survey might have acquired birds later in the period, is also valid. Furthermore, Nightingales have a short song period and once they

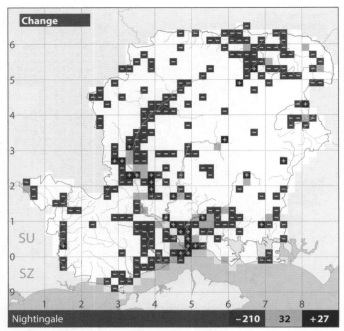

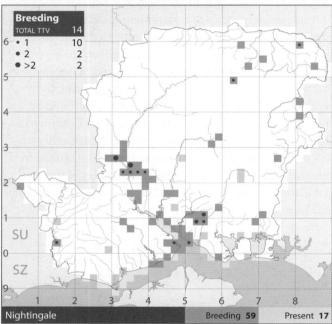

stop singing in early June become much less likely to be detected.

Despite the uncertainties, there is no doubt that a species that was once a widespread and common summer visitor in the county has become increasingly scarce, deserting many of its earlier haunts. The main areas of loss are in the upper Test Valley, the north-west and the southern fringe of the New Forest; in the north-east where the species was formerly widespread, the population has become very sparse and fragmented. Hampshire's remaining Nightingales are concentrated in three main areas, each with around 10 singing males: Botley Wood/Whiteley Pastures, Calshot/Ashlett Creek and the lower Test Valley around Romsey but even in these areas development pressures and unsympathetic habitat management are putting the populations at risk.

Nightingale, Botley Wood, April 2015 – *Trevor Codlin* (right);
undisclosed site, April 2012 – *Martin Bennett* (below)

Unless more emphasis is given to creating and maintaining
the scrub habitat favoured by this species, it seems probable
that the downward trend will continue. It is anomalous
that during a period of climatic warming when we would
be expecting birds from southern Europe to be spreading
northwards, Hampshire is at risk of losing its entire
Nightingale population.

Graham Osborne

Sponsored by Trevor Codlin

365

Pied Flycatcher
Ficedula hypoleuca

A scarce passage migrant and occasional breeder

	2007	2008	2009	2010	2011	2012
Spring	0	5	4	3	4	9
Autumn	5	17	25	15	12	32

Table 30 – Pied Flycatcher: numbers recorded 2007–12.

The Pied Flycatcher is best known as a double passage migrant in Hampshire although it has bred, the most recent occasion being in 1995. Nationally the species, which breeds in upland woodland, has been in decline since the mid-1990s with the population falling by about 50% and resulting in it being amber-listed.

In Hampshire, this species is normally less common in spring than in autumn. Numbers recorded during 2007–12 are shown in *Table 30*.

All spring records were in the April 2nd-May 24th period. Up until the publication of *BoH* in 1993, the average date of first arrival was April 18th but during the HBA period it was some ten days earlier around April 8th. Whether this advance has occurred in response to long-term climate change, or is due to a run of mild winters and early springs in the intervening years, remains to be seen. The only summer record was of a female near Holmsley on June 17th 2012 but no evidence of breeding was obtained.

Return passage occurred between July 26th and September 27th with an unusually late records at Sandy Point on October 13th/14th 2007 and IBM Lake on October 12th 2012. Records were scattered across the county, although some sites such Northney Paddocks on Hayling Island, IBM Lake and Old Winchester Hill were favoured locations.

Graham Osborne

Sponsored by Brian Sharkey

Pied Flycatcher, Rooksbury Mill, April 2010 – *Joe Stockwell* (above); Hayling Island, August 2009 – *Steve Copsey*, (below)

Black Redstart

Phoenicurus ochruros

A scarce winter visitor, passage migrant and occasional breeder

The Black Redstart is a familiar bird in towns and villages across much of south and central Europe but it is interesting to recall that, until the beginning of the 20th century, it inhabited stony ground and cliffs in montane regions rather than the urban environment. It did not breed in the UK until bomb damage during World War II provided suitable cliff-like nest sites. Today it remains a scarce and thinly distributed breeder with a population of 19–44 pairs (*APEP3*) concentrated in south-east England. The few records are still collated annually by the RBBP.

Breeding was first confirmed in Hampshire in 1943 on a bomb site in Southampton and has continued intermittently and in very small numbers to date. While most of the early breeding records were from coastal areas, by the 1970s breeding was also occurring inland, but still only occasionally. During the 1986–91 Atlas, breeding was probable at two sites: at Petersfield in 1987/88 and at Twyford in 1988. During the HBA survey, breeding was confirmed at just one site. A pair nested in a temporary building erected on Farnborough Airfield for the air show; four young were fledged around July 14th 2012. A few, apparently non-breeding, individuals were also seen in the county during the breeding season including singing males at Southampton and Portsdown Hill in 2008, and Fawley Power Station and Basingstoke in 2009. Given the species opportunistic behaviour, coupled with difficulty of access to likely sites, it is possible that some breeding pairs are overlooked but it is clear that no sustained colonisation of the county has taken place.

The species occurs more frequently in the county as a passage migrant and winter visitor. These birds are probably a mix of British breeders and Continental immigrants. In spring, passage runs from the beginning of March through to the middle of April while autumn passage is typically very late, peaking in the last week of October and the first week of November. Most passage is observed at coastal localities where counts of three or four birds may be recorded at favoured sites. Typically around six birds winter, mostly at urban locations along the coast. This mirrors the picture nationally where wintering Black Redstarts are mainly found on the coast (*Bird Atlas 2007–11*) presumably due to the mild conditions at such localities. Favoured sites in Hampshire include Sandy Point and South Hayling, Portsmouth, Gosport and Calshot.

Graham Osborne

Sponsored by Mark Cutts

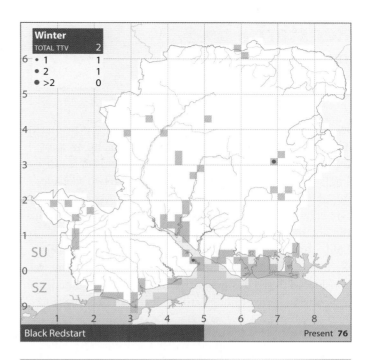

Winter
TOTAL TTV 2

• 1	1
● 2	1
● >2	0

Black Redstart — Present **76**

Black Redstart, Gosport, January 2009 – *Martin Bennett*

Redstart

Phoenicurus phoenicurus

Locally common breeding summer visitor and passage migrant

In Great Britain, this attractive summer visitor is primarily a bird of mature deciduous woodland in upland areas of the north and west. It is scarce in the lowlands of south-east England, so Hampshire is fortunate to have two sizeable populations. As the HBA breeding map shows, the New Forest has by far the most significant concentration but in the north-east, the Thames Basin and Wealden Heaths also hold important numbers. During the HBA period, there were very few sites outside these areas where breeding was considered likely. It is now extremely scarce as a breeder on agricultural land, although still widespread as a migrant.

Redstarts generally nest in natural tree holes although they will utilise a variety of other cavities and will readily take to nest boxes. In Hampshire, there is no shortage of suitable breeding sites, not only in the New Forest and the north-east heaths, but also in numerous other wooded areas across the county. Historically, the species bred sparingly in woodlands on the downs (*BoH*) and elsewhere. In fact, in the 18th century Gilbert White described the Redstart as a very common bird in fields and gardens around Selborne but, as agricultural intensification increased, numbers declined and it became effectively confined to the less-managed heathland areas. As with many other species, Redstarts appear unable to adapt to modern farming practices.

The HBA change map shows a mixed picture with a few more losses than gains. The use of the BCL approach may be introducing errors but, in this case, all the identified losses are from tetrads were breeding was probable or proved during the 1986–91 Atlas. Additional losses that could have arisen from including possible breeding records during the earlier Atlas have been eliminated.

Nationally, the population has been increasing since the mid-1970s, albeit with fluctuations. More recently there has been stronger growth with a 20% increase in England between 1995 and 2012 (*BBS*). However, these trends mask regional differences which show range declines in the southern lowlands (*Bird Atlas 2007–11*) consistent with the findings of the HBA. In Hampshire the Redstart's range appears to have contracted a little, particularly in the south-west, with breeding now restricted to about 10% of the county's tetrads. Even so, in terms of the breeding population, the overall picture is one of relative stability. The New Forest population was estimated at 400–500 pairs in 1976 and 1977 and around 1,000–1,100 pairs in the late 1980s (*BoH*). Over 2009–2011 effort-based monitoring of a 46 sq. km portion of central New Forest woodland located a maximum of 193 territories in 2011 (Ward & Wynn 2013). Scaling up based on a total woodland area of 230 sq. km gives an estimated New Forest population of 965 territories,

close to the 1980 assessment. In the Wealden Heaths SPA, counts at Woolmer Forest have been carried out since the mid-1990s. Over this period, the results have again shown a stable population with counts generally around 20 territories and peaks of 26 in both 2000 and 2009.

As a migrant, the species is more widespread, with the first incoming birds appearing in late March/early April. Passage peaks in late April and continues through May. Returning birds appear at non-breeding locations from mid-July onwards and continue through to late October. Favoured sites on, or near, the coast include Farlington Marshes, IBM Lake and Keyhaven/Lymington. Inland, sites on higher ground including Old Winchester Hill, Stockbridge Down and Martin Down see a significant passage, but birds may be found at a wide variety of locations including large gardens.

Graham Osborne

Sponsored by Jan Schubert

Redstart, New Forest, May 2009 – *Martin Bennett*

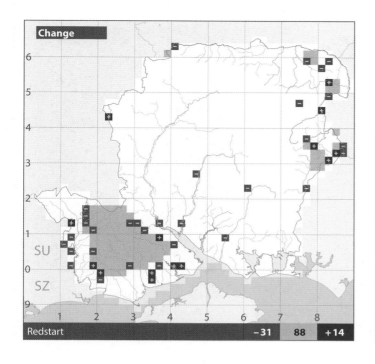

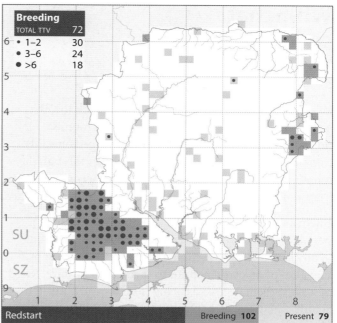

Change — Redstart — −31 | 88 | +14

Breeding — TOTAL TTV 72 — • 1–2 30 — ● 3–6 24 — ● >6 18 — Redstart — Breeding 102 | Present 79

Redstart, New Forest, June 2010 – *Martin Bennett*

Whinchat

Saxicola rubetra

A moderately common passage migrant and previous scarce breeder

Whinchats are summer visitors to Britain with the first arrivals from their sub-Saharan wintering grounds normally reaching Hampshire from mid-April onwards. Migration peaks in early May and continues through the month. Most birds pass quickly through the county on their way to more northerly and westerly breeding grounds.

BBS data indicate that a 55% fall in the UK breeding population has taken place between 1995 and 2012, but Whinchats had been declining in the south and east of England for many years prior to that. In Hampshire, *K&M* described them in 1905 as being "found in all parts of the county … but nowhere plentiful". By 1963, this was a very scarce breeding species confined largely to the New Forest (*Cohen*) and this description was still appropriate at the time of 1986–91 Atlas (*BoH*). During the HBA survey, as the accompanying maps show, no indication of likely breeding was found anywhere in the county. In fact the last confirmed Hampshire breeding record was from the New Forest in 1998. Whinchat is therefore another breeding species lost from Hampshire over the inter-Atlas period.

The nearest extant breeding population is on Salisbury Plain, which has been used as a military training area since the 19th century and has never been subject to modern intensive farming practices. This suggests that changes in agriculture may be an important factor in the species demise. Since Whinchats feed mainly on insects and other invertebrates including spiders, small snails and worms, it is likely that the widespread use of plant protection products, including fungicides, herbicides and insecticides, may be implicated. However, it is also possible that problems in their African wintering grounds are involved, as the decline in numbers mirrors the downward trend seen in many African migrants.

In autumn, return passage peaks in September but extends from July to mid-October. Numbers are generally higher in autumn than in spring and favoured coastal sites such as Farlington Marshes and Keyhaven may hold double-digit counts with birds present for several days. Passage birds may also be found inland particularly in areas of heathland, rough grassland or uncultivated hillsides, haunts somewhat akin to their favoured breeding habitats.

Graham Osborne

Sponsored by Nicky Court

Whinchat, New Forest, June 2013 – *Martin Bennett*

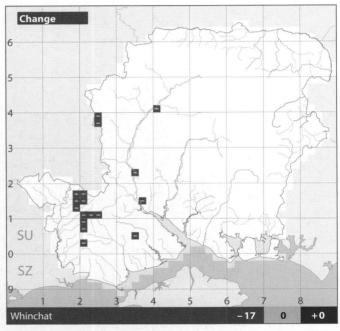

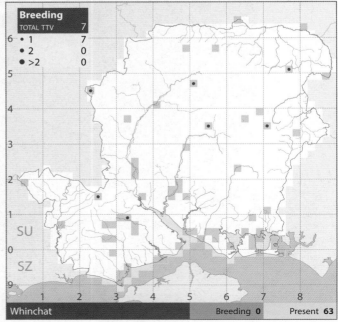

Whinchat,
New Forest, April 2013 –
Martin Bennett

Stonechat

Saxicola rubicola

A moderately common resident, passage migrant and winter visitor

During the 1968–72 national atlas, the Stonechat was widespread in Ireland, but in Britain largely restricted to coastal southern and western areas. Since the *1981–84 Winter Atlas*, the species' status has changed markedly and, due to a series of mild winters and land use changes, has undergone a 115% increase. British Stonechats are partial migrants. While more than half are resident, the remainder migrate to winter from the near Continent southwards to North Africa (Helm *et al.* 2006).

K&M record the Stonechat as a common resident in all parts of Hampshire but numerous only in those districts where furze (gorse) abounds. This suggests it was most common on the nutrient-poor, gorse-dominated soils of the New Forest and the heaths of north-east Hampshire, but that it was also to be found in a wide range of other habitats elsewhere in the county. It is impossible to speculate when Stonechat populations were at their peak; we have little idea of numbers in by-gone days. Significant habitat loss presumably occurred as a result of the 18th and 19th century Enclosure Acts and prime habitat was also greatly reduced when large swathes of heathland were appropriated by the military from the mid-1800s, or lost to development and on-going farming intensification during the 20th century. Since the 1950s the main Hampshire Stonechat populations have remained in the New Forest and on heathland in the north-east of the county; relatively few nested elsewhere in Hampshire. The county population was reduced to an estimated 100 pairs following the cold winter of 1962/63, but Stonechats are capable of rearing two or three broods in optimum seasons, so are able to quickly recover from setbacks. For example at least 545 pairs were present in the county by the late 1970s and the New Forest population was possibly as high as 1,000 pairs by the mid-1990s, with an additional 140 pairs or more on the northern heaths (*BoH*).

During the HBA period, notwithstanding cold spells and occasional heavy snowfalls in three of those winters, Stonechats were found likely to be breeding in 18% of Hampshire's tetrads, compared to 14% in 1986–91. Eighty tetrads were newly occupied since the previous survey, though 44 tetrads, in which breeding previously occurred, were vacant. Strongest population densities were again in the New Forest and isolated areas of heathland in the east and north-east of the county, though there were losses, due possibly to habitat deterioration, for example from an area in the vicinity of Portsdown Hill, from some New Forest sites and from the Avon Valley.

As the HBA maps show, the Stonechat has a much wider winter distribution than during the breeding season.

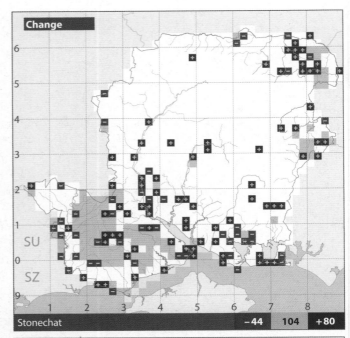

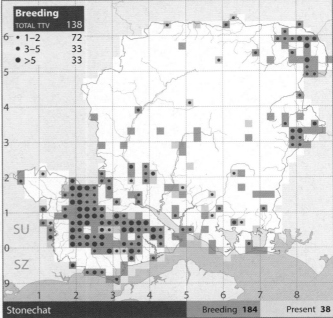

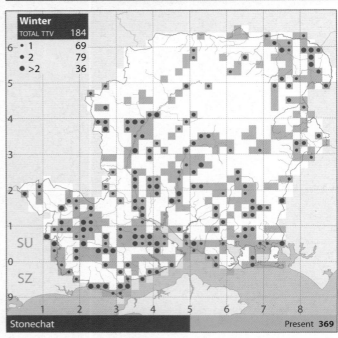

Stonechat, Bourley & Long Valley, April 2012 – *Aaron Gee* (right);
New Forest, July 2009 – *Martin Bennett* (below)

Many birds leave their heathland territories in winter, some at least moving to the coast and agricultural land, including the valleys of the River Test and Itchen.

Eddie Wiseman

Sponsored by David Shute

Wheatear
Oenanthe oenanthe

A common passage migrant; formally a scarce breeder but last proved breeding in 2005

In Hampshire, the Wheatear is best known as a common double passage migrant. This is often the first summer visitor to reach our shores with birds sometimes arriving in early March. In spring, particularly after heavy overnight rain, falls sometimes occur at coastal locations such as Sandy Point, South Hayling, Farlington Marshes and Keyhaven. During the HBA period the peak site count was 41 at Sandy Point on April 3rd 2012. Spring passage extends into late May or even early June, although numbers fall off significantly after the end of April. In autumn, the first returning birds, often juveniles, are seen from July onwards with numbers picking up in August, peaking in September and continuing through October into November. The highest numbers occur at coastal sites but birds may turn up almost anywhere inland, particularly on downland or farmland. Passage is extended, both in spring and autumn, by the migration of so-called Greenland Wheatears (race *leucorhoa*) between their Canadian breeding and African wintering grounds. Although there are occasional winter records, none were recorded during the HBA and it is the November migrants that are registered on the winter map.

The Wheatear is now restricted as a British breeding species almost entirely to the northern and western counties with just a sparse scattering of records from locations in south-east England (*Bird Atlas 2007–11*). This was not always the case. At the beginning of the 20th century, *K&M* described the species as plentiful in Hampshire, in the central hill district, suitable localities in the north and in the New Forest. Its range had expanded as a result of neglect of

Greenland Wheatear, Manor Farm CP, May 2006 – *Trevor Codlin*

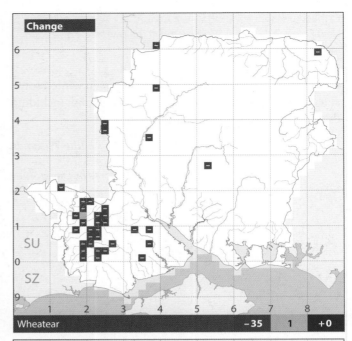

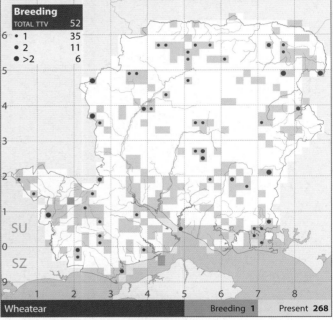

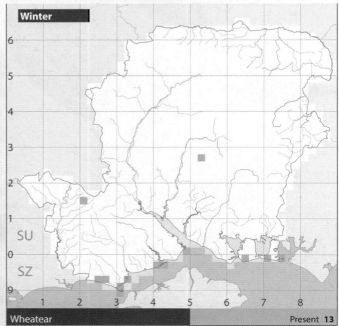

some agricultural areas but this trend was reversed in the 1930s and 1940s due to increased cultivation during and after World War II. The reduction in grazing brought about by the continuing expansion of arable at the expense of sheep farming and the loss of Rabbits due to myxomatosis in the 1950s led to further reduction in suitable close-cropped grassland habitat. By the time of the 1986–91 Atlas, breeding was confirmed in only two tetrads on the chalk, both at Porton Down. For the county as a whole, breeding was confirmed or probable in 36 tetrads, with most of these in the New Forest where they bred particularly on old airfields.

The results of the HBA survey have confirmed that, over the two decades between atlases, the decline of the Wheatear as a Hampshire breeder has continued. The species was not proved breeding anywhere in the county during the five HBA breeding seasons. Although the breeding map shows presence in 268 tetrads and likely breeding in just one, the vast majority of these records, maybe all of them, refer to migrants. The single record that met the likely breeding criteria has been included on the maps even though breeding was last confirmed in the county in 2005. If breeding has not already ceased in Hampshire, it is highly likely that it will do so in the near future.

Graham Osborne

Sponsored by Damian Offer

Wheatear, New Forest, September 2011 – *Martin Bennett*

Dunnock
Prunella modularis
An abundant resident

The Dunnock is a common but unobtrusive species, easily overlooked and often first located by its warbling song or sharp call. It is a ground-feeder and occupies a wide variety of habitats ranging from farmland hedgerows and woodland to parks, gardens and urban areas, wherever there is low, dense scrub to provide cover, feeding opportunities and suitable nest sites. For such an apparently unremarkable species, Dunnocks exhibit very complicated and unusual breeding behaviour. Females have their own territories and often mate with two or more males during the same breeding cycle. This means that the chicks in a brood may have different fathers. Other combinations involving two or more females with one male, or with two or more males, also occur (Davies 1985).

In the UK, the Dunnock population fell sharply between the mid-1970s and the mid-1980s but partially recovered over the period between the 1986–91 Atlas and the HBA. The English population grew by 12% between 1986 and 2011 (*BirdTrends*) although growth in the south-east was lower. The causes of the earlier decline are not fully understood but it is possible that reduced management of lowland woods resulting in canopy closure, combined with increased browsing by deer, reduced the quantity and suitability of scrub habitat. The removal of farmland hedges may also have contributed.

As the HBA maps show, it remains widespread in Hampshire with breeding considered likely in almost 100% of tetrads. The lowest densities occur on intensively farmed and heavily grazed downland. It is also scarce or absent in parts of the New Forest where intensive grazing has eliminated the scrub layer. In other parts of the Forest, and on the north-east heaths where grazing is less severe, Dunnocks are common in woodland and heathland scrub.

The HBA change map shows a minor contraction in the number of occupied tetrads compared with the 1986–91 Atlas. Some of the losses were from coastal tetrads with very little suitable habitat but it is possible that others were due to under-recording rather than a real reduction in range.

The HBA winter map shows little difference in the distribution between the breeding and winter seasons. This is not surprising given that the species is essentially sedentary with most birds staying very close to their natal area. Migration watches and ringing results suggest that some very limited movements do occur, mainly involving locally-bred birds but also occasionally involving Continental migrants.

Graham Osborne

Sponsored by Julie Snook

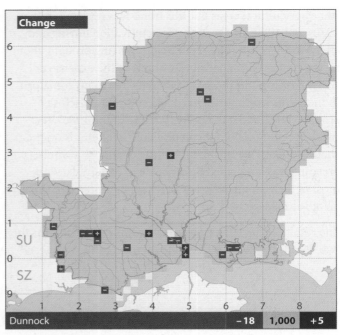

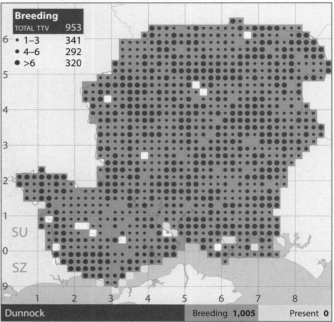

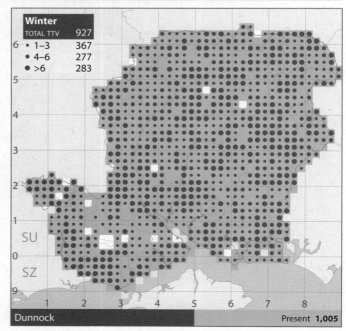

Dunnock, New Forest, May 2008 – *Martin Bennett*

House Sparrow

Passer domesticus

A numerous but declining resident

The House Sparrow is one of the most familiar birds in the UK due to its habit of breeding in proximity to humans and its bold and noisy character. It nests in colonies in both rural and suburban habitats, usually choosing a hole or crevice in a building but sometimes in creepers on a building or occasionally amongst the twigs of a tree. In recent years there has been an increased interest in the fortunes of this species from both birdwatchers and the general public and an improvement in yearly recording.

As the HBA breeding map shows, the species continues to be widespread throughout the county, with breeding considered likely in 86% of Hampshire tetrads. It is most thinly distributed in the New Forest and in the central part of the county in rural areas where the human population density is low. The highest concentrations are in more urban areas, along the coastal strip in the extreme south-west, in the Southampton metropolitan area, around the towns of Andover, Basingstoke and Portsmouth and in the north-east. Locally the species can be abundant; the highest TTV count for a single tetrad was 249. The largest site count during 2007–12 was 250 feeding on stubble at Sturt Pond on August 24th 2011.

The change map shows a 9% contraction in breeding range between 1986–91 and 2008–12. The decline is consistent with a rapid fall in UK abundance over the past 25 years (*BirdTrends*). As a result the House Sparrow was moved from the green to red list of Birds of Conservation Concern in 2002. In England, the decline has been greatest in East Anglia and the south-east, particularly London, whereas there have been some increases in the south-west and in Wales, Scotland and Ireland (*Bird Atlas 2007–11*). These regional differences suggest that reasons for the decline may be complex involving several different mechanisms.

House Sparrow, New Forest, July 2012 – *Martin Bennett*

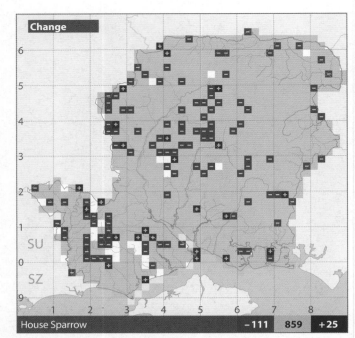

Change

House Sparrow −111 859 +25

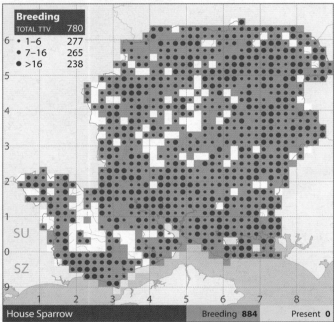

Breeding
TOTAL TTV 780
- 1–6   277
- 7–16 265
- >16   238

House Sparrow Breeding 884 Present 0

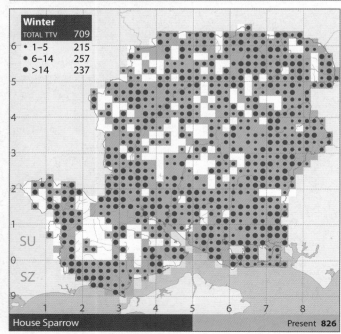

Winter
TOTAL TTV 709
- 1–5   215
- 6–14 257
- >14   237

House Sparrow Present 826

House Sparrow, New Forest, October 2009 – *Martin Bennett*

In rural, intensively-farmed areas one of these is likely to be a fall in overwinter survival as has been experienced by many farmland seed-eaters but in suburban areas breeding productivity could be the most important factor. Loss of nest sites from improved building maintenance, increases in cat predation, air pollution and the over-use of pesticides in gardens could all be involved. In Hampshire, *BBS* data suggest that the downward trend may have bottomed out as there has been little change in status in recent years.

The HBA winter map shows a similar distribution to that in the summer. This to be expected since most House

Sparrows do not move more than a few kilometres from their natal sites. Adults attend their nest sites all year round, adding material to the nest at any time; females roost in them on and off throughout the year but may join males and first-year birds in communal winter roosts. The maps suggest that the species is slightly less widespread in winter than during the breeding season. While it is possible that some marginal sites are deserted in the winter, recording differences between the seasons cannot be ruled out.

Graham Osborne

Sponsored by Colleen Hope

Spanish Sparrow

Passer hispaniolensis

A very rare vagrant

Hampshire's first Spanish Sparrow was discovered in a Calshot garden on December 3rd 2011 and remained in the area until March 23rd 2012. It was the eighth British record and the 372nd accession to the county list.

John Eyre

Spanish Sparrow, Calshot, February 2012 – *Josie Hewitt*

Tree Sparrow

Passer montanus

A very scarce and irregular visitor that formerly bred

The Tree Sparrow has an extremely large world range extending from Western Europe, including the British Isles, across Eurasia to Southeast Asia. In the Far East it is abundant in urban areas but in Europe it occupies lightly wooded countryside. There is no shortage of apparently suitable habitat in the UK, yet the species is red-listed after an estimated 95% drop in its breeding population between 1967 and 2011 (*BirdTrends*). The decline, which is the largest for any common species over this period, occurred particularly from the mid-1970s through to the early 1990s. Although recent *BBS* results suggest a small increase since then, the recovery still has a very long way to go and *Bird Atlas 2007–11* confirms that Tree Sparrows have now disappeared from much of southern England.

In Hampshire, the Tree Sparrow's population had already declined and its range had contracted by the time of the 1986–91 Atlas, when there were records from 75 tetrads with breeding confirmed in 22. During the HBA, as the change map (which is based only on proven breeding records in the first atlas) shows, no records were received indicative of likely breeding in the county. Over the past two decades, the species has disappeared as a Hampshire breeding species.

Although the mechanisms leading to the decline are uncertain, it seems likely that agricultural intensification is the underlying cause. A reduction in over-winter survival, resulting from decreases in winter stubble and weed seeds, may be the key factor. This would be consistent with declines in other resident, seed-eating species which have taken place over a similar time period.

As a winter visitor to Hampshire, the Tree Sparrow has been subject to periodic fluctuations. A reasonable breeding population was established in the 1960s and 1970s, following large autumn influxes and the appearance of winter flocks. However, by the time of the 1986–91 Atlas, the numbers recorded in autumn and winter had declined (*BoH*). This trend has continued. During the HBA winter period records of Tree Sparrows were obtained from only two tetrads. These included a bird colour-ringed as a pullus at Beckhampton, Wiltshire in 2007 coming to a feeder at Kirton Farm near Sparsholt in February 2008. Thanks to timely conservation efforts, Tree Sparrows are thriving in our neighbouring county and probably offer the best chances of re-colonisation in Hampshire.

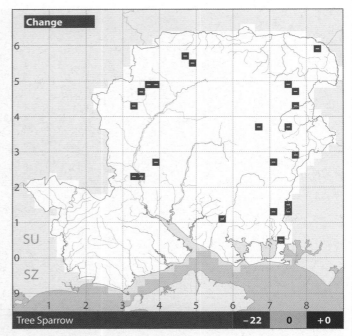

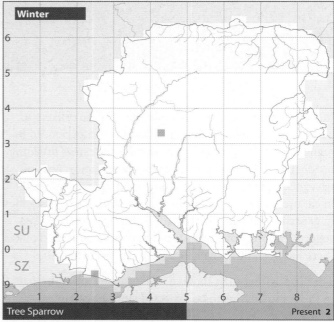

During 2007–12, but outside the HBA recording periods, a small number of additional sightings occurred in both spring and autumn. These involved mainly single birds, or very small groups, at coastal sites. In the majority of cases birds were seen on one day only or for a few days at most and that, coupled with the location, may suggest such occurrences are Continental rather than wandering British birds.

Graham Osborne

Sponsored by John Norton

Tree Sparrow, Titchfield Haven, April 2014 – *Martin Bennett*

Tree Sparrow (with House Sparrow (left)), Titchfield Haven, April 2014 – *Martin Bennett*

Yellow Wagtail

Motacilla flava

Formerly a summer visitor and common passage migrant; now rare in summer but still moderately common on passage

Yellow Wagtails winter in sub-Saharan Africa and migrate back to Europe to breed. Britain holds the bulk of the world population of the distinctive race *flavissima* with small numbers on the nearby European mainland while the Continental Blue-headed Wagtail *M. f. flava* occurs in Britain mainly as a scarce migrant and occasional breeder.

The changing status of the species in Hampshire has been well documented. In 1905, *K&M* described it as "local in its distribution … but especially plentiful in the larger river valleys, where there are large extents of water-meadows or marsh lands". In 1963, *Cohen* summarised its status as "a summer visitor in much smaller numbers than formerly. Between the two world wars this species was plentiful in the Test Valley and its tributaries, especially between Whitchurch and Stockbridge, and certainly not uncommon in the Itchen Valley and in other suitable areas. It still breeds in some numbers particularly in the Test Valley but it is nothing like as abundant as it was and in some areas has disappeared as a breeding species." *C&T* (1972) also commented on the continuing decline first noted a decade earlier. They stated that "it still breeds in some numbers in parts of the main river valleys, particularly the Test …. it is nothing like as abundant as it was and in some areas it has disappeared as a breeding species."

In 1993, following the 1986–91 Hampshire Atlas, Clark & Eyre (*BoH*) stated that its "main breeding habitats are damp meadows (especially in the Avon, Test and Itchen Valleys), coastal grassland (principally Farlington Marshes) and reclaimed land … Occasional pairs have nested around margins of gravel pits and on farmland". They reported that

Yellow Wagtails had already disappeared from much of the Test Valley in the 1970s and where, during the 1986–91 Atlas, breeding was confirmed or probable in just three tetrads. The decline was also mirrored in the Itchen Valley, where surveys recorded 27 pairs in 1976 in the Mansbridge to Bishopstoke area but just two in 1982 and none during the 1986–91 Atlas.

At the time of the 1986–91 Atlas the two remaining strongholds for Yellow Wagtails in Hampshire were the Avon Valley and Farlington Marshes. At the former site, although the Atlas confirmed breeding in most tetrads along the Hampshire stretch of the river, numbers were much reduced from an estimated 50 pairs in 1982. At Farlington Marshes, where the breeding population had increased to 12–15 pairs during the 1980s possibly as a result of reduced grazing pressure, by the end of the decade numbers were in rapid decline.

Sadly the species is now probably extinct as a breeding species in Hampshire. The last proven breeding record in the county was on Long Island in Langstone Harbour in 2003 and the HBA survey failed to register even probable breeding throughout the 2008–12 period.

The demise of the Yellow Wagtail as a Hampshire breeder is part of a more widespread range contraction which has seen the species disappear from much of southern and north-western England and parts of East Anglia (*Bird Atlas 2007–11*). As well as a considerable range contraction there has been a 72% population decline in the UK during 1970–2010 (SUKB 2012). The decline has been linked to farmland drainage, the conversion of pasture to arable land, the switch from spring- to autumn-grown cereals and the loss of insects associated with cattle.

Yellow Wagtails pass through Hampshire in spring on their way north to breed and are still recorded in reasonable numbers on return passage during mid-August through into early October. Small flocks frequent coastal grazing

Yellow Wagtail, Posbrook Floods, September 2009 – *Steve Copsey*

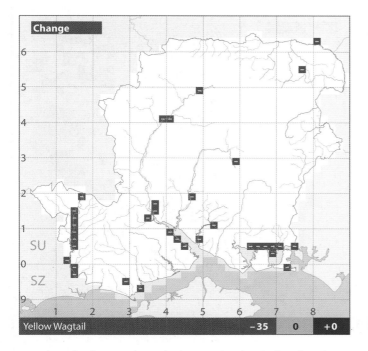

Change

Yellow Wagtail   − 35   0   + 0

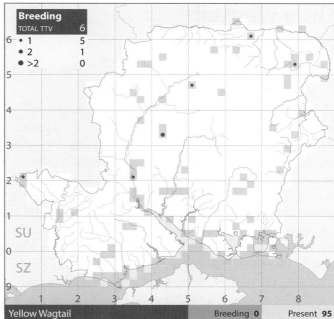

Breeding
TOTAL TTV   6
• 1   5
• 2   1
• >2   0

Yellow Wagtail   Breeding 0   Present 95

marshes, feeding with cattle during the day before heading to reed beds to roost at sites such as Farlington Marshes and Titchfield Haven. The HBA breeding map shows the distribution of migrants during the breeding season but with no indication of likely breeding. Similarly, the change map shows the total disappearance of the species from all those tetrads where breeding was considered likely during the 1986–91 Atlas. It would seem that, over the past two decades, Yellow Wagtail has been lost as a Hampshire breeder.

During the HBA period there were four records of Blue-headed Wagtail from: Titchfield Haven on April 19th 2008; Sandy Point on April 12th 2009; Testwood Lakes on May 15th 2010 and Farlington Marshes on April 6th 2011.

Peter Potts

Sponsored by Stephen Harvey

Blue-headed Wagtail, Pennington, April 2013 – *David Cuddon*

Yellow Wagtail, Woolmer, September 2009 – *Richard Ford*

Grey Wagtail

Motacilla cinerea

A moderately common resident, passage migrant and winter visitor

The Grey Wagtail wasn't described as a separate species until 1771, which explains why Gilbert White used the name Yellow Wagtail for both the Grey and Yellow species. He wrote to Pennant in 1768 that Yellow Wagtails were seen in Hampshire in both summer and winter which, of course, is true for the resident Grey but not for the migrant Yellow Wagtail. At the beginning of the 20th century *K&M* described Hampshire as "not particularly well-suited to this beautiful bird" but by 1963, *Cohen* suggests that there had been a considerable spread in its distribution in the county. Following the 1986–91 Atlas, Clark & Eyre (*BoH*) described the species as a moderately common resident, passage migrant and winter visitor, a description which remains valid today.

The Grey Wagtail's distribution in Hampshire reflects the county's network of rivers, streams and other waterways. The HBA breeding map shows the species to be widespread along the river valleys and throughout the lowlands of much of the south and north-east. They are scarce on the drier upland areas and surprisingly absent from large sections of the coast. They are usually found close to running water and are particularly fond of nesting under bridges and on other structures near streams and rivers but will also use natural cavities in banks and man-made sites including roofs, porches and sheds, sometimes a little way from water.

The HBA change map shows a mixture of gains and losses since the 1986–91 Atlas with a net breeding range contraction of just under 10%. This reduction is in line with the UK trend which saw Grey Wagtail moved from the green to amber on the list of Birds of Conservation Concern in 2002, following a 41% fall in population between 1975 and 1999. The decline has continued, with a 19% reduction in England between 1995 and 2011 (*BirdTrends*). The reason for this long-term downward trend is not clear but it is, perhaps, no coincidence that all three British wagtails are in decline. Even accepting that one of these, the Yellow Wagtail, is a summer visitor, this suggests that some common cause may be involved, perhaps involving food supply. All three species feed on invertebrates, including adult flies, mayflies, beetles, crustaceans and molluscs, often in, or close to, water. As a resident dependent on invertebrates, Grey Wagtail is also clearly affected by severe winter weather. Historically, declines were noted following most cold winters for example in 1961/62, 1962/63, 1982, 1984/85 and the severe spell in February 1991. After the latter just a single pair could be found on the Basingstoke Canal between Greywell and Ash Vale where 16 pairs had been

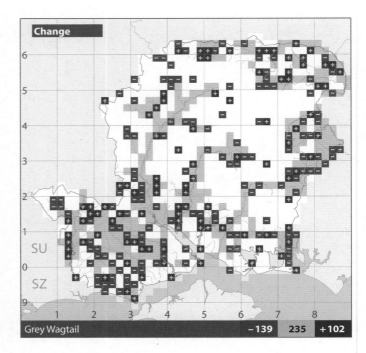

Grey Wagtail   −139   235   +102

found in 1978 (*BoH*). However, the winters between the 1986–91 Atlas and the HBA were, with a few exceptions, generally mild, so unlikely to have been responsible for the reduction in numbers.

Post-breeding dispersal and movements, both coastal and inland, occur in the autumn peaking in September and early October, therefore outside the HBA survey periods. Numbers involved are generally small. During 2007–12 the maximum site count was 155 at Barton on Sea Golf Club between September 12th and 29th 2008, with a peak day count of 22 east on September 19th.

The species' distribution in winter is very similar to that during the breeding season but, as the HBA winter map shows, with an increase in the number of occupied tetrads, particularly on the coast. Grey Wagtails are less restricted to running water in winter and can be found more commonly on ponds, sewage farms, watercress beds and flooded meadows. Historically, some large winter counts have been made including an unprecedented roost of over 180 with Pied Wagtails in reed beds at Fullerton in January 1978. Nowadays numbers are much lower, seldom reaching double figures. During the HBA period, the peak count was 11 roosting at Kings Pond, Alton, on December 8th 2007.

Ringing recoveries suggest that some of our wintering birds are from Wales, northern Britain and Continental Europe (one has been controlled with an East German ring). Although most of our breeding birds are likely to be resident, some leave the county to winter elsewhere. At least three Hampshire-bred birds have been found in the winter in France.

Peter Potts

Sponsored by Alan Snook

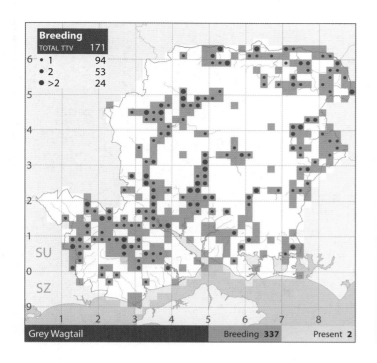

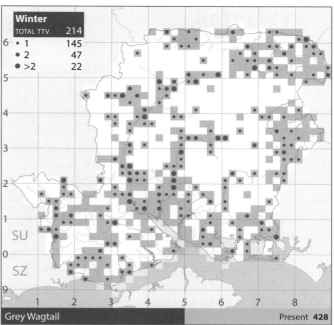

Grey Wagtail, Titchfield, February 2009 – *Steve Copsey*

Pied Wagtail

Motacilla alba yarrelli

A numerous resident, passage migrant and winter visitor

K&M (1905) touched only briefly on this species describing it as "our commonest wagtail … greatly augmented at the seasons of migration". This account still holds true today. In 1963 Cohen felt that there were indications of a decline in breeding numbers since *K&M*, although it was still widely distributed and not at all uncommon. This was of course an anecdotal observation with no survey data to back it up but a fall in numbers had apparently occurred. However, *C&T* (1972) stated that, despite the suggested decline by Cohen, the species remained widely distributed and common throughout the county. In *BoH*, Clark & Eyre (1993) described it as a numerous resident, abundant passage migrant and winter visitor.

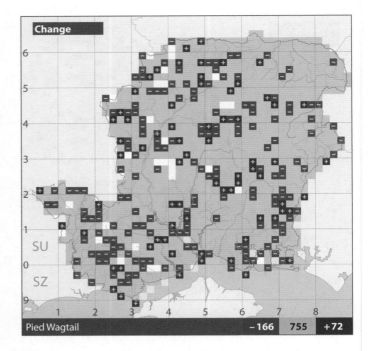

Pied Wagtail   − 166 | 755 | +72

The 1986–91 Atlas recorded Pied Wagtails present during the breeding season in 90% of Hampshire tetrads with most of the gaps being in the New Forest and on the chalk. The HBA survey shows a similar distribution, with both gains and losses but a net 10% reduction in the number of tetrads where breeding was considered likely. The losses appear scattered across the county, particularly on the chalk, with a surprising gap opening up in the middle of the New Forest. Quite why the range has contracted is unclear but is consistent with a 24% population decline in south-east England over the 1995–2012 period (*BBS*). In contrast, the national picture shows a small range gain across Great Britain since the 1968–72 Atlas (*Bird Atlas 2007–11*). Breeding densities of Pied Wagtails are highest in lowland areas of the north and west but relatively low throughout England. The population decline in south-east England matches the pattern observed for many other passerine species and raises questions about deteriorations in habitat quality and food supply.

The species prefers wet areas and is usually associated with nesting in buildings and other man-made structures. Cohen references an example of the species' ability to nest in strange places and still raise a brood. A pair once nested in a sailing dinghy at Titchfield Haven, which went out into the Solent three times a week. The female continued to incubate six eggs and the nestlings fledged successfully. Cohen also gives accounts of large roosts in Hampshire, the first documented going back to 1894–95 at Kimbridge. He also tells the remarkably sad tale of a roost of more than 600 in greenhouses in Sway that caused so much damage that drastic action was taken to keep the birds out. In so doing many were trapped inside and 325 were picked up dead. The owner estimated that the true number of casualties was nearer 600. When the roost re-formed BTO ringers trapped 148 and released them in Tring, Hertfordshire and Shoreham, Sussex but birds from

Pied Wagtail, Southampton Airport, January 2014 – *Bill Brooks*

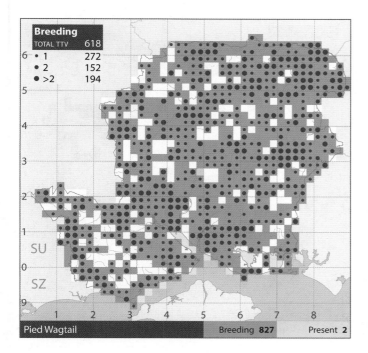

Breeding

TOTAL TTV	618
• 1	272
• 2	152
● >2	194

Pied Wagtail — Breeding **827** — Present **2**

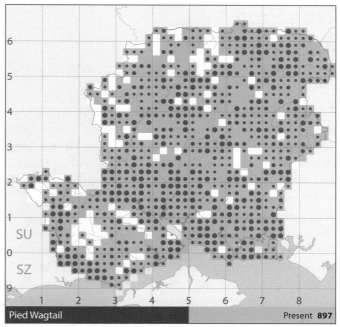

Pied Wagtail — Present **897**

both locations were subsequently re-trapped in the same greenhouse (*C&T*). A roost of 1,200 in a North Baddesley factory in January 1990 is the largest recorded to date (*BoH*).

Pied Wagtails are currently perhaps more numerous in Hampshire in the winter months. During the HBA, they were recorded in slightly more tetrads during the winter than in the breeding season. Ringing has shown that some of the Pied Wagtails wintering in Hampshire breed farther north in the UK and come south to winter in lowland England. The species is then more abundant in the south near the coast and in valleys and flood plains. Other northern breeders pass through to the Iberian Peninsula and North Africa.

Birds of the Continental race, the White Wagtail *M. a. alba*, move through Hampshire on their way to and from northern Europe, predominantly Iceland, where they breed. They winter farther south in Europe and North Africa. One Hampshire ringed Pied/White Wagtail has been recovered in Morocco. White Wagtails are predominantly recorded on the coast in Hampshire, usually between March and May in their splendidly neat breeding plumage. An exceptional count of 50 was made at Farlington Marshes during April 1959. Autumn birds are much more difficult to identify and are less frequently recorded. White Wagtails appear scarcer today in the county although considerable autumn movements of *alba* wagtails, probably involving many White Wagtails, can be recorded along the Hampshire coast.

Peter Potts

Sponsored by Katharine Wyles

Pied Wagtail, Itchen Valley, April 2008 – *Dennis Bright*

Tree Pipit

Anthus trivialis

A moderately common but declining summer visitor and passage migrant

K&M had little to say about the species, merely stating that it was found in all parts of the county but was not nearly as plentiful as the Meadow Pipit. Cohen, writing 60 years later, described it as numerous in only a few favoured localities and certainly very local in the centre and north. With the results from the 1986–91 Atlas available, Clark & Eyre in *BoH* were able to be more specific, describing it as common in parts of the New Forest, Ringwood Forest, the heaths in the Tadley area and the north-east, but locally distributed elsewhere. The county population was estimated to be in the range 600–700 pairs, comprising 300 in the New Forest, 200–250 in the north-east on the Thames Basin and Wealden Heaths and 100–150 elsewhere.

Perusal of the HBA summer and change maps show some interesting developments since the 1986–91 Atlas. In the New Forest, the species occupies clear-felled and restocked enclosures as well as open heathland with scattered trees. The central area remains occupied but birds have apparently been lost from in excess of 25 tetrads around the perimeter of the national park. This may partly be due to less complete coverage in the HBA, but numbers have certainly fallen, particularly on the heaths (A. Page, *pers. comm.*). On the Thames Basin and Wealden Heaths the distribution is broadly similar although survey data suggest that densities are now lower. Elsewhere in the county, gains have been made particularly in the Alton area and north of Andover, while losses have occurred in Ringwood Forest, in the centre north and in a scattering of tetrads across the South Downs. Many of the changes can be attributed to man's influence on the habitat. The rotational clear felling of conifers at sites such as Alice Holt and Ringwood Forests, and Ampfield and Chawton Park Woods provided much habitat at the time of the previous atlas but this is now considerably reduced. Significant habitat was provided by the Woodland Trust deciduous planting at Burkham which held a peak of 19 singing males in 2000. Numbers there have declined but birds have now occupied newly-planted areas nearby at Weston Common and adjacent to Golden Pot. Open woodlands and grassland with scattered trees, often close to low intensity arable fields on the higher chalk, also provide suitable habitat.

As indicated above, the county population has certainly fallen since the last atlas. Using atlas records and other

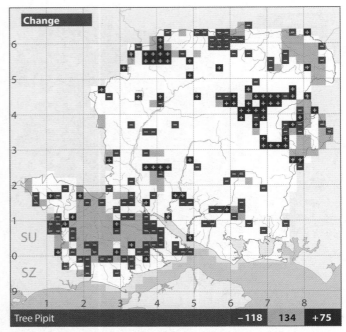

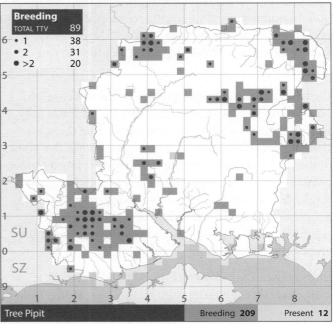

records submitted to HOS during 2008–12, there were perhaps 150–200 pairs in the New Forest, 125–150 in the north-east and 100–150 elsewhere.

Tetrads with presence indicated relate mainly to spring migrants along the coast and in other non-breeding locations.

John Clark

Sponsored by Rupert Pyrah

Tree Pipit, Ampfield, June 2005 – *Nigel Jones*

Tree Pipit, New Forest, April 2014 – *Martin Bennett*

Tree Pipit,
New Forest, May 2015 –
Martin Bennett

Meadow Pipit
Anthus pratensis
A locally common but declining resident, numerous passage migrant and winter visitor

As a breeding species, Meadow Pipit has always been widely but thinly scattered throughout the county, breeding in a range of open habitats including heathland, downland and, to a lesser degree, farmland. There has, however, been a significant decline between the 1986–91 and 2008–12 Atlases with the HBA maps showing the number of tetrads with breeding considered likely effectively halving. However, as with other migrant breeders, the absolute magnitude of the range loss is questionable because of the errors inherent in the methodology used. It is highly likely that some of the losses relate to the inclusion of migrant birds from the 1986–91 Atlas. An alternative approach is simply to compare probable and proven breeding records in that Atlas with the same categories in 2008–12, accepting that the lack of breeding evidence in the HBA will bias the outcome. On that basis, breeding was probable/proven in 308 tetrads in the first atlas and 127 in the second, a loss of 59%. Whatever method is used, it is clear that a significant range loss has occurred over the inter-atlas years. The loss of breeding birds has been most noticeable in the lower density farmland population with a contraction of the breeding range to a relatively small number of core areas. The strongholds remain the New Forest, higher altitude downland e.g. Butser Hill, Old Winchester Hill, Cheesefoot Head, Watership Down and Shipton Bellinger areas, Blackbushe and Farnborough airfields in the north-east, and the whole coastal fringe. However, even in these areas there has been a significant reduction in the breeding population.

The change map does indicate a small amount of redistribution in peripheral areas, where some of the losses are countered by gains nearby and, on a slightly more positive note, occupancy appears to have increased in the Cheesefoot Head area in particular. Nevertheless the overall decline mirrors the national trend, which has seen a 46% population decrease from 1970–2010 (*Bird Atlas 2007–11*), the losses being most noticeable in the lower density lowland areas. Meadow Pipits are partial migrants and conditions on the Iberian wintering grounds have been linked to the decline, as have losses of marginal land from parts of the breeding range (*1988–91 Atlas*).

Meadow Pipits are much more widespread in the county during the winter, with birds encountered in a wide range of open habitats. It is also one of the more conspicuous species on its diurnal migration in both spring and autumn and there are often significant movements of hundreds, or indeed thousands, of birds heading northwards during March/April and in the opposite direction in September/October.

Andy Johnson

Sponsored by Geoffrey Farwell

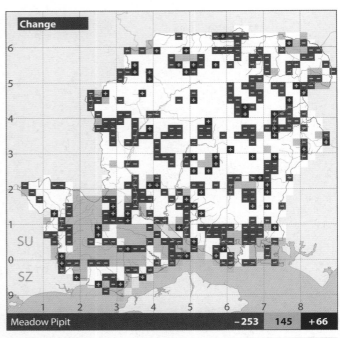

Meadow Pipit — Change − 253 | 145 | +66

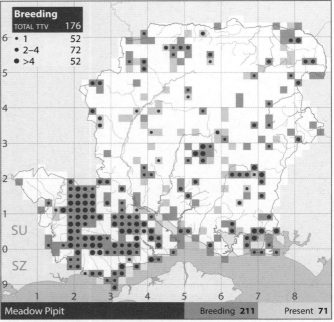

Breeding
TOTAL TTV 176
- 1 — 52
- 2–4 — 72
- >4 — 52

Meadow Pipit — Breeding 211 | Present 71

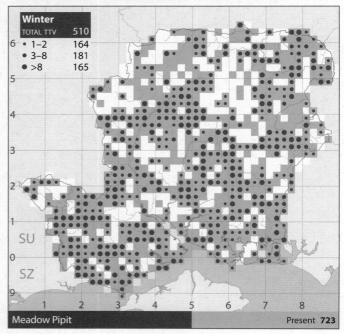

Winter
TOTAL TTV 510
- 1–2 — 164
- 3–8 — 181
- >8 — 165

Meadow Pipit — Present 723

Meadow Pipit, Blashford Lakes, March 2008 – *Martin Bennett* (above): New Forest, April 2009 – *Martin Bennett* (below)

Rock Pipit

Anthus petrosus

A scarce but increasing resident, scarce passage migrant and winter visitor

Rock Pipit has always been a relatively scarce bird in Hampshire, confined almost entirely to coastal areas. As a breeder, the species was formerly confined to the extreme south-west of the county, between Hurst Castle and Milford. This is perhaps not surprising, given that Hampshire lies towards the eastern limit of its UK breeding range; it is much more a species of northern and western rocky coasts. On a national scale, its breeding range has shown relatively little change over the 1970–2010 period (*Bird Atlas 2007–11*), but in Hampshire it has spread eastwards along the coast. Between the two atlas surveys it has expanded its range with breeding proven in ten tetrads and, based on presence during the breeding season, considered likely in an additional ten. It has used suitable habitat around Southampton Water and the eastern Solent as well as the Hurst/Milford area. Successful breeding has been reported from various man-made 'rocky' habitats including Hurst, Calshot and Southsea Castles and both Southampton and Portsmouth Docks.

Rock Pipits are much more numerous during the winter, although they are still confined to coastal habitats, including saltmarshes. Inland records are extremely rare but during the HBA winter survey there were records of single birds at Ibsley Water/Blashford Lakes in both 2008 and 2011. Compared to the breeding season, the numbers and distribution of Rock Pipits increased significantly

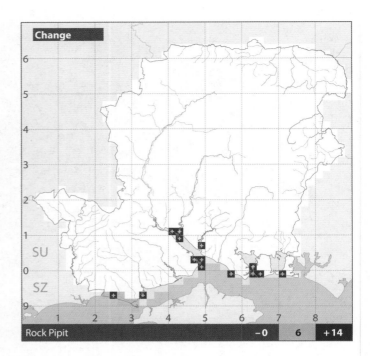

Rock Pipit   −0   6   +14

throughout the western Solent, Southampton Water (including the lower reaches of the Rivers Test, Itchen and Hamble) and the eastern harbours, with double figure flocks not uncommon in all areas.

British breeding Rock Pipits are essentially resident (*Bird Atlas 2007–11*) and hence the winter population in Hampshire is likely to be significantly augmented by Continental migrants of the subspecies *littoralis*; indeed a number of this subspecies are identified each spring as they start to acquire their distinctive breeding plumage.

Andy Johnson

Sponsored by Tim Doran

Rock Pipit, Bunny Meadows, October 2011 – *Bob Marchant*

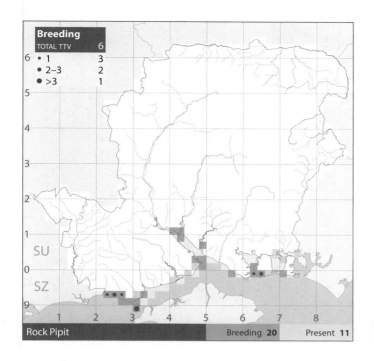

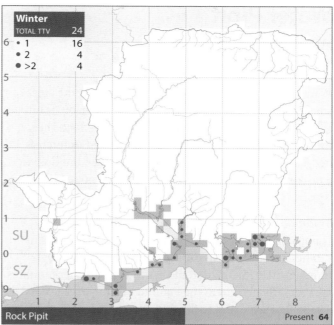

Rock Pipit, Farlington Marsh, March 2015 – *Steve Bassett*

Water Pipit

Anthus spinoletta

A scarce and declining winter visitor and passage migrant

Water Pipits are scarce winter visitors from alpine areas of southern Europe, mostly to coastal wetland habitats but also to a number of often habitual inland wetland sites, including water meadows, sewage farms and watercress beds. Birds tend to arrive from mid-October, build up to a peak in February/March, and are usually gone by mid-April.

Traditionally, the favoured locality for Water Pipits in Hampshire is the Lower Test Marshes at Totton, which can hold up to 30 birds during peak periods, although numbers may fluctuate from year to year. Smaller numbers are regularly present in the Pennington/Keyhaven Marshes, Titchfield Haven and Farlington Marshes areas, but double-figure counts at these sites are now not as regular as they used to be. Birds on passage are regularly recorded from a variety of other localities.

Inland sites mapped during the HBA survey include Blashford Lakes and the adjacent Avon Valley, the River Anton at Andover, the River Test at Compton and Camp Farm Sewage Farm in the north-east of the county.

Notably, watercress beds, including those in the upper Itchen Valley at Headbourne Worthy and in the Alresford

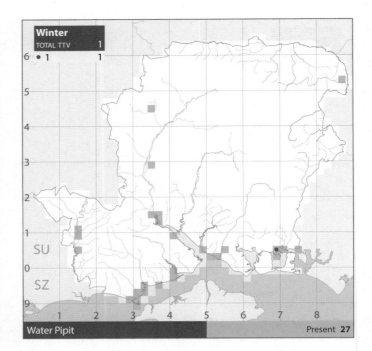

Winter
TOTAL TTV 1

Water Pipit — Present **27**

area, do not appear on the HBA map, despite these being former strongholds for the species. Over the past 30 years numbers using the beds have declined. While this is consistent with an overall fall in numbers at all sites in recent years, it is also probable that changes in the way the beds are managed have played a part.

Andy Johnson

Sponsored by Dave Pearson

Water Pipit, Blashford Lakes, March 2014 – *Gordon Small*

Richard's Pipit

Anthus richardi

A rare passage migrant usually recorded in autumn

The Richard's Pipit breeds in central and eastern Asia and migrates south to winter in the Indian subcontinent and South-east Asia. Some move west in autumn with a few reaching the UK and probably moving on to overwinter in Spain and North Africa. In Hampshire, the species was recorded in every year of the 2007–12 period. All records were from the coast and all were in the autumn between September 25th and November 18th, those late in the season occurring during the HBA winter recording season. All records are given below:

2007: Farlington, September 26th and assumed same September 30th.
Mill Rythe, East Hayling, October 2nd.
Barton on Sea, November 4th.

2008: Keyhaven, October 24th.
Barton on Sea, October 28th.

2009: Barton on Sea, September 27th.

2010: Keyhaven, November 10th/11th.

2011: Keyhaven, September 25th.
Sandy Point, October 28th.

Richards Pipit, Pennington Marsh, March 2014 – *Roger Murfitt*

2012: Becton Bunny, October 30th.
Calshot, November 17th/18th

These 11 records brought the Hampshire total to 36.

John Eyre

Tawny Pipit

Anthus campestris

A rare autumn passage migrant

The Tawny Pipit breeds in a large part of Eurasia, from Spain to Mongolia, and winters in sub-Saharan Africa, India and the Middle East. It is rare in Hampshire, occurring on passage, usually in autumn. During the 2007–12 period there were two records, the first within the HBA window. This was found in fields adjacent to New Lane, Keyhaven on June 1st 2008. It was only the second spring record for the county, following one at Sandy Point on May 10th 2005. In 2010, one was seen briefly at Keyhaven Marsh on the more usual date of August 26th. These records brought the county total to 17.

Andy Johnson

Tawny Pipit, Hayling Island, September 2015 – *David Ryves*

Brambling
Fringilla montifringilla
A moderately common winter visitor and passage migrant

Bramblings breed in the birch and pine forests of higher latitudes from Fennoscandia across to Asia, mainly wintering south of their breeding range. In the UK they occasionally breed in Scotland but, in the rest of the country including Hampshire, they are winter visitors with the lowest densities in the uplands of Scotland, northern England and Wales (*Bird Atlas 2007–11*). It is unclear whether apparent range expansions of 21% in Britain and 53% in Ireland since the *1981–84 Winter Atlas* are real or caused by increases in recording effort.

Birds generally begin to arrive in October and most have departed by mid-April with some straggling into early May. These late-leavers were recorded during the HBA breeding surveys but have not been mapped here. One of their main winter foods is Beech mast, so they tend to congregate in mature deciduous woodlands, often forming flocks with Chaffinches. The Beech trees are not successful in producing a mast crop annually so numbers of Bramblings tend to fluctuate from year to year.

In Hampshire, as the HBA map shows, winter flocks can be found throughout the county although at generally lower densities nearer the coast. Small numbers start to appear in early autumn and peak late in the winter. During the five HBA winters, numbers in the county varied between a maximum of approximately 2,200 in 2007/08 and a minimum of 230 in 2011/12. The largest flocks are usually found in winter arable crops and game strips, with high numbers recorded in some years. During the HBA period these included 1,000 at Cheesefoot Head on December 31st 2007/January 1st 2008 and at least that number at Butser Hill on January 15th 2011. Flocks in deciduous woodland tend to be smaller, the highest during the HBA period

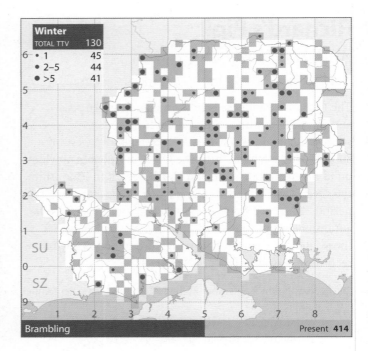

Winter
TOTAL TTV 130

● 1	45
● 2–5	44
● >5	41

Brambling — Present **414**

being 250 on November 12th 2009 in the New Forest at Mark Ash Wood.

In cold winters there is some coastal movement in response to lack of available food, with some birds probably moving to the Continent (*Migration Atlas*). Later in the winter, as natural food stocks are depleted, Bramblings are increasingly being attracted to food put down in gardens. Over the period 1996–2011 more than 4,800 have been ringed in a garden at the Straight Mile in Romsey, where black sunflower seeds provided on the ground have attracted flocks of 100 in February. A total of 5,408 have been ringed in Hampshire over the 1972–2012 period (*HBR 2012*). Recoveries have shown that Hampshire birds mainly originate from Norway.

Nigel Jones

Sponsored by Simon Woolley & Julia Casson

Brambling, Blashford Lakes, April 2011 – *Martin Bennett* (both images)

Chaffinch

Fringilla coelebs

An abundant resident, passage migrant and winter visitor

The Chaffinch is one of our commonest and most familiar birds. It is widespread in Hampshire, occurring in just about every habitat containing trees and bushes, including woodland (both coniferous and broadleaved), farmland hedgerows, scrub, heathland, parkland and gardens in towns and villages. The highest breeding densities are found in broadleaved woodland. In habitats such as hedgerows and gardens, densities are lower and depend on the number of trees and shrubs in the immediate area. It occurs at lower densities in open arable habitats where there is less suitable habitat and where agricultural intensification has had such an adverse effect on many other seed-eating birds.

The Chaffinch is successful not only because of the wide variety of habitats that it can occupy but also because it has a varied diet. It mostly feeds on seeds collected from the ground. In woods, this will be the seeds of trees and shrubs and on farmland the various crop plants such as cereals and brassicas. They do not have a specialised bill shape that some other finch species have and, as a result, are able to feed on a wider variety of seeds (Newton 1972).

Nationally, the population has been growing steadily since the early 1970s, apart from a period of slight decline during the early 1990s and again from 2005 (*BirdTrends*). This latter dip may have been caused by the severe outbreak of trichomonosis that occurred around that time (see Greenfinch, *page 404*)). The long term trend however, is upward with Chaffinch numbers increasing both at national and county level. In Hampshire, during both the 1986–91 Atlas and the HBA, they were found breeding in almost every tetrad in the county. Although they were located in slightly less tetrads during the HBA, the few losses occurred mainly in coastal tetrads where a large proportion of the land area is comprised of saltmarsh and mudflats.

British Chaffinches are thought to be sedentary with 90% moving no more than 5 km from their natal site (*Migration Atlas*). In winter the population roughly doubles as immigrants arrive from Fennoscandia. It is not surprising therefore, that the species often features prominently in autumn migration watches, both on the coast and at inland sites. British Chaffinches tend to winter in small groups in woods or hedgerows in contrast to Continental immigrants which tend to form larger feeding flocks and communal roosts.

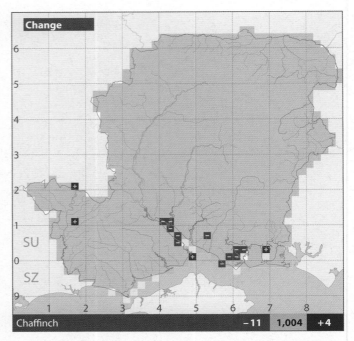

Chaffinch, Keyhaven, April 2011 – *Steve Bassett*

During the HBA winter survey, Chaffinches were again recorded in almost all tetrads. Numbers were high with indicative counts of 500 at Butser Hill on November 7th 2007, 500 at Hinton Admiral on December 11th 2007 and 750 at Mark Ash Wood on February 12th 2012. Many other localities recorded flocks of up to 300. The largest numbers were found in wooded and agricultural districts, such as across the high chalk and New Forest. In more urban areas, such as the coastal belt between Southampton and Portsmouth, numbers were lower.

Dave Unsworth

Sponsored by Julia Crossley

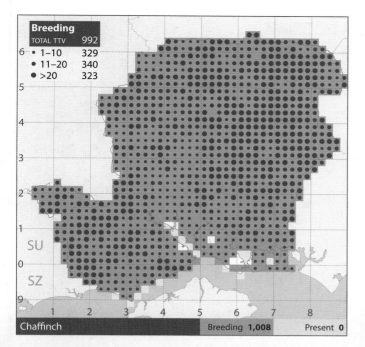

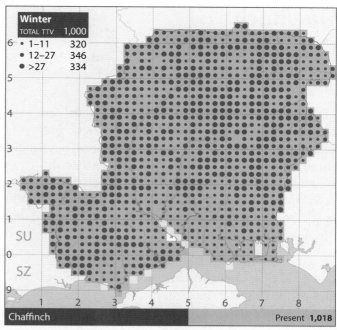

Chaffinch — Breeding **1,008** — Present **0**

Chaffinch — Present **1,018**

Chaffinch, New Forest, January 2013 – *Martin Bennett*

Hawfinch

Coccothraustes coccothraustes

A moderately common resident in the New Forest but thinly distributed elsewhere

The Hawfinch is distributed across the temperate and Mediterranean regions of the Western Palearctic and central Asia. Within the UK it has a widespread but rapidly shrinking range having been lost from many British counties over the last decade. The New Forest has recently been identified as a nationally important stronghold for the species in the UK together with the Forest of Dean and the Meirionnydd area of mid-Wales.

Hawfinch is semi-colonial with several pairs often nesting in close proximity in small, loosely associated groups. In Hampshire it breeds primarily in ancient deciduous woodland with a predominance of Beech and oak interspersed with Holly and Yew. The core of the population is found in the New Forest. A small population also exists on the chalk downland of north-west Hampshire where the species is reliant on a patchwork of Yew plantations that intersect the area. Small numbers are also known to occur at one or two locations in mid-Hampshire with fledged young reported from the East Tisted area during the HBA period. The species is undoubtedly under-recorded and could potentially be present wherever suitable habitat occurs. Hawfinches can start pair-bonding from as early as mid-February and, during the period up to late April, can be quite vocal and conspicuous. Once settled on the nest, however, they become very quiet and elusive. Post-breeding they complete a full body moult and remain very unobtrusive and difficult to locate even where reasonable numbers occur. Winter roosts and associated feeding flocks build from September onwards, reaching a peak in October.

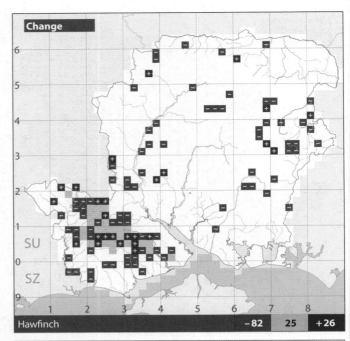

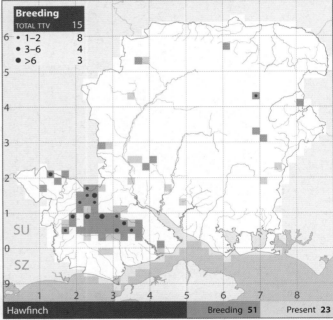

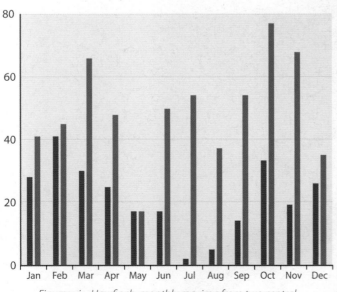

Figure xxi – Hawfinch: monthly maxima from two central New Forest roosts.

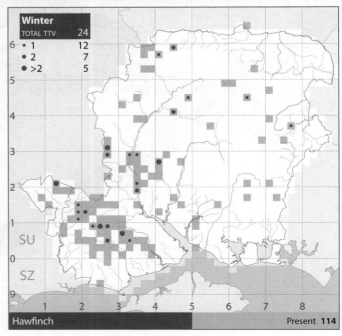

Owing to their timid nature and unobtrusive behaviour, Hawfinches are difficult to survey. On-going fieldwork that commenced in October 2011 has identified thirteen communal roost sites across the New Forest (as at December 2013), two of which were monitored weekly throughout 2012 and 2013 (see *Figure xxi*).

The breeding distribution maps show the importance of the New Forest for Hawfinch within Hampshire and reflects the national trend of the species withdrawing from the wider countryside into local strongholds. At the time of the 1986–91 Atlas, the county population was estimated at 275–500 pairs of which 150–250 pairs were within the New Forest. Current surveying of the New Forest has given an estimated population of 250 pairs. Combining this with HBA data indicates a total population of up to 300 pairs across Hampshire as a whole.

The most recent assessment puts the UK population at 500–1,000 pairs (Clements 2013) substantially below the 3,000–6,500 estimate given in the *1988–91 Atlas*. On this basis, Hampshire currently supports between 30% and 60% of the UK's Hawfinches and, even if the national total is revised upwards, it's clear that the county holds a large proportion of the population.

The recent Hawfinch roost survey has shown that the roost sites are used year-round with peaks in spring and autumn. Traditional thinking was that the New Forest received migrants through the winter months thus boosting the winter population. However, ongoing survey work suggests that the population may be largely sedentary with some birds dispersing through the winter, perhaps in leaner years. This is supported by observations of regular wintering birds appearing in non-breeding locations such as Romsey town centre, Testwood Lakes and Lakeside Country Park, Eastleigh. There is no doubt that the UK receives migrant Hawfinches as has been proven in the Forest of Dean with two Scandinavian birds being controlled in recent years. In most years small numbers are recorded at Hampshire coastal watch points, further suggesting that migrants penetrate into the county though the numbers are likely to be variable depending on the success of the seed crop farther afield.

Marcus Ward

Sponsored by Neil Lukes

Hawfinch, New Forest, March 2013 – *Martin Bennett*

Bullfinch

Pyrrhula pyrrhula

A common resident

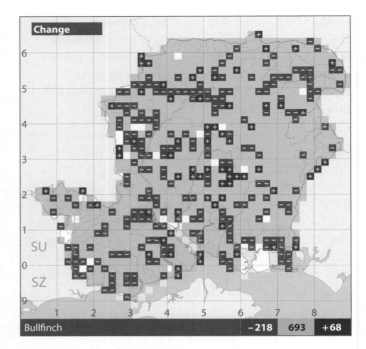

Despite the male's striking plumage, the Bullfinch is a fairly shy and retiring bird, most often encountered in pairs in areas where dense scrub is dominant, or in deciduous woodland. Its short, plaintive call is often the first indication of its presence and the subsequent encounter is frequently brief, as the pair disappears into deeper cover. Owing to its retiring nature, the species is likely to have been overlooked in some tetrads. However, it could not be described as abundant in Hampshire and, as the HBA breeding map shows, it is absent from some parts of the county including the centres of the largest conurbations and open countryside where dense scrub or woodland cover is limited.

Nationally, there was a steep fall in Bullfinch numbers from the mid-1970s through to the mid-1980s when the rate of decline eased. Since about 2000, there has been evidence of a recovery in some parts of the country with increases in northern and western Britain. However, the downward trend has continued and has been most pronounced in south-east England where *BBS* results show a 34% decrease between 1995 and 2012. The reason for the decline is unclear but, in common with many other farmland birds, has been linked to agricultural intensification. Other factors may include a reduction in feeding and nesting

opportunities brought about by changes in woodland management and also the impact of predation by a growing Sparrowhawk population (*BirdTrends*).

Against this background, there has clearly been a reduction in the range of Bullfinches in Hampshire since the 1986–91 Atlas when breeding was considered likely in 911 tetrads. During the HBA, the range has contracted to 761 tetrads – a decline of 16% over an approximate 20-year period. This reduction is thought to be genuine, rather than a result of

Bullfinch, New Forest, October 2012 – *Martin Bennett*

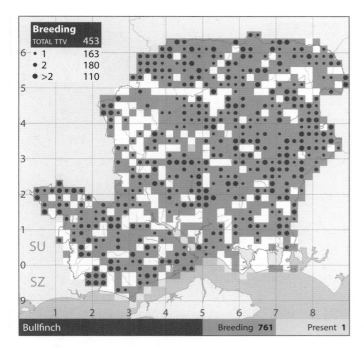

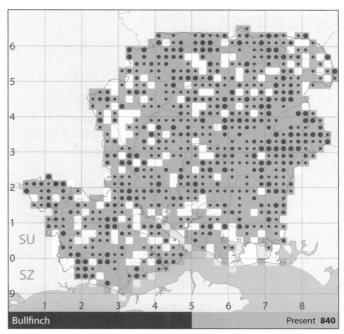

Breeding	
TOTAL TTV	453
• 1	163
• 2	180
● >2	110

Bullfinch — Breeding **761** Present **1**

Bullfinch — Present **840**

reduced observer effort during HBA fieldwork. Losses have occurred across most parts of the county. Likewise, those tetrads representing apparent range expansion are widely spread. Possibly, Bullfinches are sensitive to slight changes in habitat conditions, such as an increase or decrease in scrub cover, or the maturation of woodland, which has led to local changes in distribution.

The Bullfinch is essentially a sedentary species although ringing data and autumn migration watches indicate that some limited movement into and through the county does take place. The HBA breeding and winter distribution maps are similar but with evidence of a range expansion outside the breeding season. In winter, Bullfinches become more widespread, for example by visiting gardens where they are not recorded in summer. Flocks of ten or more are now quite unusual in the county and during the HBA, indicative counts (not necessarily of flocks) included the following: 16, Anton Lakes November 25th 2007; 16, Stockbridge January 26th 2008; 13, Itchen Valley Country Park December 14th 2008; 12, Old Winchester Hill February 14th 2009 and 24 at Dibden Bay on December 7th 2009.

Dave Unsworth

Sponsored by Graham Kesby

Common Rosefinch

Erythrina erythrina

One record prior to 2007–12

The Common Rosefinch breeds across much of northern Asia and parts of eastern and central Europe and migrates to winter on the Indian subcontinent and in south-east Asia. It occurs in the UK mainly as a scarce migrant but does breed irregularly and in very small numbers. Prior to the HBA period there had been only one record in Hampshire – a male at Titchfield Haven on August 13th 1913. On June 1st 2009, there was a second record of a singing male at Godshill Ridge in the New Forest. The former record was reviewed in 2009, along with a number of other Category B species; it was concluded that it should remain on the Hampshire list (Combridge & Clark 2010).

Dave Unsworth

Common Rosefinch, Shetland – *Hugh Harrop*

Greenfinch
Chloris chloris
A numerous resident, passage migrant and winter visitor

The Greenfinch has a delightful 'butterfly' display flight which aids easy detection during the breeding season. It is common and widespread throughout Hampshire, being found in a wide variety of habitats including villages and towns with spacious gardens, parkland and churchyards where it can find its preferred food sources. It also occurs on farmland, particularly in areas of scrub and along hedgerows, on heathland and the edges of broadleaved woodland. The species has a varied diet including weed seeds and the fruits of various bushes, showing a preference for larger seeds such as rose-hips and cereal grain, but will also eat invertebrates especially when feeding nestlings. Greenfinch numbers and survival rates have not, therefore, been affected by agricultural intensification to the same extent as those of other granivorous passerines.

The breeding distribution of the Greenfinch recorded by the HBA was very similar to that found in the 1986–91 Atlas, with breeding considered likely in close to 100% of Hampshire tetrads. However, this apparently stable situation masks a serious population decline, which has impacted on the species nationally. Greenfinch abundance showed a sustained increase from the mid-1980s through to 2006 but this was followed by a sharp decline (*BirdTrends*). This change of fortune is believed to have taken place because Greenfinch populations have been affected by the disease trichomonosis, caused by the protozoan parasite *Trichomonas gallinae*. The disease first came to prominence in the summer of 2005 when it was recorded in a number of garden species but most notably in the Greenfinch. The impact, at national level, is most clearly illustrated by results from the BTO Garden BirdWatch Survey. In 2005, Greenfinches were recorded in 74% of gardens but by 2011 this had dropped to 53% (Garden BirdWatch 2013). Over the same period, in Hampshire, the corresponding fall was smaller, from 96% to 91% of gardens and, based on the HBA results, their range has not been affected. Nevertheless, sensible hygiene precautions around garden bird feeding stations, such as regularly cleaning and disinfesting feeders and bird tables, are recommended.

The few tetrads in Hampshire where the Greenfinch was not recorded in the breeding season included parts of the New Forest and areas of the high chalk across the centre of the county. Their absence from parts of the New Forest can probably be explained by a lack of suitable feeding opportunities in the ancient and ornamental woodland and open heathland. This is a consequence of the limited shrub layer and poor ground flora resulting from grazing by livestock (Glue 1973, Irvine 1977).

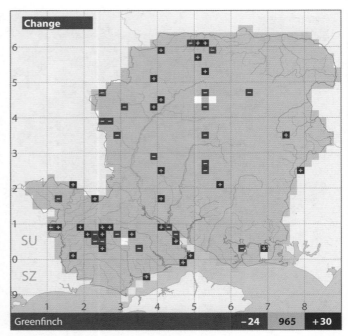

Change | Greenfinch | −24 | 965 | +30

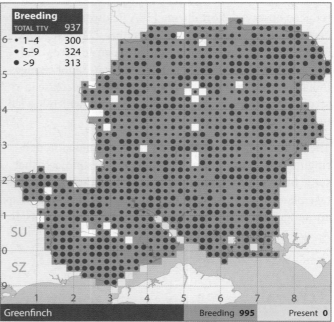

Breeding
TOTAL TTV 937
- 1–4   300
- 5–9   324
- >9   313

Greenfinch | Breeding 995 | Present 0

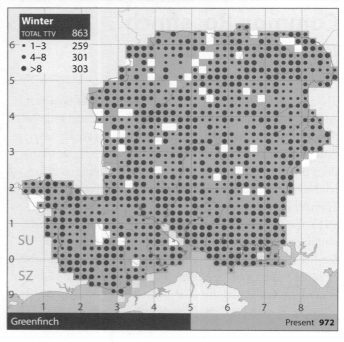

Winter
TOTAL TTV 863
- 1–3   259
- 4–8   301
- >8   303

Greenfinch | Present 972

In winter, the range is only marginally smaller than during the breeding season, with Greenfinches being recorded in 95% of tetrads. This may simply reflect a slightly lower detection rate when the birds are not singing. During the HBA period, the largest winter flock was of 300 at Walworth Trading Estate, Andover on January 10th 2009, with counts of 200 being recorded at Ibsley Water on January 16th 2010, Pennington Marsh on November 19th 2010 and at Overton on January 9th 2011. Some of these counts referred to birds going to roost.

Dave Unsworth

Sponsored by Kim Hamilton

Greenfinch, Blashford Lakes, March 2014 – *Gareth Rees*

Serin

Serinus serinus

A rare visitor

The Serin is a relatively common bird in southern and central Europe and is expanding its range northward. This is reflected in a gradual increase in the number being recorded in Hampshire, although it remains a rare bird in the county. *BoH* provides details of ten records comprising 14 individuals between 1965 and 1991, including three during the 1986–91 Atlas. Since then, a further 23 occurred prior to the start of the HBA in November 2007. During the 2008–12 period, single birds were recorded as follows: Hayling Bay on May 5th 2008; Barton on Sea on October 28th 2008; Sandy Point on November 9th 2008; Burley Street on May 11th 2009 and Testwood Lakes on April 24th 2011. These records bring the county total since *BoH* to 28 (20 coastal and eight inland) by the end of 2012.

In the 21 years from 1992 to 2012 there were sightings in all but six, with between one and four records per year. Most occurred during late April and early May as would be expected of a migrant overshooting its more southerly breeding grounds. Most records came from the Barton on Sea to Normandy Marsh area (eight records) and Hayling Island (six records). Many were seen on one date only, often being identified on call in flight and as such, the Serin is a notoriously difficult bird to see in Hampshire. *Table 31* sets out the numbers recorded during 1992–2012.

Serin, Spain – *Andy Swash*

There are no breeding records for the county, although a male held territory at Bossington in the Test Valley from May 28th to June 30th 1993. Given global warming and the birds' continuing northward spread, perhaps this is a species that may colonise Hampshire in the future.

Dave Unsworth

Sponsored by Andy Johnson

Month	Jan	Feb	Mar	Apr	May	Jun	Jul	Aug	Sep	Oct	Nov	Dec
Coast	0	0	0	6	7	1	2	0	0	3	1	0
Inland	0	1	0	3	2	1	0	0	0	0	0	1

Table 31 – Serin: Hampshire records by month of occurrence.

Linnet

Linaria cannabina

Present throughout the year as a numerous breeder and passage migrant but with numbers reduced during the winter

Linnets are widespread in Hampshire, found in open countryside, such as downland and heathland, where scrub provides suitable nest sites, or along farmland hedgerows. They can also be conspicuous in dry coastal scrub. However, this is another farmland species which has undergone a long term population decline. In England, Linnet numbers fell by around 75% between 1965 and the late 1980s (*BirdTrends*). Subsequently, the national population stabilised at a much lower level although local declines continued. *BBS* results for south-east England show a 43% drop between 1995 and 2012. The species is red-listed as a bird of conservation concern.

The main reason for the fall in population is thought to be the lower breeding success resulting from reduced availability of food on arable farmland. This has stemmed from agricultural intensification, particularly the increasing use of herbicides for weed control. This leads to a marked reduction in the numbers of several food plants that traditionally featured in the diet of nestlings (*BirdTrends*; Moorcroft *et al.* 2006). A more catastrophic decline was probably averted by the increasing availability of Oil-seed Rape, a food source that Linnets are able to utilize more effectively than most other farmland species.

In Hampshire, based on the 1986–91 Atlas data, breeding was considered likely in 827 (80%) of Hampshire tetrads. During the HBA, the corresponding number was 652 tetrads – a range decrease of 21%. As a passage migrant, Linnets can be encountered in the early summer at locations where they do not breed, so the determination of likely breeding is subject to some uncertainty. However, the direction and scale of change should be approximately correct.

The Linnet is clearly still a common breeding bird in many parts of the county, although the distribution is patchy in places. Favoured areas include the New Forest, Thames Basin and Wealden Heaths, the coastal fringe and the main chalk belt across the county. It is interesting to note that, as with the Yellowhammer, there is a gap in the species' breeding range around Southampton. This hole appears to have expanded since the 1986–91 Atlas, although not to the same extent as it has with the Yellowhammer.

Following an autumn exodus by part of the population, mainly to western France and Spain, the Linnet becomes

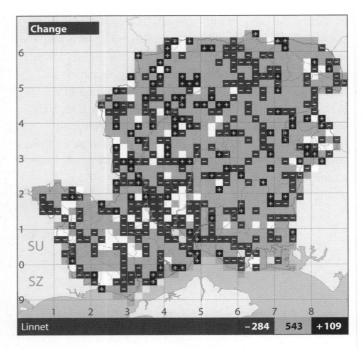

a scarcer bird in Hampshire. Although the distribution remains similar, the HBA recorded Linnets in only 49% of tetrads in winter compared with 75% in summer (although this includes migrants). However, good numbers can still be found in the county and large flocks can be attracted to locations where suitable feeding opportunities exist, such as stubble left through the winter, which provides an abundance of seeds and naturally regenerating weeds. This is reflected in two of the largest flocks recorded during the HBA: 1,200 at Chilling on December 30th 2007 decreasing to 1,000 on January 12th 2008 (with the flock finally dispersing in April) and another large count of 1,500 at South Warnborough on December 20th/21st 2009. Other notable counts included 400 at Houghton on December 26th 2007, 300 at Mapledurwell on January 13th 2009, 400 at Hurstbourne Tarrant on February 3rd 2009 and 300 at Middle Wallop on February 19th 2011. Such large flocks are invariably found during spells of severe weather.

With the exception of the Chilling flock, all these locations are from more northerly districts in the county. Farther south, Linnets are less common in winter. For example in the New Forest they are mainly confined to the western margins and coastal fringe. They are largely absent around Southampton and scarce in the Meon Valley and Portsmouth areas.

Dave Unsworth

Sponsored by Betty Hansell

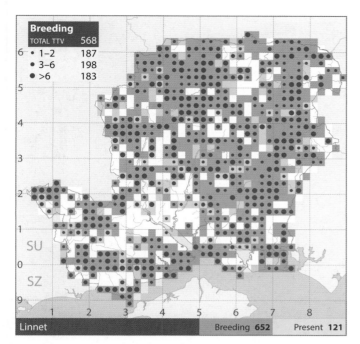

Breeding
TOTAL TTV 568
• 1–2 187
• 3–6 198
• >6 183

Linnet | Breeding **652** | Present **121**

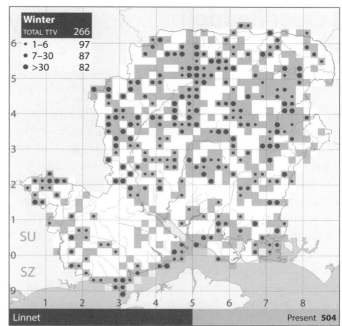

Winter
TOTAL TTV 266
• 1–6 97
• 7–30 87
• >30 82

Linnet | Present **504**

Linnet, New Forest, July 2010 – *Martin Bennett*

Lesser Redpoll
Acanthis cabaret

A moderately common passage migrant and winter visitor.
Formerly a locally common breeder that last bred in 2006

Although the taxonomy of the redpolls remains tentative, the Lesser Redpoll was restored to full species status by the BOU in 2001 when it was split from Common (previously known as Mealy) Redpoll *A. flammea* (Knox *et al.* 2001). The species was widespread as a breeding bird in lowland Britain in the 1970s but, after a period of severe decline, has withdrawn completely from large areas of eastern England. The contraction in range has been most striking in the south-east (including Hampshire) and East Anglia (*Bird Atlas 2007–11*). In contrast, numbers are increasing in Wales, western Scotland and in particular, throughout Ireland. It is thought that in some areas new forestry plantations have provided suitable habitat, whereas in others the disappearance of birch scrub as a result of woodland succession in maturing forests may have had a detrimental effect.

In Hampshire, the Lesser Redpoll was first confirmed breeding in the New Forest in 1956. Numbers remained low until about the mid-1970s when there was a rapid expansion. By 1987 there were at least 50 pairs at 20 sites in the Forest but the 1986–91 Atlas showed that breeding was confirmed or probable in about 50 tetrads (in or close to the Forest) (*BoH*) suggesting that the population could have been as high as 150–250 pairs. At around this time, a decline commenced and numbers have not returned to the levels recorded in the mid-1980s since then.

During the HBA period, Lesser Redpolls were recorded during the breeding season in around 40 tetrads in or close to the New Forest but no confirmation of breeding was obtained. Breeding was last confirmed in 2006 when a pair was seen on several occasions with young at Burley. There have been occasional sightings of juveniles subsequently, although such birds may have originated elsewhere. The strongest evidence of breeding during the 2008–12 period included five singing males recorded in a 46 sq. km block of the central New Forest in May/June 2009 and a juvenile, which may have been of local origin, seen at Blashford Lakes on July 12th of that year.

The picture is uncertain because, based on normal Atlas survey methods, it is easy to overestimate probable breeding numbers. Wintering and migrant birds can remain well into the breeding season, often singing and displaying in suitable breeding habitat. For this reason, the HBA breeding and change maps have been based on confirmed breeding records only. This may present a pessimistic view of the species' status but even if Lesser Redpoll still nests in the Forest, based on current trends, it will be lost as a breeding species in the near future. For now, it is believed that the species may just about be

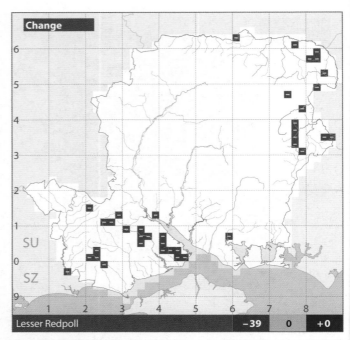

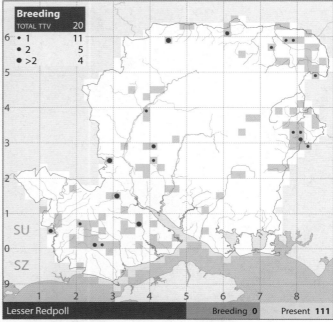

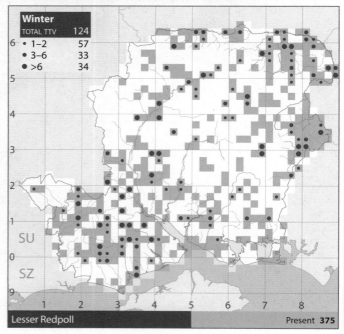

maintaining a tenuous presence as a breeding species in the Burley area (M. Ward *pers. comm.*).

Away from the New Forest, the only other area where Lesser Redpolls have nested regularly in the county is in the north-east on the Thames Basin and Wealden Heaths. For example, 35 pairs or singing males were recorded at seven sites in 1977, with notable colonies at Bourley & Long Valley, Longmoor Inclosure and Ludshott Common. The 1986–91 Atlas confirmed breeding in 16 tetrads in the area and it was considered that overall, there were between 50 and 100 pairs in the north-east during the Atlas period. In contrast, during the HBA, although Lesser Redpolls were found during the breeding season in around 40 tetrads, there was only one registration of probable breeding at Longmoor Inclosure (of two birds visiting a probable nest site on June 15th 2011).

Other records during May and June of possible breeding (away from the New Forest) came from Ampfield, Andover Down, Bourley & Long Valley, Chilbolton, Dur Hill Down, Harestock, Longparish, Old Winchester Hill, Ranvilles Lane (Fareham), Tumulus Wood and Woodley Grange Meadows. However, several or all of these may have been passage birds.

In winter, Lesser Redpolls are more widespread; during the HBA they were recorded in 36% of tetrads. The distribution to some extent reflects that in summer but with the species more widespread in the New Forest and north-east.

As with Siskins, Lesser Redpolls are thinly spread across the chalk in the middle of the county. Typically, they occur where birch trees can provide them with their preferred food source. They are found in wooded districts, areas of heathland, along the main river valleys and around gravel pits, often in association with Siskins. In general, the Lesser Redpoll is a scarcer bird than the Siskin. During the HBA, the largest flocks were found in the north-east of the county and it was noticeable that the largest numbers were recorded during the 2010/11 winter. Indicative high counts at this time included 500 at Baddesley Common on November 14th 2010; 500 at Castle Bottom, Eversley on November 26th 2010; 150 at Broxhead Common on February 20th 2011; 120 at Woolmer Pond on November 5th 2010 and 120 at Woolmer Forest on January 24th 2011. Such counts are atypical however, the species usually occurring in much smaller numbers with flocks of up to 30 being normal.

Lesser Redpolls are also readily attracted to garden feeders. Ringing in one garden at the Straight Mile, Romsey demonstrates the constant turnover of different birds though the winter. For example, in 2008 a total of 52 was ringed in November, followed by a further 33 different individuals during December.

Dave Unsworth

Sponsored by Tony Tindale

Lesser Redpoll, Blashford Lakes, April 2009 – *Martin Bennett*

Common Redpoll

Acanthis flammea

A very scarce winter visitor and passage migrant

As described for the previous species, the Redpoll complex was split into two species (Common and Lesser Redpoll) by the BOU in 2001 (Knox *et al.* 2001). At least two subspecies of Common Redpoll have been recognised in Britain and Ireland – the Mealy Redpoll (nominate *flammea*) and the Greenland Redpoll (*rostrata*). There is doubt whether birds from Iceland ('*islandica*') represent a valid separate race and it is currently excluded from the British list.

Common Redpolls breed across the boreal zone of Eurasia and North America with small numbers breeding in northern Scotland. They are prone to irruptive movements with autumn influxes occasionally reaching Britain, particularly Scotland and the east coast of England. Many of these birds then move south or west where they are recorded in central southern England, often amongst flocks of Lesser Redpolls.

At the time of the 1986-91 Atlas, the two species had not been split. Little information was provided in *BoH*, other than to say that the Mealy Redpoll was recorded in Hampshire occasionally, but was doubtless overlooked. The status of the species in recent years has become much clearer despite some birds still presenting an identification challenge. During the HBA survey, there were a number of sightings in the county although some records were submitted with insufficient detail to confirm identity. Approximate monthly totals for the five HBA winters, based on accepted records, are given in *Table 32*.

The accompanying winter map shows a thin scatter of records across the county with clusters in the north-east and Romsey areas. These are due, in part, to birds being identified thanks to ringing activities (see below).

Common Redpolls also occur on migration, sometimes in greater numbers than during the winter. Extreme dates during the 2007-12 period were April 19th 2009 at Straight

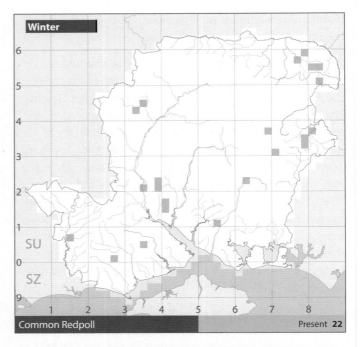

Winter	Nov	Dec	Jan	Feb
2007/08	0	0	3	0
2008/09	2	2	1	1
2009/10	0	0	1	1
2010/11	8	5	2	3
2011/12	0	0	3	0
Totals	**10**	**9**	**10**	**5**

Table 32 – Common Redpoll: monthly totals during the five HBA winters.

Mile, Romsey, and October 13th 2012 at Embley Wood. Over the period, 22 were caught by ringers. This included 15 ringed in one garden at Straight Mile, Romsey. Seven were ringed at this site between February 27th and April 19th 2009, two of which showed characteristics of the race *rostrata/islandica*. The bird feeders at Blashford Lakes were the best site in the county for those wishing to see Common Redpoll alongside its much more numerous relative. During the 2007-12 period, at least 11 were recorded there including a Greenland Redpoll which was present from March 25th to April 13th 2009.

Dave Unsworth

Common Redpoll,
Blashford Lakes, January 2014
– *Martin Bennett*

Twite

Linaria flavirostris

A very scarce winter visitor and passage migrant

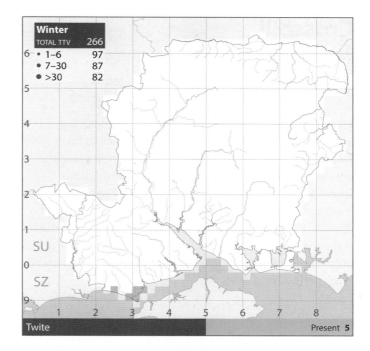

BoH describes the Twite as a scarce winter visitor and passage migrant which declined during the 1980s. That decline has continued and today the species is very scarce in Hampshire. Traditionally, coastal localities such as Farlington Marshes, Eling Great Marsh, Southampton Docks, Dibden Bay, Fawley/Calshot, and Normandy/Pennington once all held sizeable flocks in winter (*BoH*). Sadly though, such numbers no longer occur and in occasional years the species is not recorded at all in the county.

During the HBA, as shown on the accompanying map, wintering Twites were confined to the west Solent with the following being recorded: one in the Sturt Pond/Keyhaven area on several dates between December 13th 2007 and February 15th 2008; one at Pennington from November 22nd to 24th 2008; one at Keyhaven from January 28th to February 24th 2009; five on the shingle bank between Sturt Pond and Cut Bridge on December 27th 2009 and one west at Barton on Sea on November 7th 2010 (which might be better considered a passage migrant).

Other records of single birds indicative of passage during 2007–12 came from: Farlington Marshes on March 18th 2009; Iley Point on October 20th 2010; flying west at Browndown on October 21st 2010; and Hayling Seafront and Sandy Point on October 20th/21st 2011. Although strictly these sightings fall outside the Atlas period, they are given here to provide a complete picture of the occurrence of the species during the years of the survey.

Nationally, there has been a 19% decline in the breeding range since publication of the *1968–72 Atlas* (based on the number of occupied 10 km squares). Coincidentally, *Bird Atlas 2007–11* indicates a 19% increase in the winter population since the *1981–84 Winter Atlas* (mainly due to an increase in northern Britain). The nearest breeding population to Hampshire is in the Pennines, where

numbers have declined during this time; furthermore the numbers recorded wintering in South Wales, central southern England and the south-east have all shown notable declines since the first Winter Atlas was published (*Bird Atlas 2007–11*).

Twites rely on an abundant supply of seeds for feeding throughout the year and are therefore susceptible to changes in agricultural practices that reduce the availability of this food source. Breeding population declines have been attributed to the loss of species-rich hay meadows through conversion to pasture and silage, early cutting of silage, increased stocking levels and poor burning practices on heather moorlands (Langston *et al.* 2006).

Given the pressure on both breeding success and winter survival, it seems likely that the Twite will remain a very scarce bird in the county.

Dave Unsworth

Sponsored by Bart Ives

Twite, Farlington Marshes, March 2009 – *Peter Drury*

Crossbill

Loxia curvirostra

A scarce resident whose numbers are occasionally augmented by irruptions in late summer or autumn

Hampshire is unusual in southern England in having a sizeable breeding population of this distinctive finch resident in the county. Numbers can vary from year to year as the local population is swelled by immigrants from the boreal forests of Scandinavia and farther east. The reason for such movements is the failure of the cone crop particularly that of Norway Spruce *Picea abies*, which is the main food source of this species. Nationally, Crossbill populations were considered to be at a high level during the HBA period (*Bird Atlas 2007–11*).

Crossbills can breed between November and April (*Migration Atlas*) and therefore, by the start of what would be the normal breeding season for most other species, mobile family parties may already be on the wing. This should be borne in mind when considering the breeding and winter maps presented here.

The 1986–91 Hampshire Atlas recorded Crossbills present during the breeding season in 80 tetrads. For security reasons, the map published in *BoH* showed all records at the same level. The majority were recorded in the New Forest and from heathland and conifer plantations in the north-east, with a scatter of sightings from elsewhere. During the HBA, they were found in 214 tetrads with breeding considered likely in 56. Again, the majority were found in the New Forest and the north-east. The change map shows range expansion of ten tetrads where breeding was considered likely.

Crossbills are currently relatively common and widespread in the New Forest and can be found in many areas where there are extensive stands of pine or spruce. Typical sites include the Rhinefield and Bolderwood areas and several of the inclosures to the north of the A31. Away from the Forest, the HBA recorded Crossbills in a number of traditional localities in the north-east including Bourley & Long Valley, Bramshill Plantation, Holt Pound Inclosure, Longmoor Inclosure and Woolmer Forest. However, numbers at these localities were lower and less regular than those recorded in the New Forest.

In view of the Crossbill's specialised diet, it is not surprising that their winter distribution in Hampshire is very similar to that found during the breeding season with only minor differences between the numbers of tetrads occupied in the two seasons. Nevertheless, parties of Crossbills are recorded on the move during the summer and autumn in variable numbers every year. The size and extent of movement is linked to the size of the population and the availability of the food supply. When populations are high and the food supply is low, greater numbers will be recorded on the

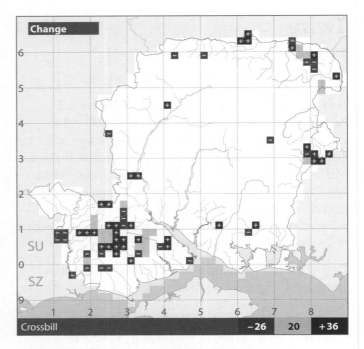

Crossbill   −26   20   +36

Crossbill, New Forest, January 2012 – *Martin Bennett*

move and this will influence the distribution and numbers recorded during the following winter. In irruption years, such movement will also include flocks of birds from abroad. The two highest winter counts recorded during the HBA were of 200 at Millyford Bridge on February 18th 2010 and 110 at the Somerley Estate on December 24th 2009, although there were numerous counts of smaller flocks of between 30 and 50 birds.

Dave Unsworth

Sponsored by Di Smith

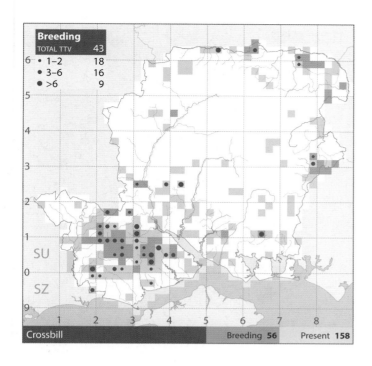

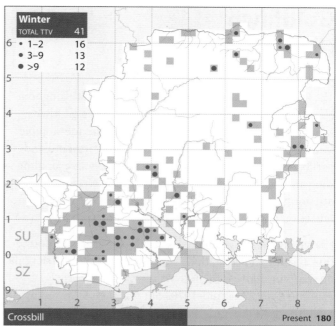

Crossbill, New Forest, November 2013 – *Martin Bennett*

Goldfinch

Carduelis carduelis

A numerous resident and passage migrant

The Goldfinch is a common and familiar bird throughout Hampshire. It can be encountered in villages and towns where waste ground and roadside verges provide suitable feeding opportunities, as well as on mixed farmland and parkland in the wider countryside. Its distinctive jangling song and flight call means that it is easily detected. The distribution presented here is considered to be an accurate reflection of the species' current range in the county.

Historically, the Goldfinch was a popular cage bird and this meant that populations were reduced until restrictions on trapping allowed them to recover. The increase continued until the mid-1970s but was then followed by a decline until the mid-1980s. Since then, numbers have continued to increase and the species is not of conservation concern. The population reduction and subsequent increase is thought to have taken place due to changes in annual survival rates caused by agricultural intensification and a reduction in weed seeds, followed by the increased use of other food sources, such as garden feeders. However, Goldfinches prefer to feed on the seed heads of the family *Compositae*, such as thistles, teasels and ragworts. These species have not been affected by agricultural intensification to the same extent as other plant species, and this may have benefited the fortunes of the Goldfinch, compared with some other farmland birds (*Migration Atlas*).

Since the publication of the 1986–91 Atlas results in *BoH*, Goldfinches have expanded and increased in numbers in the county, the HBA breeding map indicating a range expansion of approximately 8%. This increase is in line with the national trend (*Bird Atlas 2007–11*). The HBA change map clearly shows expansion in some areas such as parts of the New Forest and the intensive cereal-growing areas across the centre of the county. Based on current trends, it is expected that this expansion and consolidation will continue.

Nationally, it is estimated that approximately 80% of British Goldfinches vacate the country during the winter, with the majority heading towards the Mediterranean, particularly to France and the Iberian Peninsular. There are several ringing recoveries confirming that birds from Hampshire also visit these areas. Additionally, Goldfinches often feature prominently during visible migration watches on the Hampshire coast between September and November. In Southern Europe, the winter food plants continue to grow so that seed supplies are continually replaced and this may assist winter survival rates and therefore support the increasing breeding population. Reduced hunting pressure may also be a factor in supporting this increase (*Migration Atlas*).

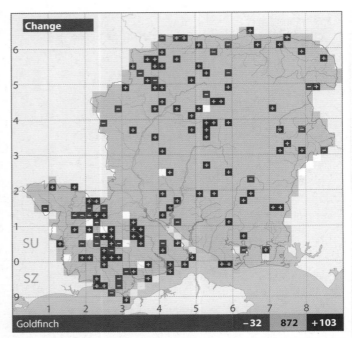

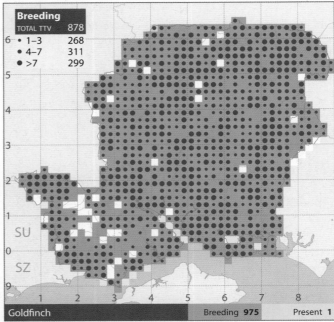

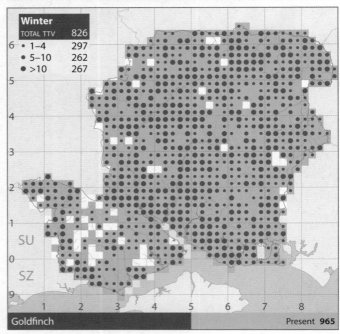

In winter, despite emigration of birds from the UK, the population of Goldfinches in Hampshire remains high. It is clearly still a widespread bird, being recorded from over 90% of all tetrads during the HBA. There is a strong association with human habitations and, where bird feeders are provided in gardens, they can be found even into the centres of larger towns and cities. Results from the BTO Garden BirdWatch indicate that, whereas Goldfinches were recorded in less than 10% of gardens in 1995, this had increased to around 50–60% in 2011 (*Bird Atlas 2007–11*). Results in Hampshire show a similar trend.

Dave Unsworth

Sponsored by Paul Matthews (of Nutbags)

Goldfinch, Pennington, October 2008 – *Martin Bennett* (both images)

Siskin

Spinus spinus

A moderately common breeder, common passage migrant and winter visitor

The Siskin is present throughout the year in Hampshire. It is restricted as a breeder mainly to the New Forest, the Thames Basin and the Wealden Heaths but is widespread as a passage migrant and winter visitor. Its preferred food source is spruce or pine seeds. Since seed production by conifers can vary significantly from year to year, this can lead to irruptive movements by the birds in the search for suitable food sources. There are many records of ringing recoveries linking the county's wintering population with breeding sites in Scotland and farther afield to Scandinavian and Baltic countries (*BoH*). The longest movement of a Siskin ever recorded in Hampshire was of a bird ringed in Leningrad on June 29th 1983 and controlled in Totton (2,415 km WSW) on February 12th 1984.

In the breeding season, Siskins are typically found in coniferous woodland. Since around 1950, the national breeding population and range have expanded. The increase has been linked to the age-profile of coniferous forests as the amount of land covered by mature conifers doubled following post-war planting (*Bird Atlas 2007–11*). This pattern is reflected in the growth of the Hampshire population up to the time of the 1986–91 Atlas. The increase in the New Forest population, which began during the 1950s and continued into the 1960s, followed by a sudden increase during the mid-1970s was summarized in *BoH*. There was a crash in 1987 and it is thought that the population did not subsequently recover to the levels found during the early 1980s. Away from the New Forest, breeding was first confirmed at Yateley Heath Wood in 1987 with further records coming from nearby locations in the Thames Basin such as Bramshill and Bourley & Long Valley, and in the Weald, from the Woolmer/Longmoor areas in subsequent years.

Based on the HBA results, this pattern of distribution has been maintained, although despite there being both gains and losses, it appears that, overall, the breeding range has contracted somewhat since the time of the 1986–91 Atlas. It should be borne in mind, however, that this species can be found singing and displaying on its winter quarters well into spring (which accounts for the large number of 'presence' records shown on the breeding map). This makes determination of likely breeding uncertain so too much weight should not be given to changes between Atlases. There may also have been changes in their distribution as a result of habitat changes as conifer plantations have matured or been harvested during the 20 years between the two Atlas periods.

In winter, Siskins occur more widely. At this season, Alder and birch seeds also feature in the diet, hence their presence

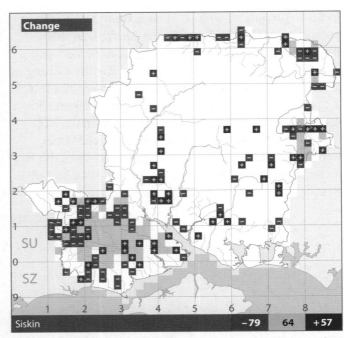

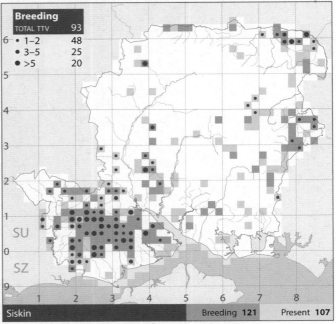

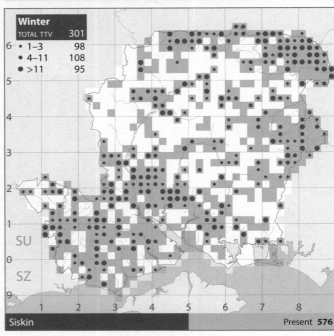

along the main river valleys and around gravel pits where these food sources are commonly found. Understandably, they are thinly spread across much of the centre of the county on the high chalk where there is less suitable habitat but, in the north and north-east, the presence of many gravel pits ensures that the Siskin is widespread and sometimes numerous at preferred locations. Indicative counts during the HBA included 600 at Fleet Pond on December 28th 2007, 740 in the Blackwater Valley between Eversley and Yateley Gravel Pits on February 18th 2011 and 500 at Darby Green on November 20th 2011. Numbers tend to be smaller elsewhere in the county with localities such as Blashford Lakes and Lakeside Country Park both attracting flocks of up to 250 in winter.

Siskins are also attracted to garden bird feeders in winter and can then be found in more urban locations where they may remain into the spring. Ringing has shown that there is a turnover of birds through individual gardens as the winter progresses. For example, in January, February and March 2008, totals of 94, 383 and 33 respectively were ringed at the Straight Mile, Romsey. Likewise, in a Fleet garden in February and March 2009, totals of 57 and 62 were ringed.

Dave Unsworth

Sponsored by Annette Clayson

Siskin, New Forest, January 2014 – *Martin Bennett* (both images)

Snow Bunting

Plectrophenax nivalis

A very scarce autumn passage migrant and winter visitor

Snow Buntings have the most northerly (circumpolar) breeding distribution of any passerine. Their confiding nature often allows the observer a close approach as the birds search for seeds amongst short vegetation habitually close to the shoreline. In flight, the snowy white flash in the wings is a reminder of their natal high-Arctic breeding grounds and the distinctive "tu tu" call also immediately grabs the observer's attention. As such, an encounter with a Snow Bunting can be the highlight of a chilly winter's day on the Hampshire coast.

Two races occur in Britain in winter: the nominate *nivalis*, which breeds from Alaska east to north-west Russia and the darker and more sedentary Icelandic race *insulae*. Most recoveries of birds ringed in Britain have been in Iceland, whereas the number of recoveries to or from Scandinavia or the Low Countries are far fewer suggesting that most Snow Buntings wintering in this country have an Icelandic origin, although some passing through Iceland from Greenland cannot be ruled out (*Migration Atlas*).

The number of records reported during the HBA shows that the Snow Bunting continues to be a scarce bird in the county. As the map indicates, this is essentially a coastal bird with records from several sites, but particularly from Barton on Sea to Hurst Beach and the coast farther east towards Needs Ore. Very few were recorded close to the shores of Southampton Water and there was only one report from Farlington Marshes. Traditionally, both of these localities have attracted Snow Buntings relatively frequently. On Hayling Island, all records came from Sandy Point or nearby sites. Indeed, the highest count during the HBA was of a group of four birds which remained near the Lifeboat Station at Sandy Point from February 2nd-25th 2012, with three remaining until March 11th. Inland records are rare. During the HBA

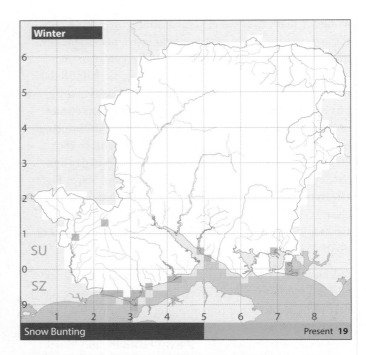

Month	Sep	Oct	Nov	Dec	Jan	Feb	Mar
Coast	0	17	57	28	16	9	9
Inland	0	0	3	2	0	1	1
Total	0	17	60	30	16	10	10

Table 33 – Snow Bunting: cumulative monthly totals 1992/3–2011/12.

period, only two such reports were received – two at Ibsley Water on December 5th 2010 and one at Cadman's Pool in the New Forest from December 4th–6th 2011.

The temporal pattern of occurrence continued as described in *BoH*, with Snow Buntings occurring more frequently as late autumn migrants rather than as wintering birds. This is demonstrated by the data in *Table 33* which gives the cumulative monthly totals (including birds flying over) for the winters 1992/93–2011/12 and shows a clear November peak.

Dave Unsworth

Sponsored by Simon Colenutt (of ECOSA Ltd)

Snow Bunting, Hurst Spit, January 2011 – *Martin Bennett*

Lapland Bunting
Calcarius lapponicus
A rare autumn passage migrant and winter visitor

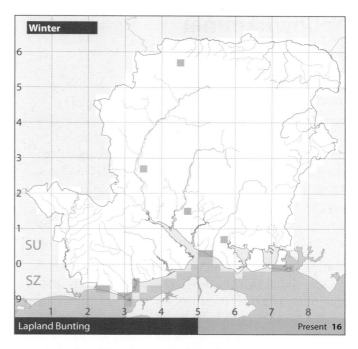

This species is generally a much rarer bird in Hampshire than its close relative the Snow Bunting. However, during the period covered by the HBA there was an exceptional influx of Lapland Buntings into Britain and Ireland in the autumn and winter of 2010/11; this resulted in far higher numbers than normal reaching Hampshire. The main causes of the influx were considered to be an unusually good breeding season in Greenland combined with weather patterns in August and September 2010 which were conducive to bringing more Lapland Buntings into the country than normal. Large numbers then remained through the winter and a substantial return migration was noted in spring 2011 (Pennington *et al.* 2012).

In Hampshire, the first was recorded on September 12th 2010 and by the end of the year, it was estimated that there were perhaps 80 birds wintering in the county. The largest numbers were recorded in the stubble fields behind Hurst Beach in the New Lane/Saltgrass Lane area where the largest single count was a minimum of 56 on November 29th 2010. Other coastal records during the winter of 2010/11 came from Barton on Sea, Milford on Sea, Keyhaven and Pennington Marshes, Brownwich, Titchfield Haven and Hayling Island.

There were also more inland records than normal as a result of this inflow with records coming from Fareham (October 31st); Michelmersh (two on November 7th); South Warnborough (one flew south on November 30th (not mapped)) and West End (December 11th). The only other inland record during the HBA period concerned one at Beacon Hill, Burghclere on November 7th 2007.

To put the 2010/11 influx into perspective, the cumulative monthly totals (including birds flying over) for the 18 winters 1992/93–2009/10 are shown in *Table 34*.

Month	Sep	Oct	Nov	Dec	Jan	Feb	Mar
Coast	2	7	7	4	4	3	3
Inland	1	3	1	1	0	0	0
Total	3	10	8	5	4	3	3

Table 34 – Lapland Bunting: cumulative monthly totals 1992/3–2009/10.

Winter	2007/08	2008/09	2009/10	2010/11	2011/12
Birds	7	1	1	80	7

Table 35 – Lapland Bunting: numbers during the five HBA winters.

During the five HBA winters, numbers were as given in *Table 35*. Although both 2007/08 and 2011/12 were above-average seasons, the size of the 2010/11 influx is clearly significant when viewed against the background of records in more 'normal' years, as indicated in the tables above.

Since the 1986–91 Atlas, there have been only two records indicative of spring passage with single birds at Keyhaven (singing) on March 27th 2004 and one, during the HBA period, at Over Wallop on April 23rd 2010.

Dave Unsworth

Lapland Bunting, Cut Bridge, January 2011 – *Martin Bennett*

Yellowhammer
Emberiza citronella
A widespread and common resident

The Yellowhammer is a bird of well-drained open countryside. This is a typical bird of the Hampshire Downs and a visit on a hot summer's day in search of orchids or butterflies is likely to be made all the more memorable by the wheezing song of the Yellowhammer as a backdrop. Nationally, Yellowhammer populations are in a long-term decline. In Britain there has been a range contraction of around 21% between the 1968–72 and 2007–11 national atlases (*Bird Atlas 2007–11*).

During the 1986–91 Hampshire Atlas the species was present and likely to be breeding in approximately 87% of the county's tetrads. There was a notable hole in its range around Southampton, including the Lower Test and Itchen Valleys, and there were gaps in the heavily wooded areas of the New Forest. It was also absent from built up areas such as Portsmouth. Throughout much of the rest of the county, Yellowhammers could still be found.

A striking feature of the HBA breeding maps is that clearly the gap in its range in the south of the county has now grown larger. The results show that the Yellowhammer was found likely to be breeding in 654 tetrads – a decrease in range of almost 27% in about 20 years. This compares with a decline in the English population of 56% between 1986 and 2011 (*BirdTrends*). The gap around Southampton has obviously expanded and the species has been lost from much of the New Forest where it previously occurred. Those birds that remain in the Forest are mainly confined to the southern fringes around Lymington and to the east of Beaulieu. Yellowhammers are also absent in a wide swathe upstream along the Test and Itchen Valleys to Romsey and Winchester. Additionally, the coastal belt between Southampton and Portsmouth (including Hayling Island) is now largely devoid of Yellowhammers. In short, the species has all but disappeared from much of the Hampshire Basin.

Elsewhere in the county, there have been obvious losses in the extreme north and east. For example, on the Thames Basin Heaths the only locality where the species is (just) surviving is Hazeley Heath. On the Wealden Heaths, there have also been significant declines and the main locality is now Longmoor Inclosure. There is also a gap in distribution around Basingstoke in SU65. It appears that, as the population declines, the species is abandoning secondary habitats such as heathland and retreating to upland agricultural areas.

The strongholds for the Yellowhammer are all on the chalk and include well-known localities such as Ashley Warren, Beacon Hill (Warnford), Butser Hill, Cheesefoot Head/ Longwood Warren, Martin Down and Old Winchester Hill amongst many others. During the HBA, there were a few tetrads (mostly on the chalk) where Yellowhammers

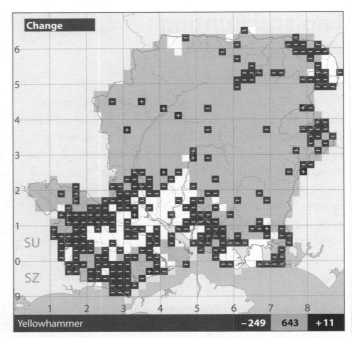

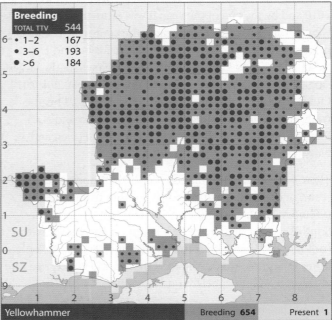

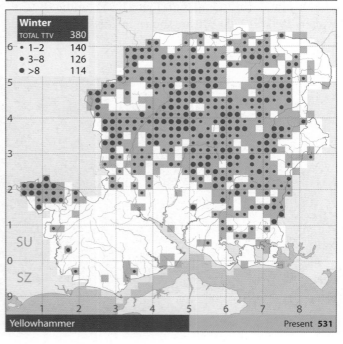

were found, having not been recorded during the 1986–91 Atlas. However, this could have been due to differences in observer coverage between the two surveys, rather than a real expansion of range.

Yellowhammers are closely associated with cereal farming where they prefer to feed on the ground. Cereal grains and other large grass seeds (e.g. *Festuca* and *Lolium*) form a significant part of their diet, particularly in winter. Declines on other types of farmland have possibly occurred because intensively managed grassland supports fewer invertebrates and weed seeds, or because dense swards reduce access to food sources (Perkins *et al.* 2000). Reductions in the availability of seed food as a result of agricultural intensification (for example, the loss of winter stubbles and a reduction in weed densities) are believed to have been a major cause of the population decline. This can be mitigated by increasing the availability of weedy stubbles or through supplementary feeding (Gillings *et al.* 2005, Siriwardena *et al.* 2007).

Urban sprawl could be an additional factor resulting in the loss of Yellowhammers from some areas, such as the coastal belt between Southampton and Portsmouth, or around Basingstoke.

The HBA winter map shows that Yellowhammers were recorded in 531 tetrads, some 19% fewer than during the breeding season. Although the birds tend to be site faithful, about 70% of adults remaining within 5 km of their breeding territories (*Winter Atlas*), they flock in winter and gather in preferred feeding locations. This may lead to their departure from certain districts at this season. The map suggests that there were fewer registrations from those areas where the breeding density is low, such as the southern fringe of the New Forest, the east and north-east and from some locations on the chalk. Yellowhammers breeding on heathland are known to leave in winter, presumably for better feeding on agricultural land.

Locations where three-figure counts (all nominally of 100) were made during the HBA winter period included Bishop's Sutton, February 2nd 2008; Chandlers Green, January 29th 2011; Cheesefoot Head, January 10th and 31st 2009; New Alresford, November 23rd 2008 and Whitchurch, January 10th 2010.

Dave Unsworth

Sponsored by Brian Sharkey

Yellowhammer, Martin Down, May 2012 – *Martin Bennett*

421

Reed Bunting
Emberiza schoeniclus
A common resident, passage migrant and winter visitor

In Hampshire, Reed Buntings are typically associated with reed beds and riverine scrub and therefore are most often encountered along the main river valleys and on coastal marshes. They also occur around lakes and gravel pits and in the New Forest and other heathland sites where they tend to be attracted to boggy areas with rank vegetation. When populations are high they can also sometimes be found in drier locations.

The majority of British Reed Buntings are sedentary although the winter population is boosted by small numbers of Continental immigrants. The population is thus largely self-contained and Reed Buntings show a high degree of breeding season site-fidelity. During the winter they do, however, spread away from riparian habitats in search of food. Outside the breeding season, Reed Buntings are largely seed-eaters and are attracted to farmland, for example where Quinoa and other seed-bearing plants are grown as conservation crops. They are also seen feeding on Purple Moor-grass on heathland and at garden feeders at this time of year. They continue to roost communally however, preferring to return to reed beds and other dense riparian scrub in the evening.

Their preference for wetland habitat is clearly reflected in the HBA breeding maps produced here, with a distribution along the Avon, Test and Itchen Valleys, and the coastal belt including Keyhaven, Needs Ore, Calshot, Lower Test Marshes, Titchfield Haven and Farlington Marshes. In the north-east of the county, Reed Buntings are associated with the network of smaller rivers and associated gravel pit complexes such as in the Blackwater Valley.

In common with many other resident seed-eating birds, there was a major reduction in the national breeding population in the 1970s. As a result, the species was red-listed but subsequently numbers have fluctuated and its status was revised to amber in 2009. *Bird Atlas 2007–11* shows that, over the past two decades, the largest declines have taken place in south-east England but these have been offset by population increases elsewhere in the country. In some arable areas, high densities are associated with Oil-seed Rape, although there appears to be no such strong association in Hampshire.

The accompanying change map indicates a breeding range contraction in Hampshire of 36% between the 1986–91 Atlas and the HBA period. This is directionally consistent with a population decline of 29% in south-east England between 1995 and 2012 (*BBS*). Locally, the decline is tempered by the discovery of Reed Buntings in many locations where they were not recorded during the 1986–91 Atlas, possibly as sites have matured and provided suitable breeding habitat. Losses are spread across the county but

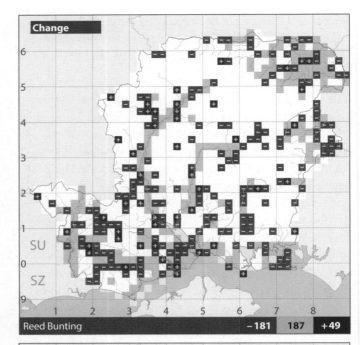

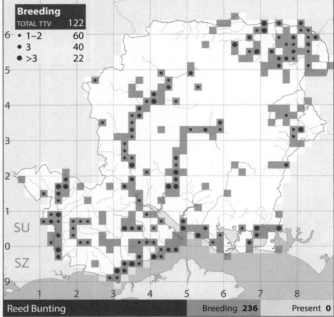

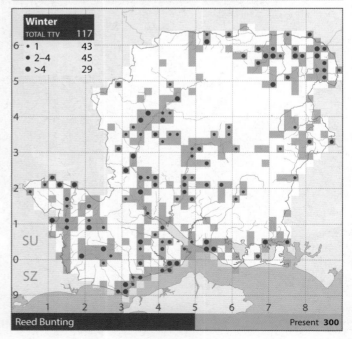

are perhaps most apparent in the New Forest, the Hamble and Meon Valleys, Hayling Island and some areas in the Thames Basin and Wealden Heaths.

As expected, the HBA maps confirm that Reed Buntings range more widely in winter than during the breeding season. They were recorded in 64 more tetrads in winter, a range increase of 27% over the summer. The winter distribution is largely a reflection of that found during the summer but with expansion into adjacent areas. The highest concentrations occurred along the coast, the main river valleys and in the north-east. During the HBA winter surveys, the highest counts were recorded as follows: 85, Fishlake Meadows on November 19th 2007; 69, Saltgrass Road, Keyhaven on November 28th 2010 and 100 at Mattingley/Chandler's Green on January 29th 2011.

An interesting fact concerning this species is that over 50% of Reed Bunting chicks are not fathered by the male of the pair, but by another male. This is the highest rate of infidelity recorded for any bird (BTO BirdFacts).

Dave Unsworth

Sponsored by Brian Sharkey

Reed Bunting,
Fordingbridge, October 2010
– *Martin Bennett* (above);
Keyhaven, April 2015
– *Martin Bennett* (below)

Corn Bunting
Emberiza calandra
A scarce and declining resident

The Corn Bunting is closely associated with arable farmland on the chalk, where it prefers open landscapes dominated by cereal fields, particularly barley, with hedgerows, fences and power lines to provide suitable song posts. British breeders appear to be largely resident, although there is only limited ring-recovery data upon which to base this (*Migration Atlas*).

Corn Bunting numbers are declining at a serious rate. Nationally, there has been a 90% reduction in the British breeding population between 1970 and 2010 (*Bird Atlas 2007–11*). The reasons for the decline are varied but in arable, lowland farming the switch from spring to autumn sowing of cereals has reduced the availability of weed-rich stubbles as a source of winter feeding. In addition, the use of pesticides has reduced the availability of invertebrate food for the young. Both of these factors are likely to have had an impact on Corn Bunting numbers in Hampshire.

During the HBA, Corn Buntings were considered likely to be breeding in just 39 tetrads, a decline of 80% since the 1986–91 Atlas. The sedentary nature of the species is a concern in that once it is lost from an area, recolonisation from elsewhere is less likely as the population becomes more fragmented. Typical breeding sites in the county include Cheesefoot Head/Longwood Warren, Martin Down, Over Wallop, Old Winchester Hill, Toyd Down and Whitsbury Down. However, numbers at all these sites are low and, at some, Corn Buntings are likely to die out within the next few years if current trends continue.

Outside the breeding season Corn Buntings occur in small flocks and although mainly sedentary, will wander in search of food. During the HBA winter survey they were recorded in fewer tetrads than during the breeding season. Two areas stand out as holding the highest numbers. These are the Cheesefoot Head/Longwood Warren/Gander Down area east of Winchester, where the largest counts during the survey were 125 on January 31st 2010 and 100 on January 31st 2012, and the Martin Down/Toyd Down area close to the Dorset-Wiltshire border in west Hampshire. The highest recorded counts in this latter area were 90 on December 28th 2009, 94 on February 27th 2010 and 100 on November 21st 2010. Other sites with smaller, but still important, winter populations include Old Winchester Hill, Danebury, Suddern Hill and Whitsbury Down.

The similarity between the breeding and winter ranges presented here is consistent with Corn Bunting being a largely sedentary bird in the county. However, counts of the winter flock at Toyd Down exceed the breeding population in the immediate vicinity. It is possible that many originate from nearby Salisbury Plain, where much larger numbers continue to breed. The winter flock in the Cheesefoot

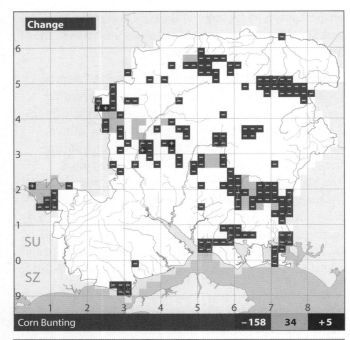

Change
Corn Bunting — −158 | 34 | +5

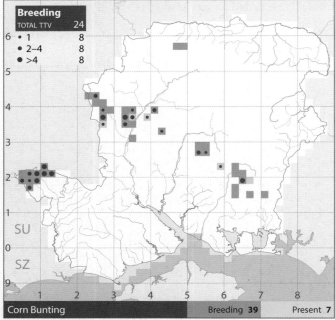

Breeding
TOTAL TTV 24
- • 1 — 8
- • 2–4 — 8
- • >4 — 8

Corn Bunting — Breeding 39 | Present 7

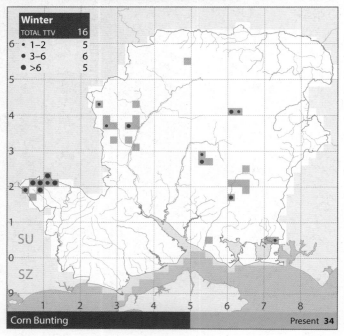

Winter
TOTAL TTV 16
- • 1–2 — 5
- • 3–6 — 6
- • >6 — 5

Corn Bunting — Present 34

Head area is also larger than the local breeding population although it is not immediately obvious where the additional birds originate. Colour-ringing studies in both areas could yield valuable information concerning winter site-fidelity and subsequent dispersal during the breeding season. This, combined with appropriate farming methods on a larger scale with support from the farming community, could yield valuable information to inform future conservation measures. Although survey data collected by HOS (Betton 2007) has been used to target funding under the Environmental Stewardship Scheme, it is clear that much more directed and effective conservation measures are needed to reverse the decline of Corn Buntings in Hampshire.

Dave Unsworth

Sponsored by Nick Wiley

Corn Bunting, Martin Down, April 2012 – *Martin Bennett* (right); Old Winchester Hill, May 2008 – *Richard Ford* (below)

Dark-eyed Junco

Junco hyemalis

A very rare, presumed ship-assisted, vagrant

Hampshire's third Dark-eyed Junco was found at Hawkshill Inclosure in the New Forest on December 22nd 2011 and remained in the area until March 11th 2012. The previous records were of one seen at Church Crookham from May 30th 1987 to March 9th 1990 and one at Picket Post, Andover on May 5th 1996. An individual on board RMS *Mauretania* while docked in Southampton on October 14th/15th 1962, was not reported on land but indicates the likely path by which some, if not all, of this American vagrant reaches our shores.

John Eyre

Dark-eyed Junco, New Forest, February 2012 – *Gordon Small*

Little Bunting

Emberiza pusilla

A rare visitor

During the HBA there was a single Little Bunting record of one at Barton's Mill, Old Basing on October 24th/25th and again on November 1st 2008.

This was the fourth Hampshire record following single birds trapped at Winnall Moors on March 18th 1986, at Titchfield Haven from February 16th to April 17th 1992 and in a Stubbington garden from February 19th to March 17th 2000.

Dave Unsworth

Little Bunting, Shetland – *Hugh Harrop*

White-throated Sparrow

Zonotrichia albicollis

A very rare, presumed ship-assisted, vagrant

During the HBA, a first-winter male was discovered at Old Winchester Hill on November 5th 2008. It remained in the area and was last seen on July 17th 2011.

There are two previous accepted records for Hampshire. The first was at Needs Ore on May 5th 1961 (which was the second British record) and another was in Southampton Docks on May 12th–13th 2007, the bird having arrived onboard *Queen Elizabeth II* from New York.

There are at least two other records of ship-assisted White-throated Sparrows arriving in Southampton Docks, but these sightings have not been reported to BBRC (*BoH*).

Dave Unsworth

White-throated Sparrow, Old Winchester Hill, April 2009 – *Keith Maycock*

Rare species recorded during 2007–12 outside the HBA period

Blue-winged Teal *Anas discors*

2009:	Titchfield Haven/ IBM Lake	An eclipse or juvenile male, August 28th/August 31st

Purple Heron *Ardea purpurea*

2007:	Titchfield Haven	Adult, May 2nd

Corncrake *Calonectris borealis*

2007:	Cholderton Estate	One, September 11th

Cory's Shearwater *Crex crex*

2007:	Sandy Point	One, July 4th
2012:	Hurst Castle	One, November 22nd

American Golden Plover *Pluvialis dominica*

2007:	Farlington Marshes	May 11th & 20th–24th

Baird's Sandpiper *Calidris bairdii*

2011:	Pennington Marshes	Juvenile, September 14th–17th
2012:	Pennington Marshes	Juvenile, September 14th

White-rumped Sandpiper *Calidris fuscicollis*

2011:	Milford on Sea	Juvenile, September 24th

Buff-breasted Sandpiper *Tryngites subruficollis*

2008:	Barton on Sea Golf Course	One, September 26th

Semipalmated Sandpiper *Calidris pusilla*

2011:	Keyhaven Marshes	Juvenile, September 24th– October 2nd

Greater Yellowlegs *Tringa melanoleuca*

2007:	Farlington Marshes	One, September 26th/27th

Lesser Yellowlegs *Tringa flavipes*

2008:	Needs Ore	Adult, September 21st

Long-billed Dowitcher *Limnodromus scolopaceus*

2009:	Ibsley North Gravel Pit	Juvenile, October 11th
2012:	Needs Ore	First-winter, March 10th

White-winged Black Tern *Chlidonias leucopterus*

2007:	Langtone Harbour/ The Kench	Juvenile, August 7th
	Langstone (Ship Inn)/ Hayling Island	Juvenile, August 19th/20th, different to above
2008:	Langstone Harbour	Juvenile, September 14th
2009:	Black Point	Juvenile, September 29th
2010:	Hurst Castle	Juvenile, September 11th
2012:	Langstone Harbour	Two juveniles, August 24th

Sabine's Gull *Xema sabinii*

2007:	Hurst Beach	First-summer, May 6th
2008:	Pennington	Two adults, September 7th
	Itchen Estuary	Juvenile, September 7th-12th
	Milford on Sea	Two juveniles, October 7th
2011:	Sopley	Adult, August 8th & 22nd
	Hinton Admiral	Adult, August 19th (presumed same as above)

2011:	Chichester Harbour Entrance	Juvenile, September 6th
	Milford on Sea	Juvenile, September 10th
	Milford on Sea	Juvenile, September 13th
	Sturt Pond	Two juveniles, September 19th-28th
	Needs Ore	Adult, September 20th

Isabelline Shrike *Lanius isabellinus*

2010:	Forton Lake, Gosport	Adult female, September 10th/11th
2011:	Moonhills, New Forest	First-winter, October 30th– November 2nd

Chough *Pyrrhocorax pyrrhocorax*

2007:	Cholderton Park	One, April 10th

Penduline Tit *Remiz pendulinus*

2010:	Titchfield Haven	Two, October 12th

Barred Warbler *Sylvia nisoria*

2007:	Sinah Gravel Pit	Juvenile, October 29th

Spectacled Warbler *Sylvia conspicillata*

2011:	Needs Ore	One, October 29th/30th

Subalpine Warbler *Sylvia cantillans*

2007:	Itchen Valley Country Park	First-summer male, April 18th
	Southampton Common	First-summer male, April 24th

Booted Warbler *Hippolais caligata*

2010:	Needs Ore	One, September 12th–15th

Melodious Warbler *Hippolais polyglotta*

2008:	Barton on Sea	One, October 8th
2011:	IBM Lake	One, August 13th

Aquatic Warbler *Acrocephalus paludicola*

2007:	Titchfield Haven	First-winter, September 29th
2008:	Farlington Marshes	Adult, August 30th
2009:	Titchfield Haven	Juvenile, August 22nd

Red-flanked Bluetail *Tarsiger cyanurus*

2010:	Sandy Point	First-winter (probably male), October 18th–23rd

Bluethroat *Luscinia svecica*

2007:	Keyhaven Marshes	September 5th & September 11th
2010:	Fishlake Meadows	First-winter male, September 30th & October 2nd

Olive-backed Pipit *Anthus hodgsoni*

2009:	Sandy Point	One, October 24th

Red-throated Pipit *Anthus cervinus*

2011:	Titchfield Haven	One, October 15th

Rustic Bunting *Emberiza rustica*

2010:	Brockenhurst	One, probably a female, March 20th/21st

Escapes and others 2007–2012

Taxonomy follows Gill, F & Donsker, D (Eds). 2015. IOC World Bird List (v 5.3)

Black-bellied Whistling Duck *Dendrocygna autumnalis*

2011:	The Vyne Watermeadows	One, May 8th

Fulvous Whistling Duck *Dendrocygna bicolor*

2007:	Titchfield Haven	Two, January 1st–March 30th, One, April–December, except July
2008:	Ibsley Water/Ivy Lake	One, May 10th
2009:	Titchfield Haven	One, January 8th then regularly reported thereafter throughout the year
	Hook Links	One, October 5th–10th (same as above)
2010:	Titchfield Haven/ Hill Head	One, intermittently throughout year though not in March, June or July
	Hook Links	One, September 5th (same as above)
	Lower Test Marshes	One, October 10th (presumably same as above)
2011:	Titchfield Haven area	January–December
	The Vyne Watermeadows	One, May 8th
2012:	Titchfield Haven	One, January 10th–October 11th
	The Vyne Lake	One, April 28th
	Springfields, Oakhanger	One, June 4th

Cape Barren Goose *Cereopsis novaehollandiae*

2009:	Titchfield Haven	September 3rd–November 28th
	Hook Links	One, September 19th & October 27th (same as above)
2012:	Marwell Zoo	One, arrived with Greylags, October 10th

Lesser White-fronted Goose *Anser erythropus*

2007:	Testbourne Lake	One, throughout the year
2008:	Testbourne Lake	One, throughout the year
2009:	Testbourne Lake	One (paired with a Greylag), throughout the year

Bar-headed Goose *Anser indicus*

2007:	Emsworth Harbour	Two, February 27th
	Blashford Lakes	One, January (two dates), July (one date), September (three dates)
	Houghton	One, June 5th
	Eastern harbours to Lymington	Probably two wide-ranging individuals at several coastal sites throughout the year
2008:	Eversley Gravel Pit	One, January 27th
	Eelmoor Marsh, Pylestock	One, May 7th
	Titchfield Haven	One, January 1st–March 3rd (on four dates) & August 11th–October 18th (on many dates)
	Lower Test Marshes	One, January 28th (same as above)
	Weston Shore	One, flying south, March 27th & on March 29th (same as above)
	Hook-with-Warsash	One, July 28th–September 1st (same as above)

2009:	Blashford Lakes	One, June 14th–July 6th, July 18th & September 25th–November 1st
	Eling/Redbridge/Lower Test Marshes/Testwood Lakes	One, June 27th, July 13th, July 25th–August 30th
	Titchfield Haven	One, September 6th
	Oxey Marshes	One, September 21st (same as above)
	Avon Valley (below Ringwood)	One, October 25th, December 20th & 31st (same as above)
2010:	Avon Causeway area	One, January, March, May, September, October
	Blashford Lakes area	February, May, July, September, October, November, December
	Needs Ore	April, May, June, July, October, November, December (possibly only one individual)
2011:	Avon Valley – Blashford Lakes/Avon Causeway	One, January 2nd & October 16th/January 16th respectively
	Needs Ore	One, January–October 1st
	Keyhaven/Pennington Marshes	One, October 15th (possibly same as above)
	Testwood Lakes	One, March 29th
	Titchfield Haven	One, April 10th & 17th, August 11th (possibly same as above)
2012:	Keyhaven–Langstone Harbour	One, March 17th–December 1st
	Hamer Warren Gravel Pit (Ringwood Forest)	Five, June 9th

Cackling Goose *Branta hutchinsii*

2009:	Titchfield Haven/ Brownwich area	One (*B.h. minima*), January 4th–March 11th & August 28th–December 31st
	Frater shore, Portsmouth Harbour	One, January 6th–10th (same as above)
	Needs Ore	One, March 7th–August 7th (same as above)
	Peak Lane, Fareham	One, September 9th (same as above)
	Hook Links	October 31st (same as above)
2010:	Titchfield Haven/ Brownwich area	One, (*B.h. minima*), January 1st–July 2nd
	Lower Test Marshes/ Testwood Lakes/ Broadlands Lake	September 19th–December 11th (on nine dates and possibly same as above, including registrations at all three sites on October 10th)
2011:	Lower Test Marshes/ Testwood Lakes/ Broadlands Lake	One (*B.h. minima*), January 1st–9th, June 26th–August 14th (same individual as from September 2010)
	Lower Test Marshes	One, December 10th (same as above)
2012:	Lower Test Marshes/ Testwood Lakes	January 13th–February 10th, September 25th & October 27th
	Needs Ore	August 2nd & 13th

Nene *Branta sandvicensis*

2009:	Alresford Pond	One, flying north, March 25th

Red–breasted Goose *Branta ruficollis*

2010:	Chichester Harbour	One (colour-ringed), October 2nd–4th, reported from Devon on October 6th and could account for following record
	Keyhaven	One, past Iley Point among 10 Dark–bellied Brent on October 5th. Probably same as above
2011:	Lower Pennington Lane	One, February 14th–24th, probably same as above

Black Swan *Cygnus atratus*

2007:	Headley Mill Pond	Pair bred & fledged 3 young
	The Vyne Watermeadows	One, November 22nd
	Wellington Country Park	One, early & late year (8 dates)
	Redbridge	One, May 19th, 3, October 13th, two, into December
	Lower Test Marshes	Up to five, September 2nd–15th
	Breamore, Searchfield Farm, Avon Valley	Two, January
	Harbridge Watermeadows	One, until April 17th (probably different from above)
	Breamore–Searchfield Farm, Avon Valley	Three, December 23rd
	Keyhaven Marshes	One, June 16th, two, July 31st–September 25th & one, October 11th
	Romsey	One, January 21st, February 18th & March 2nd
	Chichester Harbour	Two, May 17th
2008:	Headley Mill Pond	Pair attempted breeding, failing in the early year but re-nested in September; outcome unknown
	Wellington Country Park	One, throughout the year
	Tundry Pond	One, January 27th, February 10th & October 19th
	Fleet Pond	One, March 9th & April 14th
	Southampton Water (Eling/Redbridge, Riverside Park area & south to Weston Shore)	One or two in all months of the year
	Ibsley/Ibsley Water/ Breamore	One or two, January 19th–March 30th, July 20th–September 29th (on eight dates) & December 13th/14th, respectively
	Emsworth Mill Pond	January 26th–February 4th
	Idsworth Farm, Horndean	One, January 26th
	Lymington area	One, April 10th
	Needs Ore	One, April 11th (same as above)
	Martyr Worthy, Itchen Valley	One, December 28th
2009:	Wellington Country Park	One or two, January 13th–March 17th, including nesting pair on last date which subsequently failed
	Dogmersfield Lake	One, February 2nd
	Fleet Pond	One, February 15th & 22nd
	Searchfield Farm, Breamore/Ibsley Water	One, throughout year (eight dates)
2009:	Riverside Park, Southampton	Female, January 19th–February 24th & May 29th–June 29th when a nest with four eggs was occupied but failed; evidence suggested that a Mute Swan was paired with this individual
	Lower Test Marshes	March 14th–16th (above individual)
	River Itchen (near Riverside Park)	One, September 18th & December 4th (above individual)
	Laverstoke Park Lake (Test Valley)	One, September 22nd–31st December
2010:	Woolmer Pond	One, March 15th
	Searchfield/Blashford Lakes/Harbridge Watermeadows	One, February 5th, June 20th & September 7th, December 21st, respectively
	St Denys/RiversidePark (River Itchen)	One, January–March (three dates), August 16th, October 21st–December 26th (six dates)
	Laverstoke Park Lake (Test Valley)	One, throughout year (10 dates)
	Alresford Pond	One, February 14th–March 14th
2011:	Bickton	Two, early & late year & June 3rd
	Blashford Lakes	One, July 25th–August 12th (one of Bickton's birds)
	Laverstoke Park Lake (Test Valley)	One, throughout year (nine dates)
	Cobden Bridge–Woodmill (Riverside Park, Southampton)	Female, early and late year & occupied nest at Riverside Park, May 16th–June 18th; no eggs seen, though presumed predated
	Lower Test Marshes	Female, March 6th–9th (same as above)
2012:	Avon Valley (Somerley–Wiltshire border)	Two long–staying individuals
	Itchen Estuary/ Lower Test Marshes	One long–staying individual
	Laverstoke Park (Test Valley)	One long–staying individual
	Horndean (Keydell Nurseries Ponds)	Two, March 15th
	Netley	Two, May 27th
	Yateley Gravel Pit	Two, November 19th

Ruddy Shelduck *Tadorna ferruginea*

2012:	Heath Pond (Petersfield)	Pair, January 7th
	Beaulieu Estuary	Pair, January 10th

South African Shelduck *Tadorna cana*

2012:	Wellington Country Park	Pair, July 11th
	Titchfield Haven	Female, August 2nd

Paradise Shelduck *Tadorna variegata*

2012:	Titchfield Haven	Male, August 2nd

Wood Duck *Aix sponsa*

2007:	Badmiston Common Gravel Pit	Male, January–June & November–December (14 dates)
	Hook Links	Male, January (four dates)
	Eyeworth Pond	April 23rd
	Lower Avon Valley	Male, December 16th
2008:	Titchfield Haven	Male, February 3rd
	Alver Valley, Gosport	Female, February 10th–March 29th & December 31st
	Buriton	Male, February 29th & May 5th
	Curbridge	Male, March 29th
	Fleet Pond	Male, July 4th–9th
	Heath Pond (Petersfield)	Male, November 15th
2009:	Buriton	Eclipse male, February 26th
	Fort Brockhurst, Gosport	Female, disappearing into a hole beneath a window, May 8th
2010:	Dark Water (Lepe)	Male, January 10th
	Eyeworth Pond	Male, March 4th–May 22nd (apparently paired with a Mandarin Duck May 15th) & October 18th
2011:	Eyeworth Pond	Male, January 1st–17th
2012:	Eyeworth Pond	Male, February 29th–March 19th & May 7th
	Wade Hill Drove/ Testwood Lakes	Pair, March 3rd/March 11th, respectively

Maned Duck *Chenonetta jubata*

2007:	Ibsley Water, Blashford Lakes	One, January 14th
2010:	Testwood Lakes	One, September 19th & October 10th
2011:	Testwood Lakes	One, May 1st

Ringed Teal *Callonetta leucophrys*

2007:	Allington Gravel Pit	Female, early year–May 6th
	The Vyne Watermeadows	Male, May 19th (reappeared for the fourth successive year)
	Avon Causeway	One, March 3rd
	Ivy Lake, Avon Valley	One, October 31st (presumably same as above)
2009:	The Vyne Watermeadows	One, December 3rd
2010:	Ibsley Water	Pair, October 9th
2011:	Sherborne St John	July 9th

Chiloe Wigeon *Anas sibilatrix*

2007:	Riverside Park & nearby, Southampton	One, early year
	Southampton Common	One, August–October (five dates – presumably same as above)
	Allington Gravel Pit	Three (male & two females), March 17th & one or two, late year (seven dates)
	Fishtail Lagoon, Keyhaven Marshes	Male, May 9th–19th, at least
	Ibsley Water	Pair, December 8th
2009:	Titchfield Haven	Two males, January 11th
	Pennington Marshes	Male, December 9th–11th

Cinnamon Teal *Anas cyanoptera*

2011:	Titchfield Haven	Male, May 8th–July 1st & August 17th

Australian Shoveler *Anas rhynchotis*

2010:	Ibsley Water, Blashford Lakes	Male, January 3rd (race *variegata*)

Chestnut Teal *Anas castanea*

2008:	Chilland, Itchen Valley	One, presumed male, May 14th

White–cheeked Pintail *Anas bahamensis*

2007:	Southampton Common	One (a survivor from the collection there), free–flying, March–May 2nd

Speckled Teal *Anas flavirostris*

2007:	Normandy	One, January 1st–July 19th (on 8 dates), 2, November 20th,
2008:	Normandy	One, January 1st–May 25th, a female with five young on last date. Six, August 21st – presumably the same birds
2011:	Lower Pennington Lane/ Butts Lagoon	Female & three young, May 27th

Goosander *Mergus merganser*

2008:	Leckford/Longstock, River Test	Pinioned male, throughout year, with two free–flying, presumed wild redheads in late year
2009:	Leckford area, River Test	Pinioned male. Apparently paired on March 17th but no proof of breeding
2010:	Leckford area, Longstock Water Gardens	Pinioned male, with up to two free–flying redheads and apparent flightless redhead on August 18th
2011:	Leckford area, Longstock Water Gardens	Pinioned male, throughout year

Reeve's Pheasant *Syrmaticus reevesii*

2007:	Normandy Farm, Lymington	Male, January 2nd
	Lower Test Marshes	One, March 15th
2008:	Sowley Pond	Male, March 30th
2010:	Fobdown (New Alresford)	One, March 18th
2011:	Netherton Bottom	One, December 2nd

Vulture sp. (possible **Cape Vulture** *Gyps coprotheres*)

2007:	Itchen Valley Country Park/ Moorgreen Farm	One, January 27th

Vulture sp.

2008:	The Vyne Watermeadows	Unspecified May 4th & 6th

Bald Eagle *Haliaeetus leucocephalus*

2007:	Lower Test Marshes	Adult, soaring to the north, August 12th

Harris's Hawk *Parabuteo unicinctus*

2007:	Dibden Purlieu	One, March (seen regularly, no evidence of jesses)
2008:	Dibden Purlieu	One, January 1st–February 17th (no evidence of jesses)
2009:	Abbotts Ann, Andover	One, April 29th–May 30th
2012:	South Boarhunt	One, May 6th

Great Bustard *Otis tarda*

2009:	Harbridge Watermeadow	Female (tagged), January 7th–16th
	Harbridge Watermeadow	One, July 27th
	Sparsholt College, Winchester	Male, May 13th
2010:	Harbridge Watermeadow	Female, December 30th
2012:	Chilbolton/Barton Stacey	Second–winter male (no wing-tags), November 29th–March 18th 2013

Demoiselle Crane *Anthropoides virgo*

2008:	Lode Farm Sand Pit, Kingsley	1 (colour–ringed), August 27th/28th

Eurasian Eagle–Owl *Bubo bubo*

2008:	Emsworth	One, May 8th
	Game Exchange, Havant	One, June 25th/26th (same as above)
2012:	Waterlooville	One, March 29th

Lanner Falcon *Falco biarmicus*

2007:	Piper's Wait	One, April 14th
	Ashley Walk	One, May 8th
	Winchester	One, October 3rd (an escape wearing jesses)
2010:	Chichester Harbour entrance	One (pale form or hybrid), January 29th (no descriptions submitted for other claims of this species in August)

Saker Falcon *Falco cherrug*

2010:	Howen Bottom	One, May 21st (unknown origin)
2011:	Mengham Infants School (Hayling)/ Lifeoat Station (Chichester Harbour)	One (with jesses), October 19th/ October 20th, respectively

Hybrid Falcons *Falco* sp.

2008:	Hurst area/Needs Ore/ Bishops Dyke	One (reported as a Saker Falcon), April 30th, May 13th & May 23rd (presumably the same reported as a Lanner Falcon *Falco cherrug* there on 24th)
	Martin Down	One (reported as a Saker Falcon), June 4th
	Fishtail Lagoon, Keyhaven Marshes	Juvenile Lanner Falcon (reported and photographed), August 23rd; the photo suggests that the bird was a hybrid falcon, certainly with Peregrine genes in its provenance and based on size estimates by its finder, possibly a Prairie Falcon *Falco mexicanus* parent although other co–parentage such as Saker × Peregrine cannot be ruled out

Cockatiel *Nymphicus hollandicus*

2007:	Sandy Point, Hayling	One, February 26th
	Warblington Castle	One, April 27th
	Kempshott	One, August 27th
	Ibsley Water	One, September 17th
	Northney, Hayling	One, December 7th

2008:	Farnborough	One, flying south–east, May 10th
	Sandy Point, Hayling	One, August 11th
	Havant	One, September 2nd
	National Oceanography Centre, Southampton	One, September 16th
2010:	Manor Farm (Old Alresford)	One, January 11th
	Winchester Sewage Farm	One, May 18th
	Miles Hill (Fleet)	One, September 4th
2012:	Basingstoke	May 9th
	Havant	May 16th

Grey Parrot *Psittacus erithacus*

2007:	Weston Shore	One, November 4th

Senegal Parrot *Poicephalus senegalus*

2008:	Botany Bay valley, Southampton	One, January 26th

Alexandrine Parakeet *Psittacula eupatria*

2008:	Lower Pennington Lane, Lymington	One, October 5th
2011:	Lower Pennington Lane, Lymington	One, throughout the year & into 2012

Pale-headed Rosella *Platycercus adscitus*

2010:	Sandy Point/Sinah Warren, Hayling	One, calling and singing, May 24th; seen & heard, June 3rd,

Budgerigar *Melopsittacus undulatus*

2007:	Normandy, Lymington	One, June 5th
2010:	Petersfield	One, February 12th
	Sandy Point (Hayling)	One, July 19th
	Lymington	One, August 15th
2011:	Sandy Point (Hayling)	July 19th
2012:	Sandy Point (Hayling)	One, January 5th, February 9th

Zebra Finch *Taeniopygia guttata*

2009:	Titchfield Haven Sailing Club	One, September 5th
	Sandy Point estate (Hayling)	One, October 1st
2012:	Sandy Point (Hayling)	March 1st
	Ibsley Water (Blashford Lakes)	September 6th

Atlantic Canary *Serinus canaria*

2008:	Petersfield	One, in a garden, February 24th
2010:	BroadMarsh (Langstone Harbour)	One, March 11th
2012	Hampshire	

White–throated Sparrow *Zonotrichia albicollis*

2007:	Transatlantic crossing New York to Southampton	One, reported on board *QEII* and then in dockland area of Southampton on May 12th/13th

Common Yellowthroat *Geothlypis trichas*

2008:	Transatlantic crossing, St. John's, Newfoundland, Canada to Southampton	One, on board ship September 19th–22nd (probably flew ashore)

Appendix I | Contributors

David Ackland
Tracy Adams
Nicholas Aebischer
David Agombar
Belinda Ahmed
Giles Alder
Mike Alexander
Colin Allen
D P Allnutt
Samir Al-Mahrouq
Guy Anderson
I R Anderson
Karen Anderson
Jen Anderson
Edwyn Anderton
Benjamin Joseph Andrew
Ruth Angus
John Applebee
Alison Appleby
David Arch
Bruce Archer
Mike Armitage
Grant Armstrong
B S Arnold
Nicholas Ashman
Phil Ashton
Janet Atkinson
John Attiwell
J S Austin
M I Avery
Clare Bailey
Louise Bailey
John Baker
Michael Baker
Peter James Baker
Joseph Baldwin
David Ball
Kay Ball
Tim Ball
Ian David Ballam
Andrew Balmer
Dawn Elizabeth Balmer
M Bamber
Brian Banks
Michael Banks
Philip Barbagallo
Lee Barber
Jenny Barber
Mary-Anne Barber
Chris Barfield
Andy Barker
Derek Barker
Kevin Barker
S R J Barker
Cary Barnes
Edwin Barnes
Graham Barrett
John Barrett
Richard Barrett
Marc Bartolini
G S Batho
Sean Batten
Sam Bayley
Catherine Bayliss
John Bayliss
C Bealey

Billy Bean
Archibald Beattie
Ian Bell
David Bellis
Paul Benham
Stephen Bentall
Berkshire Ornithological
 Society
Tony Bertenshaw
Lt Col N W Beswick
Keith Betton
Thomas Bickerton
D T Biggs
Stella Bignold
Peter Billinghurst
Jonathan Bills
Joan Bingley
Nadya Binnis
Gavin Bird
Steven Bird
Birdguides
Birdguides-details
John Birkett
David Bishop
Graham Bishop
Sarah Bishop
Lorne Bissell
Wendy Black
David Blackmore
Emma Blair
A F Blakeley
David Blandford
Dawn Elizabeth Blight
Murray Blowfield
Andrew Bluett
William Blumsom
Trevor Blythe
Chris Bollen
Andrew Bolton
Richard Bond
Richard Bonser
Robin Borwick
Simon Boswell
Ian Bowes
Alex Sebastian Bowes
Douglas Bowker
Louise Charlotte Boyer
Pete Boylan
Reverend Paul Bradbury
Chris Bradford
Emma Bradford
Hugh Bradshaw
Ian Bradshaw
Andrew Bray
Brian Bray
M A Breakspear
R G Breakwell
Kane Brides
Matthew Brierley
Dennis Bright
R A Broad
A Broadhurst
Robert Brook
Colin Brooks
Graham Brown
Ray Brown

Stephanie Brown
William Brown
Anna Bruce
Peter Bryant
Robert Bryant
Michael Bryant
Michael Edward Buchanan
Neil Bucknell
Andrew Budd
Philip Alan Budd
A J Bull
Beryl Bull
Francis Buner
R G Burgess
N Burgum
Joanna Burkitt
James Burnett
Dave Burt
Jeff Butcher
Jennie Butler
David Butler
Edward Butler
Maaike Butter
A M B Butterworth
N J Buxton
G D Caine
Gary Calderwood
Ian Calderwood
Stephen Callister
Andrew Camp
David Campbell
George Candelin
Steven Carey
Ben Carpenter
Richard Carpenter
Trevor Carpenter
Anne Carrington-Cotton
S Carter
P E Castle
David Chadwick
Sean Chadwick
John H. Chaffe
Michael Chalmers
Chris Chapman
Colin Chapman
Peter Chapman
R A Chapman
S E Chapman
Jason W Chapman
Norman Chappell
Kate Charles
Peter Charles
P Charleton
Elisabeth Charman
Sheila Chatten
Professor Robert Cheke
Lt Cdr J M Cheverton
T J Chinn
Philip Keith Chown
Roger Christopher
David Churchill
Raymond Claridge
Frank Charles Clark
John Clark
Roger Clark
Susan Clark

Graham Clarkson
Peter Clayton
Bruno Clements
John Clements
Andy Clements
Aaron Clements-Partridge
B D Clews
Charlotte Sarah Clough
John Cloyne
Anthony Cobb
Chris Cockburn
Trevor Codlin
Deborah Cole
David Coleman
Richard John Harvey
 Collingridge
Hugh Collings
M L Collins
Barry Collins
Philip Collins
John Collman
Peter Combridge
Steve Coney
Rebecca Coneybeer
James Cook
G M Cook
Lisa Cook
Rosemary Cook
R Cook
Jane Cooke
Andrew Cooper
Julian Cooper
Margaret Cooper
Philip Cooper
Stephen Cooper
Steve Copsey
Gerald Charles Cornick
Chris Cowell
Alan Cowx
Alan Cox
Andrew Peter Cox
I N Cox
R Cox
Helen Crabtree
Richard Crawford
Mike Creighton
Richard Creighton
Kevin Crisp
Ruth Croger
Jason Crook
Claire Crook
Alison Cross
Patrick Crowley
Jenny Croxson
Michael Crutch
Sarah Lilian Cuff
Patrick Cullen
Jane Cumming
Liam Curson
Simon Curson
Colin Curtis
Charles Cuthbert
Mark Cutts
Chris Dale
Robert Dalrymple
Brian Dalton

Nolan Daly
Barbara Daniels
Giles Darvill
BTO Dataset (BBS)
BTO Dataset (GBW)
RSPB Dataset (GENERAL)
BTO Dataset (HERON)
BTO Dataset (NRS)
BTO Dataset (WeBS)
Anne Davage
Andrew Davidson
Gerry Davies
Keith Davies
Mervyn Davies
Sir Robert Allen Davies
Steve Davies
Sidney Davies
James Christopher Davies
A M Davis
Richard Dawes
Anne de Potier
Martin de Retuerto
Barry Deakin
Paul Dean
John Dedman
John Dellow
Graham Dennis
David Dicker
Lt Col R C Dickey
Tom Dingwall
Julie Dix
Mark Dixon
Malcolm Dixon
Roger Dobbs
Peter Dodsworth
Tim Doran
Robert Douthwaite
Christina Dow
John Downes
Brian Downey
John Downing
Helen Louise Downing-
 Emms
Jeffrey Dowse
Jane Elizabeth Druett
Robin Dryden
Nicola Duckworth
Chris Duffey
Francis Dummigan
Kevin Duncan
Pete Durnell
David Dyer
Robert Eames
Les Easom
T G Easterbrook
Rachel Eaton
Mark Edgeller
Maureen Edwards
Stephen Edwards
Norman Elkins
Adrian Ellis
Dr David Ellis
Nick Ellis
I M Elphick
Jennifer Elvin
Viv Erith

Dr A D Evans
Glynne Evans
Mark Evans
Mair Evans
Michael Evans
Simon Evans
Hugh Evans
Dr Libby Evans
Ed Ewitt
John Eyre
Malcolm Fairley
Charles Farrell
Geoffrey Farwell
Dr Brian Fellows
Gary David Fennemore
Amanda Fenton
Roger Ferguson
Ashley Field
Jayne Finch
Dr Robin Findlay
Stuart Leslie Fisher
Brian Fisk
Terence Flanagan
David Fleming
M R Fletcher
Paul Floyd
Jane Flux
Phil Flynn
Beryl Foote
Sean Foote
Shayne Ford
Bob Ford
Julia Ford
Natasha Forder
William Fordham
Professor Malcolm Forster
Christopher Foster
Neill Foster
Dr Mike Foulkes
Douglas Charles Fowler
Nevil Fowler
A S Fox
John Fox
Oliver Frampton
Roger Frankum
Danielle Victoria Free
Shirley Freeman
Major Arthur French
Caroline French
Petina Frost
Darren Fry
Jacky Fry
Trevor Fuller
Alan Fullforth
Christopher Furley
Lucy Gale
Dr Alexander Galloway
Neil Galton
Game & Wildlife
    Conservation Trust
Amanda Garrie
Lloyd Garvey
Jeremy Gates
Chris Gent
Imogen German
Alasdair Gibb
Caroline Gibbins
Molly Gibson
Trevor Gibson-Poole

John Gilbert
Iain Gilea
Dave Gill
Elizabeth Gill
Deborah Gillingham
Dr David William
    Gillingham
P Giovannini
James Gloyn
Dr Colin Goble
Phillip Goble
Nicholas Godden
Robert Godden
Tim Godfrey
Edward Goldingay
Clive Alexander Good
Andrew Goodall
P Goodman
J R Goodspeed
David Goodwin
Dr Sally Gordon
Diana Gorringe
Jayne Gough
S A Graham
Tim Graham
Zoe Grant
Ben Grantham
Lois Gravely
C Gray
Dr A E Green
Kaye Green
Martin Greene
Colin Greenfield
M T Greening
Stuart Greer
Gillian Margaret Gregory
Carol Greig
Robin Griffiths
R Grimmond
Clare Grindrod
Andrew Grinter
Dr Mervyn Grist
R D Gross
Derek Gruar
Andrew Guest
Mike Gunby
Anthony Gutteridge
William Haines
John Spencer William
    Hakeman
Anthony Peter Steadman
    Hale
John Hale
Derek Hale
Grace Hall
Timothy Hall
Rosamund Hall
Dr Richard Hallett
Robert Hallier
Ian Hampson
Martin Hampton
Deirdre Hanan
Derek Hankinson
B S Hansell
Michael Harding
Roger Hardy
Robin Paul Harley
Dr Andrew Harmer
Ros Harper

John Harrington
Anthony Harris
D G Harris
Joe Harris
Margaret Harris
Simon Harris
Kim Harris
Nigel Harris
Valerie Harris
Andrew Harrison
Ben Harrower
Robin Hart
Rachel Hartland
Stephen Harvey
Eddie Harwood
Robert Hastings
David Hastings
Clive Hawkins
John Hawtree
Alan Hayden
Richard Haydon
Mary Hayward
Sean Healey
Brian Hedley
Martin Henderson
James Herd
A Herrod
Dr Russ Heselden
Roger Hewitt
Christopher Hickman
Peter Hickman
R Hicks
Rupert Higgins
Jonathan Richard Hiley
Sue Hiley
Christopher Hill
Marion Hill
Roy Hilliard
Dr Dan Hoare
John Hobson
Tim Hodge
Debbie Hodges
Terry Hodkin
Julie Hogg
David Holland
John Holland
Richard Hollis
David Holt
David Holt
A N Hoodless
Hugh Horne
Rob Horne
Jane Horne
Richard Horton
Dan Houghton
Diana Housley
Peter Howard
Rodney Howard
David Hubble
R J Hubble
Margaret Irene Hudd
Mike Huddie
John Hughes
Richard Hughes
Nick Hull
Richard Humphreys
D J Humphries
Nicholas Humphrys
David Hunt

Julie Hunt
Mark Hunt
Sue Hunt
E M Husband
Dianne Hussey
J V P Hutchins
A Hutchison
Graham Huxley
Colin Hyde
Simon Ingram
Ruth Iredale
R Irwin
Peter Iver
Mark Jackson
Roger Jackson
Richard Jacobs
Robert Jacobs
David Barry Lewis James
Paul James
Mary Ann Jardine
Kevin Mark Jarvis
J E Jarvis
M Jeeves
Frances Jennings
Peter Jennings
Paul Jepson
David Jewsbury
JNCC Seabird Data
Graham John
Peter John
Kevin Johns
Keith Johnson
Lee Johnson
Andrew Johnston
Alick Jones
Alan Robert Jones
Barry Jones
Ceri Jones
Chris Jones
Howard Jones
John Jones
John Jones
N R Jones
P D Jones
Philip Jones
Peter Jones
Rosy Jones
Terence Jones
Barbara Jones
Glenn William Jones
Rebecca Jones
Tom Jordan
Simon Josey
Ian Julian
Bridget Mary Jupp
Adele Kane
Alison Kay
Philip Keane
Steve Keen
Ian James Keil
Sarah Kelman
John Kelsall
Norman Kelsey
Lucy Kemp
A D Kennelly
Jane Olivia Kenney
Hugh Kent
Graham Kesby
Vicky Kimm

David King
M King
Ann Kingston
Melvyn Kirby
G R Kirk
Karen Kita
Gareth Knass
A R Knight
A Knight
Christine Knight
David Knight
James Knight
Andrew Knight
David Koffman
Daniel Kronenberg
Alan Kydd
C Lachlan
Greg Lambe
S R Lankester
John Lansbury
C M Lansley
Jack Lavin
M R Lawn
Jackie Lawrence
Emma Sarah Lay
A R Layfield
Brian Leach
Helen Leach
David Lee
Horace Lee
J Legg
Martin Dominic Lenney
Sarah Leonard
R J Lerpiniere
Andy Lester
John Levell
A Lever
Alan Lewis
Adrian Lewis
Daliah Ley
Red Liford
Terry Lifton
Michael Liley
Christine Lindsay
Marilyn Lindsay
Jill Line
Barry Lintott
M A Litjens
Simon Lloyd
Nick Loader
Marie Lock
Anthony Locke
Stephanie Lockhart
Phillip Lomax
D F Long
Tom Lord
Kevin Lover
Stephen Lowe
Wendy Jane Lowe
Megan Lowe
Ian Loyd
Keith Lugg
Robert Lyle
Ben Macdonald
Timothy Mack
Angela Macpherson
Robert Maidment
Deirdre Major
Jenny Mallett

Lynn Mann
Anne Mansell
Jacqui Mansell
Steve Mansfield
Alun March
Robert Marchant
John Marchant
Nick Marriner
Gary Marsh
Heather Marsh
Richard Marsh
Robert Marshall
Stephen Keith Marshall
Peter Marston
Adrian Martin
Jonathan Martin
John Martin
Robert Martin
John Malcolm Maskell
Andrew Mason
Alex Massey
Ruth Masterman
Terry Matley
Melissa Matthews
Tina Matthews
Andrew Maundrell
Steve May
Keith Maycock
Caroline Maynard
Dawn McCallion
John McCarthy
Shaun McCullagh
Alistair McGowan
David Mcleod
David McNair
Keith Meacher
Ben Mead
Graham Megson
Nigel Melsom
Florence Mercer
Keith Metcalf
G P Michaels
Lord Stephen Miles
Andrew Millar
Debbie Miller
H J Miller
David Miller
Roger Milligan
David Minns
Di Mitchell
Sheila Mitchell
E Monk
Alan Monk
Joanna Monnington
John Moon
Christopher Moore
Nick Moran
Craig Morrell
Alex Morris
Peter Morrison
Mike Morton
J C Moseley
Noel Moss
Sue Moys
Sarah Louise Muddell
Paul Mulcahy
Dave Munday
Linda Munday
Barry Mung

Roger Murfitt
Gerald Murphy
Denise Murray
John Murray
Jonathan Mycock
Carl Anthony Mynott
Steve Neal
Kaitlin Neeson
Roger Nelson
M J Netherwood
Kevin New
Peter Newbound
Mark Newell
Irene Newman
M A H Newman
Philip Newman
D Newson
A C Nicholls
Lesley Nickell
Joshua Nightingale
J L Nobbs
S D Noble
Michael James Norman
Cdr A Y Norris
Glenn Norris
Stephen North
Peter Northcote
John Norton
Tristan Norton
John Nundy
Stephen Oakes
Jason Oakley
Darren Oakley-Martin
J G Oates
Damian Offer
J O'Hanlon
J C C Oliver
Martin Orchard-Webb
Nick Orson
Graham Osborne
Doreen Overy
Andrea Owen
N W Owens
Andrew Page
Steve Page
Mark Painter
Gary Palmer
Mark Palmer
Andrew Palmer
R B Palmer
Steve Palmer
Nick Papas
Adrian Parker
David Parker
Mary Parker
Owen Parker
Andrew Parkes
Christine Parkhouse
Paul Parmenter
A J Parsons
Jonathan Parsons
Kris Partridge
Richard Paulson
Anita Payne
David Payne
Nigel Peace
Adrian Pearce
Kelvin Pearce
Dave Pearson

Roger Peart
Lizzy Peat
Ronald Peck
Sarah Pendarves
Jeremy Peters
Shaun Peters
Vanessa Peters
Matthew Simon Phelps
Hywel Phillips
Roy Phillips
Robert Pickett
G D Pictor
N Pierce
Bekki Pierce
Stephen Piggott
Sir Hew Pike
Ian Pilling
Trevor Michael Pinchen
Josette Pinkney
Ben Pinnick
David Piper
Maggie Piska
Linda Pitt
Martin Pitt
Richard Pitts
Elaine Pleasance
Debbie Pledge
R Pointer
Tony Polley
Clive Poole
William John Porter
Peter Potts
Bruce Poulter
Tony Powell
Elizabeth Pratt
Joanna Priestnall
Sir Charles Pringle
Richard Prior
Chloe Pritchard
David Pritchard
Kerrie Prowting
John Proyer
Sally Puplampu
Aaron Pycroft
Rupert Pyrah
William Quantrill
A Quinn
Derek Radden
Michael Rafter
Ian Ralphs
Nicky Ranger
Jonny Rankin
Geoff Rapley
Neil Rawlings
Colin Raymond
Peter Raynes
E M Raynor
Penny Raynor
Jacqueline Redway
Ray Reedman
David Reeves
I Reid
D J Reynolds
Neil Reynolds
Andy Rhodes
Alex Rhodes
Terry Richards
Len Richardson
John Richardson

Les Rickman
Steve Ricks
Renton Righelato
BTO Ringers
John Rix
Barrie Roberts
Diana Roberts
E T Roberts
Graham Roberts
Helen Roberts
Malcolm Robertson
Peter Robinson
R Robinson
Steven Robinson
Elaine Robinson
W P Rodger
Emma Roe
Ted Rogers
Geoff Rogers
James Christopher
   Rogerson
Mark Rolfe
Rachael Rolfe
Adam Rolfe
Andrew Rooke
R Rooke
Ian Rose
Chris Ross
Ruairi Ross
Nick Rossiter
Robin Rothwell
Anne Rowe
James Rowe
G J S Rowland
Peregrine Rowse
June Roy
R S Royle
Jim Rushforth
Barry Russ
Dawn Russell
P Russell
Paul Rutter
Colin Ryall
Peter Ryder
Kevin Rylands
Alison Sainsbury
Julie Salmon
Mary Samways
Andrew Vernon Sanders
Paul Sargent
S P Satterthwaite
Roger Saunders
John Sawtell
Kevin Sayer
Vince Scannella
Richard Scarlett
Elaine Schofield
Graham Scholey
Tony Scott
Elizabeth Scott
Pat Scott
David Scott-Langley
Professor Brian Sealy
Richard Seargent
Emma Searle
Anthony Seed
Paul Selby
Peter Selby
Matthew Shaft

Brian Sharkey
G Sharp
Lesley Sharp
Richard Sharp
M J Shave
Marc Shaw
Eddie Shawyer
Alan James Shearman
P R Shepley
John Shillitoe
Peter Short
Robin Shrubsole
David Shute
Ian Sibsey
W F Simcox
Matthew Simpson
Nev Simpson
Hilary Skelton
Alf Smallbone
Jeremy Smallwood
Sally Smart
Christopher Smith
David Smith
Ian Smith
Marcus Smith
Martin Smith
M P J Smith
Maureen Smith
R G Smith
R Smith
Verity Smith
Andrew Smithen
Alan Snook
Robert Souter
Jessica Sprigens
Malcolm Spriggs
Emma Spruce
Barry Stalker
Lesley Staves
Richard Stedman
Graham Stephenson
Terry Stevens
Aisling Stewart
Graeme Stewart
Gary Stewart
Peter Stewart
Andrew Stocker
Joe Stockwell
Gavin Stoddart
Jon Stokes
David Stone
Brian Stone
Geoff Stone
Kevin Stouse
Ashley Stow
Peter Strangeman
Les Stride
Jennifer Stringer
Peter Stronach
Barry Stuckey
Bonnor Sullivan
Martin Sullivan
Alexander Patrick Sullivan
Gilly Summers
D J Sussex
Sussex Ornithological
   Society
Paul Sutton
J L Swallow

Robert Swift
Sue Sykes
Elizabeth Tarrant
Simon Tarry
Mike Taylor
Chris Taylor
Ray Teesdale
Martin Terry
Louise Tester
Brian Phillip Theakston
David Thelwell
Roger Theobald
Raymond Thomas
Brian Thompson
Joan Thompson
P G L Thompson
Teresa Thompson
Mother Carrie Thompson
G A Thornton
Justin Tilley
Antony Tindale
Richard Todd
A B Tomczynski
Mike Toms
Edward Tooth
Paul Toynton
Annette Julia Tree
David Trollope
William Howard Truckle
Robin Trundle
Mike Tubb
Jennifer Tubbs
Simon Tucker
Karen Tucker

John Turner
R Turner
Richard Turpin
Mike Turton
Sash Tusa
Roger Stanley Twigg
Peter Twine
Andrew Philip Twyman
Annette Twyman
David Tyler
Ros Tyrrell
Dave Unsworth
Geoff Upton
Nancy Urry
Alison Van De Velde
Simon Van Hear
Martyn Vann
Tim Vaughan
Dave Veal
Hugh Venables
J Vickers
Graham Vine
Michael Vokes
Donna Vose
Elizabeth Wade-Brown
Jeremy Wakeford
Robert Wakelam
Marek Walford
Stephen Walker
Tim Walker
M J Wall
David Wall
J J Walling
A P Walmsley

Laura Walsh
J M Walters
Daniel Wanklyn
David Ward
Marcus Ward
John Warren
Renee Warren
David Watkins
Barrie Watson
Daphne Watson
Jeremy Watson
Michael Watson
Peter Watson
Robert Watson
Brian Webb
Richard Webb
W J Webb
Tom Wells
Jackie Wells
Mike West
Paul Westbrook
Diana Westerhoff
I L G Weston
Eddie Whalley
Anne Wheatcroft
Jeffery Wheatley
Mike Wheeler
Mark Whitaker
Ken White
Professor Paul White
Sarah White
Brian White
Christine White
Thomas White

Stephen Whitehead
Robert David Whitehead
Peter Whiteman
A Whitfield
Kathy Whittleton
John Anthony Wichall
Mark Wiggins
J Wilcockson
Rosemary Wild
Michael Wildish
A Wilkie
Colin Wilkinson
David Wilkinson
Christopher Willard
Anne Williams
Chris Williams
G Williams
Penny Williams
Tracé Williams
Alan Williams
Carolyn Williamson
Michael Williamson
Nigel Willits
John Willmott
David Wills
Keith Wills
Colin Wilson
Gill Wilson
G E Wilson
Helen Wilson
Ian Wilson
J Wilson
S Wilson
I J Wilton

Mark Wingrove
Paul Winter
Matthew Wisby
Sylvia Wise
Eddie Wiseman
Daniel Wiseman
John Wood
J K R Wood
Martin Wood
Shaun Woodcock
Christopher Woodham
A E L Woods
Judy Woods
G Woodward
S A Woolfries
Simon Woolley
Ian Woolsey
Gerald Wordley
Ian Worsley
Angela Wright
Simon Wright
David Wyatt
Alan Wynde
Russell Wynn
Chris Yates
Duncan Yeardley
D Yelland
Colin Leslie Young
Claire Young
John Gillingham
Richard Helier
RSPB London

Appendix II | Breeding codes and dates used to define Likely Breeding

For code definitions, see *page 11*.

Species	Codes: 0 = exclude; 1 = include; Null = Record without breeding evidence																		Date range			
	F	Null	H	S	P	T	D	N	A	I	B	DD	UN	FL	ON	FF	NE	NY				
Mute Swan	0	0	0	0	0	0	1	1	1	1	1	1	1	1	1	1	1	1	01	04	31	07
Greylag Goose	0	0	0	0	0	0	1	1	1	1	1	1	1	1	1	1	1	1	01	04	31	07
Snow Goose	0	0	0	0	0	0	0	1	1	1	1	1	1	1	1	1	1	1	01	04	31	07
Canada Goose	0	0	0	0	0	0	1	1	1	1	1	1	1	1	1	1	1	1	01	04	31	07
Barnacle Goose	0	0	0	0	0	0	1	1	1	1	1	1	1	1	1	1	1	1	01	04	31	07
Egyptian Goose	0	0	0	0	0	0	0	0	0	0	0	0	0	1	1	1	1	1	01	04	31	07
Shelduck	0	0	0	0	0	0	1	1	1	1	1	1	1	1	1	1	1	1	01	04	31	07
Wood Duck	0	0	0	0	0	0	0	0	0	0	0	0	0	1	1	1	1	1	01	04	31	07
Mandarin Duck	0	1	1	1	1	1	1	1	1	1	1	1	1	1	1	1	1	1	01	04	31	07
Wigeon	0	0	0	0	0	0	0	0	0	0	0	0	0	1	1	1	1	1	01	04	31	07
Gadwall	0	1	1	1	1	1	1	1	1	1	1	1	1	1	1	1	1	1	01	05	31	07
Teal	0	0	0	0	0	0	0	0	0	0	0	0	1	1	1	1	1	1	01	04	31	07
Mallard	0	1	1	1	1	1	1	1	1	1	1	1	1	1	1	1	1	1	01	04	31	07
Pintail	0	0	0	0	0	0	0	0	0	0	0	0	0	1	1	1	1	1	01	04	31	07
Garganey	0	0	0	0	0	0	0	0	0	0	0	0	0	1	1	1	1	1	01	04	31	07
Shoveler	0	0	0	0	0	0	0	0	0	0	0	1	1	1	1	1	1	1	01	05	31	07
Red-crested Pochard	0	0	0	0	0	0	0	0	0	0	0	0	0	1	1	1	1	1	01	04	31	07
Pochard	0	0	0	0	0	0	0	0	0	0	0	1	1	1	1	1	1	1	01	05	31	07
Tufted Duck	0	1	1	1	1	1	1	1	1	1	1	1	1	1	1	1	1	1	01	05	31	08
Eider	0	0	0	0	0	0	0	0	0	0	0	0	0	1	1	1	1	1	01	04	31	07
Goosander	0	0	0	0	0	0	0	1	1	1	1	1	1	1	1	1	1	1	01	04	31	07
Ruddy Duck	0	0	0	0	0	0	1	1	1	1	1	1	1	1	1	1	1	1	01	04	31	07
Quail	1	1	1	1	1	1	1	1	1	1	1	1	1	1	1	1	1	1	15	05	15	08
Red-legged Partridge	1	1	1	1	1	1	1	1	1	1	1	1	1	1	1	1	1	1	01	04	31	07
Grey Partridge	1	1	1	1	1	1	1	1	1	1	1	1	1	1	1	1	1	1	01	04	31	07
Pheasant	1	1	1	1	1	1	1	1	1	1	1	1	1	1	1	1	1	1	01	04	31	07
Golden Pheasant	1	1	1	1	1	1	1	1	1	1	1	1	1	1	1	1	1	1	01	04	31	07
Lady Amherst's Pheasant	1	1	1	1	1	1	1	1	1	1	1	1	1	1	1	1	1	1	01	04	31	07
Cormorant	0	0	0	0	0	1	1	1	1	1	1	1	1	1	1	1	1	1	01	04	31	07
Little Egret	0	0	0	0	0	0	0	0	0	0	0	1	1	1	1	1	1	1	01	04	31	07
Grey Heron	0	0	0	0	0	0	1	1	1	1	1	1	1	1	1	1	1	1	01	03	30	06
Little Grebe	0	1	1	1	1	1	1	1	1	1	1	1	1	1	1	1	1	1	01	04	31	08
Great Crested Grebe	0	1	1	1	1	1	1	1	1	1	1	1	1	1	1	1	1	1	01	04	31	08
Black-necked Grebe	0	0	0	0	0	0	0	0	1	1	1	1	1	1	1	1	1	1	01	04	31	07
Honey-buzzard	0	0	0	0	1	1	1	1	1	1	1	1	1	1	1	1	1	1	15	05	15	08
Red Kite	0	0	0	0	0	0	1	1	1	1	1	1	1	1	1	1	1	1	01	04	31	07
Marsh Harrier	0	0	0	0	1	1	1	1	1	1	1	1	1	1	1	1	1	1	01	04	31	07
Montagu's Harrier	0	0	0	0	1	1	1	1	1	1	1	1	1	1	1	1	1	1	01	05	31	07
Goshawk	0	0	0	0	1	1	1	1	1	1	1	1	1	1	1	1	1	1	01	04	31	07
Sparrowhawk	1	1	1	1	1	1	1	1	1	1	1	1	1	1	1	1	1	1	01	04	31	07
Buzzard	1	1	1	1	1	1	1	1	1	1	1	1	1	1	1	1	1	1	01	04	31	07
Osprey	0	0	0	0	0	1	1	1	1	1	1	1	1	1	1	1	1	1	01	04	31	07
Water Rail	1	1	1	1	1	1	1	1	1	1	1	1	1	1	1	1	1	1	20	04	31	07
Spotted Crake	0	0	0	0	1	1	1	1	1	1	1	1	1	1	1	1	1	1	01	04	31	07
Moorhen	1	1	1	1	1	1	1	1	1	1	1	1	1	1	1	1	1	1	01	04	31	07
Coot	1	1	1	1	1	1	1	1	1	1	1	1	1	1	1	1	1	1	01	04	31	07

| Species | Codes: 0 = exclude; 1 = include; Null = Record without breeding evidence | | | | | | | | | | | | | | | | | | Date range | | | |
	F	Null	H	S	P	T	D	N	A	I	B	DD	UN	FL	ON	FF	NE	NY				
Crane	0	0	0	0	0	0	0	0	0	0	0	0	0	1	1	1	1	1	01	04	31	07
Great Bustard	0	0	0	0	0	0	0	0	0	0	0	0	0	1	1	1	1	1	01	04	31	07
Stone-curlew	1	1	1	1	1	1	1	1	1	1	1	1	1	1	1	1	1	1	01	04	01	09
Black-winged Stilt	0	0	0	0	1	1	1	1	1	1	1	1	1	1	1	1	1	1	01	04	31	07
Avocet	0	0	0	0	0	0	0	1	1	1	1	1	1	1	1	1	1	1	01	04	31	07
Oystercatcher	0	0	0	0	0	0	0	0	0	0	0	1	1	1	1	1	1	1	01	04	31	07
Lapwing	0	0	0	0	1	1	1	1	1	1	1	1	1	1	1	1	1	1	20	03	30	06
Little Ringed Plover	0	0	0	0	1	1	1	1	1	1	1	1	1	1	1	1	1	1	01	04	31	07
Ringed Plover	0	0	0	0	1	1	1	1	1	1	1	1	1	1	1	1	1	1	01	04	31	07
Curlew	0	0	0	0	1	1	1	1	1	1	1	1	1	1	1	1	1	1	01	04	31	07
Black-tailed Godwit	0	0	0	0	0	0	0	0	0	0	0	0	0	1	1	1	1	1	01	04	31	07
Redshank	0	0	0	0	1	1	1	1	1	1	1	1	1	1	1	1	1	1	01	04	31	07
Woodcock	1	1	1	1	1	1	1	1	1	1	1	1	1	1	1	1	1	1	01	04	31	07
Snipe	0	0	0	0	1	1	1	1	1	1	1	1	1	1	1	1	1	1	01	04	31	07
Little Tern	0	0	0	0	0	0	0	1	1	1	1	1	1	1	1	1	1	1	01	04	31	07
Sandwich Tern	0	0	0	0	0	0	0	1	1	1	1	1	1	1	1	1	1	1	01	04	31	07
Common Tern	0	0	0	0	0	0	0	1	1	1	1	1	1	1	1	1	1	1	01	04	31	07
Roseate Tern	0	0	0	0	0	0	0	1	1	1	1	1	1	1	1	1	1	1	01	05	31	07
Black-headed Gull	0	0	0	0	0	0	0	1	1	1	1	1	1	1	1	1	1	1	01	04	31	07
Mediterranean Gull	0	0	0	0	0	0	0	1	1	1	1	1	1	1	1	1	1	1	01	04	31	07
Common Gull	0	0	0	0	0	0	0	1	1	1	1	1	1	1	1	1	1	1	01	04	31	07
Lesser Black-backed Gull	0	0	0	0	0	0	0	1	1	1	1	1	1	1	1	1	1	1	01	04	31	07
Herring Gull	0	0	0	0	0	0	0	1	1	1	1	1	1	1	1	1	1	1	01	04	31	07
Yellow-legged Gull	0	0	0	0	0	0	0	1	1	1	1	1	1	1	1	1	1	1	01	04	31	07
Great Black-backed Gull	0	0	0	0	0	0	0	1	1	1	1	1	1	1	1	1	1	1	01	04	31	07
Feral Pigeon	1	1	1	1	1	1	1	1	1	1	1	1	1	1	1	1	1	1	01	04	31	07
Stock Dove	1	1	1	1	1	1	1	1	1	1	1	1	1	1	1	1	1	1	01	04	31	07
Woodpigeon	1	1	1	1	1	1	1	1	1	1	1	1	1	1	1	1	1	1	01	01	31	12
Collared Dove	1	1	1	1	1	1	1	1	1	1	1	1	1	1	1	1	1	1	01	03	31	07
Turtle Dove	1	1	1	1	1	1	1	1	1	1	1	1	1	1	1	1	1	1	01	05	31	07
Cuckoo	1	1	1	1	1	1	1	1	1	1	1	1	1	1	1	1	1	1	01	04	31	07
Barn Owl	1	1	1	1	1	1	1	1	1	1	1	1	1	1	1	1	1	1	01	03	01	09
Little Owl	1	1	1	1	1	1	1	1	1	1	1	1	1	1	1	1	1	1	01	03	31	07
Tawny Owl	1	1	1	1	1	1	1	1	1	1	1	1	1	1	1	1	1	1	01	01	31	12
Long-eared Owl	1	1	1	1	1	1	1	1	1	1	1	1	1	1	1	1	1	1	01	04	31	07
Short-eared Owl	0	0	0	0	1	1	1	1	1	1	1	1	1	1	1	1	1	1	01	04	31	07
Nightjar	1	1	1	1	1	1	1	1	1	1	1	1	1	1	1	1	1	1	15	05	31	08
Swift	0	0	0	0	0	1	1	1	1	1	1	1	1	1	1	1	1	1	01	05	31	07
Kingfisher	1	1	1	1	1	1	1	1	1	1	1	1	1	1	1	1	1	1	01	04	31	07
Green Woodpecker	1	1	1	1	1	1	1	1	1	1	1	1	1	1	1	1	1	1	01	03	31	07
Great Spotted Woodpecker	1	1	1	1	1	1	1	1	1	1	1	1	1	1	1	1	1	1	01	03	31	07
Lesser Spotted Woodpecker	1	1	1	1	1	1	1	1	1	1	1	1	1	1	1	1	1	1	01	03	31	07
Kestrel	1	1	1	1	1	1	1	1	1	1	1	1	1	1	1	1	1	1	01	04	31	07
Hobby	0	0	0	0	1	1	1	1	1	1	1	1	1	1	1	1	1	1	15	05	25	08
Peregrine	0	0	0	0	1	1	1	1	1	1	1	1	1	1	1	1	1	1	01	03	31	07
Ring-necked Parakeet	0	0	0	0	0	0	0	0	0	0	0	0	0	1	1	1	1	1	01	04	31	07
Golden Oriole	0	0	0	0	1	1	1	1	1	1	1	1	1	1	1	1	1	1	01	04	31	07
Red-backed Shrike	0	0	0	0	1	1	1	1	1	1	1	1	1	1	1	1	1	1	01	04	31	07
Magpie	1	1	1	1	1	1	1	1	1	1	1	1	1	1	1	1	1	1	01	03	31	07
Jay	1	1	1	1	1	1	1	1	1	1	1	1	1	1	1	1	1	1	01	03	31	07

Species	F	Null	H	S	P	T	D	N	A	I	B	DD	UN	FL	ON	FF	NE	NY	Date range			
Jackdaw	1	1	1	1	1	1	1	1	1	1	1	1	1	1	1	1	1	1	01	03	31	07
Rook	0	0	0	0	0	0	0	1	1	1	1	1	1	1	1	1	1	1	01	03	31	07
Carrion Crow	1	1	1	1	1	1	1	1	1	1	1	1	1	1	1	1	1	1	01	03	31	07
Raven	0	0	0	0	0	0	0	1	1	1	1	1	1	1	1	1	1	1	01	02	31	07
Goldcrest	0	1	1	1	1	1	1	1	1	1	1	1	1	1	1	1	1	1	01	04	31	07
Firecrest	0	0	1	1	1	1	1	1	1	1	1	1	1	1	1	1	1	1	01	04	31	07
Blue Tit	0	1	1	1	1	1	1	1	1	1	1	1	1	1	1	1	1	1	01	04	31	07
Great Tit	0	1	1	1	1	1	1	1	1	1	1	1	1	1	1	1	1	1	01	04	31	07
Coal Tit	0	1	1	1	1	1	1	1	1	1	1	1	1	1	1	1	1	1	01	03	31	07
Willow Tit	0	1	1	1	1	1	1	1	1	1	1	1	1	1	1	1	1	1	01	03	31	08
Marsh Tit	0	1	1	1	1	1	1	1	1	1	1	1	1	1	1	1	1	1	01	03	31	08
Bearded Tit	0	1	1	1	1	1	1	1	1	1	1	1	1	1	1	1	1	1	01	04	31	07
Woodlark	1	1	1	1	1	1	1	1	1	1	1	1	1	1	1	1	1	1	00	03	31	07
Skylark	1	1	1	1	1	1	1	1	1	1	1	1	1	1	1	1	1	1	01	04	31	07
Sand Martin	0	0	0	0	0	0	0	1	1	1	1	1	1	1	1	1	1	1	01	04	31	07
Swallow	0	1	1	1	1	1	1	1	1	1	1	1	1	1	1	1	1	1	01	04	31	07
House Martin	0	0	1	1	1	1	1	1	1	1	1	1	1	1	1	1	1	1	01	04	31	07
Cetti's Warbler	0	0	1	1	1	1	1	1	1	1	1	1	1	1	1	1	1	1	01	04	31	07
Long-tailed Tit	0	1	1	1	1	1	1	1	1	1	1	1	1	1	1	1	1	1	01	03	30	06
Wood Warbler	0	0	1	1	1	1	1	1	1	1	1	1	1	1	1	1	1	1	01	05	31	07
Chiffchaff	0	1	1	1	1	1	1	1	1	1	1	1	1	1	1	1	1	1	01	04	31	07
Willow Warbler	0	0	1	1	1	1	1	1	1	1	1	1	1	1	1	1	1	1	01	04	31	07
Blackcap	0	1	1	1	1	1	1	1	1	1	1	1	1	1	1	1	1	1	01	05	31	07
Garden Warbler	0	1	1	1	1	1	1	1	1	1	1	1	1	1	1	1	1	1	01	05	31	07
Lesser Whitethroat	0	1	1	1	1	1	1	1	1	1	1	1	1	1	1	1	1	1	01	05	31	07
Whitethroat	0	1	1	1	1	1	1	1	1	1	1	1	1	1	1	1	1	1	01	04	31	07
Dartford Warbler	0	1	1	1	1	1	1	1	1	1	1	1	1	1	1	1	1	1	01	04	31	07
Grasshopper Warbler	0	0	0	1	1	1	1	1	1	1	1	1	1	1	1	1	1	1	01	05	31	07
Savi's Warbler	0	0	0	0	1	1	1	1	1	1	1	1	1	1	1	1	1	1	01	04	31	07
Sedge Warbler	0	0	1	1	1	1	1	1	1	1	1	1	1	1	1	1	1	1	01	05	31	07
Marsh Warbler	0	0	0	0	1	1	1	1	1	1	1	1	1	1	1	1	1	1	01	06	31	07
Reed Warbler	0	1	1	1	1	1	1	1	1	1	1	1	1	1	1	1	1	1	01	04	31	07
Nuthatch	0	1	1	1	1	1	1	1	1	1	1	1	1	1	1	1	1	1	01	03	31	07
Treecreeper	0	1	1	1	1	1	1	1	1	1	1	1	1	1	1	1	1	1	01	03	31	07
Wren	1	1	1	1	1	1	1	1	1	1	1	1	1	1	1	1	1	1	01	03	31	07
Starling	0	1	1	1	1	1	1	1	1	1	1	1	1	1	1	1	1	1	01	04	31	07
Blackbird	1	1	1	1	1	1	1	1	1	1	1	1	1	1	1	1	1	1	01	03	31	07
Song Thrush	1	1	1	1	1	1	1	1	1	1	1	1	1	1	1	1	1	1	01	03	31	07
Mistle Thrush	1	1	1	1	1	1	1	1	1	1	1	1	1	1	1	1	1	1	01	04	31	07
Spotted Flycatcher	0	1	1	1	1	1	1	1	1	1	1	1	1	1	1	1	1	1	10	05	31	07
Robin	1	1	1	1	1	1	1	1	1	1	1	1	1	1	1	1	1	1	01	03	31	07
Nightingale	0	1	1	1	1	1	1	1	1	1	1	1	1	1	1	1	1	1	01	04	31	07
Pied Flycatcher	0	0	0	1	1	1	1	1	1	1	1	1	1	1	1	1	1	1	01	04	31	07
Black Redstart	0	0	0	1	1	1	1	1	1	1	1	1	1	1	1	1	1	1	01	05	31	07
Redstart	0	0	1	1	1	1	1	1	1	1	1	1	1	1	1	1	1	1	15	04	30	06
Whinchat	0	0	0	1	1	1	1	1	1	1	1	1	1	1	1	1	1	1	15	05	31	07
Stonechat	0	0	0	1	1	1	1	1	1	1	1	1	1	1	1	1	1	1	01	04	31	07
Wheatear	0	0	0	1	1	1	1	1	1	1	1	1	1	1	1	1	1	1	15	05	31	07
Dunnock	1	1	1	1	1	1	1	1	1	1	1	1	1	1	1	1	1	1	01	03	31	07
House Sparrow	1	1	1	1	1	1	1	1	1	1	1	1	1	1	1	1	1	1	01	03	31	07

Codes: 0 = exclude; 1 = include; Null = Record without breeding evidence

Species	Codes: 0 = exclude; 1 = include; Null = Record without breeding evidence																		Date range			
	F	Null	H	S	P	T	D	N	A	I	B	DD	UN	FL	ON	FF	NE	NY				
Tree Sparrow	0	0	0	0	0	0	0	0	0	0	0	0	1	1	1	1	1	1	01	04	31	07
Yellow Wagtail	0	0	1	1	1	1	1	1	1	1	1	1	1	1	1	1	1	1	01	05	31	07
Grey Wagtail	1	1	1	1	1	1	1	1	1	1	1	1	1	1	1	1	1	1	01	04	31	07
Pied/White Wagtail	1	1	1	1	1	1	1	1	1	1	1	1	1	1	1	1	1	1	01	04	31	07
Tree Pipit	0	1	1	1	1	1	1	1	1	1	1	1	1	1	1	1	1	1	01	04	31	07
Meadow Pipit	0	1	1	1	1	1	1	1	1	1	1	1	1	1	1	1	1	1	01	05	31	07
Rock Pipit	0	0	1	1	1	1	1	1	1	1	1	1	1	1	1	1	1	1	01	04	31	07
Chaffinch	1	1	1	1	1	1	1	1	1	1	1	1	1	1	1	1	1	1	01	04	31	07
Hawfinch	0	0	1	1	1	1	1	1	1	1	1	1	1	1	1	1	1	1	01	04	31	07
Bullfinch	1	1	1	1	1	1	1	1	1	1	1	1	1	1	1	1	1	1	01	04	31	07
Greenfinch	1	1	1	1	1	1	1	1	1	1	1	1	1	1	1	1	1	1	01	04	31	07
Linnet	0	0	1	1	1	1	1	1	1	1	1	1	1	1	1	1	1	1	15	04	31	07
Lesser Redpoll	0	0	0	0	0	0	0	0	0	0	0	1	1	1	1	1	1	1	01	05	31	07
Common Crossbill	0	0	0	0	1	1	1	1	1	1	1	1	1	1	1	1	1	1	01	02	31	07
Goldfinch	1	1	1	1	1	1	1	1	1	1	1	1	1	1	1	1	1	1	01	04	31	07
Siskin	0	0	1	1	1	1	1	1	1	1	1	1	1	1	1	1	1	1	01	05	31	07
Yellowhammer	1	1	1	1	1	1	1	1	1	1	1	1	1	1	1	1	1	1	01	04	31	07
Reed Bunting	1	1	1	1	1	1	1	1	1	1	1	1	1	1	1	1	1	1	01	04	31	07
Corn Bunting	0	0	1	1	1	1	1	1	1	1	1	1	1	1	1	1	1	1	01	05	31	07

Appendix III | Other taxa mentioned in the book

PLANTS

Alder	*Alnus glutinosa*
Ash	*Fraxinus excelsior*
Aspen	*Populus tremula*
Beech	*Fagus sylvatica*
Bracken	*Pteridium aquilinum*
Common Chickweed	*Stellaria media*
Common Reed	*Phragmites australis*
Cedar	*Cedrus* spp.
Cotoneaster	*Cotoneaster* spp.
Douglas Fir	*Pseudotsuga menziesii*
Eelgrass	*Zostera* spp.
Fat-hen	*Chenopodium album*
(Common) Ivy	*Hedera helix*
Hawthorn	*Craetagus monogyna*
Holly	*Ilex aquifolium*
Hornbeam	*Carpinus betulus*
Kale	*Brassica oleracea* var. *viridis*
Knotgrasses	*Polygonum aviculare*
Meadow-grasses	*Poa* spp.
New Zealand Pigmyweed	*Crassula helmsii*
Norway Spruce	*Picea abies*
(Pedunculate) Oak	*Quercus robur*
Oil-seed Rape	*Brassica napus* ssp. *oleifera*
Purple Moor-grass	*Molinia caerulea*
Quinoa	*Chenopodium quinoa*
Ragwort	*Senecio* spp.
Rhododendron	*Rhododendron* spp.
Rowan	*Sorbus aucuparia*
Rye-grasses	*Lolium* spp.
Sessile Oak	*Quercus petraea*
Silver Birch	*Betula pendula*
Small-leaved Lime	*Tilia cordata*
Teasel	*Dipsacus* spp.
Thistle	*Carduus* and *Cirsium* spp.
Turnip	*Brassica rapa* ssp. *rapa*
Willow	*Salix* spp.
Yew	*Taxus baccata*

PROTOZOA

Trichomonad protozoan	*Trichomonas gallinae*

FISH

Lamprey	*Lampetra* species
Atlantic Salmon	*Salmo salar*
Brown Trout	*Salmo trutta*

MAMMALS

(American) Mink	*Neovison vison*
(Domestic) Cat	*Feles catus*
Fallow Deer	*Dama dama*
(European) Rabbit	*Oryctolagus cuniculus*
(Brown) Rat	*Rattus norvegicus*
Grey Squirrel	*Sciurus carolinensis*
(Red) Fox	*Vulpes vulpes*
Red Squirrel	*Sciurus vulgaris*
Reeve's Muntjac	*Muntiacus reevesi*
Roe Deer	*Capreolus capreolus*
Sheep	*Ovis aries*
(Eurasian) Water Vole	*Arvicola amphibius*

Appendix IV | Gazetteer

H

Half Moon Common .... SU 2916
Hamble .... SU 4807
Hamble Country Park .... SU 4911
Hamble Estuary .... SU 4805
Hamer Warren Sand Pit .... SU 1210
Hampton Ridge .... SU 1913
Handy Cross Plain .... SU 1906
Harbridge .... SU 1410
Harestock .... SU 4631
Harewood Forest .... SU 3943
Hartley Mauditt .... SU 7436
Hartley Wintney .... SU 7656
Hasley Inclosure .... SU 1912
Hatchet Pond .... SU 3601
Hatchet Moor .... SU 3500
Havant .... SU 7106
Hawley Meadows .... SU 8559
Hawkhill Inclosure .... SU 3502
Hawley Lake .... SU 8357
Hayling Bay .... SZ 7298
Hayling Island .... SU 7101
Hayling Oysterbeds .... SU 7102
Hazeley Heath .... SU 7558
Headbourne Worthy .... SU 4832
Headley Mill Pond .... SU 8134
Heath Pond (Petersfield) .... SU 7522
Highland Water Inclosure .... SU 2409
Hill Head .... SU 5402
Hillside Marsh .... SU 7550
Hinton Admiral .... SZ 2095
Hoglands Park (Soton.) .... SU 4211
Holm Hill .... SU 2602
Holmsley .... SU 2200
Holt Pound (Alice Holt) .... SU 8144
Hook-with-Warsash .... SU 4905
Hook Links .... SU 4904
Hook Spit .... SU 4805
Hordle .... SZ 2695
Horndean .... SU 7013
Houghton .... SU 3432
Howen Bottom .... SU 2315
Hucklesbrook .... SU 1509
Hundred Acres (Wickham) .... SU 5911
Hursley .... SU 4225
Hurst Beach .... SZ 3090
Hurst Spit .... SZ 3189
Hurstbourne Tarrant .... SU 3853
Hurst Castle .... SZ 3189

I

IBM Lake (Cosham) .... SU 6404
Ibsley Bridge .... SU 1409
Ibsley Common .... SU 1710
Ibsley North GP (Blashford) .... SU 1509
Ibsley Water (Blashford) .... SU 1408
Idsworth Farm (Horndean) .... SU 7414
Iley Lane (Keyhaven) .... SZ 3193
Iley Point (Keyhaven) .... SZ 3191
Itchen Estuary .... SU 4309
Itchen Valley CP .... SU 4616
Ivy Lake (Blashford) .... SU 1507

K

Kempshott .... SU 6049
Kench (The) .... SZ 6999
Kentford Lake .... SU 3219
Kentsboro .... SU 3140
Keyhaven Marsh .... SZ 3192
Keyhaven .... SZ 3191
Kimbridge .... SU 3225
Kingston (Avon Valley) .... SU 1401

L

Lakeside CP (Eastleigh) .... SU 4417
Langdown .... SU 4306
Langstone Harbour .... SU 6802
Langstone Mill Pond .... SU 7105
Lasham .... SU 6743
Latchmore Bottom .... SU 1812
Laverstoke .... SU 4948
Leaden Hall .... SU 2015
Leckford .... SU 3737
Lee (Nursling) .... SU 3617
Lepe .... SZ 4598
Little London (Andover) .... SU 3749
Locks Heath .... SU 5107
Lode Farm (Kingsley) .... SU 7737
Long Beech Inclosure .... SU 2512
Long Down (Hambledon) .... SU 6619
Long Island .... SU 7004
Longmoor Inclosure .... SU 7930
Longparish .... SU 4344
Longstock .... SU 3636
Long Valley (Bourley) .... SU 8352
Longwood Warren .... SU 5226
Lordshill .... SU 3815
Lower Froyle .... SU 7644
Lower Pennington .... SZ 3193
Lower Test Marshes .... SU 3614
Ludshott Common .... SU 8535
Lymington NR .... SZ 3494
Lymington River .... SZ 3494
Lyndhurst .... SU 2908
Lyndridge Farm (Eversley) ...... SU 7760

M

Manor Farm (Old Alresford) ..... SU 5833
Mansbridge (River Itchen) ...... SU 4415
Mapledurwell .... SU 6851
Marchwood .... SU 3909
Mark Ash Wood .... SU 2407
Marsh Court (Stockbridge) ...... SU 3533
Martin .... SU 0619
Martin Down .... SU 0419
Martyr Worthy .... SU 5132
Mattingley .... SU 7357
Meon Valley GC .... SU 5513
Micheldever Wood .... SU 5337
Michelmersh .... SU 3525
Middle Wallop .... SU 2937
Midgham Wood .... SU 1412
Milford on Sea .... SZ 2891
Milkham .... SU 2110
Millbrook .... SU 3813
Mill Field (Old Basing) .... SU 6653

(continued)

Mill Rythe .... SU 7300
Millyford Bridge .... SU 2607
Milton Common .... SZ 6700
Moody's Down .... SU 4338
Moonhills .... SU 4002
Mottisfont .... SU 3227

N

Needs Ore .... SZ 4297
Nether Wallop .... SU 3036
Netherton .... SU 3757
Netherton Bottom .... SU 3856
Netley .... SU 4508
New Copse Inclosure .... SU 3202
Newlands Farm .... SU 5604
New Lane .... SZ 2991
New Milton .... SZ 2395
Newtown (Weston) .... SU 4510
Noar Hill .... SU 7431
Normandy Marsh .... SZ 3394
North Baddesley .... SU 3919
North Camp (Aldershot) .... SU 8652
Northam Bridge .... SU 4312
Northington Lake .... SU 5636
Northney .... SU 7303
Nursling .... SU 3515

O

Oakford Coppice .... SU 0412
Ocknell Plain .... SU 2311
Odiham .... SU 7450
Ogdens Purlieu .... SU 1811
Old Basing .... SU 6652
Old Winchester Hill .... SU 6420
Otterbourne .... SU 4623
Ovington .... SU 5631
Overton .... SU 5149
Over Wallop .... SU 2838
Ower .... SU 3216
Oxey Marsh .... SZ 3393

P

Pamber Forest .... SU 6161
Passfield Pond .... SU 8234
Paulsgrove Reclamation .... SU 6305
Pauncefoot Hill .... SU 3420
Pennington Marsh .... SZ 3292
Petersfield .... SU 7423
Pig Bush .... SU 3604
Pilot Hill .... SU 3959
Piper's Wait .... SU 2416
Pitts Deep .... SZ 3795
Plastow Green .... SU 5361
Potbridge Fishery .... SU 7454
Portchester Castle .... SU 6204
Porton Down .... SU 2135
Portsdown Hill .... SU 6406
Portsea Island .... SU 6600
Portsmouth .... SZ 6497
Portsmouth Harbour .... SU 5902
Preston Candover .... SU 6041
Pylewell .... SZ 3595

Appendix V | References and abbreviations

Often-used abbreviations:

BBRC	British Birds Rarities Committee.
BBS	Breeding Bird Survey.
BTO	British Trust for Ornithology.
BOU	British Ornithologists' Union.
CBC	Common Bird Census.
GWCT	Game and Wildlife Conservation Trust.
HBA	Hampshire Bird Atlas 2007–12.
HIWWT	Hampshire and Isle of Wight Wildlife Trust.
HOS	Hampshire Ornithological Society.
RBBP	Rare Breeding Birds Panel.
RSPB	Royal Society for the Protection of Birds.
WeBS	Wetland Bird Survey.
WWT	Wildfowl & Wetlands Trust.

Frequently used and abbreviated references:

1968–72 Atlas
Sharrock, J.T.R. 1976. *The Atlas of Breeding Birds in Britain and Ireland*. BTO, Tring.

1981–84 Winter Atlas
Lack, P. 1986. *The Atlas of Wintering Birds in Britain and Ireland*. T. & A.D. Poyser, Staffs.

1988–91 Atlas
Gibbons, D.W., Reid, J.B. & Chapman, R.A. 1993. *The New Atlas of Breeding Birds in Britain and Ireland: 1988–1991*. T. & A.D. Poyser, London.

APEP3
Avian Population Estimates Panel, 3rd report. Musgrove, A.J., Aebischer, N., Eaton, M., Hearn, R., Newson, S., Noble, D., Parsons, M., Risley, K. & Stroud, D. 2013. Population estimates of birds in Great Britain and the United Kingdom. *British Birds* 106: 64–100.

BBS
Breeding Bird Survey.
http://www.bto.org/volunteer-surveys/bbs

Bird Atlas 2007–11
Balmer, D.E., Gillings, S., Caffrey, B.J., Swann, R.L., Downie, I.S. & Fuller, R.J. 2013. *Bird Atlas 2007–11. The breeding and wintering birds of Britain and Ireland*. BTO Books, Thetford.

BirdTrends
BirdTrends 2013: trends in numbers, breeding success and survival for UK breeding birds.
http://www.bto.org/about-birds/birdtrends/2013

BoH
Clark, J.M. & Eyre, J.A. eds. 1993. *Birds of Hampshire*. Hampshire Ornithological Society.

BWP
Cramp, S. & Perrins, C.M. eds. 1977–96. *The Birds of the Western Palearctic*. Oxford University Press.

Cohen
Cohen, E. 1963. *Birds of Hampshire & the Isle of Wight*. Oliver & Boyd, Edinburgh and London.

C&T
Cohen, E. & Taverner, J. 1972. *A Revised List of Hampshire and Isle of Wight Birds*. Oxford Illustrated Press.

GBW
BTO Garden BirdWatch.
http://www.bto.org/volunteer-surveys/gbw

HBR
Hampshire Bird Report. Published annually by HOS. If a date follows the abbreviation it is the date of the annual report being referenced.

HBW
Del Hoyo, J., Elliott, A. Sargatal, J. & Christie, D.A. eds. 1992–2013. *Handbook of the Birds of the World*. Lynx Edicions, Barcelona.

K&M
Kelsall, J.E. & Munn, P.W. 1905. *The Birds of Hampshire and the Isle of Wight*. Witherby & Co. London.

Migration Atlas
Wernham, C., Siriwardena, G.M., Toms, M., Marchant, J., Clark, J.A., Baillie, S. 2002. *The Migration Atlas: Movements of the Birds of Britain and Ireland*. Helm.

RBBP2009
Holling, M. and the Rare Breeding Birds Panel 2011. Rare breeding birds in the United Kingdom in 2009. *British Birds* 104: 476–537.

RBBP2012
Holling, M. and the Rare Breeding Birds Panel 2014. Rare breeding birds in the United Kingdom in 2012. *British Birds* 107: 504–560.

Seabird 2000
Mitchell, P.I., Newton, S.F., Ratcliffe, N. and Dunn T.E. eds. 2004. *Seabird Populations of Britain and Ireland: results of the Seabird 2000 census (1998–2002)*. T. and A.D. Poyser, London.

SUKB
The State of the UK's Birds. Available on-line from the WeBSites of the BTO, RSPB and WWT. If a date follows the abbreviation it is the date of the annual report being referenced.

WeBS
Wetland Bird Survey report, *Waterbirds in the UK*. Available on line at http://www.bto.org/volunteer-surveys/WeBS/publications/WeBS-annual-report/waterbirds-in-the-uk. If a date follows the abbreviation it is the date of the report being referenced.

Author and source references:

Betton, K.F. 2007. A Breeding Season Survey of Corn Buntings in Hampshire, 2005. *HBR 2005*: 206–210, HOS.

Betton, K. F. & Jacobs, R. J. 2009. The Red Kite in Hampshire – past and present. *HBR 2008*: 236–242, HOS

Bijlsma, R.G. 2004. What is the predation risk of European Honey-buzzards *Pernis apivorus* in Dutch forests inhabited by food-stressed Northern Goshawks *Accipiter gentilis*? *De Takkeling* 12: 185–197 (Dutch with English Summary).

Blaker, B.G. 1933. The Barn Owl in England – Results of the Census. *Bird Notes & News* 15: 169–172, 207–211.

Brown, A. 2007. One hundred years of notable avian events in *British Birds*. *British Birds* 100: 214–243.

Brown, A., Gilbert, G. & Wotton, S. 2012. Bitterns and Bittern Conservation in the UK. *British Birds* 105: 58–87.

Broughton, R.K. 2009. Separation of Willow Tit and Marsh Tit in Britain: a review. *British Birds* 102: 604–616.

BTO Birdfacts http://blx1.bto.org/birdfacts/results/bob18770.htm

BOU 2013. The British List: A Checklist of Birds of Britain (8th edition). *Ibis*, 155: 635–676.

Cabot, D. 1996. Performance of the Roseate Tern population breeding in north-west Europe – Ireland, Britain and France, 1960–94. *Proceedings of the Royal Irish Academy* 96B: 55–68.

Carpenter, J. 2008. *An investigation of causes of population decline in the Marsh Tit* Poecile palustris *in Britain*. DPhil Thesis, University of Oxford.

Carpenter, J., Smart, J., Amar, A., Gosler, A., Hinsley, S. & Charman, E. 2010. National-scale analyses of habitat associations of Marsh Tits *Poecile palustris* and Blue Tits *Cyanistes caeruleus*: two species with opposing population trends in Britain. *Bird Study* 57: 31–43.

Carr, P. 2009. The Hampshire Little Egret Breeding Population – Ten Years On. *HBR 2008*: 208–213, HOS.

Channel Coastal Observatory 2008. *Solent Dynamic Coast Project Main Report*. New Forest District Council/ Channel Coast Observatory.

Clark, J.M. 1979. The numbers and distribution of breeding Grebes and Wildfowl in Hampshire in 1978. *HBR 1978*: 61–76, HOS.

Clark, J.M. 2007. Invasion of Waxwings *Bombycilla garrulus* into Hampshire, December 2004–May 2005. *HBR 2005*: 211–215, HOS.

Clark, J.M. 2009. Feral Barnacle and Snow Geese in the upper Loddon and Blackwater valleys. *Berkshire Bird Report 2005*: 11–15.

Clark, J.M. 2011a. Dartford Warblers in Hampshire, 1994–2011. *HBR 2010*: 206–212, HOS.

Clark, J.M. 2011b. Exceptional numbers of Redwings roosting in Hampshire. *British Birds* 104: 276–7.

Clark, J.M. 2013. Invasion of Waxwings *Bombycilla garrulus* into Hampshire, November 2010–April 2011. *HBR 2011*: 211–219, HOS.

Clements, R. 2013. A UK population estimate for the Hawfinch. *British Birds* 106: 43–44.

Cloyne, J. 2007. The Status of Wetland Birds in the Itchen Valley. *HBR 2006*: 221–231, HOS.

Combridge, P. & Clark, J.M. 2010. Category B species on the Hampshire List: a review. *HBR 2009*: 209–219, HOS.

Conway, G.J., Burton, N.H.K., Handschub, M. & Austin, G.E. 2008. UK population estimates from the 2007 Breeding Little Ringed Plover and Ringed Plover surveys. *BTO Research Report 510*. BTO, Thetford.

Conway, G., Wotton, S.R., Henderson, I., Langston, R., Drewitt, A. & Currie, F. 2007. Status and distribution of European Nightjars *Caprimulgus europaeus* in the UK in 2004. *Bird Study* 54: 98–111.

Conway, G., Wotton, S.R., Henderson, I., Eaton, M., Drewitt, A. & Spencer, J. 2009. The status of breeding Woodlarks *Lullula arborea* in Britain in 2006. *Bird Study* 56: 310–325.

Countryside Survey 2007. www.countrysidesurvey.org.uk. Accessed November 2014.

Cramp, S. ed. 1977. *The Handbook of the Birds of Europe, The Middle East and North Africa. The Birds of the Western Palearctic*. Vol 1, Oxford University Press. Oxford.

Davies, N.B. 1985. Cooperation and conflict among dunnocks, *Prunella modularis*, in a variable mating system. *Animal Behaviour*, 33: 628–648.

Denby Wilkinson, C. 1950. The annual immigration of the Wood-Pigeon and Stock-Dove on the coast of East Sussex. *British Birds* 43: 233–238.

Defra 2009. http://archive.defra.gov.uk/environment/ biodiversity/documents/indicator/200904f4.pdf Accessed November 2014

Douglas, D. J. T., Newson, S. E., Leech, D. I., Noble, D. G. & Robinson, R. A. (2010), How important are climate-induced changes in host availability for population processes in an obligate brood parasite, the European cuckoo? *Oikos*, 119: 1834–1840.

Duffin, B.S. 1991. *The Birds of Titchfield Haven*. Pekkari Books, Hill Head.

Duffin, B.S. 2003. Savi's Warblers breeding in Hampshire - a historical perspective. *HBR 2002*: 205–209, HOS.

Eaton, M.A., Brown, A.F., Noble, D.G., Musgrove, A.J., Hearn, R.D., Aebischer, N.J., Gibbons, D.W., Evans, A. & Gregory, R.D. 2009. Birds of Conservation Concern 3: the population status of birds in the United Kingdom, Channel Islands and the Isle of Man. *British Birds* 102: 296–341.

Ecomare. http://www.ecomare.nl/en/encyclopedia/ animals-and-plants/animals/birds/other-birds/ spoonbill/ Accessed November 2014.

Environment Agency 2012. *Greater working with natural processes in flood and coastal erosion risk management*. http://www.wessexwater.co.uk/WorkArea/ DownloadAsset.aspx?id=8978 Accessed November 2014.

Eyre, J.A. 2007. The status of Woodlarks in Hampshire: results of the 2006 survey. *HBR 2006*: 198–203, HOS.

Ferguson-Lees, J., Castle, P., Combridge, P., Cranswick, P. & Edwards, S. eds. 2007. *Birds of Wiltshire*, Wiltshire Ornithological Society, Devizes.

Fjeldså, J. 1973. Distribution and geographical variation of the horned grebe *Podiceps auritus* (Linnaeus, 1758). *Ornis Scandinavica*, 4(1): 55–86.

Fox, R., Parsons, M.S., Chapman, J.W., Woiwod, I.P., Warren, M.S. & Brooks, D.R. 2013 *The State of Britain's Larger Moths 2013*. Butterfly Conservation and Rothamsted Research, Wareham, Dorset, UK.

Fraser, P. & Ryan, J. 1995. Status of the Great Grey Shrike in Britain and Ireland. *British Birds* 88: 478–484.

Fuisz, T.I. & de Kort, S.R. 2007. Habitat-dependent call divergence in the common cuckoo: is it a potential signal for assortative mating? *Proc. R. Soc. B* 274: 2093–2097.

Fuller, R.J., Noble, D.G., Smith, K.W. & Vanhinsbergh, D. 2005. Recent declines in populations of woodland birds in Britain: a review of possible causes. *British Birds* 98: 116–143.

Gamauf, A., Tebb, G., & Nemeth, E. 2013. Honey-buzzard *Pernis apivorus* nest site selection in relation to habitat and distribution of Goshawk *Accipiter gentilis*. *Ibis* 155 -2: 258–270.

Garden BirdWatch 2013. BTO Garden BirdWatch Results. www.bto.org/volunteer-surveys/gbw/results.

Gillings, S., Newson, S.E., Noble, D.G., & Vickery, J.A., 2005. Winter availability of cereal stubbles attracts declining farmland birds and positively influences breeding population trends. *Proc. R. Soc. B* 272: 733–739.

Glue, D.E., 1973. The breeding birds of a New Forest valley. *British Birds* 66: 461–472.

Green, R. E., Tyler, G.A. & Bowden, C.G.R. 2000. Habitat selection, ranging behaviour and diet of the Stone Curlew in southern England. *Journal of Zoology* 250: 161–183.

Helm, B., Fiedler, W. & Callion, J. 2006. Movements of European Stonechats *Saxicola torquata* according to ringing recoveries. *Ardea* 94: 33–44.

Hinge, M.D.C. 2014. *New Forest Woodcock Group study report*.

Holloway, S. 1996. *The Historical Atlas of Breeding Birds in Britain and Ireland 1875–1900*. Poyser.

Holt, C.A., Fuller, R.J. & Dolman, P.M. 2010. Experimental evidence that deer browsing reduces habitat suitability for breeding Common Nightingales *Luscinia megarhynchos*. *Ibis* 152, Issue 2: 335–346

Holt, C.A., Hewson, C.H. & Fuller, R.J. 2012. The Nightingale in Britain: status, ecology and conservation needs. *British Birds* 105, 172–187.

Hoodless, A.N. & Powell, A. 2010. *Origins of Wintering Woodcocks: initial findings*. Game & Wildlife Conservation Trust.

IPCC 2014. *Climate Change 2014 Synthesis Report*. http://www.ipcc.ch/pdf/assessment-report/ar5/syr/SYR_AR5_SPM.pdf Accessed November 2014

Irvine, J. 1977. Breeding Birds in New Forest Broad-Leaved Woodland. *Bird Study* 24: 105–111.

JNCC 2014 Seabird Population Trends and Causes of Change: 1986–2013 Report http://www.jncc.defra.gov.uk/page-3201. Joint Nature Conservation Committee. Accessed November 2014.

Jones J.R. 2010. A Survey of Gulls Nesting on Roofs in Southampton in 2009. *HBR 2009*: 220–227, HOS.

Knox, A.G., Helbig, A.J., Parkin, D.T. & Sangster, G. 2001. The taxonomic status of Lesser Redpoll. *British Birds* 94: 260–267.

Lack, D. & Ridpath, M.G. 1955. Do English Woodpigeons migrate? *British Birds* 48: 289–292.

Langston, R.H.W., Smith, T., Brown, A.E., & Gregory, R.D. 2006. Status of breeding Twite *Carduelis flavirostris* in the UK. *Bird Study* 53: 55–63.

Ławicki, Ł. 2014. The Great White Egret in Europe: population increase and range expansion since 1980. *British Birds* 107: 8–25.

Lehikoinen, A. & Jaatinen, K. 2011. Delayed autumn migration in northern European waterfowl. *J Ornithol* DOI 10.1007/s10336–011–0777–z.

Lever, C. 2009. *The Naturalised Animals of Britain and Ireland*. New Holland Publishers (UK) Ltd.

Lewis, A. J., Amar, A., Cordi-Piec, D. & Thewlis, R. M. 2007. Factors influencing Willow Tit site occupancy: a comparison of abandoned and occupied woods. *Ibis*, 149: 205–213.

LPO 2014. (Ligue pour la Protection des Oiseaux) https://www.lpo.fr/les-cigognes-blanches/le-retour-de-la-cigogne-blanche-en-france-et-en-charente-maritime. Accessed November 2014.

Marchant, J.H., Hudson, R., Carter, S.P. & Whittington, P.A. 1990. *Population Trends in British Breeding Birds*. BTO, Tring.

Marchant, J.H., Prater, A.J., & Hayman, P. 1986. *Shorebirds: an identification guide to the waders of the world*. Helm, London.

Mason, C.F. & Macdonald, S.M. 1999. Habitat use by Lapwings *Vanellus vanellus* and Golden Plovers *Pluvialis apricaria*. *Wildfowl* 50: 205–207.

Mead, C. 2000. *The State of the Nation's Birds*. Whittet Books.

Mikkola, H. 1983. *Owls of Europe*. T. & A.D. Poyser, Staffs.

Moksnes, A., Røskaft, E. & Stokke, B. G. 2011. Gjøkens forunderlige verden. Historien om gjøken og vitenskapen. Tapir Akademisk Forlag, Oslo.

Moorcroft, D., Wilson, J.D. & Bradbury, R.B., 2006. Diet of nestling Linnets *Carduelis cannabina* on lowland farmland before and after agricultural intensification. *Bird Study* 53: 156–162.

Morris, A., Burges, D., Fuller, R.J., Evans, A.D. & Smith, K.W. 1994. The status and distribution of Nightjars *Caprimulgus europaeus* in Britain in 1992. *Bird Study* 41: 181–191.

Newson, S.E., Marchant, J.H., Ekins, G.R. & Sellers, R.M. 2007. The status of inland-breeding Great Cormorants in England. *British Birds* 100: 265–318.

Munn, P.W. 1920. Notes on Birds of Hampshire and the Isle of Wight. *Proc. Hants Field Club Archaeol. Soc.* 9 (1): 23–36. Newton, I., 1972. *Finches*. Collins, London.

O'Brien, S.H., Wilson, L.J., Webb, A. & Cranswick, P.A. 2008. Revised estimate of wintering Red-throated Divers *Gavia Stellata* in Great Britain. *Bird Study* 55: 152–160.

Ockendon, N., Hewson, C.N., Johnston, A. & Atkinson, P.W. 2012. Declines in British-breeding populations of Afro-Palaearctic migrant birds are linked to bioclimatic wintering zone in Africa, possibly via constraints on arrival time advancement. *Bird Study* 59: 111–125.

Ogilvie, M.A., 1978. *Wild Geese*. Poyser, Berkhamsted.

Parr, S.J. 1985. The breeding ecology and diet of the Hobby *Falco subbuteo* in southern England. *Ibis* 127: 60–73.

Pennington, M.G., Riddington, R. & Miles, W.T.S. 2012. The Lapland Bunting influx in Britain and Ireland in 2010/11. *British Birds* 105: 654–671.

Perkins, A.J., Whittingham, M.J., Bradbury, R.B., Wilson, J.D., Morris, A.J. & Barnett, P.R. 2000. Habitat characteristics affecting the use of lowland agricultural grassland by birds in winter. *Biological Conservation* 95: 279–294.

Petty, S.J., Anderson, D.I.K., Davison, M., Little, B., Sherratt, T.N., Thomkas, C.J. & Lambin, X. 2003, The decline of Common Kestrels *Falco tinnunculus* in a forested area of northern England: the role of predation by Northern Goshawks *Accipiter gentilis, Ibis* 145: 472–483.

Rands, M. 1985. Pesticide use on cereals and the survival of Grey Partridge chicks: a field experiment. *Journal of Applied Ecology* 22: 49–54.

Risely, K., Massimino, D., Newson, S.E., Eaton, M.A., Musgrove, A.J., Noble, D.G., Proctor, D. & Baillie, S.R. 2013. *The Breeding Bird Survey 2012*. BTO Research Report 645. BTO, Thetford.

RSPB 2014. www.rspb.org.uk/news/360162-tiny-tag-reveals-recordbreaking-bird-migration. Accessed November 2014.

Santoro, S., Máñez, M., Green, A.J. & Figuerola, J. 2010. Formation and growth of a heronry in a managed wetland in Doñana, Spain. *Bird Study* 57: 515–524.

Sharkey, B. 2007. BTO Tawny Owl Survey 2005. *HBR 2005:* 199–201, HOS.

Sharrock, J.T.R. 1976. *The Atlas of Breeding Birds in Britain and Ireland*. BTO, Tring.

Shawyer, C.R. 1987. *The Barn Owl in the British Isles: its past, present and future*. The Hawk Trust, London.

Shillitoe, J.R.D. 2007. The 2003/04–2005/06 winter gull roost survey. *HBR 2006:* 236–238, HOS.

Shillitoe, J.R.D. 2008. BTO Breeding Ringed and Little Ringed Plovers. *HBR 2007:* 199–202, HOS.

Siriwardena, G.M. 2006. Avian nest predation, competition and the decline of British Marsh Tits *Parus palustris. Ibis* 148: 255–265.

Siriwardena, G.M., Stevens, D.K., Anderson, G.Q.A., Vickery, J.A., Galbrade, N.A. & Dodds, S., 2007. The effect of supplementary winter seed food on breeding populations of farmland birds: evidence from two large-scale experiments. *Journal of Applied Ecology* 44: 920–932.

Steventon, D.J. 1985. Breeding Ringed Plover Survey, 1984. *HBR 1984:* 81–84, HOS.

Suffern, C. & Ferguson-Lees, I.J. 1964. Cetti's Warbler in Hampshire. *British Birds* 57: 365–366.

Taverner, J.H. 1962. *Wildfowl in Hampshire.* Warren and Son Ltd. Winchester.

Taylor M. & Marchant J.H. 2011. *Norfolk Bird Atlas – Summer and Winter Distributions, 1999–2007*. BTO, Thetford.

Toms, M. 2010. Collared Dove: Out of India. *Bird Table* 63: 14–16. BTO, Thetford.

Tubbs, C.R. 1997. *The Ecology, Conservation and History of The Solent*. Packard. Chichester.

Tubbs, C.R. & Tubbs, J.M. 1982. Brent Geese *Branta bernicla bernicla* and their food in The Solent, Southern England. *Biol. Conserv.* 31: 141–165.

Unsworth, D.J. 2003. Solent Waterbird population changes 1986/87–2000/01. *HBR 2002:* 188–193, HOS.

Ward, M. & Wynn, R.B. 2013. Results of targeted surveys of Firecrests and other woodland species in the central New Forest from 2009–2011. *HBR 2012:* 196–203, HOS.

WeBS 2008. Austin, G.E., Collier, M.P., Calbrade, N.A., Hall. C. & Musgrove, A.J. 2008. *Waterbirds in the UK 2006/07: The Wetland Bird Survey.* BTO/WWT/RSPB/JNCC, Thetford.

WeBS 2012. *Waterbirds in the UK 2011/12.* http://blx1.bto.org/WeBS-reporting/

WeBS 2014. Austin, G.E., Read, W.J., Calbrade, N.A., Mellan, H.J., Musgrove, A.J., Skellorn, W., Hearn, R.D., Stroud, D.A., Wotton, S.R. & Holt, C. A. 2014. *Waterbirds in the UK 2011/12: The Wetland Bird Survey.* BTO, RSPB and JNCC, in association with WWT. BTO, Thetford.

Wetlands International 2002. (Compiled by Simon Delany and Derek Scott). *Waterbird Population Estimates - Third Edition.* Wetlands International, Global Series No. 12. Wageningen, The Netherlands.

White, G. 1789. *The Natural History and Antiquities of Selborne.*

Wilson, A.M., Vickery, J.A., Brown, A., Langston, R.H.W., Smallshire, D., Wotton, S.R. & Vanhinsbergh, D. 2005 Changes in the numbers of breeding waders on lowland wet grasslands in England and Wales between 1982 and 2002. *Bird Study* 52: 55–69.

Wiseman, E.J. 2012. Honey-buzzards in southern England. *British Birds* 105: 23–28.

Witherby, H.F. 1939. *The Handbook of British Birds* Vol 3: 131. H. F. & G. Witherby, London.

Wotton, S. R., Carter, I., Cross, A.V., Etheridge, B., Snell, N., Duffy, K. & Gregory, R.D. 2002. Breeding status of the Red Kite in Britain in 2000. *Bird Study*, 49: 278–286.

Wotton, S.R., Grantham, N., Moran, N. & Gilbert, G. 2011. Eurasian Bittern distribution and abundance in the UK during the 2009/10 winter. *British Birds* 104: 636–641.

Wynn, R.B. 2012. An exceptional inshore movement of Great and Arctic Skuas off southeast England in spring 2012. *British Birds* 105: 626–628.

Index